# Forecasting & Predictive Analytics
## with ForecastX™

# Forecasting & Predictive Analytics with ForecastX™

Seventh Edition

**Barry Keating**
*University of Notre Dame*

**J. Holton Wilson**
*Central Michigan University*

**John Galt Solutions, Inc.**
*Chicago*

Boston   Burr Ridge, IL   Dubuque, IA   New York   San Francisco   St. Louis Bangkok
Bogotá   Caracas   Kuala Lumpur   Lisbon   London   Madrid   Mexico City   Milan
Montreal   New Delhi   Santiago   Seoul   Singapore   Sydney   Taipei   Toronto

FORECASTING AND PREDICTIVE ANALYTICS: WITH FORECASTX™, SEVENTH EDITION

Published by McGraw-Hill Education, 2 Penn Plaza, New York, NY 10121. Copyright © 2019 by McGraw-Hill Education. All rights reserved. Printed in the United States of America. Previous editions © 2018, 2009, and 2007. No part of this publication may be reproduced or distributed in any form or by any means, or stored in a database or retrieval system, without the prior written consent of McGraw-Hill Education, including, but not limited to, in any network or other electronic storage or transmission, or broadcast for distance learning.

Some ancillaries, including electronic and print components, may not be available to customers outside the United States.

This book is printed on acid-free paper.

1 2 3 4 5 6 7 8 9 LCR 21 20 19 18

ISBN 978-1-259-90391-5
MHID 1-259-90391-5

Portfolio Manager: *Noelle Bathurst*
Product Developers: *Michele Janicek and Tobi Phillips*
Marketing Manager: *Harper Christopher*
Content Project Managers: *Daryl Horrocks and Erika Jordan*
Buyer: *Sandy Ludovissy*
Design: *Matt Diamond*
Content Licensing Specialists: *Shannon Manderscheid*
Cover Image: *©VLADGRIN/Getty Images*
Compositor: *MPS Limited*

All credits appearing on page or at the end of the book are considered to be an extension of the copyright page.

**Library of Congress Cataloging-in-Publication Data**

Keating, Barry, 1945- author. | Wilson, J. Holton, 1942- author.
    Business forecasting : with ForecastX™ / Barry Keating, University of
    Notre Dame, J. Holton Wilson, Central Michigan University.
    Seventh edition. | New York, NY : McGraw-Hill/Irwin, [2018] |
    J. Holton Wilson appears as first named author on earlier editions.
    LCCN 2017055980 | ISBN 9781259903915 (alk. paper)
    LCSH: Business forecasting.
    LCC HD30.27 .W56 2018 | DDC 658.4/03550285554—dc23 LC record available at
    https://lccn.loc.gov/2017055980

The Internet addresses listed in the text were accurate at the time of publication. The inclusion of a website does not indicate an endorsement by the authors or McGraw-Hill Education, and McGraw-Hill Education does not guarantee the accuracy of the information presented at these sites.

mheducation.com/highered

To: Maryann, John, Ingrid, Vincent, Katy, Alice, Mike, and Casey Keating
To: Zhihong Ren

# Preface

The seventh edition of *Forecasting and Predictive Analytics with ForecastX™* builds on the success of the first six editions. While a number of significant changes have been made in this seventh edition, it remains a book about prediction methods for managers, forecasting practitioners, data scientists, and students who will one day become business professionals and have a need to understand practical issues related to prediction in all its forms. Our emphasis is on authentic learning of the forecasting and analytics methods that practitioners have found most useful. *Forecasting and Predictive Analytics with ForecastX™* is written for students and others who want to know how forecasting is really done.

## Content Updates

Major overall updates for this edition include:

- Four new chapters on predictive analytics
- The addition of Learning Objectives to all chapters
- Updated data throughout the book
- Updated and clarified ForecastX™ software sections

Today, most business planning routinely begins with a sales forecast. Whether you are an accountant, a marketer, a human resources manager, a data scientist, or a financial analyst, you will have to predict something sooner or later. This book is designed to lead you through the most helpful techniques to use in any prediction effort.

The analytics materials included in the sixth edition have been expanded to include four full chapters in the seventh edition; this is a recognition of the importance of these tools in today's prediction efforts. The examples we offer are, for the most part, based on actual historical data, much like that you may encounter in your own forecasts. The techniques themselves are explained as procedures that you may replicate with your own data.

Specific chapter updates include:

### Chapter 1. Introduction to Business Forecasting and Predictive Analytics

- Added Stages in the development of business forecasting are added.
- Steps to obtain better forecasts are added.
- A discussion of survey results is added showing what functional areas in an organization contribute to a forecast and which area owns the forecast.

### Chapter 2. The Forecast Process, Data Considerations, and Model Selection

- New exercises and updated data in others are added.
- Discussion of trend, seasonal, and cyclical components of a time series, including new data, is added.

### Chapter 3. Extrapolation 1. Moving Averages and Exponential Smoothing

- Sections on Simple, Holt's and Winters' exponential smoothing models are completely rewritten to clarify how they work and how to interpret the results.
- The use of all methods for dealing with seasonal data is discussed, including the deseasonalizing of data, making the forecast, then putting the seasonality back into the forecast.
- "Event Modeling" section is expanded to include a complete example.
- New exercises and updated data in others are added.

### Chapter 4. Extrapolation 2. Introduction to Forecasting with Regression Trend Models

- A comparison of the look of regression results from Excel and from ForecastX™ is added to show that they are equivalent, even if the formatting is different.
- An explanation of seasonal indices and how to get seasonal indices using ForecastX™ is added.
- A complete explanation of calculating the mean absolute percent error (MAPE) is added, including a table with an example.
- An example of cross sectional forecasting is added.
- The steps to use when evaluating a regression model are clarified.

### Chapter 5. Explanatory Models 1. Forecasting with Multiple Regression Causal Models

- The discussion of steps to use when evaluating regression models is expanded and clarified.
- An example of accounting for a recession in a multiple regression model with an introduction to business cycle information from FRED is added.
- Discussion of how missing variables may affect serial correlation is clarified, with an example.
- Discussion of the use of a seasonal Durbin-Watson statistic $DW_4$ versus $DW_1$ is added.
- An appendix concerning forecast combinations (ensembles) with a full discussion of detecting bias is added.

### Chapter 6. Explanatory Models 2. Time-Series Decomposition

- Discussion of ways to estimate cycle turning points using actual private housing starts data with detailed graphics is added.

### Chapter 7. Explanatory Models 3. ARIMA (Box-Jenkins)–Type Forecasting Models

- The ARIMA philosophy of modelling is introduced.
- An intuitive approach to explaining ARIMA is used to reduce complexity.
- The individual components of ARIMA (autoregressive models and moving average models) are explained.
- Stationarity is explained and the handling of nonstationarity is demonstrated.

- Numerous examples are included.
- The application of ARIMA to time-series data is detailed.
- "Overfitting" is explained along with detection and correction.

### Chapter 8. Predictive Analytics: Helping to Make Sense of Big Data

- Entirely new chapter.
- The field of predictive analytics as an extension of forecasting is introduced.
- The three primary tools of analytics are defined.
- The new vocabulary and terminology used in analytics are listed.
- The importance of correlation is stressed.
- The "steps" in any data mining/analytics process are described.
- The data used in analytics is differentiated from the data commonly used in forecasting.
- The new diagnostic statistics used by data scientists are described.

### Chapter 9. Classification Models: The Most Used Models in Analytics

- Entirely new chapter.
- The most used technique in analytics, classification algorithms, is introduced.
- The use of the kNN algorithm is taught.
- CART models (a second type of classification algorithm) is demonstrated.
- A third classification algorithm is introduced: the Naive Bayes algorithm.
- The final classification technique, Logit, is detailed.
- Actual examples of each technique are covered in detail.

### Chapter 10. Ensemble Models and Clustering

- Entirely new chapter.
- Ensemble models are introduced with the rationale for their use in analytics.
- Two important ensemble techniques are discussed and demonstrated: bagging and boosting.
- A third, newer ensemble is detailed: random forests.
- Clustering is introduced as a completely different class of analytics technique.
- Each of the techniques in the chapter is demonstrated step-by-step with actual examples.

### Chapter 11. Text Mining

- Entirely new chapter.
- Text mining (and all its variants) is introduced first in a general manner.
- The concept of data reduction is demonstrated, and its importance is demonstrated in the context of text mining.
- The "bag of words" approach to text mining is used with examples and software.
- "Bag of words" analysis is detailed in an extended example involving newsgroups.
- The newer approach to text mining involves "natural language processing;" this is shown with an extended example.
- Text mining and the more traditional data mining are combined through example to demonstrate the power of using both together.

**Chapter 12. Forecast/Analytics Implementation**

- Graphics related to the forecasting process are added.

# McGraw-Hill Connect® Learn Without Limits!

Connect® is a teaching and learning platform that is proven to deliver better results for students and instructors. Connect® empowers students by continually adapting to deliver precisely what they need, when they need it, and how they need it, so your class time is more engaging and effective.

New to the seventh edition, Connect® includes SmartBook®, instructor resources, and student resources. For access, visit **connect.mheducation.com** or contact your McGraw-Hill sales representative.

## Auto-Graded End-of-Chapter Questions

Connect® includes selected questions from the end of chapter in an auto-graded format that instructors can assign as homework and practice for students. Filtering and reporting capabilities for learning objective, topic, and level of difficulty are also available.

## SmartBook®

Proven to help students improve grades and study more efficiently, SmartBook® contains the same content within the print book but actively tailors that content to the needs of the individual. SmartBook®'s adaptive technology provides precise, personalized instruction on what the student should do next, guiding the student to master and remember key concepts, targeting gaps in knowledge and offering customized feedback, and driving the student toward comprehension and retention of the subject matter. Available on desktops and tablets, SmartBook® puts learning at the student's fingertips—anywhere, anytime.

## Instructor Resources

The Instructor's Edition within Connect® is password-protected and a convenient place for instructors to access course supplements that include the complete solutions to all problems and cases, PowerPoint slides that include both lecture materials for nearly every chapter and nearly all the figures (including all the spreadsheets) in the book, and the Test Bank, which now includes filters for topic, learning objective, and level of difficulty for choosing questions and reporting on them, and is available in three ways:

- As Word files, with both question-only and answer files.
- In TestGen, a desktop test generator and editing application for instructors to provide printed tests that can incorporate both McGraw-Hill's and instructors' questions.
- As a Connect® assignment for online testing and automatic grading; can be used for actual exams or assigned as quizzes or practice.

## Student Resources

As described above, SmartBook® provides a powerful tool to students for personalized instruction. Connect® also provides access to other course supplements of interest to students. For the convenience of students, we also are providing the website www.mhhe.com/Keating7e that will contain all of the Excel files used to generate the data and the images in the chapters. This page will also include access information to the software referred to in this text.

# Software Partnerships

## ForecastX™

As with the sixth edition, we again use the ForecastX™ software as the tool to implement the methods described in the text. This software is made available through an agreement with John Galt Solutions, Inc. Every forecasting method discussed in the text can be implemented with this software (the predictive analytics techniques, however, require separate software). Based on our own experiences and those of other faculty members who have used the sixth edition, we know that students find the ForecastX™ software easy to use, even without a manual or other written instructions. However, we have provided a brief introduction to the use of ForecastX™ at the end of each relevant chapter. There is also an extensive User's Guide within the software itself for those who may want more extensive coverage, including information on advanced issues not covered in the text but included in the software.

John Galt Solutions provides us with the ForecastX™ software that does contain proprietary algorithms, which in some situations do not match exactly with the results one would get if the calculations were done by hand. Their proprietary methods, however, have proven successful in the marketplace as well as in forecast competitions.

We are confident that faculty and students will enjoy using this widely adopted, commercially successful software. However, the text also can be used without reliance on this particular package. All data files are provided in Excel format so that they can be easily used with almost any forecasting or statistical software. As with previous editions, nearly all data in the text is real, such as jewelry sales, book store sales, and total houses sold. In addition, we have continued the use of an ongoing case involving forecasting sales of The Gap, Inc., at the end of most chapters to provide a consistent link. Additionally, a number of excellent sources of data are referenced in the text. These are especially useful for student projects and for additional exercises that instructors may wish to develop.

## Analytic Solver® for Education

**Analytic Solver® for Education** (hereafter referred to as Analytic Solver) can be used with Microsoft Excel for Windows (as an add-in), or "in the cloud" at AnalyticSolver.com using any device (PC, Mac, tablet) with a web browser. It offers comprehensive features for prescriptive analytics (optimization, simulation, decision analysis) and predictive analytics (forecasting, data mining, text mining); its optimization features are upward compatible from the standard Solver in Excel. Analytic Solver includes:

- A more interactive user interface, with optimization, simulation, and data mining elements always visible alongside the main spreadsheet.
- A model analysis tool that reveals the characteristics of an optimization model (e.g., whether it is linear or nonlinear, smooth or nonsmooth).
- Faster/more powerful 'solver engines' for optimization, plus the ability to solve problems with uncertainty using simulation optimization, robust optimization, and stochastic programming methods.
- The ability to build and run sophisticated Monte Carlo simulation models for risk analysis.
- An interactive simulation mode that allows simulation results to be shown instantly whenever a change is made to a simulation model.
- Parameterized optimization, simulation, and 'what-if' analysis reports see the effect of varying data in a model in a systematic way.
- Tools to build and solve decision trees within a spreadsheet.
- A full range of time series forecasting, data mining, and text mining algorithms, from logistic regression to neural networks.
- The ability to draw summarized results and statistically representative samples from SQL databases and Apache Spark 'Big Data' clusters.
- Basic data visualization features, plus direct links to advanced data visualization tools such as Tableau and Power BI.

If interested in having students get individual licenses for class use, instructors should send an email to support@solver.com to get their course code and receive student pricing and access information. Note that this software is no longer free with the purchase of this text, but low-cost student licenses are available.

## Prevedere

Prevedere is an industry insights and predictive analytics company, helping business leaders make better decisions by providing a real-time view of their company's future. Our external real-time insights engine constantly monitors the world's data, identifying future threats or opportunities to business performance. Along with a team of industry experts, data scientist, and economists, Prevedere helps business leaders make the right decisions in an ever-changing world. Instructors interested in getting complimentary access to Prevedere for themselves and their students should go to www.prevedere.com or call 1-888-686-7746 and ask for University Relations.

## Acknowledgements

The authors would like to thank the students at the University of Notre Dame and Central Michigan University for their help in working with materials included in this book during its development. Their comments were invaluable in preparing clear expositions and meaningful examples for this seventh edition. Comments from students at other universities in the United States and elsewhere have also been appreciated. It has been particularly gratifying to hear from students who have found what they learned from a course using this text to be useful in their professional careers. We are accessible; drop us an email if you have a comment.

The final product owes a great debt to the inspiration and comments of our colleagues, especially Professors Thomas Bundt of Hillsdale College and Tunga Kiyak at Michigan State University. In addition, we would like to thank the staff at John Galt Solutions for facilitating our use of the ForecastX™ software. We also thank Professor Eamonn Keogh at the University of California, Riverside, for sharing with you his illuminating examples of data mining techniques.

Adopters of the first six editions who have criticized, challenged, encouraged, and complimented our efforts deserve our thanks. The authors are particularly grateful to the following faculty and professionals who used earlier editions of the text and/or have provided comments that have helped to improve this seventh edition.

**Paul Altieri**
*Central Connecticut State University*

**Peter Bruce**
*Statistics.com*

**Margaret M. Capen**
*East Carolina University*

**Thomas P. Chen**
*St. John's University*

**Ronald L. Coccari**
*Cleveland State University*

**Lewis Coopersmith**
*Rider University*

**Ali Dogramaci**
*Rutgers, the State University of New Jersey*

**Farzad Farsio**
*Montana State University*

**Robert Fetter**
*Yale University*

**Benito Flores**
*Texas A & M University*

**Dan Fylstra**
*Frontline Systems*

**Kenneth Gaver**
*Montana State University*

**Rakesh Gupta**
*Adelphi University*

**Joseph Kelley**
*California State University, Sacramento*

**Thomas Kelly**
*BMW of Canada*

**Eamonn Keogh**
*University of California, Riverside*

**Krishna Kool**
*University of Rio Grande*

**Paul Mackie**
*John Galt Solutions*

**John Mathews**
*University of Wisconsin–Madison*

**Joseph McCarthy**
*Bryant College*

**Elam McElroy**
*Marquette University*

**Rob Roy McGregor**
*University of North Carolina, Charlotte*

**Jared Myers**
*Prevedere*

**John C. Nash**
*University of Ottawa*

**Thomas Needham**
*US Bancorp*

**Anne Omrod**
*John Galt Solutions*

**Nitin Patel**
*Massachusetts Institute of Technology*

**Gerald Platt**
*San Francisco State University*

**Melissa Ramenofsky**
*University of Southern Alabama*

**Helmut Schneider**
*Louisiana State University*

**Stanley Schultz**
*Cleveland State University*

**Nancy Serafino**
*United Telephone*

**Galit Shmueli**
*University of Maryland*

**Donald N. Stengel**
*California State University, Fresno*

**Kwei Tang**
*Louisiana State University*

**Rich Wagner**
*Prevedere*

**Dick Withycomb**
*University of Montana*

We are especially grateful to have worked with the following publishing professionals on our McGraw-Hill book team: Noelle Bathurst, Tobi Philips, Michele Janicek, Erika Jordan, Daryl Horrocks, and Harper Christopher.

We hope that all of the above, as well as all new faculty, students, and business professionals who use the text, will be pleased with the seventh edition.

*Barry Keating*
*Barry.P.Keating.1@nd.edu*

*J. Holton Wilson*
*Holt.Wilson@cmich.edu*

# Brief Contents

# Contents

## Chapter 3
## Extrapolation 1. Moving Averages and Exponential Smoothing    92

## Chapter 4
## Extrapolation 2. Introduction to Forecasting with Regression Trend Models    159

## Chapter 5
## Explanatory Models 1. Forecasting with Multiple Regression Causal Models    220

# Chapter 6
# Explanatory Models 2. Time-Series Decomposition    302

# Chapter 7
# Explanatory Models 3. ARIMA (Box-Jenkins) Forecasting Models    336

# Chapter One

# Introduction to Business Forecasting and Predictive Analytics

## INTRODUCTION

I believe that forecasting or demand management may have the potential to add more value to a business than any single activity within the supply chain. I say this because if you can get the forecast right, you have the potential to get everything else in the supply chain right. But if you can't get the forecast right, then everything else you do essentially will be reactive, as opposed to proactive planning.

*Al Enns, Director of Supply Chain Strategies, Motts North America, Stamford, Connecticut*[1]

## LEARNING OBJECTIVES

After studying this chapter, you should be able to:

1. Explain the three stages of prediction evolution.
2. Explain how the organization of this text relates to the stages of prediction.
3. Distinguish between qualitative and quantitative forecasting.
4. Discuss four types of qualitative forecast methods.
5. Explain how forecasting relates to supply chain efficiency.
6. Discuss forecasting for new products.
7. Describe the naive forecasting method.
8. Explain what the MAPE is and how it is used in forecasting.

[1] Sidney Hill, Jr., "A Whole New Outlook," *Manufacturing Systems* 16, no. 9 (September 1998), pp. 70–80.

# FORECASTING IS ESSENTIAL FOR SUCCESS IN BUSINESS

If you are reading this text as part of the course requirements for a college degree, consider yourself fortunate. Many college graduates, even those with degrees in business or economics, do not ever study forecasting, except as a sidelight in a course that has other primary objectives. And yet, we know that forecasting is an essential element of most business decisions.

The need for personnel with forecasting expertise is growing. For example, Levi Strauss only started its forecast department in 1995 and within four years had a full-time forecasting staff of 30. Many people filling these positions have had little formal training in forecasting and are paying thousands of dollars to attend educational programs. In annual surveys conducted by the Institute of Business Forecasting, it has been found that there are substantial increases in the staffing of forecasters in full-time positions within American companies.

## Stages in the Development of Business Forecasting

We might think of business forecasting as having developed in three stages. One way of looking at this development is illustrated in Figure 1.1. Almost anything

**FIGURE 1.1**
**Stages of light bulb and forecasting evolution.**

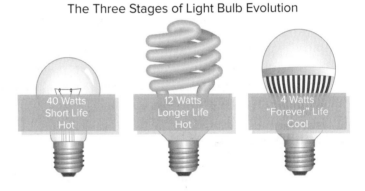

The Three Stages of Light Bulb Evolution

40 Watts
Short Life
Hot

12 Watts
Longer Life
Hot

4 Watts
"Forever" Life
Cool

The Three Stages of Prediction Evolution

| Stage I Time Series Models | Stage II Demand Planning Models | Stage III Predictive Analytics Models |
|---|---|---|
| Naïve Model | | Classification |
| Moving Average Model | | Clustering/Segmentation |
| Simple Ex. Smoothing | Simple Regression | Association Rule Mining |
| Holt's Ex. Smoothing | Multiple Regression | Text Mining |
| Holt Winter's Model | Nonlinear Regression | Entity Analytics |
| Decomposition Model | Event Model | Sentiment Analysis |
| ARIMA | | Willingness to Purchase |

you think about has gone through some evolution. In lighting, we went from primitive torches to kerosene to the first light bulbs developed by Edison in the late 1870s. Incandescent light bulbs like the one at the left in the top panel of Figure 1.1 became a worldwide standard for many years. Such light bulbs had a relatively short life, were hot, and were not energy efficient. In the late 20th century, new, more energy-efficient, longer lasting, but still hot bulbs became common. Then, in the early 21st century, LED bulbs that were cool, energy efficient, and long-lasting became the new norm.

Forecasting has gone through an evolution as well. Very early forecasting was judgmental (or subjective). In your reading, you will see that judgmental forecasting has only brief coverage. A variety of quantitative tools have been shown to outperform judgmental forecasting in most situations. However, judgments will always be important in forecasting in selecting the right forecast tools, cleaning data files, and adjusting final forecasts when human judgments are needed to adjust forecasts to account for factors not included in the data history. We will come back to this later in the chapter.

Quantitative methods have allowed organizations to forecast more accurately. The first stage of the development of quantitative forecasting relied on various time series models. Time series methods that extrapolate historical data patterns to make predictions about the future are widely used. The most common of these are included in this text. Examples are shown in the left side of the lower panel in Figure 1.1.

As research moved forward, forecasters began using causal models. These models help an organization "shape" the future rather that accept an extrapolation of historical patterns. By modelling causality, one can mold the future and better plan for the demand that lies ahead. For example, one can develop causal regression models that include independent variable that can be adjusted to meet an organizations needs. For example, promotions may be incorporated into a forecast model. Forecast methods that allow for causality are included in the text, as shown in the middle panel at the bottom of Figure 1.1.

The emergence of "Big Data" has brought with it an increased need for other analytical tools. Today every organization is confronted with a deluge of data. Organizations have more data than can easily be converted into actionable information using traditional statistical methods. New predictive analytical tools such as data or text mining have emerged and are being used by organizations globally. This has moved us into "Stage III" in the evolution of forecasting and predictive analytics.

# THE STRUCTURE OF THIS TEXT

We have divided the coverage of business forecasting and predictive analytics into three major sections. These are designed to help you progress in your ability to understand and use tools/methods in a logical way that will help you master the material.

## Section 1: Time Series Models

We begin with this current chapter ("Introduction to Business Forecasting and Predictive Analytics") in which you will get acclimated to some forecasting terminology, see examples of forecasting success, understand the difference between qualitative (subjective) and quantitative (objective) forecasts, understand judgmental, extrapolation and explanatory approaches to forecasting, as well as learn some ways to deal with new product forecasting for which we have little or no historical data. Throughout the remainder of the text, our primary focus will be on quantitative forecast applications that have come to dominate business forecasting. You will also get your first introduction to the ForecastX$^{TM}$ software. This software is quite sophisticated. It is software widely used in the business world both in the United States and abroad. For predictive analytics, we will use XLMiner; this software will allow you to estimate and experience the algorithms used in analytics (including text mining).

In Chapter 2, "The Forecast and Prediction Process: Data Considerations, and Model Selection," you will learn about the three major components of time series data, review some basic statistical concepts, start to think about when different methods would be most likely to lead to good forecasts, continue with the Gap, Inc. example that will be seen often through the text, and see some introductory forecast examples. In addition, your ability to work with the ForecastX$^{TM}$ software will be expanded.

In Chapter 3, "Extrapolation 1: Moving Averages and Exponential Smoothing," you really get into the meat of forecasting. This chapter focusses on some of the forecasting methods that analyze historical data, then replicate the patterns observed in the past to make predictions (forecasts) for the future. You will learn when moving averages can be used to forecast, how to use and interpret a variety of exponential smoothing models (including why they are called *exponential* smoothing models), what is meant by an "Event" model and when/how such a model can be used, look deeper into new product forecasting, and see application of the material in Chapter 3 to the Gap example. Your ability to use the ForecastX$^{TM}$ software will be extended to the appropriate methods from the chapter.

In Chapter 4, "Extrapolation 2: Introduction to Forecasting with Regression Trend Models," takes the concepts from Chapter 3 in a slightly different direction. In this chapter, you will learn how to apply regression analysis to make predictions about the future. Most students taking this class will have had some prior exposure to regression analysis. However, we have structured the discussion so that even with no prior background, one can learn the material. You will learn to apply simple trends for prediction and to use a causal regression model. You will also learn how you can modify a simple trend to take into account seasonal variations in data. An important element of your learning in this chapter will be how to evaluate whether a regression model is truly useful. Again you will see an application to the Gap data and will learn how to implement regression forecasts using ForecastX$^{TM}$.

## Section 2: Demand Planning

Chapter 5, "Explanatory Models 1: Forecasting with Multiple Regression Causal Models," builds on the information you learned in Chapter 4 to explicitly take into account causality. You will see that the evaluation of a causal regression model necessitates one additional step to be sure causal variables do not have too much overlap in the degree of their causality. Examples will help you master the concepts. One of the examples will be an extension of your ability to forecast the data in the ongoing Gap example. At the end of the chapter, you will learn how to use ForecastX™ to make a causal regression forecast in different ways. This depends on whether you want to specify values of the causal variables in the forecast horizon, whether you want ForecastX™ to predict those for you, or whether you prefer a mix of these approaches. There is an appendix to Chapter 4 that explains how you can use regression to combine forecasts from different methods. You will learn that often one can obtain forecast improvement by doing so.

In Chapter 6, "Explanatory Models 2: Times-Series Decomposition," you will learn about a classical approach to forecasting. This method explicitly breaks a time series of data into individual components, with the most important in forecasting being trend, seasonality and cycle. The method forecasts each component separately and then puts them together to form a forecast of the original series. Time series decomposition (TSD) is an appealing method in part because the math involved is quite simple. In fact, in days gone by, it was actually done by hand. One very useful result from TSD is that it generates an explicit measure of the degree of seasonality. Once more, TSD will be applied to forecasting the Gap data series.

Chapter 7, "Explanatory Models 3: ARIMA (Box-Jenkins) Forecasting Models" introduces you to a method of forecasting that often out performs others. However, performance comes with a price. That price in the case of ARIMA is overfitting. You will learn to use the power of ARIMA along with details of how to avoid its most serious shortcoming. ARIMA forecasts are often used as baseline forecasts allowing you to compare how other models perform compared to ARIMA.

## Section 3: Analytics

In Chapter 8, "Predictive Analytics: Helping to Make Sense of Big Data Results," you will learn the language of predictive analytics along with the new diagnostic measures that are commonly used by data scientists. This chapter is a departure from previous ones since it introduces a new and different form of prediction. The new algorithms will seem strange at first, but their predictive power is becoming more evident each year.

In Chapter 9, "Classification Models: The Most Used Models in Analytics," you will learn that all predictive analytics algorithms can be divided into a few categories; classification models are by far the most often used of these categories. As with all prediction, there is no one model that qualifies as the "best one." You will learn that each classification model has limitations as well as advantages in actual practice. These supervised learning techniques are used in a wide variety of business situations.

Chapter 10, "Ensemble Models and Clustering," continues the discussion in Chapter 9 by adding new classification models to your toolkit. In that process, you will improve your understanding of both the new diagnostic statistics and some common methods for enhancing most of the classification algorithms. You will also learn about two other classes of predictive analytics models: association rules and cluster analysis. This will be your first look at "unsupervised learning."

Chapter 11, "Text Mining: The Use of Unstructured Data," may seem to you to be the strangest of all the techniques you have learned. However, it is also the one that allows you to analyze the largest trove of unstructured data available: text. E-mails, blogs, social media, reviews, warranty claims, and internet documents are mainly text. Up to this point in your study of prediction, that text has remained outside of your ability to analyze and go from data to information. In this chapter, textual data of all types becomes available as an input to many of the algorithms you have already learned. Text mining is not so much a new algorithm as it is a method for introducing text as an input to the models we already have.

In Chapter 12, "Forecast/Analytics Implementation," you will learn some of the practical aspects of applying the knowledge learned in the first 11 chapters. In this chapter, you will learn a nine-step procedure that can be helpful in establishing a forecasting process that works in a wide variety of organizations.

## QUANTITATIVE FORECASTING HAS BECOME WIDELY ACCEPTED

We think of forecasting as a set of tools that helps decision makers make the best possible predictions about future events. In today's rapidly changing business world, such predictions can mean the difference between success and failure. It is not reasonable to rely solely on intuition, or one's "feel for the situation," in projecting future sales, inventory needs, personnel requirements, and other important economic or business variables.

Quantitative methods have been shown to be helpful in making better predictions about the future course of events than judgments alone.[2] Sophisticated computer software packages make quantitative methods readily accessible to nearly everyone. In a survey done a decade ago, it was found that about 80 percent of forecasting was done with quantitative methods.[3] The trend toward more and deeper analytics makes this even more true today. Sophisticated software such as ForecastX$^{TM}$ make it relatively easy to implement quantitative methods in a forecasting process. There is a danger, however, in using forecasting software unless you are familiar with the concepts upon which the programs are based. Thus, in this text, you will learn about a variety of methods as well as how to implement them.

This text and its accompanying computer software (ForecastX$^{TM}$) have been carefully designed to provide you with an understanding of the conceptual basis

---

[2] J. Holton Wilson and Deborah Allison-Koerber, "Combining Subjective and Objective Forecasts Improves Results," *Journal of Business Forecasting* 11, no. 3 (Fall 1992), pp. 12–16.

[3] Chaman Jain, "Benchmarking Forecasting Models," *Journal of Business Forecasting* 26, no. 4 (Winter 2007–08), p. 17.

Personal judgments based on practical experience and/or thorough research should always play an important role in the preparation of any forecast.

for many modern quantitative forecasting models, along with programs that have been written specifically for the purpose of allowing you to put these methods to use. You will find both the text and the software to be extremely user-friendly. After studying the text and using the software to replicate the examples we present, you will be able to forecast economic and business variables with greater accuracy than you might now expect. But a word of warning is appropriate. Do not become so enamored with quantitative methods and computer results that you fail to ***think*** carefully about the series you wish to forecast. In the evolution of forecasting over the last several decades, there have been many changes, but the move to more quantitative forecasting has been the most dramatic. This has been due primarily to the availability and quality of data and to the increased accessibility of user-friendly forecasting software.[4] Personal judgments based on practical experience and/or thorough research should always play an important role in the preparation of any forecast.

## FORECASTING IN BUSINESS TODAY

Forecasting in today's business world is becoming increasingly important as firms focus on increasing customer satisfaction while reducing the cost of providing products and services. Six Sigma initiatives and lean thinking are representative of moves in this direction. The term *lean* has come to represent an approach to removing waste from business systems while providing the same, or higher, levels of quality and output to customers (business customers as well as end users). Major business costs involve inventory, raw materials, various supplies, and final products. Through better forecasting, inventory costs can be reduced and wasteful inventory eliminated.

Two professional forecasting organizations offer programs specifically aimed at increasing the skills and abilities of business professionals who find forecasting an important part of their job responsibilities. The International Institute of Forecasters (IIF) offers many events at which professional forecasters share ideas with others and can participate in various tutorials and workshops designed to enhance their skills (https://forecasters.org/ ). With the leadership of Len Tashman, in 2005 the IIF started a practitioner-oriented journal, *Foresight: The International Journal of Applied Forecasting,* aimed at forecast analysts, managers, and students of forecasting.

The Institute of Business Forecasting (IBF) offers a variety of programs for business professionals where they can network with others and attend seminars and workshops to help enhance their forecasting skills (see www.ibf.org). Examples include the "Demand Planning and Forecasting Best Practices Conference," "Supply Chain Forecasting Conference," and "Business Forecasting Tutorials." The IBF also publishes a journal that focuses on applied forecasting issues (*The Journal of Business Forecasting*).

Both IIF and IBF offer forecast certification programs. IIF offers three levels of certification as a Certified Professional Demand Forecaster (CPDF); see

[4] Barry Keating et al., "Evolution in Forecasting: Experts Share Their Journey," *Journal of Business Forecasting* 25, no. 1 (Spring 2006), p. 15.

www.cpdftraining.org. IBF offers two levels of certification as a Certified Professional Forecaster (CPF); see www.ibf.org/certjbf.cfm. Both organizations present a variety of workshops and training sessions to prepare business professionals for certification. After completing this course, you will have a good knowledge base to get started toward certification from these organizations.

Business decisions almost always depend on some forecast about the course of events. Virtually every functional area of business makes use of some type of forecast. For example:

1. Accountants rely on forecasts of costs and revenues in tax planning.
2. The personnel department depends on forecasts as it plans recruitment of new employees and other changes in the workforce.
3. Financial experts must forecast cash flows to maintain solvency.
4. Production managers rely on forecasts to determine raw-material needs and the desired inventory of finished products.
5. Marketing managers use a sales forecast to establish promotional budgets.

Because forecasting is useful in so many functional areas of an organization it is not surprising that this activity is found in many different areas. Consider the following survey results concerning forecasting responsibility within their organizations:[5]

| Functional Area | Percent Contributing Information to the Forecast | Percent That "Own" the Forecast |
|---|---|---|
| Sales | 84% | 43% |
| Marketing | 81% | 31% |
| Finance | 48% | 18% |
| Planning | 43% | 21% |
| Production | 38% | 4% |
| Logistics | 24% | 7% |
| Purchasing | 12% | 4% |

The sales forecast is often the root forecast from which others, such as employment requirements, are derived.

The sales forecast is often the root forecast from which others, such as employment requirements, are derived. As early as the mid-1980s, a study of large American-operated firms showed that roughly 94 percent made use of a sales forecast.[6] The ways in which forecasts are prepared and the manner in which results are used vary considerably among firms.

As a way of illustrating the application of forecasting in the corporate world, we will look at two examples of successes with business forecasting. In these examples, you may see some terms with which you are not fully familiar at this time. However, you probably have a general understanding of them, and when you have completed the text, you will understand them all quite well.

[5] Adapted from T. M. McCarthy, D. F. Davis, S. L. Golicic, and J. T. Mentzer, "The Evolution of Sales Forecasting Management," *Journal of Forecasting*, 25, (2006): 303-324, p. 309.
[6] Wilson and Allison-Koerber, pp. 12–16.

Due to a manual and high-level forecasting process, Post Foods struggled to plan production timely and accurately. Forecasts were produced mainly by input from the sales team, which focused on recent events, driving short-term volatility of the forecast. Forecasts were produced at the national and monthly level, making it difficult to plan by location or incorporate the promotional demand that drives Post's business. To maintain customer service levels, Post was forced to drive up inventory to compensate.

Post selected John Galt Solutions to drive a new statistical forecasting and planning process. This allowed Post to drive their forecasts by item and location, giving the production team the detail they needed to produce an accurate plan.

In the first few months of implementation, **Post was able to reduce finished goods inventory 12 percent** while maintaining customer service. With the superior forecast accuracy, Post could plan their material requirements far into the future, enabling them to use sophisticated hedging strategies to improve their procurement costs and meet strategic objectives. Post has also been able to reduce the number of changes to the production schedule, making it easier for them to sustain their plan over time and reducing cost further. In addition, by managing the planning process, Post eliminated the delays in forecast entry, gaining further efficiency and making effective decision-making possible.

Since 1991, Radio Systems and their Petsafe and Invisible Fence brands have led the industry in pet training, containment, safety, and lifestyle product solutions. Radio Systems released the world's first do-it-yourself electronic pet fence in 1991 and followed up in 1998 with the world's first wireless electronic pet fence. With Radio Systems products, pet owners can rest secure in the knowledge that their pets are protected humanely.

During a period of rapid growth, Radio Systems recognized the importance of a one-number consensus forecast. With 12 sales managers dispersed throughout the United States and three in Europe, reconciling the forecast posed a major technical challenge. Forecast accuracy and inventory management were also crucial, due to the international sourcing of many of Petsafe's components.

In order to improve supply chain performance, Radio Systems sought to produce a forecast that was both grounded in solid statistics and reflected the numerous opinions of the sales managers. The solution that they chose had to be able to centralize those numerous plans from worldwide sources, be easy for the sales managers to understand and use, and not require major installation at the overseas locations.

Petsafe determined that the Planning Portal from John Galt was uniquely able to meet their global collaboration needs. The Planning Portal's Web-based architecture enables far-flung collaborators to contribute to a one-number plan without implementing a bulky software package on the client side. In addition, they obtained the world's most advanced statistical baseline to build the consensus.

The sales team was able to pick up on the software in only a few hours, allowing Radio Systems to quickly work on producing their consensus.

Radio Systems' planners were able to not only build a one-number consensus forecast but also to construct a formal supply and operations planning (S&OP) process that includes project managers and SKU directors.

Ocean Spray is one example of a company that faces many global challenges that affect forecasting.

Sean Reese, a demand planner at Ocean Spray Cranberries, Inc., summarized some issues that are particularly important for anyone involved in forecasting in a global environment. First, units of measurement differ between the United States and most other countries. Where the United States uses such measures as ounces, pounds, quarts, and gallons, most other countries use grams, kilograms, milliliters, and liters. Making appropriate conversions and having everyone involved understand the relationships can be a challenge.[7]

Second, seasonal patterns reverse between the Northern and Southern Hemispheres, so it makes a difference whether one is forecasting for a Northern or Southern Hemisphere market. Third, such cultural differences as preference for degree of sweetness, shopping habits, and perception of colors can impact sales. The necessary lead time for product and ingredient shipments can vary a great deal depending on the geographic regions involved. Further, since labels are different, one must forecast specifically for each country rather than the system as a whole. Consider, for example, two markets that may at first appear similar: the United States and Canada. These two markets use different units of measurement, and in Canada labels must have all information equally in both French and English. Thus, products destined to be sold in one market cannot be sold in the other market, so each forecast must be done separately.

# FORECASTING IN THE PUBLIC AND NOT-FOR-PROFIT SECTORS

The need to make decisions based on judgments about the future course of events extends beyond the profit-oriented sector of the economy. Hospitals, libraries, blood banks, police and fire departments, urban transit authorities, credit unions, and a myriad of federal, state, and local governmental units rely on forecasts of one kind or another. Social service agencies such as the Red Cross and the Easter Seal Society must also base their yearly plans on forecasts of needed services and expected revenues. The following three examples will help you see that the importance of forecasting goes well beyond for profit businesses.

## A Police Department

Brooke Saladin, working with the research and planning division of the police department in a city of about 650,000 people, was effective in forecasting the demand for police patrol services.[8] This demand is measured by using a call-for-service workload level in units of hours per 24-hour period. After a thorough statistical analysis, five factors were identified as influential determinants of the call-for-service work load ($W$):

[7] Sean Reese, "Reflections of an International Forecaster," *Journal of Business Forecasting* 22, no. 4 (Winter 2003–04), pp. 23, 28.

[8] Brooke A. Saladin, "A Police Story with Business Implications and Applications," *Journal of Business Forecasting* 1, no. 6 (Winter 1982–83), pp. 3–5.

POP   a population factor
ARR   an arrest factor
AFF   an affluence factor
VAC   a vacancy factor
DEN   a density factor

You will learn how to develop, evaluate, and apply multiple regression models in Chapter 5. The following multiple regression model was developed on the basis of a sample of 40 cruiser districts in the city:

$$W = 5.66 + 1.84\text{POP} + 1.70\text{ARR} - 0.93\text{AFF} + 0.61\text{VAC} + 0.13\text{DEN}$$

Using the remaining 23 cruiser districts to test this model, Saladin found that "the absolute error in forecasting workload ranged from 0.07827 to 1.49764, with an average of 0.74618."[9] This type of model is useful in planning the needs for both personnel and equipment.

## The Texas Legislative Board

In Texas, the Legislative Budget Board is required to forecast the growth rate for Texas personal income, which then governs the limit for state appropriations. The state comptroller's office also needs forecasts of such variables as the annual growth rates of electricity sales, total nonagricultural employment, and total tax revenues. Richard Ashley and John Guerard have used techniques like those to be discussed in this text to forecast these variables and have found that the application of time-series analysis yields better one-year-ahead forecasts than naive constant-growth-rate models.[10]

## The California Legislative Analysis Office

Dr. Jon David Vasche, senior economist for the California Legislative Analysis Office (LAO), needed to prepare economic and financial forecasting for the state. He has noted that these forecasts are essential, since the state's budget must be prepared long before actual economic conditions are known.[11] The key features of the LAO's forecasting approach are:

1. *Forecasts of national economic variables.* The Wharton econometric model is used with the adaptations that reflect the LAO's own assumptions about such policy variables as monetary growth and national fiscal policies.

2. *California economic submodel.* This model forecasts variables such as trends in state population, personal income, employment, and housing activity.

---

[9] Ibid., p. 5.

[10] Richard Ashley and John Guerard, "Applications of Time-Series Analysis to Texas Financial Forecasting," *Interfaces* 13, no. 4 (August 1983), pp. 46–55.

[11] Jon David Vasche, "Forecasting Process as Used by California Legislative Analyst's Office," *Journal of Business Forecasting* 6, no. 2 (Summer 1987), pp. 9–13; and "State Demographic Forecasting for Business and Policy Applications," *Journal of Business Forecasting*, Summer 2000, pp. 23–30.

3. *State revenue submodels.* These models are used to forecast the variables that affect the state's revenue. These include such items as taxable personal income, taxable sales, corporate profits, vehicle registrations, and cash available for investment.

4. *Cash-flow models.* These models are used to forecast the flow of revenues over time.

In developing and using forecasting models, "the LAO has attempted to strike a balance between comprehensiveness and sophistication on the one hand, and flexibility and usability on the other."[12] LAO's success is determined by how accurately it forecasts the state's revenues. In the three most recent years reported, the "average absolute value of the actual error was only about 1.6 percent."[13]

# FORECASTING AND SUPPLY CHAIN MANAGEMENT

In recent years, there has been increased attention to supply chain management issues. In a competitive environment, businesses are forced to operate with maximum efficiency and with a vigilant eye toward maintaining firm cost controls, while continuing to meet consumer expectations in a profitable manner. To be successful, businesses must manage relationships along the supply chain more fully than ever before. This can be aided by effectively using the company's own sales organization and making forecasting an integral part of the sales and operations planning (S&OP) process.

We can think of the supply chain as encompassing all of the various flows between suppliers, producers, distributors (wholesalers, retailers, etc.), and consumers. Throughout this chain, each participant, prior to the final consumer, must manage supplies, inventories, production, and shipping in one form or another. For example, a manufacturer that makes cellular phones needs a number of different components to assemble the final product and ultimately ship it to a local supplier of cellular phone services or some other retailer. One such component might be a leather carrying case. The manufacturer of the carrying case may have suppliers of leather, clear plastic for portions of the case, fasteners, dyes, and possibly other components. Each one of these suppliers has its own suppliers back one more step in the supply chain. With all of these businesses trying to reduce inventory costs (for raw materials, goods in process, and finished products), reliability and cooperation across the supply chain becomes essential.

Forecasting has come to play an important role in managing supply chain relationships. If the supplier of leather phone cases is to be a good supply chain partner, it must have a reasonably accurate forecast of the needs of the cellular phone company. The cellular phone company, in turn, needs a good forecast of sales to be able to provide the leather case company with good information. It is probably obvious that if the cellular phone company is aware of a significant change in

[12] Vasche, "Forecasting Process," pp. 9, 12.
[13] Ibid., p. 12.

sales for a future period, that information needs to be communicated to the leather case company in a timely manner.

To help make the entire supply chain function more smoothly, many companies have started to use collaborative forecasting systems in which information about the forecast is shared throughout the relevant portions of the supply chain. Often, in fact, suppliers have at least some input into the forecast of a business further along the supply chain in such collaborative forecasting systems.[14] Having good forecasts at every stage is essential for efficient functioning of the supply chain.

At the beginning of the text, at the very start of page 1, you read the following quote from Al Enns, director of supply chain strategies, at Motts North America:

> I believe that forecasting or demand management may have the potential to add more value to a business than any single activity within the supply chain. I say this because *if you can get the forecast right, you have the potential to get everything else in the supply chain right.* But if you can't get the forecast right, then everything else you do essentially will be reactive, as opposed to proactive planning.[15]

Daphney Barr, a planning coordinator for Velux-America, a leading manufacturer of roof windows and skylights, has similarly observed that:

> Demand planning is the key driver of the supply chain. Without knowledge of demand, manufacturing has very little on which to develop production and inventory plans while logistics in turn has limited information and resources to develop distribution plans for products among different warehouses and customers. *Simply stated, demand forecasting is the wheel that propels the supply chain forward* and the demand planner is the driver of the forecasting process.[16]

These are two examples of the importance business professionals give to the role of forecasting.

There is another issue that is partially related to where a business operates along the supply chain that is important to think about when it comes to forecasting. As one gets closer to the consumer end of the supply chain, the number of items to forecast tends to increase. For example, consider a manufacturer that produces a single product that is ultimately sold through discount stores. Along the way, it may pass through several intermediaries. That manufacturer only needs to forecast sales of that one product (and, of course, the potentially many components that go into the product). But consider Wal-Mart, which sells the product to consumers throughout the United States. Just think of the tens of thousands of stockkeeping units (SKUs) that Wal-Mart sells and must forecast. Clearly the methods that the

In left margin: *To help make the entire supply chain function more smoothly, many companies have started to use collaborative forecasting systems in which information about the forecast is shared throughout the relevant portions of the supply chain.*

[14] Many forecasting software packages facilitate collaborative forecasting by making the process Web-based so that multiple participants can potentially have access to, and in some cases input into, the forecast process.

[15] Sidney Hill, Jr., "A Whole New Outlook," *Manufacturing Systems* 16, no. 9 (September 1998), pp. 70–80. (*Emphasis* added.)

[16] Daphney P. Barr, "Challenges Facing a Demand Planner: How to Identify and Handle Them," *Journal of Business Forecasting* 21, no. 2 (Summer 2002), pp. 28–29. (*Emphasis* added.)

manufacturer considers in preparing a forecast can be much more labor intensive than the methods that Wal-Mart can consider. An organization like Wal-Mart will be limited to applying forecasting methods that can be easily automated and can be quickly applied. This is something you will want to think about as you study the various forecast methods discussed in this text.

# COLLABORATIVE FORECASTING

The recognition that improving functions throughout the supply chain can be aided by appropriate use of forecasting tools has led to increased cooperation among supply chain partners. In the simplest form, the process is as follows: A manufacturer that produces a consumer good computes its forecast. That forecast is then shared with the retailers that sell that product to end-use consumers. Those retailers respond with any specific knowledge that they have regarding their future intentions related to purchases based on known promotions, programs, shutdowns, or other proprietary information about which the manufacturer may not have had any prior knowledge. The manufacturer then updates the forecast including the shared information. In this way, the forecast becomes a shared collaborative effort between the parties.

All participants in the supply chain stand to benefit. With so much to gain, it's no wonder that there are many companies that have successfully implemented collaborative forecasting partnerships. Companies that have adopted collaborative forecasting programs have generally seen very positive results.

The value of information sharing has been documented in many studies. Consider one such study of a small to midsized retailer with about $1 billion in annual sales. This retailer operates at more than 20 locations each with multiple retail outlets including department stores, mass merchandisers, and convenience stores. As a result of sharing information in the supply chain, the retailer achieved supply chain savings at the two biggest locations of about 15 percent and 33 percent.[17]

To effectively use collaborative planning, forecasting, and replenishment (CPFR), a company must be prepared to share information using electronic data transfer via the Internet. A number of software developers offer programs that are designed to create that data link between parties. It is this link to electronic data and the use of the Internet that is the first hurdle companies must overcome when considering CPFR. A company needs to be committed to an electronic data platform including available hardware, software, and support staff. Depending on the size of the company and the complexity of the integration, the amount of resources can vary greatly.

One of the most interesting problems to consider when establishing a collaborative relationship is how to deal with a nonparticipant. That is, if a manufacturer

---

[17] Tonya Boone and Ram Ganeshan, "The Value of Information Sharing in the Retail Supply Chain: Two Case Studies," *Foresight*, 9 (Spring 2008), pp. 12–17.

sells to two customers—one that enters the collaborative relationship and one that doesn't—are they both entitled to the benefits that result? At the center of the issue is the preferential delivery of goods to the customer with the collaborative relationship. If that customer is guaranteed first delivery of goods over the nonparticipating customer, then the nonparticipant bears nearly all the risk of stock-outs.

Information surrounding collaboration, such as new product launches and special promotions, is very sensitive and could be at risk. Securing this information and ensuring that it doesn't become public knowledge add to the importance of the job of the software administrator. At the very least, the issue of confidentiality must be addressed between the parties, and proper measures should be put in place to ensure all parties are satisfied that their interests are protected.

# COMPUTER USE AND QUANTITATIVE FORECASTING

In today's business environment, computers are at the heart of business analytics, including forecasting. The widespread availability of computers has contributed to the use of quantitative forecasting techniques, many of which would not be practical to carry out by hand. Most of the methods described in this text fall into the realm of quantitative forecasting techniques that are reasonable to use only when appropriate computer software is available. A number of software packages, at costs that range from about $100 to many thousands of dollars, are currently marketed for use in developing forecasts. You will find that the software that accompanies this text will enable you to apply the most commonly used quantitative forecasting techniques to data of your choosing.

The use of personal computers in forecasting has been made possible by rapid technological changes that have made desktop and laptop computers very fast and capable of storing and processing large amounts of data. User-friendly software makes it easy for people to become proficient in using forecasting and other analytic programs in a short period of time. The dominance of PC forecasting software is clear at the annual meetings of the major forecasting associations. At these meetings various vendors of PC-based forecasting software packages display and demonstrate their products.

The importance of quantitative methods in forecasting has been stressed by Charles W. Chase, Jr., who was formerly director of forecasting at Johnson & Johnson Consumer Products, Inc., and now is at the SAS Institute, Inc. He says, "Forecasting is a blend of science and art. Like most things in business, the rule of 80/20 applies to forecasting. By and large, forecasts are driven 80 percent mathematically and 20 percent judgmentally."[18]

[18] Charles W. Chase, Jr., "Forecasting Consumer Products," *Journal of Business Forecasting* 10, no. 1 (Spring 1991), p. 2.

# QUALITATIVE OR SUBJECTIVE FORECASTING METHODS

Quantitative techniques using the power of the computer have come to dominate the forecasting landscape. However, there is a rich history of forecasting based on subjective and judgmental methods, some of which remain useful even today. These methods are probably most appropriately used when the forecaster is faced with a severe shortage of historical data and/or when quantitative expertise is not available. In some situations, a judgmental method may even be preferred to a quantitative one. Very long range forecasting is an example of such a situation. The computer-based models that are the focal point of this text have less applicability to such things as forecasting the type of home entertainment that will be available 40 years from now than do those methods based on expert judgments. In this section, several subjective or judgmental forecasting methods are reviewed.

## Sales Force Composites

The sales force can be a rich source of information about future trends and changes in buyer behavior. These people have daily contact with buyers and are the closest contact most firms have with their customers. If the information available from the sales force is organized and collected in an objective manner, considerable insight into future sales volumes can be obtained.

Members of the sales force are asked to estimate sales for each product they handle. These estimates are usually based on each individual's subjective "feel" for the level of sales that would be reasonable in the forecast period. Often a range of forecasts will be requested, including a most optimistic, a most pessimistic, and a most likely forecast. Typically, these individual projections are aggregated by the sales manager for a given product line and/or geographic area. Ultimately, the person responsible for the firm's total sales forecast combines the product-line and/or geographic forecasts to arrive at projections that become the basis for a given planning horizon.

While this process takes advantage of information from sources very close to actual buyers, a major problem with the resulting forecast may arise if members of the sales force tend to underestimate sales for their product lines and/or territories. This behavior is particularly likely when the salespeople are assigned quotas on the basis of their forecasts and when bonuses are based on performance relative to those quotas. Such a downward bias can be very harmful to the firm. Scheduled production runs are shorter than they should be, raw-material inventories are too small, labor requirements are underestimated, and in the end, customer ill will is generated by product shortages. The sales manager with ultimate forecasting responsibility can offset this downward bias, but only by making judgments that could, in turn, incorporate other bias into the forecast.

## Surveys of Customers and the General Population

In some situations, it may be practical to survey customers for advanced information about their buying intentions. This practice presumes that buyers plan their purchases and follow through with their plans. Such an assumption is probably more realistic for industrial sales than for sales to households and individuals. It is also more realistic for big-ticket items such as cars than for convenience goods such as toothpaste or tennis balls.

Survey data concerning how people feel about the economy are sometimes used by forecasters to help predict certain buying behaviors. One of the commonly used measures of how people feel about the economy comes from a monthly survey conducted by the University of Michigan Survey Research Center (SRC). The SRC produces an Index of Consumer Sentiment (UMICS) based on a survey of individuals, 40 percent of whom are respondents who participated in the survey six months earlier and the remaining 60 percent new respondents selected on a random basis. This index has its base period in 1966, when the index was 100. High values of the UMICS indicate more positive feelings about the economy than do lower values. Thus, if the UMICS goes up, one might expect that people are more likely to make certain types of purchases.

## Jury of Executive Opinion

The judgments of experts in any area are a valuable resource. Based on years of experience, such judgments can be useful in the forecasting process. Using the method known as the *jury of executive opinion,* a forecast is developed by combining the subjective opinions of the managers and executives who are most likely to have the best insights about the firm's business. To provide a breadth of opinions, it is useful to select these people from different functional areas. For example, personnel from finance, marketing, and production might be included.

The person responsible for making the forecast may collect opinions in individual interviews or in a meeting where the participants have an opportunity to discuss various points of view. The latter has some obvious advantages such as stimulating deeper insights, but it has some important disadvantages as well. For example, if one or more strong personalities dominate the group, their opinions will become disproportionately important in the final consensus that is reached.

## The Delphi Method

The Delphi method is similar to the jury of executive opinion in taking advantage of the wisdom and insight of people who have considerable expertise about the area to be forecast. It has the additional advantage, however, of anonymity among the participants. The experts, perhaps five to seven in number, never meet to discuss their views; none of them even knows who else is on the panel.

The Delphi method can be summarized by the following six steps:

1. Participating panel members are selected.
2. Questionnaires asking for opinions about the variables to be forecast are distributed to panel members.
3. Results from panel members are collected, tabulated, and summarized.
4. Summary results are distributed to the panel members for their review and consideration.

5. Panel members revise their individual estimates, taking account of the information received from the other, unknown panel members.

6. Steps 3 through 5 are repeated until no significant changes result.

Through this process, there is usually movement toward centrality, but there is no pressure on panel members to alter their original projections. Members who have strong reason to believe that their original response is correct, no matter how widely it differs from others, may freely stay with it. Thus, in the end, there may not be a consensus.

The Delphi method may be superior to the jury of executive opinion, since strong personalities or peer pressures have no influence on the outcome. The processes of sending out questionnaires, getting them back, tabulating, and summarizing has been made much more efficient by using Internet-based processes.

### Some Advantages and Disadvantages of Subjective Methods

Subjective (i.e., qualitative or judgmental) forecasting methods are sometimes considered desirable because they do not require any particular mathematical background of the individuals involved. As future business professionals, like yourself, become better trained in quantitative forms of analysis, this advantage will become less important. Historically, another advantage of subjective methods has been their wide acceptance by users. However, our experience suggests that users are increasingly concerned with how the forecast was developed, and with most subjective methods, it is difficult to be specific in this regard. The underlying models are, by definition, subjective.

This subjectivity is nonetheless the most important advantage of this class of methods. There are often forces at work that cannot be captured by quantitative methods. They can, however, be sensed by experienced business professionals and can make an important contribution to improved forecasts. Wilson and Allison-Koerber have shown this dramatically in the context of forecasting sales for a large item of food-service equipment produced by the Delfield Company.[19] Quantitative methods reduced errors to about 60 percent of those that resulted from the subjective method that had been in use. When the less accurate subjective method was combined with the quantitative methods, errors were further reduced to about 40 percent of the level when the subjective method was used alone. It is clear from this result, and others, that there is often important information content in subjective methods.

# NEW-PRODUCT FORECASTING

Quantitative forecasting methods, which are the primary focus of this text, are not usually well suited for predicting sales of new products, because they rely on a historical data series for products upon which to establish model parameters. Often judgmental methods are better suited to forecasting new-product sales because

---

[19] Wilson and Allison-Koerber, "Combining Subjective and Objective Forecasts," p. 15.

there are many uncertainties and few known relationships. However, there are ways to make reasonable forecasts for new products. These typically include both qualitative judgments and quantitative tools of one type or another. One way to deal with the lack of known information in the forecasting of new products is to incorporate a modified version of the Delphi method.

## Using Marketing Research to Aid New-Product Forecasting

Various market research activities can be helpful in new-product forecasting. Surveys of potential customers can provide useful preliminary information about the propensity of buyers to adopt a new product. Test-market results and results from the distribution of free samples can also provide estimates of initial sales. On the basis of predictions about the number of initial innovators who will buy a product, an S-shaped market-penetration curve can be used to forecast diffusion of the new product throughout the market.

Whitlark, Geurts, and Swenson have used customer purchase intention surveys as a tool to help prepare forecasts of new products.[20] They describe a three-step process that starts with the identification of a demographic profile of the target market, then the probability of purchase is estimated from survey data, and finally a forecast is developed by combining this probability with information on the size of the target market. A sample of consumers from the target market is asked to respond to an intent-to-purchase scale such as: definitely will buy; probably will buy; might or might not buy; probably will not buy; and definitely will not buy. Probabilities are then assigned to each of the intention-to-buy categories, using empirical evidence from a longitudinal study of members of the target market covering a length of time comparable to the length of time for the proposed forecast horizon. An example of these probabilities for a three- and a six-month time horizon is shown in Table 1.1. Note that the probabilities of purchase increase as the time horizon increases.

**TABLE 1.1**
**Probabilities Assigned to Purchase-Intention Categories**

| Intention-to-Purchase Category | Three-Month Time Horizon | Six-Month Time Horizon |
|---|---|---|
| Definitely will buy | 64% | 75% |
| Probably will buy | 23 | 53 |
| Might or might not buy | 5 | 21 |
| Probably will not buy | 2 | 9 |
| Definitely will not buy | 1 | 4 |

Source: Whitlark, David B., Geurts, Michael D., and Swenson, Michael J. "New Product Forecasting with a Purchase Intention Survey," *Journal of Business Forecasting* 10, no. 3 (Fall 1993), pp. 18–21.

[20] David B. Whitlark, Michael D. Geurts, and Michael J. Swenson, "New Product Forecasting with a Purchase Intention Survey," *Journal of Business Forecasting* 10, no. 3 (Fall 1993), pp. 18–21.

Applying this method to two products produced good results. For the first product, the three-month forecast purchase rate was 2.9 percent compared with an actual purchase rate of 2.4 percent. In the six-month time horizon, the forecast and actual rates were 15.6 percent and 11.1 percent, respectively. Similar results were found for a second product. In the three-month horizon, the forecast and actual percents were 2.5 percent versus 1.9 percent, while in the six-month forecast horizon, the forecast was 16.7 percent and the actual was 16.3 percent.

## The Product Life Cycle Concept
## Aids in New-Product Forecasting

The concept of a product life cycle (PLC), such as is shown in Figure 1.2, can be a useful framework for thinking about new-product forecasting. During the introductory stage of the product life cycle, only consumers who are classified as "innovators" are likely to buy the product. Sales start low and increase slowly at first; then, near the end of this stage, sales start to increase at an increasing rate. Typically, products in this introductory stage are associated with negative profit margins as high front-end costs and substantial promotional expenses are incurred.

As the product enters the growth stage of the life cycle, sales are still increasing at an increasing rate as "early adopters" enter the market. Eventually, in this stage the rate of growth in sales starts to decline and profits typically become positive. Near the end of the growth stage, sales growth starts to level off substantially as the product enters the maturity stage. Here profits normally reach the maximum level. Businesses often employ marketing strategies to extend this stage as long as possible. However, all products eventually reach the stage of decline in sales and are, at some point, removed from the market (such as Oldsmobile cars, which had been in the automobile market for a century).

This notion of a product life cycle can be applied to a product class (such as personal passenger vehicles), to a product form (such as sport utility vehicles), or to a brand (such as the GMC Yukon). Product life cycles are not uniform in shape or duration and vary from industry to industry. For high-tech electronic

**FIGURE 1.2**

**A product life cycle curve.**

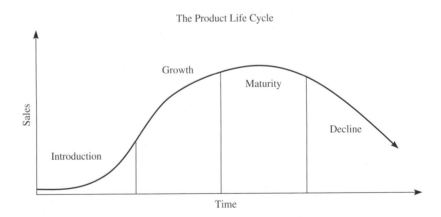

The Product Life Cycle

products, life cycles may be as short as six to nine months. An example would be a cell phone.

The forecasting approach that is best will vary depending on where a product or product class is in the life cycle. Once the mid-to-late growth stage is reached, there is probably sufficient historical data to consider a wide array of quantitative methods. The real forecasting problems occur in the introductory stage (or in the preintroductory product development stage). Here the forecaster finds traditional quantitative methods of limited usefulness and must often turn to marketing research techniques and/or qualitative forecasting techniques.

## Analog Forecasts

The basic idea behind the analog method is that the forecast of the new product is related to information that you have about the introduction of other similar products in the past. Suppose that you work for a toy company that sells toys to children in the 4-to-14 age group. Two years ago for the Christmas season, you introduced a toy that was based on a popular animated Christmas movie. The percentage of total market households that purchased that product was 1.3 percent, 60 percent of potential toy stores stocked the product, and your company spent $750,000 on promotions. Now you have a new toy to bring to market this Christmas season, and you need some estimate of sales. Suppose that this new product appeals to a narrower age range such that the likely percentage of households that would purchase the product is 1.1 percent and that you can expect comparable promotional support as well as comparable acceptance by retailers in stocking the product. Assuming that the only change is the percentage of households likely to purchase the product, the relation of sales of the new product to the old one would be 1.1 ÷ 1.3 (which equals 0.84615). If the previous product sold 100,000 units in the first quarter of introduction and 120,000 in the second quarter of introduction, you might forecast sales for your new product as 84,615 in the first quarter and 101,538 in the second quarter. If the size of the relevant population, the percentage of stores stocking the product, or the promotional effort changes, you would adjust the forecast accordingly.

## Test Marketing

Test marketing involves introducing a product to a small part of the total market before doing a full product roll-out. The test market should have characteristics that are similar to those of the total market along relevant dimensions. For example, usually we would look for a test market that has a distribution similar to the national market in terms of age, ethnicity, and income, as well as any other characteristics that would be relevant for the product in question. The test market should be relatively isolated in terms of the product being tested to prevent product and/or information flow to or from other areas. For example, Kansas City, Missouri, would not usually be a good test market because there would be a good deal of crossover between Kansas City, Missouri, and Kansas City, Kansas. Indianapolis, Indiana, on the other hand, might be a better choice of a test market for many types of products because it has a demographic mix that is similar to the entire country and is relatively isolated in the context discussed here. Suppose we do a test market in one or more test cities and sell an average of 1.7 units per 10,000 households. If, in the total market, there are 100 million households, we might project sales to be 17,000 units ([1.7 ÷ 10,000] × 100,000,000 = 17,000). The cost of doing a local roll-out is far less than a national roll-out and can provide significant new information.

## Product Clinics

The use of product clinics is a marketing research technique in which potential customers are invited to a specific location and are shown a product mock-up or prototype, which in some situations is essentially the final product. These people are asked to "experience the product," which may mean tasting a breakfast cereal, using a software product, or driving a test vehicle. Afterward, they are asked to evaluate the product during an in-depth personal interview and/or by filling out a product evaluation survey. Part of this evaluation would normally include some measure of likelihood to purchase the product. From these results, a statistical probability of purchase for the population can be estimated and used to predict product sales. The use of in-home product evaluations is a similar process. A panel of consumers is asked to try the product at home for an appropriate period of time and then is asked to evaluate the product, including an estimate of likelihood to purchase.

## Type of Product Affects New-Product Forecasting

All products have life cycles and the cycles have similar patterns, but there may be substantial differences from one product to another. Think, for example, about products that are fashion items or fads in comparison with products that have real staying power in the marketplace. Fashion items and products that would be considered fads typically have a steep introductory stage followed by short growth and maturity stages and a decline that is also very steep.

## The Bass Model for New-Product Forecasting

The Bass model for sales of new products, first published in 1969, is probably the most notable model for new-product forecasting. Its importance is highlighted by the fact that it was republished in *Management Science* in December 2004.[21] This model gives rise to product diffusion curves that look like those illustrated in Figure 1.3. The Bass model was originally developed for application only to durable goods. However, it has been adapted for use in forecasting a wide variety of products with short product life cycles and new products with limited historical data.

The model developed by Bass is:

$$S_t = pm + (q - p) * Y_t - (q/m) * Y_t^2$$

---

[21] Frank M. Bass, "A New Product Growth Model for Consumer Durables," *Management Science* 50, no. 12S (December 2004), pp. 1825–32. See also Gary Lilien, Arvind Rangaswamy, and Christophe Van den Bulte, "Diffusion Models: Managerial Applications and Software," ISBM Report 7-1999, Institute for the Study of Business Markets, Pennsylvania State University. Available at http://www.ebusiness.xerox.com/isbm/dscgi/ds.py/Get/File-89/7-1999.pdf.

**FIGURE 1.3**  **Examples of new-product diffusion curves.**

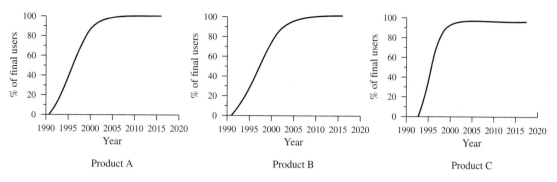

Product A          Product B          Product C

Where:

$S_t$ = Sales at time period $t$.

$p$ = Probability of initial purchase at time $t = 0$. This reflects the importance of innovators and is called the coefficient of innovation.

$m$ = Number of initial purchases of product over the life cycle (excludes replacement purchases).

$q$ = Coefficient of imitation representing the propensity to purchase based on the number of people who have already purchased the product.

$Y_t$ = Number of previous buyers at time $t$.

The values for $p$, $q$, and $m$ can be estimated using a statistical tool called *regression analysis,* which is covered in Chapters 4 and 5 of this text. The algebraic form for the regression model is:

$$S_t = a + b\,Y_{t-1} + c\,Y_{t-1}^2$$

From the regression estimates for $a$, $b$, and $c$ the values of $p$, $q$, and $m$ can be derived. Note that:

$$a = pm$$
$$b = q - p$$
$$c = -q/m$$

Bass shows that:

$$p = a/m \qquad q = -mc \qquad \text{and} \qquad m = (-b \pm [b^2 - 4ac]^{0.5})/2c$$

Getting the estimates of the three parameters in the Bass model is the difficult part. If the product is entirely new and in a prelaunch stage, we might gather data for an analogous product for which a sales history is known, such as a previous model of a cell phone. Once the product has been launched, knowing even four or five values of sales we can get preliminary estimates of the parameters. As a sales history develops, these estimates can be refined.

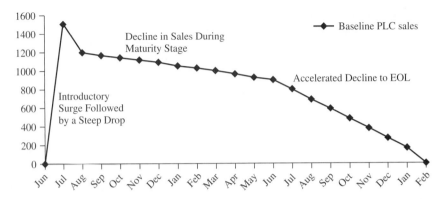

**FIGURE 1.4**

**A Typical PLC for a short-lived product.** An initial product launch is followed by a sharp decline, then a more modest drop in sales, and finally a steeper drop to the end of the PLC. (Data are in the c1t2&f3,4 file.)

## Forecasting Sales for New Products That Have Short Product Life Cycles

In an age of rapid change there are many products that have short product life cycles. This is especially true of high-tech products for which technological change and/or marketing strategies make products obsolete relatively quickly. Cell phones would be a good example. New cell phones with a variety of enhancements seem to appear almost weekly. Such products may have a life cycle of perhaps 12 to 24 months, which means that there is little time to gather historical data upon which to base a forecast. It also means that the initial forecasts are exceptionally important because there is less time to recover from either over- or underprojecting sales.

The life cycle for this type of situation may look something like that shown in Figure 1.4. Upon introduction, sales are typically high then drop quickly, level out to a slower rate of decline for some period, followed by a more rapid drop to the end of the product's life cycle (EOL). We illustrate this in Figure 1.4 for a product with a 20-month PLC. The data shown in such a graph can frequently be developed by looking at the historic PLC for similar products, such as past generations of cell phones.[22]

Suppose that we know that there has been a seasonal pattern for similar products in the past. Based on this knowledge, a natural bump to sales can be expected during the back-to-school period in August and September, followed by increased buying during the holiday season and another bump when people get tax returns in March. Based on knowledge from past product introductions, the seasonal indices are estimated to be:

August, 1.15
September, 1.10
November, 1.10
December, 1.30
March, 1.05

You will see how such seasonal indices are computed later in the text. A complete list of the seasonal indices (SI) for this product is shown in Table 1.2.

---

[22] The work of Burress and Kuettner at Hewlett-Packard provides a foundation for this example. See Jim Burress and Dorothea Kuettner, "Forecasting for Short-Lived Products: Hewlett-Packard's Journey," *Journal of Business Forecasting* 21, no. 4 (Winter 2002–03), pp. 9–14.

**TABLE 1.2**  Modifying a Baseline Forecast for a Product with a Short PLC     (c1t2)

The baseline forecast for each month is multiplied by the seasonal index for that month (SI) as well as by factors that represent the percentage change in sales expected from other factors such as price cut (P) or various promotional strategies (H and S). The influence of factors such as SI, P, H, and S could be additive if they are expressed in number of units rather than as a percent adjustment. (c1t2&f4,5)

| Month | Baseline PLC Sales | SI | Price Cut (P) | Holiday Promotion (H) | School Promotion (S) | After SI Adj | After SI & P Adj | After SI, P, & H Adj | After SI, P, H, & S Adj |
|---|---|---|---|---|---|---|---|---|---|
| Jun | 0 | 0.80 | 1.00 | 1.00 | 1.00 | 0.00 | 0.00 | 0.00 | 0.00 |
| Jul | 1,500 | 0.80 | 1.00 | 1.00 | 1.00 | 1,200.00 | 1,200.00 | 1,200.00 | 1,200.00 |
| Aug | 1,200 | 1.15 | 1.00 | 1.00 | 1.05 | 1,380.00 | 1,380.00 | 1,380.00 | 1,449.00 |
| Sep | 1,170 | 1.10 | 1.00 | 1.00 | 1.05 | 1,287.00 | 1,287.00 | 1,287.00 | 1,351.35 |
| Oct | 1,140 | 0.90 | 1.15 | 1.00 | 1.00 | 1,026.00 | 1,179.90 | 1,179.90 | 1,179.90 |
| Nov | 1,110 | 1.10 | 1.10 | 1.00 | 1.00 | 1,221.00 | 1,343.10 | 1,477.41 | 1,477.41 |
| Dec | 1,080 | 1.30 | 1.05 | 1.10 | 1.00 | 1,404.00 | 1,474.20 | 1,621.62 | 1,621.62 |
| Jan | 1,050 | 0.65 | 1.00 | 1.00 | 1.00 | 682.50 | 682.50 | 682.50 | 682.50 |
| Feb | 1,020 | 0.70 | 1.00 | 1.00 | 1.00 | 714.00 | 714.00 | 714.00 | 714.00 |
| Mar | 990 | 1.05 | 1.00 | 1.00 | 1.00 | 1,039.50 | 1,039.50 | 1,039.50 | 1,039.50 |
| Apr | 960 | 0.85 | 1.00 | 1.00 | 1.00 | 816.00 | 816.00 | 816.00 | 816.00 |
| May | 930 | 0.80 | 1.00 | 1.00 | 1.00 | 744.00 | 744.00 | 744.00 | 744.00 |
| Jun | 900 | 0.80 | 1.00 | 1.00 | 1.00 | 720.00 | 720.00 | 720.00 | 720.00 |
| Jul | 795 | 0.80 | 1.10 | 1.00 | 1.00 | 636.00 | 699.60 | 699.60 | 699.60 |
| Aug | 690 | 1.15 | 1.05 | 1.00 | 1.04 | 793.50 | 833.18 | 833.18 | 866.50 |
| Sep | 585 | 1.10 | 1.00 | 1.00 | 1.04 | 643.50 | 643.50 | 643.50 | 669.24 |
| Oct | 480 | 0.90 | 1.00 | 1.00 | 1.00 | 432.00 | 432.00 | 432.00 | 432.00 |
| Nov | 375 | 1.10 | 1.00 | 1.05 | 1.00 | 412.50 | 412.50 | 433.13 | 433.13 |
| Dec | 270 | 1.30 | 1.00 | 1.05 | 1.00 | 351.00 | 351.00 | 368.55 | 368.55 |
| Jan | 165 | 0.65 | 1.00 | 1.00 | 1.00 | 107.25 | 107.25 | 107.25 | 107.25 |
| Feb | 0 | 0.70 | 1.00 | 1.00 | 1.00 | 0 | 0 | 0 | 0 |

We can also incorporate the marketing plans for the product into the PLC forecast. Suppose that the marketing mix for the product calls for a skimming introductory price followed by a price cut three months after the product launch. This price cut is expected to increase sales by 15 percent the first month of the cut (October, in our example), followed by 10 and 5 percent increases in the following two months (November and December), after which time the market has fully adjusted to the price drop. A similar price cut is planned for the following July to help prop up sales as the life cycle moves into a more rapid rate of decline. Typically, a price cut this late in the PLC has less effect, as can be seen in Table 1.2.

In addition, two promotional campaigns are planned for the product: one designed to promote the product as a holiday gift, and the other to communicate the benefits to students of having the product as the school year gets under way. The holiday promotion is expected to have a 10 percent lift in both the first November and December and a 5 percent lift the next holiday season. The back-to-school promotion is expected to add 5 percent to sales the first August and September and 4 percent at the beginning of the following school year.

These seasonal and marketing mix constructs are used to adjust the baseline new-product life cycle, as illustrated in Table 1.2. The baseline forecast is first

**FIGURE 1.5**

**Adjusted baseline forecasts.** The upper graph shows the new-product life cycle baseline forecast adjusted only for seasonality (S). The bottom graph shows the baseline forecast and the forecast after adjustment for seasonality, and marketing mix strategies including pricing (P), a holiday promotion (H), and a back-to-school promotion (S). (c1t2&f3,4)

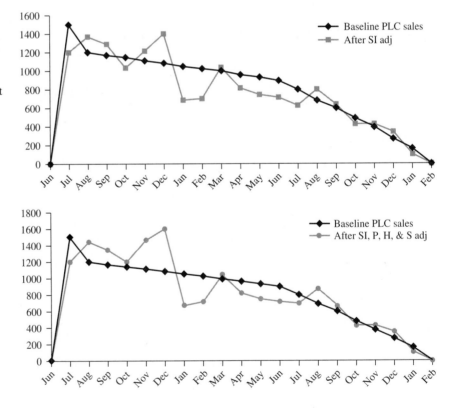

multiplied by the seasonal indices, then by the factors representing the expected effect of each part of the marketing mix. Additional marketing mix relationships, such as distribution and awareness strategies, could be included in a similar manner.

The sales forecast based on the seasonal adjustment (the column headed "After SI Adj") is found by multiplying the baseline forecast by the seasonal indices (SI). The baseline forecast and the seasonally adjusted forecast are shown in the top of Figure 1.5. Each subsequent adjustment for marketing mix elements is done in a similar manner until the final adjusted forecast is developed. This final forecast is shown in the right-hand column of Table 1.2. The baseline and final adjusted forecast are shown in the bottom graph of Figure 1.5.

# A SIMPLE NAIVE FORECASTING MODEL

The simplest of all forecasting methods is to assume that the next period will be identical to the present. You may have used this method often in deciding what clothes to wear. If you had not heard a professional weather forecast, your decision about today's weather might be based on the weather you observed yesterday. If yesterday was clear and the temperature was 70°F, you might assume today to be the same. If yesterday was snowy and cold, you might expect a similar wintry day today. In fact, without evidence to suggest otherwise, such a weather forecast is quite reasonable. Forecasts based solely on the most recent observation of the variable of interest are often referred to as "naive forecasts."

In this section, we will use the naive method to forecast the monthly value of the University of Michigan Index of Consumer Sentiment (UMICS). For this example, we use data from January 2016 through December 2016. These data are given and shown graphically in Figure 1.6. In both forms of presentation, you can see that the UMICS varied considerably throughout this period, from a low

**FIGURE 1.6**   **University of Michigan Index of Consumer Sentiment (UMICS).** (c1f6 c1f7 c1t3)

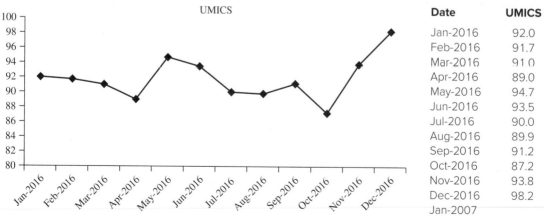

| Date | UMICS |
|------|-------|
| Jan-2016 | 92.0 |
| Feb-2016 | 91.7 |
| Mar-2016 | 91.0 |
| Apr-2016 | 89.0 |
| May-2016 | 94.7 |
| Jun-2016 | 93.5 |
| Jul-2016 | 90.0 |
| Aug-2016 | 89.9 |
| Sep-2016 | 91.2 |
| Oct-2016 | 87.2 |
| Nov-2016 | 93.8 |
| Dec-2016 | 98.2 |
| Jan-2007 | |

of 87.2 in October 2016 to a high of 98.2 in December 2016. The fluctuations in most economic and business series (variables) are usually best seen after converting the data into graphic form, as you see in Figure 1.6. You should develop the habit of observing data in graphic form when forecasting.

The simplest naive forecasting model, in which the forecast value is equal to the previous observed value, can be described in algebraic form as follows:

$$F_t = A_{t-1}$$

where $F_t$ represents the forecast value for time period $t$ and $A_{t-1}$ represents the observed value one period earlier $(t - 1)$. In terms of the UMICS data we wish to forecast, the model may be written as:

$$UMICSF_t = UMICS_{t-1}$$

where $UMICSF_t$ is the University of Michigan Index of Consumer Sentiment naive forecast at time period $t$ and $UMICS_{t-1}$ is the observed University of Michigan Index of Consumer Sentiment one period earlier $(t -1)$. This naive forecast was done using Excel. The results are shown in Table 1.3 .

Note that each forecast value simply replicates the actual value for the preceding month. The results are presented in graphic form in Figure 1.7 , which clearly shows the one-period shift between the two series. The forecast for every month is exactly the same as the actual value for the month before.

**TABLE 1.3**
**The Actual UMICS and a Naive Forecast of the UMICS.**
(c1f6 c1f7 c1t3)

Table 1.3 (c1f6 c1f7 c1t3)

| Date | UMICS | Naive Forecast |
|------|-------|----------------|
| Jan-2016 | 92 | |
| Feb-2016 | 91.7 | 92 |
| Mar-2016 | 91 | 91.7 |
| Apr-2016 | 89 | 91 |
| May-2016 | 94.7 | 89 |
| Jun-2016 | 93.5 | 94.7 |
| Jul-2016 | 90 | 93.5 |
| Aug-2016 | 89.8 | 90 |
| Sep-2016 | 91.2 | 89.8 |
| Oct-2016 | 87.2 | 91.2 |
| Nov-2016 | 93.8 | 87.2 |
| Dec-2016 | 98.2 | 93.8 |
| Jan-2017 | | 98.2 |

**FIGURE 1.7**
**The University**
**Index of Consumer**
**Sentiment (UMICS)**
**and a naive forecast.**
Note how the naive
forecast (dotted line)
lags the actual
values (solid line).
(c1f6 c1f7 c1t3)

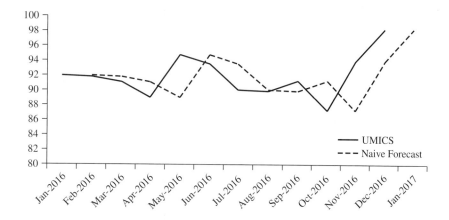

# EVALUATING FORECASTS

You have now looked at a forecasts of the University of Michigan Index of Consumer Sentiment. How do we evaluate how well that forecast, or any other, actually works? One can not rely on a simple visual inspection of the actual values and the predicted values in a graph such as Figure 1.7.

It is rare to find one model that is always best for any given set of business or economic data.

We need some way to evaluate the accuracy of forecasting models over a number of periods so that we can identify the model that generally works the best. Among a number of possible criteria that could be used, seven common ones are the mean error (ME), the mean absolute error (MAE), the mean percentage error (MPE), the mean absolute percentage error (MAPE), the mean-squared error (MSE), the root-mean-squared error (RMSE), and Theil's U. We will focus mainly on MAPE, which is widely used by professional business forecasters.

To illustrate how each of these is calculated, let

$$A_t = \text{Actual value in period } t$$

$$F_t = \text{Forecast value in period } t$$

$$n = \text{Number of periods used in the calculation}$$

1. The mean error is calculated as:

$$\text{ME} = \frac{\sum (A_t - F_t)}{n}$$

2. The mean absolute error is then calculated as:

$$\text{MAE} = \frac{\sum |A_t - F_t|}{n}$$

3. The mean percentage error is calculated as:

$$\text{MPE} = \frac{\sum [(A_t - F_t)/A_t]}{n}$$

4. The mean absolute percentage error is calculated as:

$$\text{MAPE} = \frac{\sum |(A_t - F_t)/A_t|}{n}$$

5. The mean-squared error is calculated as:

$$\text{MSE} = \frac{\sum (A_t - F_t)^2}{n}$$

6. The root-mean-squared error is:

$$\text{RMSE} = \sqrt{\frac{\sum (A_t - F_t)^2}{n}}$$

7. Theil's U can be calculated in several ways, two of which are shown here.

$$U = \sqrt{\sum (A_t - F_t)^2} \div \sqrt{\sum (A_t - A_{t-1})^2}$$
$$U = \text{RMSE}(\text{model}) \div \text{RMSE}(\text{no-change model})$$

The no-change model used in calculating Theil's U is the basic naive forecast model described above, in which $F_t = A_{t-1}$.

For criteria one through six, lower values are preferred to higher ones. For Theil's U, a value of zero means that the model forecast perfectly (no error in the numerator). If $U < 1$, the model forecasts better than the consecutive-period no-change naive model; if $U = 1$, the model does only as well as the consecutive-period no-change naive model; and if $U > 1$, the model does not forecast as well as the consecutive-period no-change naive model.

The MAPE for the forecast of the University of Michigan Index of Consumer Sentiment is shown in Table 1.4 From this, we see that on average, there was an error of 2.95 percent. Note that by using absolute values (values that ignore the algebraic sign), positive and negative errors do not cancel each other out. There could be a very bad forecast with a zero mean error since positive and negative values could potentially add to zero. Because the MAPE is calculated with absolute values, this problem is averted.

This MAPE of 2.95 percent is neither good nor bad. It is just one commonly used metric that allows us to compare different forecasts. Of course, a lower MAPE is preferred to a higher MAPE.

Mean error (ME) and mean percentage error (MPE) are not often used as measures of forecast accuracy because large positive errors ($A_t > F_t$) can be offset by large negative errors ($A_t < F_t$). In fact, a very bad model could have an ME or MPE of zero. ME and MPE are, however, very useful as measures of forecast bias. A negative ME or MPE suggests that, overall, the forecasting model overstates the forecast, while a positive ME or MPE indicates forecasts that are generally too low.

The other measures (MAE, MAPE, MSE, RMSE, and Theil's U) are best used to compare alternative forecasting models for a given series. Because of different units used for various series, only MAPE and Theil's U should be interpreted across series. For example, a sales series may be in thousands of units, while the

**TABLE 1.4**  Calculation of the Mean Absolute Percentage Error (MAPE) (c1t4)

| Date | UMICS = A | Naive Forecast = F | Error (A − F) | Absolute Error | Absolute % Error (Absolute Error/ A)*100 |
|---|---|---|---|---|---|
| Jan-2016 | 92 | NA | NA | NA | NA |
| Feb-2016 | 91.7 | 92 | −0.3 | 0.3 | 0.33 |
| Mar-2016 | 91 | 91.7 | −0.7 | 0.7 | 0.77 |
| Apr-2016 | 89 | 91 | −2 | 2 | 2.25 |
| May-2016 | 94.7 | 89 | 5.7 | 5.7 | 6.02 |
| Jun-2016 | 93.5 | 94.7 | −1.2 | 1.2 | 1.28 |
| Jul-2016 | 90 | 93.5 | −3.5 | 3.5 | 3.89 |
| Aug-2016 | 89.8 | 90 | −0.2 | 0.2 | 0.22 |
| Sep-2016 | 91.2 | 89.8 | 1.4 | 1.4 | 1.54 |
| Oct-2016 | 87.2 | 91.2 | −4 | 4 | 4.59 |
| Nov-2016 | 93.8 | 87.2 | 6.6 | 6.6 | 7.04 |
| Dec-2016 | 98.2 | 93.8 | 4.4 | 4.4 | 4.48 |
| Jan-2017 | NA | 98.2 | NA | NA | NA |
| | | | | MAPE = | 2.95 |

prime interest rate is a percentage. Thus, MAE, MSE, and RMSE would be lower for models used to forecast the prime rate than for those used to forecast sales.

Throughout this text, we will focus on the mean absolute percentage error (MAPE) to evaluate the relative accuracy of various forecasting methods. The MAPE is easy for most people to interpret because of its simplicity and it is one of the most commonly used measures of forecast accuracy.

All quantitative forecasting models are developed on the basis of historical data. When measures of accuracy, such as MAPE, are applied to the historical period, they are often considered measures of how well various models **fit** the data (i.e., how well they work "in sample"). To determine how **accurate** the models are in actual forecasts ("out of sample"), a holdout period is often used for evaluation. It may be that the best model "in sample" may not hold up as the best "out of sample." It is common to test models for their accuracy by preparing forecasts for which actual values are known and see how the MAPE (or other metric) compares when calculated on data that was not used in developing the forecast. For example, if one has eight years of quarterly data, they might not use (hold out) the last four quarters and use those values as a true test of the forecast model's accuracy. Once they find the model that works best for the out of sample data, they would redo the forecast using all eight years of quarterly data. This helps us in selecting an appropriate model.

## USING MULTIPLE FORECASTS

When forecasting sales or some other business or economic variable, it is usually a good idea to consider more than one model. We know it is unlikely that one model will always provide the most accurate forecast for any series. Thus, it makes sense to "hedge one's bets," in a sense, by using two or more forecasts. This may involve making a "most optimistic," a "most pessimistic," and a "most likely" forecast. Suppose that we have two forecasts. We could take the forecast with the lowest MAPE as the most optimistic, the forecast with the highest MAPE as the most pessimistic, and the average value as the *most likely*. The latter can be calculated as the mean of the two other forecast values in each month. That is:

$$\text{Most likely forecast} = \frac{\text{UMICSF1} + \text{UMICSF2}}{2}$$

This is the simplest way to combine forecasts. Actually, it is unlikely that the simple mean will provide the best combination of forecasts. Later we will see one way of determining the optimal weights for each forecast in the combination.

*In making a final forecast, we again stress the importance of using well-reasoned judgments based on expertise regarding the series under consideration.*

The purpose of a number of studies has been to identify the best way to combine forecasts to improve overall accuracy. After we have covered a wider array of forecasting models, we will come back to this issue of combining different forecasts (see the appendix to Chapter 5 ). For now, we just want to call attention to the desirability of using more than one method in developing any forecast. In making a final forecast, we again stress the importance of using well-reasoned judgments based on expertise regarding the series under consideration.

## SOURCES OF DATA

The quantity and type of data needed in developing forecasts can vary a great deal from one situation to another. Some forecasting techniques require only the data series that is to be forecast. These methods include the naive method discussed above, as well as more sophisticated time-series techniques such as time-series decomposition, exponential smoothing, and ARIMA models, which will be discussed in subsequent chapters of this text. On the other hand, multiple-regression methods require a data series for each variable included in the forecasting model. This may mean that a large number of data series must be maintained to support the forecasting process.

The most obvious sources of data are the internal records of the organization itself. Such data include unit product sales histories, employment and production records, total revenue, shipments, orders received, inventory records, and so forth. However, it is surprising how often an organization fails to keep historical data in a form that facilitates the development of forecasting models. Another problem with using internal data is getting the cooperation necessary to make them available both in a form that is useful and in a timely manner. As better information systems are developed and made available, internal data will become more useful in the preparation of forecasts.

For many types of forecasts, the necessary data come from outside the firm. Various trade associations are a valuable source of such data, which are usually available to members at a nominal cost and sometimes to nonmembers for a fee. But the richest sources of external data are various governmental and syndicated services (such as Prevedere, discussed in Chapter 5).

You will find a wealth of data available on the Internet.[23] Using various search engines, you can uncover sources for most macroeconomic series that are of interest to forecasters.

## FORECASTING TOTAL NEW HOUSES SOLD

In each chapter of the text where new forecasting techniques are developed, we will apply at least one of the new methods to preparing a forecast of total new houses sold in the United States (TNHS). As you will see, there is a fair amount of variability in how well different methods work for this very important economic series. The data we will be using are shown graphically in Figure 1.8. As you see from the graph, we have monthly TNHS from January 2010 through December 2016. The data represent sales in thousands of units and have not been seasonally adjusted.

In Figure 1.9, you see how a naive forecast looks for total new houses sold in the United States. At first, you might think it looks pretty good because the actual and forecast lines appear to be fairly close. The problem is that our eyes can be deceiving. We may only see the horizontal difference between the lines. However, the errors are the vertical distances between the lines at each observation. Looking at the graph this way, we see that the errors are quite large. When data are seasonal, such as TNHS, a naive model will typically make for very poor forecasts.

**FIGURE 1.8   Total new houses sold (TNHS).**   This graph shows TNHS in thousands of units per month from January 2010 through December 2016. (c1f8)

**FIGURE 1.9 Total new houses sold (TNHS) and a naive forecast.** This graph shows TNHS in thousands of units per month from January 2010 through December 2016, along with a naive forecast. (c1f9)

TNHS and a Naive Forecast
60
50
40
30
20
10
0
TNHS (000)
Naïve Forecast (000)
Jan-10
May-10
Sep-10
Jan-11
May-11
Sep-11
Jan-12
May-12
Sep-12
Jan-13
May-13
Sep-13
Jan-14
May-14
Sep-14
Jan-15
May-15
Sep-15
Jan-16
May-16
Sep-16
Jan-17

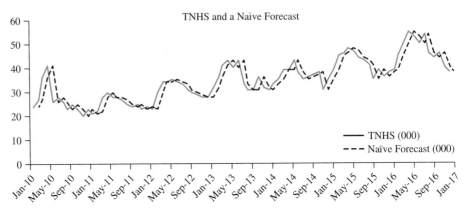

## STEPS TO BETTER TIME SERIES FORECASTS

Judgmental or qualitative forecasts rarely are as good as forecasts based on quantitative methods. Figure 1.10 shows a hierarchy of time series forecast methods starting at the bottom with the methods that are least likely to provide good forecasts. As one moves up and to the right, the methods become more sophisticated and generally can provide better forecasts when applied to data series for which they are appropriate. In Chapter 2, we provide more guidance about selection of appropriate methods.

**FIGURE 1.10**
**Steps to improving forecasts of time series data.**

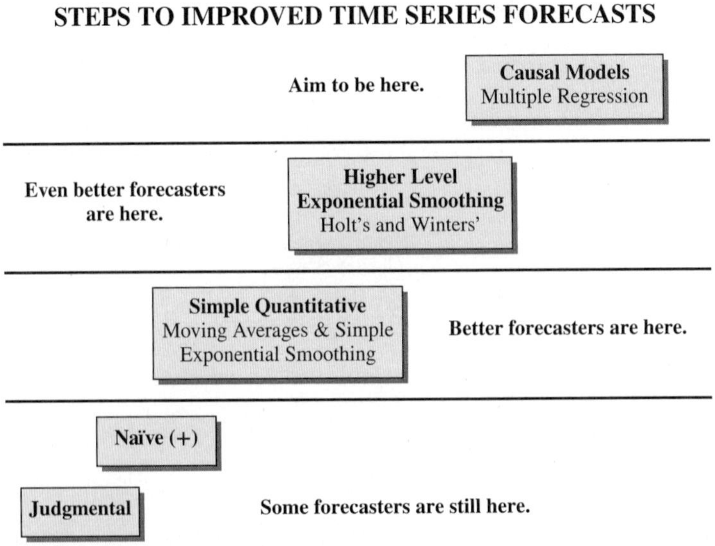

STEPS TO IMPROVED TIME SERIES FORECASTS
Aim to be here.
Causal Models
Multiple Regression
Even better forecasters are here.
Higher Level
Exponential Smoothing
Holt's and Winters'
Simple Quantitative
Moving Averages & Simple Exponential Smoothing
Better forecasters are here.
Naïve (+)
Judgmental
Some forecasters are still here.

# INTEGRATIVE CASE: FORECASTING SALES OF THE GAP

## Background of the Gap and Gap Sales

We will be using The Gap sales in an integrative case at the end of most chapters. In these chapters, concepts from the chapter will be applied to this sales series. In this chapter, we provide an overview of the company as well as of applying a forecasting concept.

The first Gap store was opened in 1969 by founder Donald Fisher, who decided to open a store after he had a problem exchanging a pair of Levi's jeans that were an inch too short. He felt that there was a need for a store that would sell jeans in a full array of sizes. He opened his first store in San Francisco and advertised that it had "four tons" of Levi's. The store was an instant success, and The Gap stores were on their way to national prominence. Levi's were the mainstay of The Gap's business, and due to Levi Strauss & Company's fixed pricing, Fisher originally maintained a 50 percent margin on the sales of these jeans. This changed in 1976, however, when the Federal Trade Commission prohibited manufacturers from dictating the price that retailers could charge for their products. There was suddenly massive discounting on Levi's products, which drastically cut The Gap's margins. Fisher recognized the need to expand his product offerings to include higher-margin items and therefore began to offer private-label apparel.

In 1983, Fisher recruited Millard Drexler as president, with his objective being to revamp The Gap. Drexler did this by liquidating its existing inventories and focusing on simpler, more classic styles that offered the consumer "good style, good quality, good value." The Gap started to design its own clothes to fit into this vision. The Gap already had formed strong relationships with manufacturers from its earlier entry into the private-label business. This enabled it to monitor manufacturing closely, which kept costs low and quality high. The Gap's strategy didn't end with high-quality products. Drexler paid equally close attention to the visual presence of the stores. He replaced the old pipe racks and cement floors with hardwood floors and attractive tables and shelves with merchandise neatly folded, which made it easier for the customers to shop. As new merchandise came in, store managers were given detailed "plannograms," which told them precisely where the items would go. With this control, Drexler ensured that each Gap store would have the same look and would therefore present the same image to the customer.

Drexler's retailing prowess also became evident when he turned around the poor performance of the Banana Republic division. In 1983, The Gap bought Banana Republic, which featured the then-popular safari-style clothing. This trend toward khakis had been brought on by the popularity of movies such as *Raiders of the Lost Ark* and *Romancing the Stone*. By 1987, Banana Republic's sales had reached $191 million. Then the safari craze ended, and this once-popular division lost roughly $10 million in the two years that followed. Banana Republic was repositioned as a more upscale Gap, with fancier decor as well as more updated fashions that offered a balance between sophistication and comfort.

In the early 1990s, the market became flooded with "Gap-like" basics. Other retailers were also mimicking their presentation strategy and started folding large-volume commodity items such as jeans, T-shirts, and fleece, some selling them at substantially lower prices. Drexler and his team recognized that several major changes were taking place in the retailing environment and they needed to identify ways to respond to this competition if they were to continue to grow.

One way The Gap responded to increasing competition was to revise its merchandise mix. Customers were shifting away from the basics toward more fashion items in gender-specific styles. To respond to this trend, The Gap took advantage of aggressive changes already under way in its inventory management programs, which gave it faster replenishment times. This enabled The Gap to reduce its inventories in basics by as much as 40 percent, giving it more room for hot-selling, high-profit items. In addition to shifting to more fashion, The Gap also fine-tuned its product mix so that merchandise would be more consistent between stores.

Another way that The Gap responded to increased competition and changing retailing trends was by entering into strip malls. Many strip malls offer their customers easier access to stores and more convenient parking than they could in larger indoor mall locations.

Gap launched the Old Navy Clothing Co. in April 1994 to target consumers in households with lower to middle incomes. Old Navy stores carry a different assortment of apparel than traditional Gap stores. They differentiated themselves from The Gap stores by offering alternative versions of basic items, with different fabric blends that enable them to charge lower retail prices. To help keep costs down, it also scaled down the decor of these stores, with serviceable concrete floors and shopping carts instead of the hardwood floors found in The Gap. Old Navy stores further positioned themselves as one-stop-shopping stores by offering clothing for the whole family in one location.

With its current mix of stores, The Gap has successfully carved out a position for itself in many retail clothing categories. Table 1.5 shows the distribution of store types by geographic regions. Although there have been some hurdles along

**TABLE 1.5**

**The Gap Store Count**

Source: http://www.gapinc.com/content/gapinc/html/investors/realestate.html (click on Historical Store Count by country).

| Stores | As of 2017 |
|---|---|
| Gap North America | 844 |
| Gap Asia | 311 |
| Gap Europe | 164 |
| Old Navy North America | 1,043 |
| Old Navy Asia | 13 |
| Banana Republic North America | 601 |
| Banana Republic Asia | 48 |
| Banana Republic Europe | 1 |
| Athleta North America | 132 |
| Intermix North America | 43 |
| Company-Operated Stores | 3,200 |
| Franchise | 459 |
| Total | 3,659 |

the way, Gap has proven that it has the ability to respond to changes in the retail environment and has, therefore, managed to stay in the race.

Gap's quarterly sales are shown in Table 1.6 and in Figure 1.11 . Table 1.6 and Figure 1.11 also have a modified naive forecast for The Gap sales using a four-quarter lag.

**TABLE 1.6**   **The Gap Sales and a Modified Naive Forecast (Forecast = Sales [−4])** (c1t6&f11).

The Gap sales data are in thousands of dollars by quarter.

The months indicated in the date columns represent the end month in The Gap's financial quarter.

The first quarter of Gap's fiscal year includes February, March, and April.

Gap data from ycharts.com.

| Date | Gap Sales ($M) | Gap Sales Modified Naïve Forecast (M$) | Date | Gap Sales ($M) | Gap Sales Modified Naïve Forecast (M$) |
|---|---|---|---|---|---|
| Apr-06 | 3,441 | | Apr-12 | 3,487 | 3,295 |
| Jul-06 | 3,714 | | Jul-12 | 3,575 | 3,386 |
| Oct-06 | 3,851 | | Oct-12 | 3,864 | 3,585 |
| Jan-07 | 4,919 | | Jan-13 | 4,725 | 4,283 |
| Apr-07 | 3,549 | 3,441 | Apr-13 | 3,729 | 3,487 |
| Jul-07 | 3,685 | 3,714 | Jul-13 | 3,868 | 3,575 |
| Oct-07 | 3,854 | 3,851 | Oct-13 | 3,976 | 3,864 |
| Jan-08 | 4,675 | 4,919 | Jan-14 | 4,575 | 4,725 |
| Apr-08 | 3,384 | 3,549 | Apr-14 | 3,774 | 3,729 |
| Jul-08 | 3,499 | 3,685 | Jul-14 | 3,981 | 3,868 |
| Oct-08 | 3,561 | 3,854 | Oct-14 | 3,972 | 3,976 |
| Jan-09 | 4,082 | 4,675 | Jan-15 | 4,708 | 4,575 |
| Apr-09 | 3,127 | 3,384 | Apr-15 | 3,657 | 3,774 |
| Jul-09 | 3,245 | 3,499 | Jul-15 | 3,898 | 3,981 |
| Oct-09 | 3,589 | 3,561 | Oct-15 | 3,857 | 3,972 |
| Jan-10 | 4,236 | 4,082 | Jan-16 | 4,385 | 4,708 |
| Apr-10 | 3,329 | 3,127 | Apr-16 | 3,438 | 3,657 |
| Jul-10 | 3,317 | 3,245 | Jul-16 | 3,851 | 3,898 |
| Oct-10 | 3,654 | 3,589 | Oct-16 | 3,798 | 3,857 |
| Jan-11 | 4,364 | 4,236 | Jan-17 | 4,429 | 4,385 |
| Apr-11 | 3,295 | 3,329 | Apr-17 | | 3,438 |
| Jul-11 | 3,386 | 3,317 | Jul-17 | | 3,851 |
| Oct-11 | 3,585 | 3,654 | Oct-17 | | 3,798 |
| Jan-12 | 4,283 | 4,364 | Jan-18 | | 4,429 |

**FIGURE 1.11** **The Gap sales in thousands of dollars and a modified naive forecast.** The data are quarterly, so a four-quarter lag was used for a modified naive forecast. (c1t6&f11)

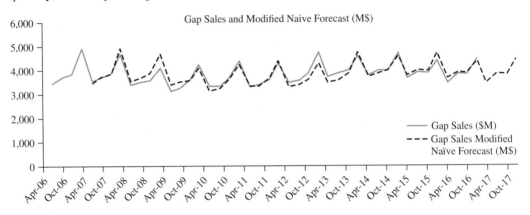

**Case Questions**

1. Based on the tabular and the graphic presentations of The Gap sales data, what do you think explains the seasonal pattern in its sales data?

2. Why do you think a modified naive forecasting method, rather than the simple naive method, was used for Gap sales? Using Excel with only Gap data from April 2005 through January 2016, make your own forecast of The Gap sales for the four quarters from April 2016 through January 2017. Based on inspection of your graph, what is your expectation in terms of forecast accuracy?

3. Calculate the MAPE for your forecast of those four quarters, given the actual sales that are in a **bold** font shown in Table 1.6.

**Solutions to Case Questions**

Data are in the c1t6&f11 file.

1. The seasonal pattern is one in which sales typically have a modest increase from the first to the second quarter, followed by another similar increase in the third quarter, then a large increase in the fourth quarter. The increase in the fourth quarter is caused by the holiday shopping season.

2. The model would be: GAPF = GAPSALES(−4). GAPF represents the forecast values, while GAPSALES(−4) is the actual value four periods earlier. An inspection of The Gap sales series would lead us to expect that a naive forecasting model with a lag of four periods would pick up the seasonality as well as the downward trend in The Gap sales. This can be seen in the graph of actual and predicted values in Figure 1.10.

3. The actual and predicted values for April 2016 through January 2017 are shown below. The MAPE for these four quarters is: MAPE = 2.5 percent.

| Date | Gap Sales ($M) | Gap Sales Modified Naive Forecast | Error | Absolute Error | Absolute %Error |
|------|------|------|------|------|------|
| April 2016 | 3,438 | 3,657 | −219 | 219 | 6.4 |
| July 2016 | 3,851 | 3,898 | −47 | 47 | 1.2 |
| October 2016 | 3,798 | 3,857 | −59 | 59 | 1.6 |
| January 2017 | 4,429 | 4,385 | 44 | 44 | 1.0 |

MAPE = 2.5%

## Case References

http://www.gapinc.com
http://money.cnn.com/2005/02/23/news/fortune500/Gap/?cnn5yes

## AN INTRODUCTION TO FORECASTX™

ForecastX™ is a family of forecasting tools capable of performing the most complex forecast methods and requires only a brief learning curve that facilitates immediate, simple, and accurate operation regardless of user experience.

### Forecasting with the ForecastX Wizard™

The following provides a brief description of some features of the ForecastX Wizard™ and how to use them while forecasting. A complete manual can be found in the "Wizard Users Guide.pdf" file, which is in the Help subfolder of the ForecastX™ folder within the Programs folder (or wherever you have installed the software). You will get instructions on how to download the software from your instructor,

Open the "Gap Practice Data" file by clicking on c1 Gap Practice Data.
When the spreadsheet opens, click in any cell that contains data; for example, B4.

Click the ForecastX Wizard™ icon [ Forecast ] to start the Wizard.

## USING THE FIVE MAIN TABS ON THE OPENING FORECASTX™ SCREEN

Use The Gap sales data you have opened, and follow the directions in the following screen shots to get a first look at how ForecastX™ works.

## The Data Capture Tab

This tab appears when you first start ForecastX™.

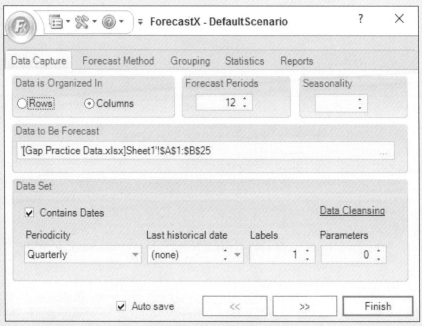

The purpose of the Data Capture screen is to tell ForecastX™ about your data.

When the ForecastX Wizard™ captures your data, the Intelligent Data Recognizer determines the following:

a. *Organization:* Indicates whether the data is in rows or columns.

b. *Data to Be Forecast:* Specifies the range of the data to be forecasted.

c. *Dates:* Specifies whether the data has dates and the periodicity of the dates.

d. *Labels:* Indicates the number of rows of descriptive labels in the data.

e. *Parameters:* Indicates the number of DRP (Distribution Resource Planning) fields in your data. For the purposes of this text, you will not need to use this functionality.

f. *Seasonality:* You can either select the seasonality of the data or allow ForecastX™ to determine it. Here you see that ForecastX™ correctly identified the data as quarterly. It is almost always correct. These fields must follow the labels information in your underlying data.

g. *Forecast Periods:* Set the number of periods to forecast out into the future. The default is 12.

## Forecast Method Tab

The ForecastX Wizard™ allows you to select individual forecasting techniques and their parameters. To select a Forecasting Technique:

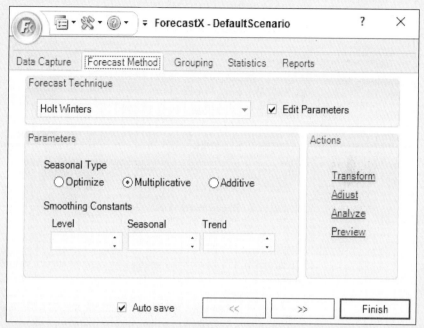

Source: John Galt Solutions

From the Forecasting Technique drop-down menu, select a particular method from over 20 forecasting techniques. For this example, select "Holt Winters," as shown above. Later you will understand why you would select this method.

## The Group By Tab

In this text, we only discuss forecasting a single series, so you will not need this tab. However, should you want to forecast product groups, see the "Wizard Users Guide.pdf" file.

## The Statistics Tab

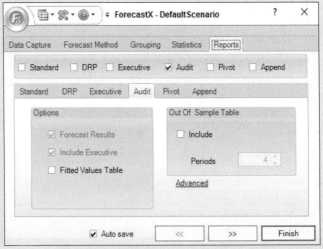

Source: John Galt Solutions

The ForecastX Wizard™ allows you to select statistical analyses to include on the Audit Trail report. ForecastX™ supports more than 40 statistics from both descriptive and accuracy measurement categories. For this example, just select the MAPE, as shown above.

The "More Statistics" option offers advanced statistics. The Root Mean Squared Error (RMSE) and many other metrics are available. Statistics for regression models are located in this dialog box. To access the Advanced Statistics dialog, click the "More Statistics" button on the Statistics screen.

## The Reports Tab

Source: John Galt Solutions

The ForecastX Wizard™ offers five report choices with specific options for each. Checking any of the report boxes in the upper grouping of check boxes automatically includes it in the output. You may check more than one if desired. Each type of report will produce its own Excel workbook but may contain several series within one workbook. In this text, we will use only the "Audit" and "Standard" reports. Detailed information about all these tabs can be found in the "Wizard Users Guide.pdf" file.

### Standard Report

The Standard Report is built for speed and handling of large volumes of data. It produces a side-by-side report listing the actual values compared to the forecasted values. It also includes selected metrics and statistics: Mean Absolute Percentage Error (MAPE), R-Squared Value, and Standard Deviation.

### Audit Report

The Audit Report produces the most detailed analysis of the forecast. Those who need to justify their forecasts with statistics generally use the Audit Trail report. A partial section of the Audit Trail report that you have generated by following these instructions is shown below. (see c1Gap Gap Practice Data)

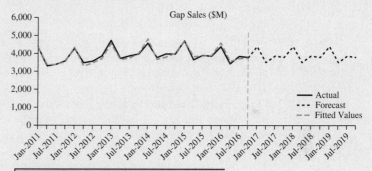

| Forecast – Holt-Winters Selected | | |
|---|---|---|
| | | Forecast |
| Date | Quarterly | Annual |
| Jan-2017 | 4,396.35 | |
| Apr-2017 | 3,510.72 | |
| Jul-2017 | 3,867.98 | |
| Oct-2017 | 3,798.00 | 15,573.05 |
| Jan-2018 | 4,396.35 | |
| Apr-2018 | 3,510.72 | |
| Jul-2018 | 3,867.98 | |
| Oct-2018 | 3,798.00 | 15,573.05 |
| Jan-2019 | 4,396.35 | |
| Apr-2019 | 3,510.72 | |
| Jul-2019 | 3,867.98 | |
| Oct-2019 | 3,798.00 | 15,573.05 |
| **Accuracy Measures** | | **Value** |
| MAPE | | 2.52% |

*Note:* **Throughout the text you may find some situations in which the standard calculations that we show do not match exactly with the ForecastX™ results. This is because they, at times, invoke proprietary alterations from the standard calculations. The results are always very close but sometimes do not match perfectly with "hand" calculations.**

## Suggested Readings and Web Sites

Adams, F. Gerard. *The Business Forecasting Revolution*. New York: Oxford University Press, 1986.

Armstrong, J. Scott. "Forecasting for Environmental Decision Making." In *Tools to Aid Environmental Decision Making*, eds. V. H. Dale and M. E. English. New York: Springer-Verlag, 1999, pp. 192–225.

Armstrong, J. Scott; Kesten C. Green; and Andreas Graefe. "Golden Rule of Forecasting." *Journal of Business Research*, 68, no. 8 (August 2015). pp. 1717–1731.

Armstrong, J. Scott. *Principles of Forecasting: A Handbook for Researchers and Practitioners*. Norwell, MA: Kluwer Academic Publishers: The Netherlands, 2001.

Blessington, Mark. "Sales Quota Accuracy and Forecasting," *Foresight*, 40, (Winter 2016), pp. 44–49.

Byrne, Teresa M. McCarthy. "Omnichannel: How Will It Impact Retail Forecasting and Planning Processes?" *Journal of Business Forecasting* 35, no. 4 (Winter 2016–2017), pp. 4–9.

Chase, Charles W. Jr. *Demand-Driven Forecasting*. 2nd ed. Hoboken, NJ: John Wiley & Sons, 2013.

Duguay, Andrew. "The Top 10 External Factors That Impact Forecast Accuracy." www.prevedere.com, (January 21, 2016), pp. 1–3.

Ellis, Joseph H. *Ahead of the Curve: A Commonsense Guide to Forecasting Business and Market Cycles*. Boston, MA.: Harvard Business School Press, 2005.

Goodwin, P. "Predicting the Demand for New Products," *Foresight,* no. 9 (2008), pp. 8–10.

Kahn, Kenneth B.; and John Mello. "Lean Forecasting Begins with Lean Thinking on the Demand Forecasting Process." *Journal of Business Forecasting* 23, no. 4 (Winter 2004–05), pp. 30–40.

Lapide, Larry. "Execution Needs the S&OP Plans." *Journal of Business Forecasting* 35, no. 1 (Spring 2016). pp. 19–22.

Meade, N. "Evidence for the Selection of Forecasting Methods." *Journal of Forecasting* 19, no. 6 (2000), pp. 515–35.

Shore, H.; and D. Benson-Karhi (2007) "Forecasting S-Shaped Diffusion Processes via Response Modeling Methodology," *Journal of the Operational Research Society*, 58, pp. 720–28.

Wagner, Rich. "Why External Data Are Vital to Demand Forecasts." *Journal of Business Forecasting* 35, no. 1 (Spring 2016). pp. 30–34.

Wilson, J. Holton; and Deborah Allison-Koerber. "Combining Subjective and Objective Forecasts Improves Results." *Journal of Business Forecasting* 11, no. 3 (Fall 1992), pp. 12–16.

**http://www.economagic.com**

**http://www.forecasters.org**

**http://www.forecastingprinciples.com**

**http://www.johngalt.com**

**www.ibf.org**

## Exercises

1. Describe the three phases of the evolution of forecasting/prediction.

2. How does the organization of the material in this book relate to the stages of the evolution of prediction?

3. Write a paragraph in which you compare what you think are the advantages and disadvantages of subjective forecasting methods. How do you think the use of quantitative methods relates to these advantages and disadvantages?

4. Explain how forecasting relates to having an efficient supply chain.

5. The process of forecasting new products is difficult. Why? How can new products be forecast?

6. In this chapter, you saw an example of a naive forecast. Why do you think it is given that name? Describe how the naive forecast is developed.

7. In the chapter, you learned about many metrics that can be used to evaluate forecast accuracy. The MAPE was one of those that may be the most common in use. Explain what the MAPE tells a forecaster.

8. Suppose that you work for a U.S. senator who is contemplating writing a bill that would put a national sales tax in place. Because the tax would be levied on the sales revenue of retail stores, the senator has asked you to prepare a forecast of retail store sales for year 8, based on data from year 1 through year 7. The data are:

| (c1p8) | Year | Retail Store Sales |
|---|---|---|
| | 1 | $ 1,225 |
| | 2 | 1,285 |
| | 3 | 1,359 |
| | 4 | 1,392 |
| | 5 | 1,443 |
| | 6 | 1,474 |
| | 7 | 1,467 |

*a.* Use the naive forecasting model presented in this chapter to prepare a forecast of retail store sales for each year from 2 through 8.

*b.* Prepare a time-series graph of the actual and forecast values of retail store sales for the entire period. (You will not have a forecast for year 1 or an actual value for year 8.)

*c.* Calculate the MAPE for your forecast series using the values for year 2 through year 7.

9. Suppose that you work for a major U.S. retail department store that has outlets nationwide. The store offers credit to customers in various forms, including store credit cards, and over the years has seen a substantial increase in credit purchases. The manager of credit sales is concerned about the degree to which consumers are using credit and has started to track the ratio of consumer installment credit to personal income. She calls this ratio the credit percent, or CP, and has asked that you forecast that series for year 8. The available data are:

| (c1p9) | Year | CP |
|---|---|---|
| | 1 | 12.96 |
| | 2 | 14.31 |
| | 3 | 15.34 |
| | 4 | 15.49 |
| | 5 | 15.70 |
| | 6 | 16.00 |
| | 7 | 15.62 |

*a.* Use the first naive model presented in this chapter to prepare forecasts of CP for years 2 through 8.

*b.* Plot the actual and forecast values of the series for the years 1 through 8. (You will not have an actual value for year 8 or a forecast value for year 1.)

*c.* Calculate the MAPE for your forecasts for years 2 through 7.

10. Go to the library and look up annual data for population in the United States from 2000 through the most recent year available. This series is available at a number of Internet sites, including http://www.economagic.com. Plot the actual data along with the forecast you would get by using the basic naive model discussed in this chapter.

11. CoastCo Insurance, Inc., is interested in developing a forecast of larceny thefts in the United States. It has found the following data:

| (c1p11) | Year | Larceny Thefts* | Year | Larceny Thefts* |
|---|---|---|---|---|
| | 1 | 4,151 | 10 | 7,194 |
| | 2 | 4,348 | 11 | 7,143 |
| | 3 | 5,263 | 12 | 6,713 |
| | 4 | 5,978 | 13 | 6,592 |
| | 5 | 6,271 | 14 | 6,926 |
| | 6 | 5,906 | 15 | 7,257 |
| | 7 | 5,983 | 16 | 7,500 |
| | 8 | 6,578 | 17 | 7,706 |
| | 9 | 7,137 | 18 | 7,872 |

Plot this series in a time-series plot and make a naive forecast for years 2 through 19. Calculate the MAPE for years 2 through 18. On the basis of these measures and what you see in the plot, what do you think of your forecast? Explain.

12. As the world's economy becomes increasingly interdependent, various exchange rates between currencies have become important in making business decisions. For many U.S. businesses, the Japanese exchange rate (in yen per U.S. dollar) is an important decision variable. This exchange rate (EXRJ) is shown in the following table by month for a two-year period:

| (c1p12) | Period | EXRJ | Period | EXRJ |
|---|---|---|---|---|
| | Year 1 | | Year 2 | |
| | M1 | 127.36 | M1 | 144.98 |
| | M2 | 127.74 | M2 | 145.69 |
| | M3 | 130.55 | M3 | 153.31 |
| | M4 | 132.04 | M4 | 158.46 |
| | M5 | 137.86 | M5 | 154.04 |
| | M6 | 143.98 | M6 | 153.70 |
| | M7 | 140.42 | M7 | 149.04 |
| | M8 | 141.49 | M8 | 147.46 |
| | M9 | 145.07 | M9 | 138.44 |
| | M10 | 142.21 | M10 | 129.59 |
| | M11 | 143.53 | M11 | 129.22 |
| | M12 | 143.69 | M12 | 133.89 |

Prepare a time-series plot of this series, and use the naive forecasting model to forecast EXRJ for each month from year 1 M2 (February) through year 3 M1 (January). Calculate the MAPE for the period from year 1 M2 through year 2 M12.

# Chapter Two

# The Forecast Process, Data Considerations, and Model Selection

## INTRODUCTION

In this chapter, we will outline a forecasting process that is a useful guide to the establishment of a successful forecasting system. It is important that forecasting be viewed as a process that contains certain key components. This process includes the selection of one or more forecasting techniques applicable to the data that need to be forecast. This selection, in turn, depends on the type of data that are available. In selecting a forecasting model, one should first evaluate the data for trend, seasonal, and cyclical components.

In evaluating a data series for its trend, seasonal, and cyclical components, it is useful to look at the data in graphic form. In this chapter, we evaluate data for the U.S. population, total new houses sold, disposable personal income, and The Gap sales to see which time-series components exist in each. This chapter also includes a review of statistics and an introduction to the use of autocorrelation coefficients, which can provide useful information about the underlying components in a time series.

## LEARNING OBJECTIVES

After studying this chapter, you should be able to:
1. Explain a process for developing forecasts.
2. Distinguish between trend, seasonal, and cyclical data patterns.
3. Identify forecasting methods that would be good candidates for a given series to be forecast.
4. Explain the differences between the mean, median, and mode for a set of data.
5. Explain the most common measures of dispersion in data.
6. Discuss the normal and Student's t distributions.
7. Describe three common forms of statistical hypotheses.

8. Explain what a statistical correlation measures.

9. Explain how an autocorrelation function (ACF) can be useful in forecasting.

# THE FORECAST PROCESS

The forecast process begins with recognizing the need to make decisions that depend on the future—and unknown—value(s) of some variable(s). It is important for managers who use forecasts in making decisions to have some familiarity with the methods used in developing the forecast. It is also important for the individuals involved in developing forecasts to have an understanding of the needs of those who make decisions based on the forecasts. Thus, good communication among all involved with forecasting is paramount.

There are a variety of ways in which we could outline the overall forecasting process. We have found the sequence shown below to be a useful paradigm.

1. Specify objectives.
2. Determine what to forecast.
3. Identify time dimensions.
4. Data considerations.
5. Model selection.
6. Model evaluation.
7. Forecast preparation.
8. Forecast presentation.
9. Tracking results.

This flow of relationships in the forecasting process will be discussed in more detail in Chapter 12, after a base of understanding of quantitative forecasting methods has been established.

It may seem obvious that the forecasting process should begin with a clear statement of objectives that includes how the forecast will be used in a decision context. Objectives and applications of the forecast should be discussed between the individual(s) involved in preparing the forecast and those who will utilize the results. Good communication at this phase will help ensure that the effort that goes into developing the forecast results in improved decision outcomes.

The second step of the process involves specifying explicitly what to forecast. For a traditional sales forecast, you must decide whether to forecast unit sales or dollar sales. Should the forecast be for total sales, or sales by product line, or sales by region? Should it include domestic sales, export sales, or both? A hospital may want to forecast patient load, which could be defined as admissions, discharges, patient-days, or acuity-days. In every forecasting situation, care must be taken to carefully determine exactly what variable(s) should be forecast.

Next, two different issues that relate to the time dimensions of the forecast need to be considered. One of these dimensions involves the length and periodicity of the forecast. Is the forecast needed on an annual, quarterly, monthly, weekly, or daily basis? In some situations, an even shorter time period may be necessary, such as in forecasting electricity demand for a generating facility. The second time dimension to be considered is related to the urgency of the forecast. If there is little time available before the forecast is needed, the choice of methods that can be used will be limited. When forecasting involves hundreds, or thousands, or tens of thousands SKUs (stock keeping units), a forecaster will be limited to methods that can be automated and done in an efficient manner.

The fourth element of the forecasting process involves a consideration of the quantity and the type of data that are available. Some data may be available internally, while other data may have to be obtained from external sources. Internal data are often the easiest to obtain, but not always. Sometimes data are not retained in a form useful for the development of a forecast. It is surprising how frequently we find that data are kept only on an annual basis rather than for shorter periods, such as quarterly or monthly. Similarly, we often run into situations where only dollar values are available rather than units. External data are available from a wide variety of sources, some of which were discussed in Chapter 1. Most external sources provide data in an electronic form.

Model selection, the fifth phase of our forecasting process, depends on a number of criteria, including:

1. The pattern exhibited by the data
2. The quantity of historic data available
3. The length of the forecast horizon

Table 2.1 summarizes how these criteria relate to the quantitative forecasting methods that are included in this text. While all of these criteria are important, the first is the most important. We will discuss the evaluation of patterns in data and model selection in greater detail after completing a review of the forecasting process.

*Fit* refers to how well the model works retrospectively. *Accuracy* relates to how well the model works in the forecast horizon

The sixth phase of the forecasting process involves testing models on the specific series to be forecast. This is often done by evaluating how each model works in a retrospective sense. That is, we see how well the results fit the historic data that were used in developing the models. A measures such as the mean absolute percentage error (MAPE) is typically used for this evaluation. We often make a distinction between *fit* and *accuracy* in evaluating a forecast model. *Fit* refers to how well the model works retrospectively. *Accuracy* relates to how well the model works in the forecast horizon (i.e., outside the period used to develop the model). When we have sufficient data, we often use a "holdout" period to evaluate forecast accuracy. For example, suppose that you have 10 years of historic quarterly sales data and want to make a two-year

**TABLE 2.1** **A Guide to Selecting a Traditional Forecasting Method* ****

| Forecasting Method | Data Pattern | Quantity of Historical Data (Number of Observations) | Forecast Horizon |
|---|---|---|---|
| Naive | Stationary | 1 or 2 | Very short |
| Moving averages | Stationary | Number equal to the periods in the moving average | Very short |
| Exponential smoothing | | | |
|   Simple | Stationary | 5 to 10 | Short |
|   Adaptive response | Stationary | 10 to 15 | Short |
|   Holt's | Linear trend | 10 to 15 | Short to medium |
|   Winters' | Trend and seasonality | At least 4 or 5 per season | Short to medium |
|   Bass model | S-curve | Small, 3 to 10 | Short to Medium |
| Regression-based | | | |
|   Trend | Linear and nonlinear trend with or without seasonality | Minimum of 10 with 4 or 5 per season if seasonality is included | Short to medium |
|   Causal | Can handle nearly all data patterns | Recommend a minimum of 10 per independent variable | Short, medium, and long |
| Time-series decomposition | Can handle trend, seasonal, and cyclical patterns | Enough to see two peaks and two troughs in the cycle | Short, medium, and long |
| ARIMA | Stationary or transformed to stationary | Minimum of 50 | Short, medium, and long |

*The methods presented in this table are the most commonly used techniques. There are many other methods available, most of which are included in the ForecastX™ software that accompanies this text.

** Data and text mining methods that are discussed in Chapters 8 through 11 are based on different criteria.

forecast. In developing and evaluating potential models, you might use just the first eight years of data to forecast the last two years of the historical series. MAPEs could then be calculated for the two holdout years to determine which model or models provide the most accurate forecasts. These models would then be respecified using all 10 years of historic data, and a forecast would be developed for the true forecast horizon. If the models selected in phase 6 did not yield an acceptable level of accuracy, you would return to step 5 and select an alternative model.

Phase 7, forecast preparation, is the natural result of having found models that are believed to produce acceptably accurate results. We recommend that more than one technique be used whenever possible. When two, or more, methods that have different information bases are used, their combination will frequently provide better forecasts than would either method alone. The process of combining forecasts is sufficiently important that the appendix to Chapter 5 is devoted to this topic.

The eighth phase of the forecasting process involves the presentation of forecast results to those who rely on them to make decisions. Here, clear communication is critical. Sometimes analysts who develop forecasts become so enamored with the sophistication of their models that they focus on technical issues rather than on the substance of the forecast. In both written and oral presentations, the use of objective visual representations of the results is very important.[1]

Finally, the forecasting process should include continuous tracking of how well forecasts compare with the actual values observed during the forecast horizon. Over time, even the best of models are likely to deteriorate in terms of accuracy and need to be respecified, or replaced with an alternative method. Forecasters can learn from their mistakes. A careful review of forecast errors may be helpful in leading to a better understanding of what causes deviations between the actual and forecast series.

# TREND, SEASONAL, AND CYCLICAL DATA PATTERNS

The data that historically have been used most often in forecasting are time series. For example, you might have sales data by month from January 2010 through December 2017, or you might have the number of visitors to a national park every year for a 30-year period, or you might have stock prices on a daily basis for several years. These would all be examples of time-series data.

Such time series can display a wide variety of patterns when plotted over time. Displaying data in a time-series plot is an important first step in identifying various component parts of the time series. A time series is likely to contain some, or all, of the following components:

Trend
Seasonal
Cyclical
Irregular (often called random)

We will first define and discuss each of these in general terms, and then we will look at several specific data series to see which components we can visualize through graphic analyses.

Data are considered *stationary* when there is neither a positive nor a negative trend.

The *trend* in a time series is the long-term change in the level of the data. If, over an extended period of time, the series moves upward, we say that the data show a positive trend. If the level of the data diminishes over time, there is a negative trend. Data are considered ***stationary*** when there is neither a positive nor a negative trend (i.e., the series is essentially flat in the long term).

[1] An excellent discussion of how to present information in graphic form can be found in Edward R. Tufte, *The Visual Display of Quantitative Information* (Cheshire, CT: Graphics Press, 1983).

A *seasonal* pattern occurs in a time series when there is a regular variation in the level of the data that repeats itself at the same time each year.

A *seasonal* pattern occurs in a time series when there is a regular variation in the level of the data that repeats itself at the same time each year. For example, ski lodges in Killington, Vermont, have very regular high occupancy rates during December, January, and February (as well as regular low occupancy rates in the spring of the year). Housing starts are always stronger in the spring and summer than during the fall and winter. Retail sales for many products tend to peak in November and December because of holiday sales. Most university enrollments are higher in the fall than in the winter or spring and are typically the lowest in the summer. All of these patterns recur with reasonable regularity year after year. No doubt you can think of many other examples of time-series data for which you would expect similar seasonal patterns.

A *cyclical* pattern is represented by wavelike upward and downward movements of the data around the long-term trend. Cyclical fluctuations are of longer duration and are less regular than are seasonal fluctuations. The causes of cyclical fluctuations are less readily apparent as well. They are usually attributed to the ups and downs in the general level of business activity that are frequently referred to as *business cycles*.

The *irregular* component of a time series contains the fluctuations that are not part of the other three components. These are often called *random* fluctuations. As such, they are the most difficult to capture in a forecasting model. There is always some noise in the data that would be a part of this irregular component.

To illustrate these components, let us analyze three specific sets of data. One of these is a quarterly series for the population in the United States (POP), which is an important driver for many types of business activities. POP tends to increase at a fairly constant linear rate. The second series is monthly data for total new houses sold (TNHS), which is also important for many businesses to forecast since it drives so many other types of sales (such as drapes, furniture, appliances, etc.). TNHS has a lot of seasonality, some upward trend since 2010, and a cyclical component. The third series is disposable personal income (DPI, in billions of dollars), which also has a positive trend. The trend is slightly nonlinear with DPI increasing at an increasing rate. DPI is also sometimes referred to as a prime mover because income is the revenue source for personal consumption.

The top panel of Figure 2.1 shows a times-series plot of population on a quarterly basis starting with the first quarter of 2000 and ending with the last quarter of 2016. From a visual inspection of this graph, it is fairly easy to see that there has been a positive trend to POP over the period shown. The long-term linear trend is shown by the dotted red line in the lower panel of Figure 2.1. (In later chapters, you will learn how to determine an equation for this long-term trend line.) You see that population is nonstationary. Because POP is nonstationary, some models would not be appropriate in forecasting POP (see Table 2.1).

Total new houses sold (TNHS) is plotted in Figure 2.2 for the period from January 1978 through July 2007. Probably the most striking feature of this visualization of the TNHS data is the regular and sharp upward and downward movements

**FIGURE 2.1** **Total population of the United States in thousands.**

The upper graph shows the U.S. population growth from the first quarter of 2000 through the last quarter of 2016. The bottom graph illustrates how closely a linear trend approximates the actual population growth. (c2f1)

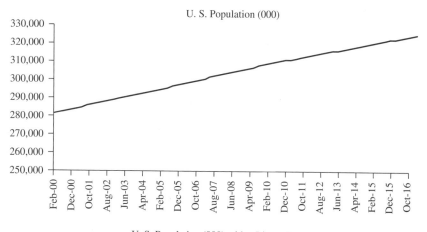

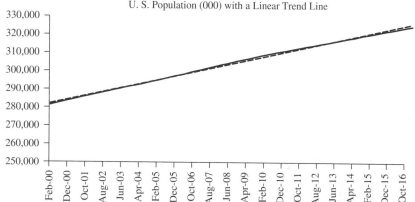

that repeat year after year. This indicates a seasonal pattern, with housing sales reaching a peak in the spring of each year. Overall, there also appears to be some upward trend to the data and some cyclical movement as well.

The straight solid line in Figure 2.2 shows the long-term trend in the TNHS series. The dotted line, which moves above and below the long-term trend but is smoother than the plot of TNHS, is what the TNHS series looks like after the seasonality has been removed. Such a series is said to be "deseasonalized," or "seasonally adjusted" (SA). By comparing the deseasonalized series with the trend, the cyclical nature of houses sold becomes clearer. You will learn how to deseasonalize data in Chapter 6.

Now let us turn to a visual analysis of disposable personal income per capita (DPIPC). Figure 2.3 shows DPIPC from the first quarter of 1959 through the last quarter of 2016. Clearly, there is an upward trend in the data, and it is a trend that appears to be accelerating slightly (i.e., becoming increasingly steep). You will learn to forecast such nonlinear trends later in this text. There does not appear to be a cyclical component to the series, and there is no seasonality.

**FIGURE 2.2** Total new houses sold by month in thousands: January 2002 through December 2016. The solid dark line shows the actual values of houses sold. The dashed straight line shows the long-term linear trend of total new houses sold, while the lighter wavelike line shows the cyclical nature of new houses sold over time. (c2f2)

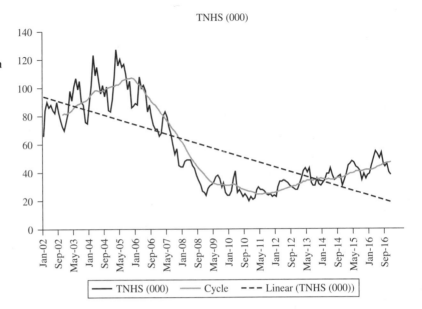

You can see in the top graph of Figure 2.3 that the linear trend would over-forecast DPIPC from the first quarter or 1970 through the second quarter of 2003. After that the linear trend under-forecasts DPIPC. However, the quadratic (nonlinear) trend in the lower graph provides a better basis for forecasting.

## DATA PATTERNS AND MODEL SELECTION

The pattern that exists in the data is an important consideration in determining which forecasting techniques are appropriate.

As discussed earlier in this chapter, the pattern that exists in the data is an important consideration in determining which forecasting techniques are appropriate. On the basis only of the pattern of data, let us apply the information in Table 2.1 to determine which methods might be good candidates for forecasting each of the three specific series just discussed and plotted in Figures 2.1 through 2.3.

For POP, which has a trend but no cycle and no seasonality, the following might be most appropriate:

Holt's exponential smoothing
Linear regression trend

Total new houses sold (TNHS) has a trend, seasonality, and a cycle. Therefore, some likely candidate models for forecasting TNHS would include:

Winters' exponential smoothing
Linear regression trend with seasonal adjustment
Causal regression
Time-series decomposition

**FIGURE 2.3**

**Disposable personal income per capita in the United States.** The solid line in the upper graph shows the actual DPIPC from the first quarter of 1959 through the last quarter of 2016, The dashed line in the lower graph shows a linear trend for DPIPI. The bottom graph illustrates how a quadratic trend (shown by the dashed line) approximates the actual DPIPC more accurately than the linear trend. (c2f3)

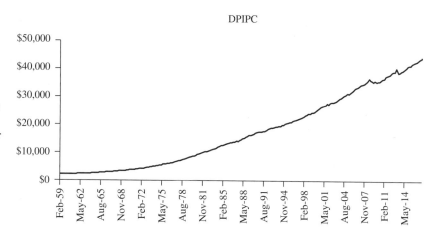

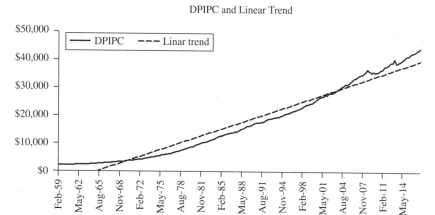

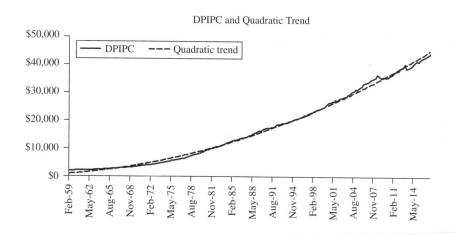

The existence of a cycle component would suggest that the latter two may be the best candidates.

For disposable personal income per capita (DPIPC), there is a nonlinear trend, with no seasonality and no cycle. Thus, the models most likely to be successful are:

Nonlinear regression trend
Causal regression
Holt's exponential smoothing

In subsequent chapters of the text, we will return to these series from time to time as examples. By the time you finish with the text, you will be able to develop good forecasts for series that exhibit a wide variety of data patterns. After a review of some statistical concepts, we will return to an evaluation of data patterns that goes beyond the simple, yet powerful, visualization of data and that will be of additional help in selecting appropriate forecasting techniques.

# A STATISTICAL REVIEW[2]

The approach that we will take in this discussion is more intuitive than theoretical. Our intent is to help you recall a small part of what is normally covered in an introductory statistics course. We begin by discussing descriptive statistics, with an emphasis on measures of central tendency and measures of dispersion. Next we review two important statistical distributions. These topics lead to statistical inference, which involves making statements about a population based on sample statistics. We then present an overview of hypothesis testing and finish with a discussion of correlation.

## Descriptive Statistics

We often want to use numbers to describe one phenomenon or another. For example, we might want to communicate information concerning the sales of fast-food restaurants in a community. Or we might want to describe the typical consumption of soft drinks in U.S. households. Or we might want to convey to someone the rate at which sales have been increasing over time. All of these call for the use of descriptive statistics.

When we want to describe the general magnitude of some variable, we can use one or more of several *measures of central tendency*. The three most common measures of central tendency are the mean, median, and mode. To grasp each of these measures, let us consider the data in Table 2.2. These data represent 25 consecutive months of computer sales for a small office-products retailer. The *mode* is the response that occurs most frequently. If you count the number of times each value for sales is found in Table 2.2, you obtain the following results:

---

[2] Students with a good statistical background may be able to skip this section.

**TABLE 2.2**
**Twenty-Five**
**Consecutive Months**
**of Total Sales** (c2t2)

| Month | Sales | Month | Sales |
|-------|-------|-------|-------|
| 1 | 3 | 14 | 4 |
| 2 | 4 | 15 | 7 |
| 3 | 5 | 16 | 3 |
| 4 | 1 | 17 | 4 |
| 5 | 5 | 18 | 2 |
| 6 | 3 | 19 | 5 |
| 7 | 6 | 20 | 7 |
| 8 | 2 | 21 | 4 |
| 9 | 7 | 22 | 5 |
| 10 | 8 | 23 | 2 |
| 11 | 1 | 24 | 6 |
| 12 | 13 | 25 | 4 |
| 13 | 4 | | |

| Sales | Number of Occurrences |
|-------|-----------------------|
| 1 | 2 |
| 2 | 3 |
| 3 | 3 |
| 4 | 6 |
| 5 | 4 |
| 6 | 2 |
| 7 | 3 |
| 8 | 1 |
| 13 | 1 |
| Total | 25 |

Since the largest number of occurrences is 6 (for sales of four computers), the mode is 4.

The *median* is the value that splits the responses into two equal parts when they are arrayed from smallest to largest. In this set of data, the median is 4. This is shown in the following diagram:

Responses Arrayed from Low to High

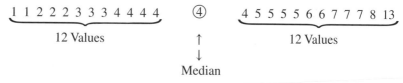

1 1 2 2 2 3 3 3 4 4 4 4    ④    4 5 5 5 5 6 6 7 7 7 8 13

12 Values        ↑        12 Values
                 ↓
                 Median

There are 12 numbers to the left of the circled 4, and 12 numbers to the right. When there are an even number of observations, the median is the midpoint of the two center values. For example, in the series 1, 4, 6, 10, the median is 5. Note that the median may be a number that is not actually in the data array.

The *mean* is the arithmetic average of all the numbers in the data set. To find the mean, add up all the values and divide by the number of observations. If the set of numbers is a population, rather than a sample, the mean is designated by the Greek mu ($\mu$). It is calculated as:

$$\mu = \sum_{i=1}^{N} X_i / N$$

where the subscript $i$ is used to identify each $X$ value and

$$\sum_{i=1}^{N} X_i$$

means the sum of all the values of $X_i$, in which $i$ ranges from 1 to $N$. $X$ is simply a shorthand way of representing a variable. For the data in Table 2.2, $X_3 = 5$ and $X_{15} = 7$. $N$ represents the total number of elements, or observations, in the population. In this case $N = 25$. Adding up all 25 values, we get:

$$\Sigma X = 115$$

Note that we have dropped the subscript here. This will often be done to simplify the notation. The population mean is then:

$$\mu = \Sigma X / N = 115 / 25 = 4.6$$

If the data represent a sample (i.e., a portion of the entire population), the mean is designated $\overline{X}$ and the number of elements in the sample is designated $n$. Thus, a sample mean is:

$$\overline{X} = \sum_{i=1}^{n} X_i / n$$

If the data in Table 2.2 represented a sample of months, the mean would be calculated as:

$$\overline{X} = \Sigma X / n = 115 / 25 = 4.6$$

All three of these measures of central tendency provide some feel for what we might think of as a "typical case." For example, knowing that the median and mode for sales are both 4 and the mean is 4.6 gives you an idea about what is a typical month's sales.

These sales data are plotted over time in Figure 2.4, along with the trend line. You see in this plot that sales fluctuate around a nearly flat trend. Thus, this sales series is stationary.

We have seen that for the data in Table 2.2, the mean is 4.6, and both the mode and the median are 4.0. Note that the mean is above both of the other measures of central tendency. This can result when there is one relatively large value (in this example, the 13). That large value pulls up the mean but has little or no effect on the median or mode. Without that observation, the median and mode for this example would still be 4, but the mean would be 4.25 (4.25 = 102/24).

**FIGURE 2.4 Sales and sales trend (c2f4).** For this sales series, the trend is almost perfectly flat, so that the data are stationary. Note that the level of the trend line is fairly close to the sample mean of 4.6.

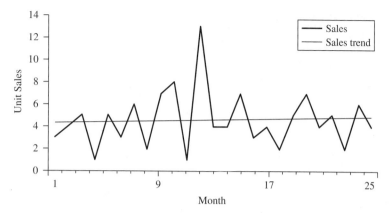

Let us now consider dispersion in data. A measure of dispersion tells us something about how spread out (or dispersed) the data are. Such information helps us to gain a clearer picture of the phenomenon being investigated than we get by looking just at a measure of central tendency. Look, for example, at the following two data sets marked *A* and *B*:

| *A:* | 18 | 19 | 20 | 21 | 22 |
|---|---|---|---|---|---|
| *B:* | 0 | 10 | 20 | 30 | 40 |

In both cases, the mean and median are 20. (Since no value occurs more frequently than the others, there is no mode.) However, the two data sets are really very different. Measures of dispersion can be helpful in conveying such a difference.

The simplest measure of dispersion is the *range,* which is the difference between the smallest value and the greatest value. In Table 2.2, the smallest value is 1 (observations 4 and 11); the greatest is 13 (observation 12). Thus,

$$\text{Range} = \text{Greatest value} - \text{Smallest value}$$
$$= 13 - 1$$
$$= 12$$

For the two data sets *A* and *B* just given, the range for *A* is 4 and the range for *B* is 40.

Think for a moment about the different perception you get from the following two statements:

"The data set *A* has a mean of 20 and a range of values equal to 4, from 18 to 22."
"The data set *B* has a mean of 20 and a range of values equal to 40, from 0 to 40."

You can see how much your perception is affected by knowing this measure of dispersion in addition to the mean.

Two other measures of dispersion, the variance and the standard deviation, are probably the ones that are most used. The standard deviation is a measure of the "average" spread of the data around the mean. Thus, it is based on the mean and tells us how spread out the data are from the mean. The variance is the square of the standard deviation.

The calculation of sample and population standard deviations and variances can be shown in the shorthand of mathematical expressions as follows (let $X_i$ represent the $i$th observation):

| | For a Sample | For a Population |
|---|---|---|
| Standard deviation | $S = \sqrt{\dfrac{\Sigma(X_i - \overline{X})^2}{n-1}}$ | $\sigma = \sqrt{\dfrac{\Sigma(X_i - \mu)^2}{N}}$ |
| Variance | $S^2 = \dfrac{\Sigma(X_i - \overline{X})^2}{n-1}$ | $\sigma^2 = \dfrac{\Sigma(X_i - \mu)^2}{N}$ |

For the computer sales data in Table 2.2, the calculations of the standard deviation and variance are illustrated in Table 2.3. Note that the sum of the unsquared differences between each observation and the mean is equal to zero. This is always true. Squaring the differences gets around the problem of offsetting positive and negative differences. The standard deviation for the sales data is (assuming the data represent a sample) 2.582 units around a mean of 4.6. That is, the "average" spread around the mean is 2.582. The corresponding variance is 6.667 "units squared." You can see that the interpretation of the variance is a bit awkward. What is a "squared computer"? Because of this squaring of the units of measurement, the variance is less useful in communicating dispersion than is the standard deviation. In statistical analysis, however, the variance is frequently far more important and useful than the standard deviation. Thus, both are important to know and understand.

Look back at the two small data sets $A$ and $B$ referred to earlier. For both sets, the mean was 20. Assuming that these are both samples, the standard deviations are:

For $A$:  $S = 1.58$
For $B$:  $S = 15.8$

You see that knowing both the mean and the standard deviation gives you a much better understanding of the data than you would have if you knew only the mean.

## The Normal Distribution

Many statistical distributions are important for various applications. Two of them—the normal distribution and Student's $t$-distribution—are particularly useful for the applications in forecasting to be discussed in this text. In this section,

**TABLE 2.3**
Calculation of the
Standard Deviation
and Variance for
the Computer Sales
Data (Assuming a
Sample)  (c2t3)

| Observation Number | Computer Sales ($X_i$) | $(X_i - \bar{X})$ | $(X_i - \bar{X})^2$ |
|---|---|---|---|
| 1 | 3 | −1.6 | 2.56 |
| 2 | 4 | −0.6 | 0.36 |
| 3 | 5 | 0.4 | 0.16 |
| 4 | 1 | −3.6 | 12.96 |
| 5 | 5 | 0.4 | 0.16 |
| 6 | 3 | −1.6 | 2.56 |
| 7 | 6 | 1.4 | 1.96 |
| 8 | 2 | −2.6 | 6.76 |
| 9 | 7 | 2.4 | 5.76 |
| 10 | 8 | 3.4 | 11.56 |
| 11 | 1 | −3.6 | 12.96 |
| 12 | 13 | 8.4 | 70.56 |
| 13 | 4 | −0.6 | 0.36 |
| 14 | 4 | −0.6 | 0.36 |
| 15 | 7 | 2.4 | 5.76 |
| 16 | 3 | −1.6 | 2.56 |
| 17 | 4 | −0.6 | 0.36 |
| 18 | 2 | −2.6 | 6.76 |
| 19 | 5 | 0.4 | 0.16 |
| 20 | 7 | 2.4 | 5.76 |
| 21 | 4 | −0.6 | 0.36 |
| 22 | 5 | 0.4 | 0.16 |
| 23 | 2 | −2.6 | 6.76 |
| 24 | 6 | 1.4 | 1.96 |
| 25 | 4 | −0.6 | 0.36 |
| Total | 115 | 0.0 | 160.00 |

$$\text{Mean} = \bar{X} = \frac{\Sigma X_i}{n} = \frac{115}{25} = 4.6$$

$$\text{Variance} = S^2 = \frac{\Sigma(X_i - \bar{X})^2}{n-1} = \frac{160}{25-1} = 6.667$$

$$\text{Standard deviation} = S = \sqrt{\frac{\Sigma(X_i - \bar{X})^2}{n-1}} = \sqrt{\frac{160}{24}} = \sqrt{6.667} = 2.582$$

we will describe the normal distribution. We will consider the *t*-distribution in a later section.

The normal distribution for a continuous random variable is fully defined by just two characteristics: the mean and the variance (or standard deviation) of the

**FIGURE 2.5**

**Three normal distributions.**

The top and middle distributions have the same mean but different standard deviations. The top and bottom distributions have the same standard deviation but different means.

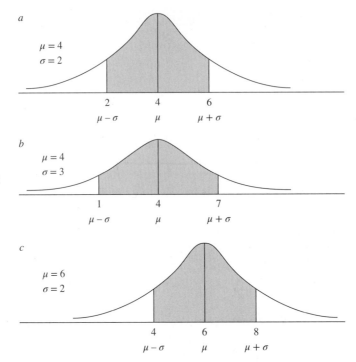

variable. A graph of the normal distribution has a bell shape such as the three distributions shown in Figure 2.5.[3] All such normal distributions are symmetrical around the mean. Thus, 50 percent of the distribution is above the mean and 50 percent is below the mean. It follows that the median must equal the mean when the distribution is normal.

In Figure 2.5, the top graph represents the normal curve for a variable with a population mean of 4 and a standard deviation of 2. The middle graph is for a variable with the same mean but a standard deviation of 3. The lower graph is for a normal distribution with a mean of 6 and a standard deviation of 2. While each is unique, the three graphs have similar shapes, and they have an important common feature: for each of these graphs the shaded area represents roughly 68 percent of the area under the curve.

This brings us to an important property of all normal curves. The area between one standard deviation above the mean and one standard deviation below

---

[3] Technically, these are probability density functions, for which the area under the curve between any two points on the horizontal axis represents the probability of observing an occurrence between those two points. For a continuous random variable, the probability of any particular value occurring is considered zero, because there are an infinite number of possible values in any interval. Thus, we discuss only probabilities that values of the variable will lie between specified pairs of points.

the mean includes approximately 68 percent of the area under the curve. Thus, if we were to draw an element at random from a population with a normal distribution, there is a 68 percent chance that it would be in the interval $\mu \pm 1\sigma$. This 68 percent is represented by the shaded areas of the graphs in Figure 2.5.

If you remember that the normal distribution is symmetrical, you will realize that 34 percent must be in the shaded area to the left of the mean and 34 percent in the shaded area to the right of the mean. Since the total area to the right (or left) of the mean is 50 percent, the area in either tail of the distribution must be the remaining 16 percent (these are the unshaded regions in the graphs in Figure 2.5).

If you extend the range to plus or minus two standard deviations from the mean, roughly 95 percent of the area would be in that interval. And if you go out three standard deviations in both directions from the mean, over 99.7 percent of the area would be included. These concepts can be summarized as follows:

$\mu \pm 1\sigma$ includes about 68 percent of the area
$\mu \pm 2\sigma$ includes about 95 percent of the area
$\mu \pm 3\sigma$ includes over 99 percent of the area

These three rules of thumb are helpful to remember.

In Figure 2.5, you saw three similar yet different normal distributions. How many such distributions are there? There may be billions of them. Every variable or measurement you might consider could have a different normal distribution. And yet any statistics text you look in will have just one normal distribution. The reason for this is that every other normal distribution can be transformed easily into a *standard* normal distribution called the Z-distribution. The transformation is simple:

$$Z = \frac{X - \mu}{\sigma}$$

In this way, any observed value ($X$) can be standardized to a corresponding Z-value. The Z-value measures the number of standard deviations by which $X$ differs from the mean. If the calculated Z-value is positive, then $X$ lies to the right of the mean ($X$ is larger than $\mu$). If the calculated Z-value is negative, then $X$ lies to the left of the mean ($X$ is smaller than $\mu$).

The standard normal distribution is shown in Table 2.4. Note that it is centered on zero. For every value of $X$, there is a corresponding value for $Z$, which can be found by using the transformation shown in the preceding equation. For example, let us calculate the Z-values that correspond to $X = 40$ and to $X = 65$ assuming a standard deviation of 10:

$$Z = \frac{X - \mu}{\sigma}$$

For $X = 40$, $\qquad Z = \frac{40 - 50}{10} = -1$

For $X = 65$, $\qquad Z = \frac{65 - 50}{10} = 1.5$

## TABLE 2.4   The Standard Normal Distribution*

**Source:** Hall, Jr., Owen P. and Adelman, Harvey M. *Computerized Business Statistics* (Homewood, Ill.: Richard D. Irwin, 1987), p. 91.

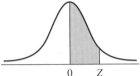

| Z | .00 | .01 | .02 | .03 | .04 | .05 | .06 | .07 | .08 | .09 |
|---|---|---|---|---|---|---|---|---|---|---|
| 0.0 | .0000 | .0040 | .0080 | .0120 | .0160 | .0199 | .0239 | .0279 | .0319 | .0359 |
| 0.1 | .0398 | .0438 | .0478 | .0517 | .0557 | .0596 | .0636 | .0675 | .0714 | .0753 |
| 0.2 | .0793 | .0832 | .0871 | .0910 | .0948 | .0987 | .1026 | .1064 | .1103 | .1141 |
| 0.3 | .1179 | .1217 | .1255 | .1293 | .1331 | .1368 | .1406 | .1443 | .1480 | .1517 |
| 0.4 | .1554 | .1591 | .1628 | .1664 | .1700 | .1736 | .1772 | .1808 | .1844 | .1879 |
| 0.5 | .1915 | .1950 | .1985 | .2109 | .2054 | .2088 | .2123 | .2157 | .2190 | .2224 |
| 0.6 | .2257 | .2291 | .2324 | .2357 | .2389 | .2422 | .2454 | .2486 | .2518 | .2549 |
| 0.7 | .2580 | .2612 | .2642 | .2673 | .2704 | .2734 | .2764 | .2794 | .2823 | .2852 |
| 0.8 | .2881 | .2910 | .2939 | .2967 | .2995 | .3023 | .2051 | .3078 | .3106 | .3133 |
| 0.9 | .3159 | .3186 | .3212 | .3238 | .3264 | .3289 | .3315 | .3340 | .3365 | .3389 |
| 1.0 | .3413 | .3438 | .3461 | .3485 | .3508 | .3531 | .3554 | .3577 | .3599 | .3621 |
| 1.1 | .3643 | .3665 | .3686 | .3708 | .3729 | .3749 | .3770 | .3790 | .3810 | .3830 |
| 1.2 | .3849 | .3869 | .3888 | .3907 | .3925 | .3944 | .3962 | .3980 | .3997 | .4015 |
| 1.3 | .4032 | .4049 | .4066 | .4082 | .4099 | .4115 | .4131 | .4147 | .4162 | .4177 |
| 1.4 | .4192 | .4207 | .4222 | .4236 | .4251 | .4265 | .4279 | .4292 | .4306 | .4319 |
| 1.5 | .4332 | .4345 | .4357 | .4370 | .4382 | .4394 | .4406 | .4418 | .4429 | .4441 |
| 1.6 | .4452 | .4463 | .4474 | .4484 | .4495 | .4505 | .4515 | .4525 | .4535 | .4545 |
| 1.7 | .4554 | .4564 | .4573 | .4582 | .4591 | .4599 | .4608 | .4616 | .4625 | .4633 |
| 1.8 | .4641 | .4649 | .4656 | .4664 | .4671 | .4678 | .4686 | .4693 | .4699 | .4706 |
| 1.9 | .4713 | .4719 | .4726 | .4732 | .4738 | .4744 | .4750 | .4756 | .4761 | .4767 |
| 2.0 | .4772 | .4778 | .4783 | .4788 | .4793 | .4798 | .4803 | .4808 | .4812 | .4817 |
| 2.1 | .4821 | .4826 | .4830 | .4834 | .4838 | .4842 | .4846 | .4850 | .4854 | .4857 |
| 2.2 | .4861 | .4864 | .4868 | .4871 | .4875 | .4878 | .4881 | .4884 | .4887 | .4890 |
| 2.3 | .4893 | .4896 | .4898 | .4901 | .4904 | .4906 | .4909 | .4911 | .4913 | .4916 |
| 2.4 | .4918 | .4920 | .4922 | .4925 | .4927 | .4929 | .4931 | .4932 | .4934 | .4936 |
| 2.5 | .4938 | .4940 | .4941 | .4943 | .4945 | .4946 | .4948 | .4949 | .4951 | .4952 |
| 2.6 | .4953 | .4955 | .4956 | .4957 | .4959 | .4960 | .4961 | .4962 | .4963 | .4964 |
| 2.7 | .4965 | .4966 | .4967 | .4968 | .4969 | .4970 | .4971 | .4972 | .4973 | .4974 |
| 2.8 | .4974 | .4975 | .4976 | .4977 | .4977 | .4978 | .4979 | .4979 | .4980 | .4981 |
| 2.9 | .4981 | .4982 | .4982 | .4983 | .4984 | .4984 | .4985 | .4985 | .4986 | .4986 |
| 3.0 | .49865 | .4987 | .4987 | .4988 | .4988 | .4989 | .4989 | .4989 | .4990 | .4990 |
| 4.0 | .49997 | | | | | | | | | |

*Z is the standard normal variable. Other variables can be transformed to Z as follows:

$$Z = \frac{X - \mu}{\sigma}$$

For Z = 1.96, the shaded area in the distribution is 0.4750 (found at the intersection of the 1.9 row and the .06 column).

Through this process every normal variable can be transformed to the standard normal variable Z.

The normal distribution provides a background for many types of data analysis. However, it is not typically appropriate for work with sample data, and in business we almost always have sample data. When working with sample data, we use the *t*-distribution.

## The Student's *t*-Distribution

When the population standard deviation is not known, or when the sample size is small, the Student's *t*-distribution should be used rather than the normal distribution. The Student's *t*-distribution resembles the normal distribution but is somewhat more spread out for small sample sizes. As the sample size becomes very large, the two distributions become the same. Like the normal distribution, the *t*-distribution is centered at zero (i.e., has a mean of zero) and is symmetrical.

Since the *t*-distribution depends on the number of degrees of freedom (*df*), there are many *t*-distributions. The number of degrees of freedom appropriate for a given application depends on the specific characteristics of the analysis. Throughout this text, we will specify the value for *df* in each application. Table 2.5 has a *t*-distribution for 29 different degrees of freedom plus infinity. The body of this table contains *t*-values such that the shaded area in the graph is equal to the subscript on *t* at the top of each column for the number of degrees of freedom (*df*) listed along the left.

To learn how to read the *t*-table, let us consider three examples. First, what value of *t* would correspond to 5 percent of the area in the shaded region if there are 15 degrees of freedom? To answer this, go to the row for 15 degrees of freedom, then to the column that has .050 for the subscript on *t*. The *t*-value at the intersection of that row and column is 1.753. Second, if there are 26 degrees of freedom and the *t*-value is 2.479, how much area would be in the shaded region? Looking across the row for 26 degrees of freedom, we see that 2.479 is in the column for which *t* is subscripted with .010. Thus, 1 percent of the area would be in that tail.

For our third example, consider the following question: If there are 85 degrees of freedom, what value of *t* would be associated with finding 97.5 percent of the area in the unshaded portion of the curve? For any number of degrees of freedom greater than 29, we would use the infinity (Inf.) row of the table. If we want 97.5 percent in the clear area, then 2.5 percent must be in the shaded region. Thus, we need the column for which *t* is subscripted with .025. The *t*-value at the intersection of this row and column is found to be 1.960. (Note that this is the same as the Z-value for which 2.5 percent would be in the tail, or 0.4750 is in the shaded section of the normal distribution shown in Table 2.4.)

While *t*-tables are usually limited to four or five areas in the tail of the distribution and perhaps 30 levels for degrees of freedom, most statistical software incorporates the equation for the *t*-distribution and will give exact areas, given any

**TABLE 2.5**
Student's
*t*-Distribution*

**Source:** Hall, Jr., Owen
P. and Adelman, Harvey
M. *Computerized
Business Statistics*
(Homewood, Ill.: Richard
D. Irwin, 1987), p. 91.

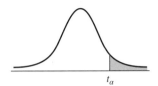

$t_\alpha$

| df | $t_{.100}$ | $t_{.050}$ | $t_{.025}$ | $t_{.010}$ | $t_{.005}$ |
|-----|-----|-----|-----|-----|-----|
| 1 | 3.078 | 6.314 | 12.706 | 31.821 | 63.657 |
| 2 | 1.886 | 2.920 | 4.303 | 6.965 | 9.925 |
| 3 | 1.638 | 2.353 | 3.182 | 4.541 | 5.841 |
| 4 | 1.533 | 2.132 | 2.776 | 3.747 | 4.604 |
| 5 | 1.476 | 2.015 | 2.571 | 3.365 | 4.032 |
| 6 | 1.440 | 1.943 | 2.447 | 3.143 | 3.707 |
| 7 | 1.415 | 1.895 | 2.365 | 2.998 | 3.499 |
| 8 | 1.397 | 1.860 | 2.306 | 2.896 | 3.355 |
| 9 | 1.383 | 1.833 | 2.262 | 2.821 | 3.250 |
| 10 | 1.372 | 1.812 | 2.228 | 2.764 | 3.169 |
| 11 | 1.363 | 1.796 | 2.201 | 2.718 | 3.106 |
| 12 | 1.356 | 1.782 | 2.179 | 2.681 | 3.055 |
| 13 | 1.350 | 1.771 | 2.160 | 2.650 | 3.012 |
| 14 | 1.345 | 1.761 | 2.145 | 2.624 | 2.977 |
| 15 | 1.341 | 1.753 | 2.131 | 2.602 | 2.947 |
| 16 | 1.337 | 1.746 | 2.120 | 2.583 | 2.921 |
| 17 | 1.333 | 1.740 | 2.110 | 2.567 | 2.898 |
| 18 | 1.330 | 1.734 | 2.101 | 2.552 | 2.878 |
| 19 | 1.328 | 1.729 | 2.093 | 2.539 | 2.861 |
| 20 | 1.325 | 1.725 | 2.086 | 2.528 | 2.845 |
| 21 | 1.323 | 1.721 | 2.080 | 2.518 | 2.831 |
| 22 | 1.321 | 1.717 | 2.074 | 2.508 | 2.819 |
| 23 | 1.319 | 1.714 | 2.069 | 2.500 | 2.807 |
| 24 | 1.318 | 1.711 | 2.064 | 2.492 | 2.797 |
| 25 | 1.316 | 1.708 | 2.060 | 2.485 | 2.787 |
| 26 | 1.315 | 1.706 | 2.056 | 2.479 | 2.779 |
| 27 | 1.314 | 1.703 | 2.052 | 2.473 | 2.771 |
| 28 | 1.313 | 1.701 | 2.048 | 2.467 | 2.763 |
| 29 | 1.311 | 1.699 | 2.045 | 2.462 | 2.756 |
| Inf. | 1.282 | 1.645 | 1.960 | 2.326 | 2.576 |

*The t-distribution is used for standardizing when the population standard deviation is unknown and the sample standard deviation is used in its place.

$$t = \frac{\bar{X} - \mu}{s/\sqrt{n}}$$

*t*-value and the appropriate number of degrees of freedom. *We will rely on the t-distribution extensively in* Chapters 4 *and* 5 *as part of the evaluation of statistical significance in regression models.*

## From Sample to Population: Statistical Inference

We are usually much less interested in a sample than in the population from which the sample is drawn. The reason for looking at a sample is almost always to provide a basis for making some inference about the whole population. For example, suppose we are interested in marketing a new service in Oregon and want to know something about the income per person in the state. Over 3.5 million people live in Oregon. Clearly, trying to contact all of them to determine the mean income per person would be impractical and very costly. Instead we might select a sample and make an inference about the population based on the responses of the people in that sample of Oregon residents.

*A sample statistic is our best point estimate of the corresponding population parameter.* While it is best, it is also likely to be wrong. Thus, in making an inference about a population, it is usually desirable to make an interval estimate.

For example, an interval estimate of the population mean is one that is centered on the sample mean and extends above and below that value by an amount that is determined by how confident we want to be, by how large a sample we have, and by the variability in the data. These elements are captured in the following equation for a confidence interval:

$$\mu = \bar{X} \pm t(s/\sqrt{n})$$

The ratio $s/\sqrt{n}$ is called the standard error of the sample mean and measures dispersion for sample means. The *t*-value is determined from Table 2.5 after choosing the number of degrees of freedom ($n - 1$ in this case) and the level of confidence we desire as reflected by the area in the shaded tail of the distribution.

If we want a 95 percent confidence interval that is symmetrical around the mean, we would want a total of 5 percent in the two extreme tails of the distribution. Thus, 2.5 percent would be in each tail. The following diagram will help you see this:

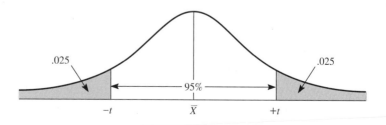

The *t*-value that would correspond to 2.5 percent in each tail can be determined from Table 2.5, given the appropriate number of degrees of freedom. Several examples follow:

| Number of Degrees of Freedom | *t*-Value for 95% Confidence Interval |
|---|---|
| 5 | 2.571 |
| 10 | 2.228 |
| 20 | 2.086 |
| 50 | 1.960 |
| 100 | 1.960 |

Suppose that a sample of 100 responses gives a mean of $25,000 and a standard deviation of $5,000. Our best point estimate for the population mean would be $25,000, and a 95 percent confidence interval would be:

$$\mu = 25,000 \pm 1.96(5,000/\sqrt{100})$$
$$= 25,000 \pm 980$$

that is,

$$24,020 \leq \mu \leq 25,980$$

See if you can correctly find the endpoints for a 90 percent confidence interval given this same set of sample results.[4]

## Hypothesis Testing

Frequently we have a theory or hypothesis that we would like to evaluate statistically. For example, we might hypothesize that the mean expenditure on entertainment in some city is equal to the national average for all age groups. Or we may theorize that consumption of soft drinks by retired people is less than the national level. Or we may want to evaluate the assumption that women professionals work more than the standard 40-hour work week. All of these can be evaluated by using an appropriate hypothesis testing procedure.

The process begins by setting up two hypotheses, the null hypothesis (designated $H_0$:) and the alternative hypothesis (designated $H_1$:). These two hypotheses should be structured so that they are mutually exclusive and exhaustive. For example, if we hypothesize that the mean expenditure on entertainment by people in some city is different from the national average, the null and alternative

*The process begins by setting up two hypotheses, the null hypothesis (designated $H_0$:) and the alternative hypothesis (designated $H_1$:). These two hypotheses should be structured so that they are mutually exclusive and exhaustive.*

[4] The lower bound is $24,177.5; the upper bound is $25,822.5. Notice that at this lower confidence level, the value of *t* is smaller (other things equal), and thus the confidence interval is narrower.

hypotheses would be (let $\mu_0$ = the national average and $\mu$ = this city's population mean):

$$\text{Case I}\begin{cases} \text{H}_0: & \mu = \mu_0 \\ \text{i.e., } \text{H}_0: & \text{The city mean equals the national mean.} \\ \text{H}_1: & \mu \neq \mu_0 \\ \text{i.e., } \text{H}_1: & \text{The city mean is not equal to the national mean.} \end{cases}$$

If we theorize that the consumption of soft drinks by retired people is *less* than the national average, the null and alternative hypotheses would be (let $\mu_0$ = the national average and $\mu$ = the mean for retired people):

$$\text{Case II}\begin{cases} \text{H}_0: & \mu \geq \mu_0 \\ \text{i.e., } H_0: & \text{The mean for retired people is greater than or} \\ & \text{equal to the national average.} \\ H_1: & \mu < \mu_0 \\ \text{i.e., } H_1: & \text{The mean for retired people is less than the} \\ & \text{national average.} \end{cases}$$

If we want to evaluate the assumption that women professionals work *more* than the standard 40-hour work week, the null and alternative hypotheses would be (let $\mu_0$ = the standard work week and $\mu$ = the mean for professional women):

$$\text{Case III}\begin{cases} \text{H}_0: & \mu \leq \mu_0 \\ \text{i.e., } H_0: & \text{The mean for professional women is less than} \\ & \text{or equal to the standard.} \\ H_1: & \mu > \mu_0 \\ \text{i.e., } H_1: & \text{The mean for professional women is greater} \\ & \text{than the standard.} \end{cases}$$

In each of these cases, the null and alternative hypotheses are mutually exclusive and exhaustive.

In statistical hypothesis testing, the approach is to see whether you find sufficient evidence to reject the null hypothesis. If so, the alternative is found to have support. For questions of the type we are considering, this is done by using a *t*-test. To perform a *t*-test, we must first determine how confident we want to be in our decision regarding whether or not to reject the null hypothesis. In most business applications, a 95 percent confidence level is used. A measure that is closely related to the confidence level is the significance level for the test. The significance level, often denoted $\alpha$ (alpha), is equal to 1 minus the confidence level. Thus, a 95 percent confidence level is the same as a 5 percent significance level. The significance level is the probability of rejecting the null hypothesis when in fact it is true.

In testing hypotheses, there are four possible outcomes, two of which are good and two of which are bad. These are summarized in Table 2.6. If we reject $H_0$: when in fact it is true, we have what is termed a *type I error*. The other possible

**TABLE 2.6** **Type I and Type II Errors**

| Statistical Decision | The Truth | |
|---|---|---|
| | $H_0$: Is True | $H_0$: Is Not True |
| Reject $H_0$: | Type I error | No error |
| Fail to Reject $H_0$: | No error | Type II error |

error results when we fail to reject a null hypothesis that is in fact incorrect. This is a *type II error*. These two errors are related in that by reducing the chance of a type I error we increase the chance of a type II error and vice versa. Most of the time, greater attention is given to type I errors. The probability of making a type I error is determined by the significance level ($\alpha$) we select for the hypothesis test. If the cost of a type I error is large, we would use a low $\alpha$, perhaps 1 percent or less.

Hypothesis tests may be one- or two-tailed tests. When the sign in the alternative hypothesis is an unequal sign ($\neq$), the test is a two-tailed test. Otherwise, a one-tailed test is appropriate. For a two-tailed test, the significance level ($\alpha$) is split equally into the two tails of the distribution. For a one-tailed test, the entire significance level ($\alpha$) goes in the one tail of the distribution that is indicated by the direction of the inequality sign in the alternative hypothesis. Consider the three situations described a few paragraphs back. These are summarized in the following diagrams, which show where the significance level would be (a 5 percent significance level is used in all three cases).

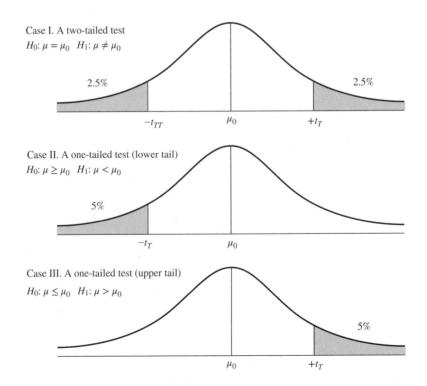

Case I. A two-tailed test
$H_0: \mu = \mu_0 \quad H_1: \mu \neq \mu_0$

2.5%

2.5%

$-t_{TT}$

$\mu_0$

$+t_T$

Case II. A one-tailed test (lower tail)
$H_0: \mu \geq \mu_0 \quad H_1: \mu < \mu_0$

5%

$-t_T$

$\mu_0$

Case III. A one-tailed test (upper tail)
$H_0: \mu \leq \mu_0 \quad H_1: \mu > \mu_0$

5%

$\mu_0$

$+t_T$

The $t_T$ values are determined from a $t$-distribution, such as that in Table 2.5, at the appropriate number of degrees of freedom ($n - 1$, in the examples used here) and for the tail areas indicated in these diagrams ($\alpha/2$ for two-tailed tests and $\alpha$ for one-tailed tests).

For each hypothesis test, a $t$-value is calculated ($t_{calc}$) and compared with the critical value from the $t$-distribution ($t_T$). If the calculated value is further into the tail of the distribution than the table value, we have an observation that is extreme, given the assumption inherent in $H_0$, and so $H_0$ is rejected. That is, we have sufficient evidence to reject the null hypothesis ($H_0$) when the *absolute value* of $t_{calc}$ is greater than $t_T$. Otherwise we fail to reject the premise in $H_0$.

The calculated $t$-statistic is found as follows:

$$t_{calc} = \frac{\bar{X} - \mu_0}{s/\sqrt{n}}$$

where $\bar{X}$ is our sample mean and our best point estimate of $\mu$. The value we are testing against is $\mu_0$. The sample standard deviation is s and the sample size is $n$.

Let us now apply these concepts to our three situations. Starting with case I, let us assume that a sample of 49 people resulted in a mean of $200 per month with a standard deviation of $84. The national average is $220 per month. The hypotheses are:

$$H_0{:}\mu = 220$$
$$H_1{:}\mu \neq 220$$

The calculated value is:

$$t_{calc} = \frac{200 - 220}{84/\sqrt{49}} = \frac{-20}{12} = -1.67$$

If we want a 95 percent confidence level ($\alpha = 0.05$), the critical or table value of $t$ is $\pm 1.96$. Notice that the $t_{.025}$ column of Table 2.5 was used. This is because we have a two-tailed test, and the $\alpha$ of 0.05 is split equally between the two tails. Since our calculated $t$-value ($t_{calc}$) has an absolute value that is less than the critical value from the $t$-table ($t_T$), we fail to reject the null hypothesis. Thus, we conclude that the evidence from this sample is not sufficient to say that entertainment expenditures by people in this city are any different from the national average.

This result is summarized in the following diagram:

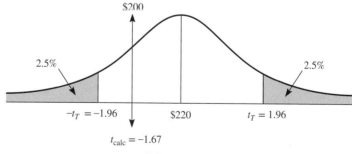

Fail to Reject $H_0$

We see here that the observed mean of $200 or its corresponding $t$-value $(-1.67)$ is not extreme. That is, it does not fall into either of the shaded areas. These shaded areas taken together are often called the *rejection region*, because $t_{calc}$ values in the shaded areas would call for rejection of $H_0$.

Let us now look at case II. Assume that for a sample of 25 retired people the mean was 1.2 six-packs per week with a standard deviation of 0.6. The national average $(\mu_0)$ is 1.5. The hypotheses are:

$$H_0: \mu \geq 1.5$$
$$H_1: \mu < 1.5$$

The calculated $t$-value is:

$$t_{calc} = \frac{1.2 - 1.5}{0.6/\sqrt{25}} = \frac{-0.3}{0.12} = -2.50$$

The critical value from the $t$-distribution in Table 2.5, assuming a 95 percent confidence level $(\alpha = 0.05)$, is $t_T = -1.711$. Note that there are 24 degrees of freedom. Since the absolute value of $t_{calc}$ is greater than the table value of $t$, we reject $H_0$. Thus, we conclude that there is sufficient evidence to support the notion that retired people consume fewer soft drinks than the national average.

This result is shown in graphic form as follows:

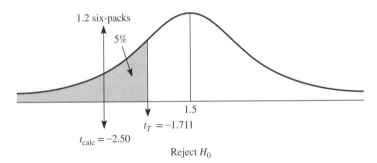

Here we see that the sample mean of 1.2 is extreme, given $\alpha = 0.05$ and $df = 24$, and so we reject $H_0$. The calculated value of $t$ falls in the rejection region.

Finally, let us consider case III. We will assume that we have a sample of 144 professional women and that the mean number of hours per week worked for that sample is 45 with a sample standard deviation of 29. The national norm is the 40-hour work week. The hypotheses are:

$$H_0: \mu \leq 40$$
$$H_1: \mu > 40$$

Our calculated $t$-value is:

$$t_{calc} = \frac{45 - 40}{29/\sqrt{144}} = \frac{5}{2.42} = 2.07$$

The relevant table value is 1.645 ($\alpha = 0.05$ and $df = 143$). Since $t_{calc} > t_T$, we reject the null hypothesis and conclude that the mean for professional women is greater than 40 hours per week.

This result is shown graphically as follows:

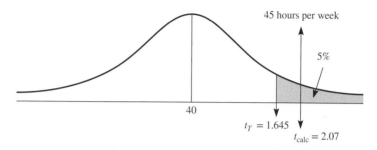

The calculated $t$-value lies in the shaded (or rejection) region, and so $H_0$ is rejected.

The $t$-tests illustrated in this section involved making judgments about a population mean based on information from a sample. In each $t$-test, the calculated value of $t$ was determined by dividing some difference $(\overline{X} - \mu_0)$ by a standard error $(s/\sqrt{n})$. All $t$-statistics are calculated in this general way:

$$t = \frac{\text{the difference being evaluated}}{\text{the corresponding standard error}}$$

We will use this general form later in this chapter as well as in subsequent chapters of the text when $t$-tests are appropriate.

There are other statistical tests and other distributions that are applicable to forecasting. These include $F$-tests, Durbin-Watson tests, and chi-square tests, which will be discussed later in the text as they are applied. If you have a basic understanding of the use of $t$-tests, these other statistical tests will not be difficult to use.

## Correlation

It is often useful to have a measure of the degree of association between two variables. For example, if you believe that sales may be affected by expenditures on advertising, you might want to measure the degree of association between sales and advertising. One measure of association that is often used is the Pearson product-moment correlation coefficient, which is designated $\rho$ (rho) for a population and $r$ for a sample. There are other measures of correlation, but Pearson's is the most common and the most useful for the type of data encountered in forecasting situations. Thus, when we refer to correlation or a correlation coefficient, we mean the Pearson product-moment correlation.

There are several alternative ways to write the algebraic expression for the correlation coefficient. For our purposes, the following is the most instructive:

$$r = \frac{\Sigma(X - \overline{X})(Y - \overline{Y})}{\sqrt{\left[\Sigma(X - \overline{X})^2\right]\left[\Sigma(Y - \overline{Y})^2\right]}}$$

where $X$ and $Y$ represent the two variables of interest (e.g., advertising and sales). This is the sample correlation coefficient. The calculation of the population correlation coefficient ($\rho$) is strictly analogous except that the population means for $X$ and $Y$ would be used rather than the sample means. It is important to note that the correlation coefficient defined here measures the degree of linear association between $X$ and $Y$.

The correlation coefficient can have any value in the range from $-1$ to $+1$. A perfect positive correlation would be $r = +1$, while a perfect negative correlation would be $r = -1$. These cases are shown in scatterplots $A$ and $B$ of Figure 2.6. You can see that when there is a perfect correlation (positive or negative) all of the data points fall along a straight line.

In scatterplot $C$, it appears that in general when $X$ increases, $Y_C$ increases as well. That is, there appears to be a positive (or direct) association between $X$ and $Y_C$. However, all five points do not fall along a single straight line, and so there is not a perfect linear association. In this case, the correlation coefficient is $+0.79$. Scatterplot $D$ shows a negative (or inverse) association between $X$ and $Y_D$, but one that is not perfectly linear. For scatterplot $D$, $r = -0.89$.

The remaining two scatterplots in Figure 2.6 illustrate cases for which the correlation coefficient is zero. In both cases, there is no linear association between the variables. However, note that in panel $F$ there is a clear nonlinear association between $X$ and $Y_F$.

We could perform a hypothesis test to determine whether the value of a sample correlation coefficient ($r$) gives us reason to believe that the true population correlation coefficient ($\rho$) is significantly different from zero. If it is not, then there would be no linear association between the two measures. The hypothesis test would be:

$$H_0: \rho = 0$$
$$H_1: \rho \neq 0$$

and $t$ would be calculated as:

$$t = \frac{r - 0}{\sqrt{(1 - r^2)/(n - 2)}}$$

where $\sqrt{(1 - r^2)/(n - 2)}$ is the standard error of $r$.

Let us apply this to the data in scatterplots $C$ and $D$ of Figure 2.6. In both of these cases, for a two-tailed test, with $\alpha = 0.05$ and $n = 5$, the table value of $t_T$ is 3.182 (there are $n - 2$, or 3 degrees of freedom for this test). For panel $C$ the calculated value of $t$ is:

$$t_{\text{calc}} = \frac{0.79 - 0}{\sqrt{[1 - (0.79)^2]/(5 - 2)}}$$
$$= \frac{0.79}{\sqrt{0.3759/3}} = \frac{0.79}{\sqrt{0.1253}} = -2.2318$$

Since $t_{\text{calc}}$ is in the interval between $\pm t_T$ (i.e., $\pm 3.182$), we would fail to reject the null hypothesis on the basis of a sample of five observations at a 95 percent

**FIGURE 2.6**　**Representative scatterplots with the corresponding correlation coefficients.**

These scatterplots show correlation coefficients that range from a perfect positive correlation (*A*) and a perfect negative correlation (*B*) to zero correlations (*E* and *F*).

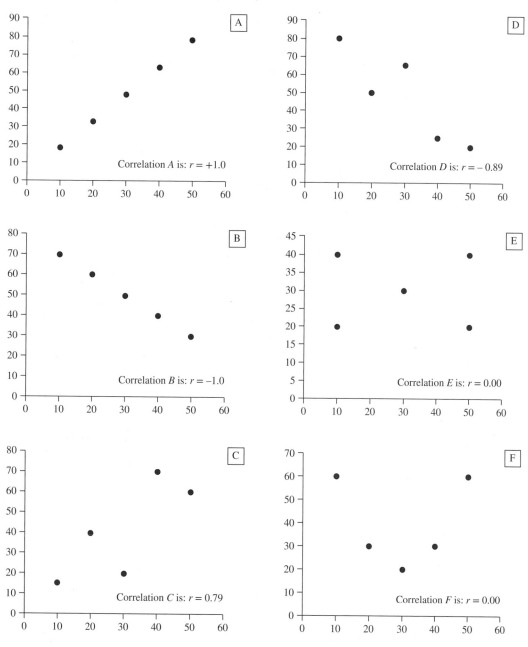

confidence level ($\alpha = 0.05$). Thus, we conclude that there is not enough evidence to say that $\rho$ is different from zero. While the $r = 0.79$ is a fairly strong correlation, we are not able to say it is significantly different from zero in this case, largely because we have such a small sample. If $n = 50$ and $r = 0.79$, the calculated value for $t$ would be 26.06, and the table value would be 1.96, so that the null hypothesis would be rejected.

For the data in panel $D$, the calculated value of $t$ is:

$$t_{\text{calc}} = \frac{-0.89 - 0}{\sqrt{(1 - 0.89^2)/(5 - 2)}} = -3.3808$$

Since this $t_{\text{calc}}$ is not in the interval between $\pm t_T$, we would reject $H_0$ and would conclude that we do have enough evidence to suggest that $\rho$ is different from zero (at a 95 percent confidence level, or $\alpha = 0.05$, and on the basis of a sample of five observations).

# CORRELOGRAMS: ANOTHER METHOD OF DATA EXPLORATION

In evaluating a time series of data, it is useful to look at the correlation between successive observations over time. This measure of correlation is called an *autocorrelation*.

In evaluating a time series of data, it is useful to look at the correlation between successive observations over time. This measure of correlation is called an *autocorrelation* and may be calculated as follows:

$$r_k = \frac{\sum_{t=1}^{n-k} (Y_{t-k} - \overline{Y})(Y_t - \overline{Y})}{\sum_{t-1}^{n} (Y_t - \overline{Y})^2}$$

where:

$r_k$ = Autocorrelation for a $k$-period lag

$Y_t$ = Value of the time series at period $t$

$Y_{t-k}$ = Value of time series $k$ periods before period $t$

$\overline{Y}$ = Mean of the time series

If the time series is stationary, the value of $r_k$ should diminish rapidly toward zero as $k$ increases. If, on the other hand, there is a trend, $r_k$ will decline toward zero slowly. If a seasonal pattern exists, the value of $r_k$ may be significantly different from zero at $k = 4$ for quarterly data, or $k = 12$ for monthly data. (For quarterly data, $r_k$ for $k = 8$, $k = 12$, $k = 16, \ldots$ may also be large. For monthly data, a large $r_k$ may also be found for $k = 24$, $k = 36$, etc.)

A $k$-period plot of autocorrelations is called an *autocorrelation function* (ACF), or a *correlogram*. We will look at a number of such graphics as we further analyze disposable personal income, total houses sold, and The Gap data.

To determine whether the autocorrelation at lag $k$ is significantly different from zero, the following hypothesis test and rule of thumb may be used:

$$H_0 : \rho_k = 0$$
$$H_1 : \rho_k \neq 0$$

For any $k$, reject $H_0$ if $|r_k|>2/\sqrt{n}$, where $n$ is the number of observations. This rule of thumb is for a 95 percent confidence level.[5]

The use of autocorrelations and correlograms can be illustrated by looking at some of the data used earlier in this chapter. Let us begin with the disposable personal income (DPIPC) data graphed in Figure 2.7. From that plot it is clear that DPIPC has a positive trend, so that we might expect high autocorrelation coefficients. The quarter-to-quarter change in DPIPC ($\Delta$DPIPC) is shown along with DPIPC in Figure 2.7. While there is a great deal of fluctuation in $\Delta$DPIPC, the series is much more flat than are the data for DPIPC.

The autocorrelation structures of DPIPC and $\Delta$DPIPC are shown in Figure 2.8. For DPIPC, 69 observations were used. Thus, $2/\sqrt{n} = 2/\sqrt{69} = 0.241$. Since

**FIGURE 2.7**
**DPIPC and change in DPIPC ($\Delta$DPIPC).** We see that there is a strong positive trend in DPIPC, but the quarter-to-quarter change is essentially flat. (c2f7)

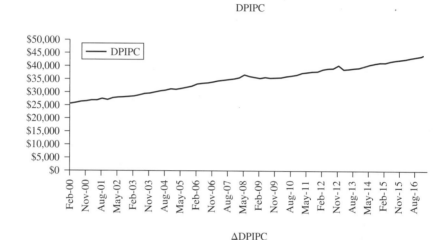

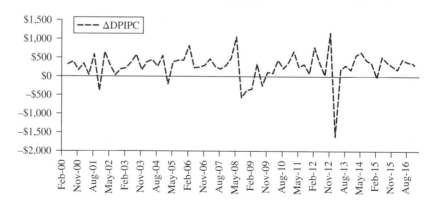

[5] The complete $t$-test would be to reject $H_0$ if $|t_{calc}| > t_T$, where:

$$t_{calc} = \frac{(r_k - 0)}{1/\sqrt{(n-k)}}$$

and $t_T$ is from the $t$-table for $a/2$ and $n-k$ degrees of freedom ($n$ = number of observations, $k$ = period of the lag).

all of the autocorrelation coefficients in Figure 2.8 are greater than 0.241, we can conclude that they are all significantly different from zero. Therefore, we have additional evidence of a trend in the DPIPC data.[6] The actual 95 percent confidence interval is shown by the two horizontal lines labeled "Upper limit" and "Lower limit."

If we want to try a forecasting method for DPIPC that requires stationary data, we must first transform the DPIPC data to a stationary series. Often this

**FIGURE 2.8**

**The ACF graphs for DPIPC and ΔDPIPC.** From the upper graph, we see evidence that DPIPC does have a positive trend. The lower graph suggests that quarter-to-quarter ΔDPIPC is stationary. (c2f8)

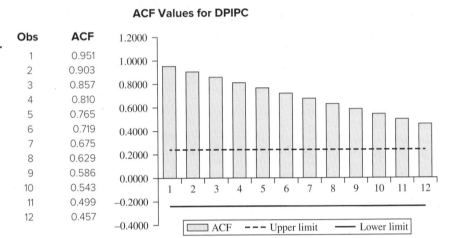

| Obs | ACF |
|-----|-------|
| 1 | 0.951 |
| 2 | 0.903 |
| 3 | 0.857 |
| 4 | 0.810 |
| 5 | 0.765 |
| 6 | 0.719 |
| 7 | 0.675 |
| 8 | 0.629 |
| 9 | 0.586 |
| 10 | 0.543 |
| 11 | 0.499 |
| 12 | 0.457 |

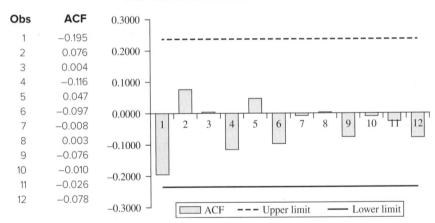

| Obs | ACF |
|-----|--------|
| 1 | −0.195 |
| 2 | 0.076 |
| 3 | 0.004 |
| 4 | −0.116 |
| 5 | 0.047 |
| 6 | −0.097 |
| 7 | −0.008 |
| 8 | 0.003 |
| 9 | −0.076 |
| 10 | −0.010 |
| 11 | −0.026 |
| 12 | −0.078 |

[6] The more formal hypothesis test is:

$$H_0 : \rho_k = 0$$
$$H_1 : \rho_k \neq 0$$

and the calculated $t$-ratio is:

$$t_{calc} = \frac{r_k - 0}{1/\sqrt{n-k}}$$

For example, for $k = 12$ where $r_k = 0.8124$,

$$t_{calc} = \frac{0.8124 - 0}{1/\sqrt{199 - 12}} = 11.109$$

which is greater than the table value of 1.96 at $\alpha/2 = 0.025$ (a 95 percent confidence level).

can be done by using first differences. For DPIPC, the first differences can be calculated as:

$$\Delta DPIPC_t = DPIPC_t - DPIPC_{t-1}$$

where $\Delta DPIPC_t$ is the first difference (or change) in DPIPC. We can check for stationarity in $\Delta DPIPC$ by examining the autocorrelation structure for $\Delta DPIPC$ as shown in Figure 2.8. For $\Delta DPIPC$, the autocorrelations are all within the upper and lower bounds, so this series is stationary.

## TOTAL NEW HOUSES SOLD: EXPLORATORY DATA ANALYSIS AND MODEL SELECTION

Let us apply exploratory data analysis techniques to the total new houses sold data that were introduced in Chapter 1 and that often will be used as an example in the text. Figure 2.9 shows the raw data for total houses sold (TNHS) and a trend line. In this plot, we see several things of interest. First, there appear to be fairly regular, sharp up-and-down movements that may be a reflection of seasonality in TNHS. Second, the long-term trend appears negative. The autocorrelation structure of TNHS is shown in Figure 2.10.

We see that the autocorrelations for TNHS do not fall quickly to zero. The autocorrelation coefficients are all significantly different from zero. Thus, we have evidence of a significant trend in TNHS. We also show the ACF for the quarter-to-quarter change of TNHS in Figure 2.10.

**FIGURE 2.9** **Total new houses sold.** This graph shows total new houses sold (in thousands) by month from January 2002 through December 2016, along with the long-term trend. (c2f9)

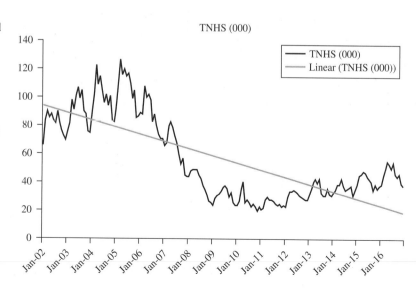

## FIGURE

**2.10   ACF values for total new houses sold and changes in total new houses sold.**   All coefficients are outside the 95 percent confidence band, indicating the positive trend in TNHS. For the change in TNHS, the coefficients fall quickly and are mainly within the 95 percent confidence band, indicating no trend in the month-to-month changes in TNHS. (c2f10)

| Obs | ACF |
| --- | --- |
| 1 | .9741 |
| 2 | .9484 |
| 3 | .9164 |
| 4 | .8869 |
| 5 | .8730 |
| 6 | .8562 |
| 7 | .8558 |
| 8 | .8520 |
| 9 | .8608 |
| 10 | .8716 |
| 11 | .8764 |
| 12 | .8778 |

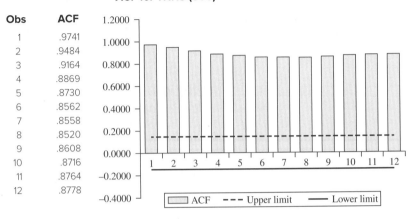

ACF for TNHS (000)

| Obs | ACF |
| --- | --- |
| 1 | −.0239 |
| 2 | .1351 |
| 3 | −.0506 |
| 4 | −.3191 |
| 5 | .0859 |
| 6 | −.3447 |
| 7 | .0675 |
| 8 | −.2432 |
| 9 | −.0477 |
| 10 | .1141 |
| 11 | .0578 |
| 12 | .5779 |

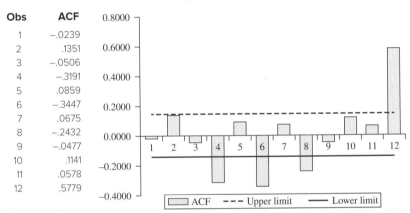

ACF for Change in TNHS

# Business Forecasting: A Process, Not an Application

**1**

### Charles W. Chase, Jr.

Current literature and experience dictate that the best forecasting system provides easy access, review, and modification of forecast results across all corporate disciplines; provides alternative modeling capabilities (multidimensional); includes the ability to create a knowledge base by which future forecasts can be refined; and provides timely and accurate automated link/feed interfaces with other systems such as I.R.I. (Information Resources Inc.)/Nielsen syndicated databases and the mainframe shipment database. The present industry trend has been redirected away from mainframe systems toward PC-based software applications due to the lack of flexibility associated with mainframe access and reporting. Mainframes are being utilized primarily as storage bins for PC-based systems to extract and store information.

**Source:** Chase, Charles, Jr. Business Forecasting: A Process, Not an Application, *Journal of Business Forecasting* 11, no. 3 (Fall 1992), pp. 12–13.

From this exploratory analysis of the total new houses sold, we can conclude that there is trend and seasonality. From Table 2.1, we can, therefore, suggest the following as potential forecasting methods for total houses sold:

Winters' exponential smoothing
Regression trend with seasonality
Causal regression
Time-series decomposition

# INTEGRATIVE CASE: THE GAP

The Gap sales year starts in February and ends the following January. This means the first quarter includes February, March, and April. The fourth quarter includes November, December, and January.

## Data Analysis of the Gap Sales Data

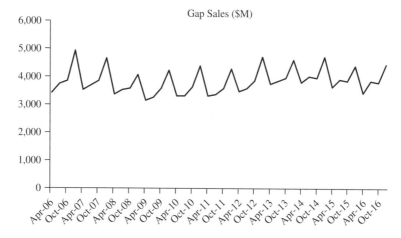

From this graph, it is clear that The Gap sales are seasonal and essentially stationary. There does not appear to be a cycle. The Gap sales year starts in February and ends the following January. (C2 Gap Sales Data)

## Case Questions

1. In 2016, The Gap sales by quarter were as given below:

| Quarter | Gap Sales ($M) |
| --- | --- |
| 2016Q1 | 3,438 |
| 2016Q2 | 3,851 |
| 2016Q3 | 3,798 |
| 2016Q4 | 4,429 |

Calculate the mean and standard deviation for this set of quarterly sales. See the following file: C2 Gap Sales Data.

2. The Gap sales on an annual basis are shown in the following table.

| Year | Annual Gap Sales ($M) |
|------|------------------------|
| 2006 | 15,925 |
| 2007 | 15,763 |
| 2008 | 14,526 |
| 2009 | 14,197 |
| 2010 | 14,664 |
| 2011 | 14,549 |
| 2012 | 15,651 |
| 2013 | 16,148 |
| 2014 | 16,435 |
| 2015 | 15,797 |
| 2016 | 15,516 |

   Plot these data in a time-series plot. Based on this graph, what pattern do you see in The Gap's annual sales? See the following file: C2 Gap Sales Data.

3. Using data for 2006Q1 through 2016Q4, construct the correlogram (plot of the autocorrelations) for lags of 1 through 12. (The quarterly data are in the following file: C2 Gap Sales Data.)

4. Based on the plot of The Gap quarterly sales and on what you learned from question 3, what forecasting methods might you suggest if you were to forecast The Gap's quarterly sales?

## Solutions to Case Questions

1. The sum of the four quarters is 15,516 which when divided by 4 gives a mean of 3,879. The standard deviation (assuming this is a sample of data) is 410.01. See the following file: C2 Gap Sales Data.

2.

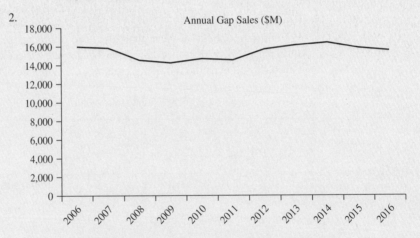

Annual Gap Sales ($M)

3. As you see from the autocorrelations (ACF) and correlogram below, the autocorrelations do not decline gradually. Thus, we have evidence that there is not a significant trend in The Gap data during the period for which we have data. The higher bars outside the upper 95 percent confidence band suggest seasonality in the fourth quarters. The data are in the following file: C2 Gap Sales Data.

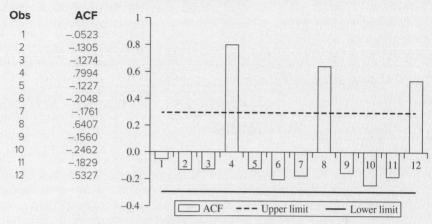

**ACF for Gap Sales ($M)**

| Obs | ACF |
|-----|-------|
| 1 | −.0523 |
| 2 | −.1305 |
| 3 | −.1274 |
| 4 | .7994 |
| 5 | −.1227 |
| 6 | −.2048 |
| 7 | −.1761 |
| 8 | .6407 |
| 9 | −.1560 |
| 10 | −.2462 |
| 11 | −.1829 |
| 12 | .5327 |

4. Based on the plot of The Gap's quarterly sales, as well as the data analysis from question 3, the following forecasting methods might be suggested from the information in Table 2.1:

> Winters' exponential smoothing
> Regression trend with seasonality
> Causal regression
> Time-series decomposition

# Comments from the Field    Anchorage    2.1

## Economic Development Center Secures Time-Saving Forecasting Accuracy

Anchorage Economic Development Center (AEDC) is a private, nonprofit corporation that has been in operation since 1987 and is seeking to improve the economic conditions in Anchorage by expanding value-added industries, increasing business services, and developing tourism. The AEDC needed to accurately forecast the economic outlook for such industries as mining, government, finance, insurance, real estate, manufacturing, construction, transportation, communications, utilities, trade, and services.

Using historical data from the Alaska Department of Labor, the AEDC had used ratio-to-moving averages classical decomposition formulas in Microsoft Excel to forecast the economic outlook. But this long and fairly complicated process usually took about one month to complete. The results, though complete, were not as accurate as they should be.

The AEDC determined that John Galt Solutions could provide software (ForecastX™ Wizard) that would more accurately—and efficiently—define and forecast the economic conditions in Anchorage. AEDC wanted a solution that would minimize its time formatting and forecasting data and allow more time for analyzing and marketing the results of the forecasts.

The AEDC found ForecastX™ to be an easy-to-integrate tool that required no data preparation. AEDC was also happy to continue using Microsoft Excel and still have the ability to use the advanced forecasting methods. Flawlessly integrated, ForecastX™ Wizard provided the AEDC with Procast (expert selection); the ability to handle unlimited amounts of data; and the ability to forecast data on a monthly, quarterly, or yearly basis.

With the advanced features and functionality of ForecastX™ and its ease of use, AEDC was able to cut its forecasting prep time down to one week. More time, therefore, could be spent focusing on evaluating the results of forecasts and bringing more businesses to Anchorage. ForecastX™ Wizard provided AEDC with the tool it needed to more efficiently and accurately complete its forecasts.

## USING FORECASTX™ TO FIND AUTOCORRELATION FUNCTIONS

The most difficult calculations in this chapter were the autocorrelation coefficients. These can be calculated easily in the ForecastX™ software that accompanies your text. What follows is a brief discussion of how to use ForecastX™ for this purpose. This also serves as a good introduction to the ease of use of ForecastX™.

First, put your data into an Excel spreadsheet in column format such as the sample of The Gap data shown in C2 Gap Sales Data. Once you have your data in this format, while in Excel highlight the data you want to use and then start ForecastX™. The following dialog box appears:

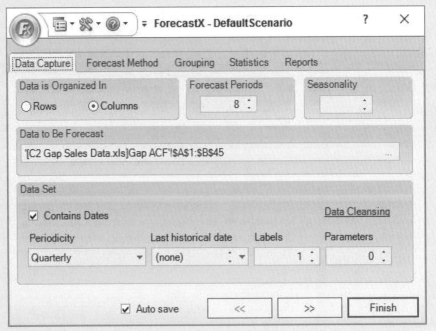

Source: John Galt Solutions

Check the Periodicity box to be sure that it matches the periodicity of your data (**Quarterly** for this example), then click the **Forecast Method** tab at the top and the following screen appears:

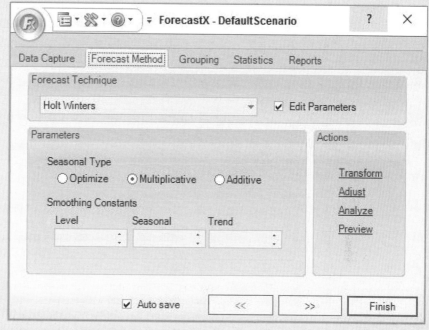

Source: John Galt Solutions

You may get a different forecast method than shown here (Holt Winters) but for now this does not matter. Now click the **Analyze** button in the right side panel and the following screen appears. Click **Export**, and the results will be saved to a new Excel book.

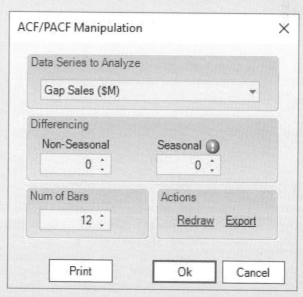

Source: John Galt Solutions

You will have the results shown below (along with some other results) in a new Excel book.

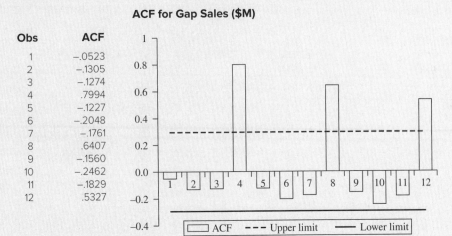

**ACF for Gap Sales ($M)**

| Obs | ACF |
|-----|--------|
| 1 | −.0523 |
| 2 | −.1305 |
| 3 | −.1274 |
| 4 | .7994 |
| 5 | −.1227 |
| 6 | −.2048 |
| 7 | −.1761 |
| 8 | .6407 |
| 9 | −.1560 |
| 10 | −.2462 |
| 11 | −.1829 |
| 12 | .5327 |

*Note:* **Throughout the text, you may find some situations in which the standard calculations that we show do not match exactly with the ForecastX™ results. This is because they, at times, invoke proprietary alterations from the standard calculations. The results are always very close but sometimes do not match perfectly with "hand" calculations.**

## Suggested Readings

Aghazadeh, Seyed-Mahmoud; and Jane B. Romal. "A Directory of 66 Packages for Forecasting and Statistical Analyses." *Journal of Business Forecasting* 11, no. 2 (Summer 1992), pp. 14–20.

"Beyond the Business Cycle?" *The Economist* 353, no. 8142 (October 1999), p. 90.

Chatterjee, Satyajit. "From Cycles to Shocks: Progress in Business-Cycle Theory." *Business Review*, Federal Reserve Bank of Philadelphia (March/April 2000), pp. 27–37.

Chen, Rong, et al. "Forecasting with Stable Seasonal Pattern Models with an Application to Hawaiian Tourism Data." *Journal of Business & Economic Statistics* 17, no. 4 (October 1999), pp. 497–504.

Drumm, William J. "Living with Forecast Error." *Journal of Business Forecasting* 11, no. 2 (Summer 1992), p. 23.

Ermer, Charles M. "Cost of Error Affects the Forecasting Model Selection." *Journal of Business Forecasting* 10, no. 1 (Spring 1991), pp. 10–11.

Huff, Darrell. *How to Lie with Statistics*. New York: W. W. Norton, 1954.

Makridakis, Spyros. "Forecasting: Its Role and Value for Planning and Strategy." *International Journal of Forecasting* 12, no. 4 (December 1996), pp. 513–37.

Mentzer, John T.; and Carol C. Bienstock. *Sales Forecasting Management*. Thousand Oaks, CA: Sage Publications, 1998.

Mentzer, John T.; and Kenneth B. Kahn. "Forecasting Technique Familiarity, Satisfaction, Usage, and Application." *Journal of Forecasting* 14, no. 5 (September 1995), pp. 465–76.

———. "State of Sales Forecasting Systems in Corporate America." *Journal of Business Forecasting* 16, no. 1 (Spring 1997), pp. 6–13.

O'Clock, George; and Priscilla M. O'Clock. "Political Realities of Forecasting." *Journal of Business Forecasting* 8, no. 1 (Spring 1989), pp. 2–6.

Sawhney, Mohanbir S., et al. "A Parsimonious Model for Forecasting Gross Box-Office Revenues of Motion Pictures." *Marketing Science* 15, no. 2 (1996), pp. 113–31.

Smith, Michael. "Modeling and Short-Term Forecasting of New South Wales Electricity System Load." *Journal of Business & Economic Statistics* 18, no. 4 (October 2000), pp. 465–78.

Tufte, Edward R. *Envisioning Information.* Cheshire, CT: Graphics Press, 1990.

———. *The Visual Display of Quantitative Information.* Cheshire, CT: Graphics Press, 1983.

Winklhofer, Heidi; Adamantios Diamantopoulos; and Stephen F. Witt. "Forecasting Practice: A Review of the Empirical Literature and an Agenda for Future Research." *International Journal of Forecasting* 12, no. 2 (June 1996), pp. 193–221.

**Exercises**

1. The mean volume of sales for a sample of 100 sales representatives is $25,350 per month. The sample standard deviation is $7,490. The vice president for sales would like to know whether this result is significantly different from $24,000 at a 95 percent confidence level. Set up the appropriate null and alternative hypotheses, and perform the appropriate statistical test.

2. Larry Bomser has been asked to evaluate sizes of tire inventories for retail outlets of a major tire manufacturer. From a sample of 120 stores, he has found a mean of 310 tires. The industry average is 325. If the standard deviation for the sample was 72, would you say that the inventory level maintained by this manufacturer is significantly different from the industry norm? Explain why. (Use a 95 percent confidence level.)

3. Twenty graduate students in business were asked how many credit hours they were taking in the current quarter. Their responses are shown as follows (c2p3):

| Student Number | Credit Hours | Student Number | Credit Hours | Student Number | Credit Hours |
|---|---|---|---|---|---|
| 1 | 2 | 8 | 8 | 15 | 10 |
| 2 | 7 | 9 | 12 | 16 | 6 |
| 3 | 9 | 10 | 11 | 17 | 9 |
| 4 | 9 | 11 | 6 | 18 | 6 |
| 5 | 8 | 12 | 5 | 19 | 9 |
| 6 | 11 | 13 | 9 | 20 | 10 |
| 7 | 6 | 14 | 13 | | |

   *a.* Determine the mean, median, and mode for this sample of data. Write a sentence explaining what each means.

   *b.* It has been suggested that graduate students in business take fewer credits per quarter than the typical graduate student at this university. The mean for all graduate students is 9.1 credit hours per quarter, and the data are normally distributed. Set up the appropriate null and alternative hypotheses, and determine whether the null hypothesis can be rejected at a 95 percent confidence level.

4. Arbon Computer Corporation (ACC) produces a popular PC clone. The sales manager for ACC has recently read a report that indicated that sales per sales representative for other producers are normally distributed with a mean of $255,000. She is interested in knowing whether her sales staff is comparable. She picked a random sample of 16 salespeople and obtained the following results (c2p4):

| Person | Sales | Person | Sales |
|--------|---------|--------|---------|
| 1 | 177,406 | 9 | 110,027 |
| 2 | 339,753 | 10 | 182,577 |
| 3 | 310,170 | 11 | 177,707 |
| 4 | 175,520 | 12 | 154,096 |
| 5 | 293,332 | 13 | 236,083 |
| 6 | 323,175 | 14 | 301,051 |
| 7 | 144,031 | 15 | 158,792 |
| 8 | 279,670 | 16 | 140,891 |

At a 5 percent significance level, can you reject the null hypothesis that ACC's mean sales per salesperson was $255,000? Draw a diagram that illustrates your answer.

5. Assume that the weights of college football players are normally distributed with a mean of 205 pounds and a standard deviation of 30.

   a. What percentage of players would have weights greater than 205 pounds?

   b. What percentage of players would weigh less than 250 pounds?

   c. Ninety percentage of players would weigh more than what number of pounds?

   d. What percentage of players would weigh between 180 and 230 pounds?

6. Mutual Savings Bank of Appleton has done a market research survey in which people were asked to rate their image of the bank on a scale of 1 to 10, with 10 being the most favorable. The mean response for the sample of 400 people was 7.25, with a standard deviation of 2.51. On this same question, a state association of mutual savings banks has found a mean of 7.01.

   a. Clara Weston, marketing director for the bank, would like to test to see whether the rating for her bank is significantly greater than the norm of 7.01. Perform the appropriate hypothesis test for a 95 percent confidence level.

   b. Draw a diagram to illustrate your result.

   c. How would your result be affected if the sample size had been 100 rather than 400, with everything else being the same?

7. In a sample of 25 classes, the following numbers of students were observed (c2p7):

| Class | Number of students | Class | Number of students |
|-------|--------------------|-------|--------------------|
| 1 | 40 | 14 | 37 |
| 2 | 50 | 15 | 35 |
| 3 | 42 | 16 | 44 |
| 4 | 20 | 17 | 10 |
| 5 | 29 | 18 | 40 |
| 6 | 39 | 19 | 36 |
| 7 | 49 | 20 | 20 |
| 8 | 46 | 21 | 20 |
| 9 | 52 | 22 | 29 |
| 10 | 45 | 23 | 58 |
| 11 | 51 | 24 | 51 |
| 12 | 64 | 25 | 54 |
| 13 | 43 | | |

   a. Calculate the mean, median, standard deviation, variance, and range for this sample.

   b. What is the standard error of the mean based on this information?

*c.* What would be the best point estimate for the population class size?

*d.* What is the 95 percent confidence interval for class size? What is the 90 percent confidence interval? Does the difference between these two make sense?

8. CoastCo Insurance, Inc., is interested in forecasting annual larceny thefts in the United States using the following data (c2p8):

| Year | Larceny Thefts | Year | Larceny Thefts |
|------|------|------|------|
| 1972 | 4,151 | 1984 | 6,592 |
| 1973 | 4,348 | 1985 | 6,926 |
| 1974 | 5,263 | 1986 | 7,257 |
| 1975 | 5,978 | 1987 | 7,500 |
| 1976 | 6,271 | 1988 | 7,706 |
| 1977 | 5,906 | 1989 | 7,872 |
| 1978 | 5,983 | 1990 | 7,946 |
| 1979 | 6,578 | 1991 | 8,142 |
| 1980 | 7,137 | 1992 | 7,915 |
| 1981 | 7,194 | 1993 | 7,821 |
| 1982 | 7,143 | 1994 | 7,876 |
| 1983 | 6,713 | | |

*a.* Prepare a time-series plot of these data. On the basis of this graph, do you think there is a trend in the data? Explain.

*b.* Look at the autocorrelation structure of larceny thefts for lags of 1, 2, 3, 4, and 5. Do the autocorrelation coefficients fall quickly toward zero? Demonstrate that the critical value for $r_k$ is 0.417. Explain what these results tell you about a trend in the data.

*c.* On the basis of what is found in parts *a* and *b*, suggest a forecasting method from Table 2.1 that you think might be appropriate for this series.

9. Use exploratory data analysis to determine whether there is a trend and/or seasonality in mobile home shipments (MHS). The data by quarter are shown in the following table (c2p9):

| Period | MHS | Period | MHS | Period | MHS | Period | MHS |
|--------|-----|--------|-----|--------|-----|--------|-----|
| Mar-81 | 54.9 | Dec-84 | 66.2 | Sep-88 | 59.2 | Jun-92 | 52.8 |
| Jun-81 | 70.1 | Mar-85 | 62.3 | Dec-88 | 51.6 | Sep-92 | 57 |
| Sep-81 | 65.8 | Jun-85 | 79.3 | Mar-89 | 48.1 | Dec-92 | 57.6 |
| Dec-81 | 50.2 | Sep-85 | 76.5 | Jun-89 | 55.1 | Mar-93 | 56.4 |
| Mar-82 | 53.3 | Dec-85 | 65.5 | Sep-89 | 50.3 | Jun-93 | 64.3 |
| Jun-82 | 67.9 | Mar-86 | 58.1 | Dec-89 | 44.5 | Sep-93 | 67.1 |
| Sep-82 | 63.1 | Jun-86 | 66.8 | Mar-90 | 43.3 | Dec-93 | 66.4 |
| Dec-82 | 55.3 | Sep-86 | 63.4 | Jun-90 | 51.7 | Mar-94 | 69.1 |
| Mar-83 | 63.3 | Dec-86 | 56.1 | Sep-90 | 50.5 | Jun-94 | 78.7 |
| Jun-83 | 81.5 | Mar-87 | 51.9 | Dec-90 | 42.6 | Sep-94 | 78.7 |
| Sep-83 | 81.7 | Jun-87 | 62.8 | Mar-91 | 35.4 | Dec-94 | 77.5 |
| Dec-83 | 69.2 | Sep-87 | 64.7 | Jun-91 | 47.4 | Mar-95 | 79.2 |
| Mar-84 | 67.8 | Dec-87 | 53.5 | Sep-91 | 47.2 | Jun-95 | 86.8 |
| Jun-84 | 82.7 | Mar-88 | 47 | Dec-91 | 40.9 | Sep-95 | 87.6 |
| Sep-84 | 79 | Jun-88 | 60.5 | Mar-92 | 43 | Dec-95 | 86.4 |

On the basis of your analysis, do you think there is a significant trend in MHS? Is there seasonality? What forecasting methods might be appropriate for MHS according to the guidelines in Table 2.1?

10. Home sales are often considered an important determinant of the future health of the economy. Thus, there is widespread interest in being able to forecast home sales (HS). Quarterly data for HS are shown in the following table in thousands of units (c2p10):

| Date | Home sales (000) per Quarter | Date | Home sales (000) per Quarter | Date | Home sales (000) per Quarter |
|---|---|---|---|---|---|
| Mar-89 | 161 | Jun-95 | 185 | Sep-01 | 216 |
| Jun-89 | 179 | Sep-95 | 181 | Dec-01 | 199 |
| Sep-89 | 172 | Dec-95 | 145 | Mar-02 | 240 |
| Dec-89 | 138 | Mar-96 | 192 | Jun-02 | 258 |
| Mar-90 | 153 | Jun-96 | 204 | Sep-02 | 254 |
| Jun-90 | 152 | Sep-96 | 201 | Dec-02 | 220 |
| Sep-90 | 130 | Dec-96 | 161 | Mar-03 | 256 |
| Dec-90 | 100 | Mar-97 | 211 | Jun-03 | 299 |
| Mar-91 | 121 | Jun-97 | 212 | Sep-03 | 294 |
| Jun-91 | 144 | Sep-97 | 208 | Dec-03 | 239 |
| Sep-91 | 126 | Dec-97 | 174 | Mar-04 | 314 |
| Dec-91 | 116 | Mar-98 | 220 | Jun-04 | 329 |
| Mar-92 | 159 | Jun-98 | 247 | Sep-04 | 292 |
| Jun-92 | 158 | Sep-98 | 218 | Dec-04 | 268 |
| Sep-92 | 159 | Dec-98 | 200 | Mar-05 | 328 |
| Dec-92 | 132 | Mar-99 | 227 | Jun-05 | 351 |
| Mar-93 | 154 | Jun-99 | 248 | Sep-05 | 326 |
| Jun-93 | 183 | Sep-99 | 221 | Dec-05 | 278 |
| Sep-93 | 169 | Dec-99 | 185 | Mar-06 | 285 |
| Dec-93 | 160 | Mar-00 | 233 | Jun-06 | 300 |
| Mar-94 | 178 | Jun-00 | 226 | Sep-06 | 251 |
| Jun-94 | 185 | Sep-00 | 219 | Dec-06 | 216 |
| Sep-94 | 165 | Dec-00 | 199 | Mar-07 | 214 |
| Dec-94 | 142 | Mar-01 | 251 | Jun-07 | 240 |
| Mar-95 | 154 | Jun-01 | 243 | | |

a. Prepare a time-series plot of THS. Describe what you see in this plot in terms of trend and seasonality.

b. Calculate and plot the first 12 autocorrelation coefficients for HS. What does this autocorrelation structure suggest about the trend?

11. Exercise 12 of Chapter 1 includes data on the Japanese exchange rate (EXRJ) by month. On the basis of a time-series plot of these data and the autocorrelation structure of EXRJ, would you say the data are stationary? Explain your answer. (c2p11)

| Period | EXRJ | Period | EXRJ |
|--------|--------|--------|--------|
| 1 | 127.36 | 13 | 144.98 |
| 2 | 127.74 | 14 | 145.69 |
| 3 | 130.55 | 15 | 153.31 |
| 4 | 132.04 | 16 | 158.46 |
| 5 | 137.86 | 17 | 154.04 |
| 6 | 143.98 | 18 | 153.7 |
| 7 | 140.42 | 19 | 149.04 |
| 8 | 141.49 | 20 | 147.46 |
| 9 | 145.07 | 21 | 138.44 |
| 10 | 142.21 | 22 | 129.59 |
| 11 | 143.53 | 23 | 129.22 |
| 12 | 143.69 | 24 | 133.89 |

# Chapter **Three**

# Extrapolation 1. Moving Averages and Exponential Smoothing

Consider the situation facing a manager who must periodically forecast the inventories for hundreds or thousands of products. Each day or week or month, updated forecasts for the many inventories are required within a short time period. While it might well be possible to develop sophisticated forecasting models for each of the items, in many cases some very simple short-term forecasting tools are adequate for the job.

A manager facing such a task is likely to use some form of time-series *smoothing*. All the time-series smoothing methods use a form of weighted average of past observations to smooth up-and-down movements, that is, some statistical method of suppressing short-term fluctuations. The assumption underlying these methods is that the fluctuations in past values represent random departures from some smooth curve that, once identified, can plausibly be extrapolated into the future to produce a forecast or series of forecasts.

We will examine five basic smoothing techniques in this chapter. All five of these have the common characteristic that only a past history of the time series to be forecast is necessary to produce the forecast. Further, all are based on the concept that there is some underlying pattern to the data; that is, all time-series data to be forecast are assumed to have some cycles or fluctuations that tend to recur. The five methods, to be examined in turn, are:

1. Moving averages
2. Simple exponential smoothing
3. Holt's exponential smoothing
4. Winters' exponential smoothing
5. Adaptive–response-rate single exponential smoothing

# LEARNING OBJECTIVES

After studying this chapter, you should be able to:

1. Explain what a moving average is and how to use one to make a forecast.
2. Distinguish between simple moving averages and exponential smoothing models.
3. Explain why the term *exponential* is used in naming exponential smoothing models.
4. Explain when simple exponential smoothing would be an appropriate forecast method.
5. Explain when Holt's exponential smoothing would be an appropriate forecast method.
6. Explain when Winter's exponential smoothing would be an appropriate forecast method.
7. Explain some methods that can be used to forecast new products.
8. Explain what an event model is and when such a model might be used to make a forecast.

# MOVING AVERAGES

*The simple statistical method of moving averages may mimic some data better than a complicated mathematical function.*

The simple statistical method of moving averages may mimic some data better than a complicated mathematical function. Figure 3.1 shows the exchange rate between the Japanese yen and the U.S. dollar from 1980Q1 through 2016Q4. Figure 3.1 does not exhibit a simple linear, exponential, or quadratic trend similar to those we will examine in Chapters 4 and 5. Instead, the series appears to show

**FIGURE 3.1**   **Exchange Rate of the Japanese Yen Against the U.S. Dollar**   (c3t1)

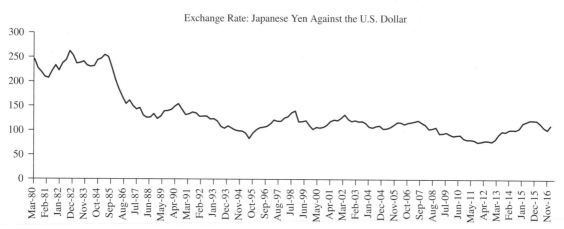

Exchange Rate: Japanese Yen Against the U.S. Dollar

substantial randomness, which we may be able to eliminate with a technique that averages the most recent values.

To illustrate how a moving average is used, consider Table 3.1, which contains data for the exchange rate between the Japanese yen and one U.S. dollar, as shown in Figure 3.1. To calculate the three-quarter moving average first requires

**TABLE 3.1**   **Exchange Rate: Japanese Yen Against the US Dollar**   (c3t1)

| Date | Exchange Rate: Japanese Yen Against the US Dollar | Three Quarter Moving Average (MA3) | Forecast Based on MA3 | Five Quarter Moving Average (MA5) | Forecast Based on MA5 |
|---|---|---|---|---|---|
| Mar-80 | 245.52 | NA | NA | NA | NA |
| Jun-80 | 227.27 | NA | NA | NA | NA |
| Sep-80 | 219.17 | 230.65 | NA | NA | NA |
| Dec-80 | 209.79 | 218.74 | 230.65 | NA | NA |
| Mar-81 | 207.73 | 212.23 | 218.74 | 221.89 | NA |
| Jun-81 | 221.45 | 212.99 | 212.23 | 217.08 | 221.89 |
| Sep-81 | 233.40 | 220.86 | 212.99 | 218.31 | 217.08 |
| Dec-81 | 223.13 | 225.99 | 220.86 | 219.10 | 218.31 |
| Mar-82 | 238.09 | 231.54 | 225.99 | 224.76 | 219.10 |
| Jun-82 | 244.35 | 235.19 | 231.54 | 232.08 | 224.76 |
| Sep-82 | 262.49 | 248.31 | 235.19 | 240.29 | 232.08 |
| Dec-82 | 253.79 | 253.54 | 248.31 | 244.37 | 240.29 |
| Mar-83 | 237.39 | 251.22 | 253.54 | 247.22 | 244.37 |
| Jun-83 | 238.59 | 243.26 | 251.22 | 247.32 | 247.22 |
| Sep-83 | 241.59 | 239.19 | 243.26 | 246.77 | 247.32 |
| Dec-83 | 233.26 | 237.81 | 239.19 | 240.92 | 246.77 |
| Mar-84 | 231.00 | 235.28 | 237.81 | 236.37 | 240.92 |
| Jun-84 | 232.01 | 232.09 | 235.28 | 235.29 | 236.37 |
| Sep-84 | 244.23 | 235.75 | 232.09 | 236.42 | 235.29 |
| Dec-84 | 247.43 | 241.22 | 235.75 | 237.59 | 236.42 |
| Mar-85 | 255.07 | 248.91 | 241.22 | 241.95 | 237.59 |
| Jun-85 | 250.67 | 251.06 | 248.91 | 245.88 | 241.95 |
| Sep-85 | 230.02 | 245.25 | 251.06 | 245.48 | 245.88 |
| Dec-85 | 204.66 | 228.45 | 245.25 | 237.57 | 245.48 |
| Mar-86 | 184.33 | 206.34 | 228.45 | 224.95 | 237.57 |
| Jun-86 | 167.99 | 185.66 | 206.34 | 207.53 | 224.95 |
| Sep-86 | 154.63 | 168.99 | 185.66 | 188.33 | 207.53 |
| Dec-86 | 161.31 | 161.31 | 168.99 | 174.59 | 188.33 |
| Mar-87 | 150.38 | 155.44 | 161.31 | 163.73 | 174.59 |
| Jun-87 | 143.64 | 151.78 | 155.44 | 155.59 | 163.73 |
| Sep-87 | 146.09 | 146.70 | 151.78 | 151.21 | 155.59 |
| Dec-87 | 131.18 | 140.30 | 146.70 | 146.52 | 151.21 |
| Mar-88 | 126.62 | 134.63 | 140.30 | 139.58 | 146.52 |

**TABLE 3.1** (continued)

| Date | Exchange Rate: Japanese Yen Against the US Dollar | Three Quarter Moving Average (MA3) | Forecast Based on MA3 | Five Quarter Moving Average (MA5) | Forecast Based on MA5 |
|------|------|------|------|------|------|
| Jun-88 | 127.29 | 128.37 | 134.63 | 134.97 | 139.58 |
| Sep-88 | 134.04 | 129.32 | 128.37 | 133.05 | 134.97 |
| Dec-88 | 124.30 | 128.54 | 129.32 | 128.69 | 133.05 |
| Mar-89 | 129.61 | 129.32 | 128.54 | 128.37 | 128.69 |
| Jun-89 | 139.76 | 131.22 | 129.32 | 131.00 | 128.37 |
| Sep-89 | 140.68 | 136.68 | 131.22 | 133.68 | 131.00 |
| Dec-89 | 142.94 | 141.13 | 136.68 | 135.46 | 133.68 |
| Mar-90 | 150.03 | 144.55 | 141.13 | 140.60 | 135.46 |
| Jun-90 | 154.50 | 149.16 | 144.55 | 145.58 | 140.60 |
| Sep-90 | 143.30 | 149.28 | 149.16 | 146.29 | 145.58 |
| Dec-90 | 132.33 | 143.38 | 149.28 | 144.62 | 146.29 |
| Mar-91 | 134.33 | 136.65 | 143.38 | 142.90 | 144.62 |
| Jun-91 | 137.82 | 134.83 | 136.65 | 140.46 | 142.90 |
| Sep-91 | 135.86 | 136.00 | 134.83 | 136.73 | 140.46 |
| Dec-91 | 128.76 | 134.14 | 136.00 | 133.82 | 136.73 |
| Mar-92 | 129.34 | 131.32 | 134.14 | 133.22 | 133.82 |
| Jun-92 | 129.14 | 129.08 | 131.32 | 132.18 | 133.22 |
| Sep-92 | 123.35 | 127.27 | 129.08 | 129.29 | 132.18 |
| Dec-92 | 124.19 | 125.56 | 127.27 | 126.95 | 129.29 |
| Mar-93 | 119.21 | 122.25 | 125.56 | 125.04 | 126.95 |
| Jun-93 | 108.26 | 117.22 | 122.25 | 120.83 | 125.04 |
| Sep-93 | 105.11 | 110.86 | 117.22 | 116.02 | 120.83 |
| Dec-93 | 109.76 | 107.71 | 110.86 | 113.31 | 116.02 |
| Mar-94 | 105.55 | 106.81 | 107.71 | 109.58 | 113.31 |
| Jun-94 | 101.59 | 105.64 | 106.81 | 106.06 | 109.58 |
| Sep-94 | 99.30 | 102.15 | 105.64 | 104.26 | 106.06 |
| Dec-94 | 98.72 | 99.87 | 102.15 | 102.98 | 104.26 |
| Mar-95 | 94.93 | 97.65 | 99.87 | 100.02 | 102.98 |
| Jun-95 | 83.90 | 92.51 | 97.65 | 95.69 | 100.02 |
| Sep-95 | 94.81 | 91.21 | 92.51 | 94.33 | 95.69 |
| Dec-95 | 102.06 | 93.59 | 91.21 | 94.88 | 94.33 |
| Mar-96 | 106.11 | 100.99 | 93.59 | 96.36 | 94.88 |
| Jun-96 | 107.35 | 105.17 | 100.99 | 98.85 | 96.36 |
| Sep-96 | 108.99 | 107.48 | 105.17 | 103.86 | 98.85 |
| Dec-96 | 114.48 | 110.27 | 107.48 | 107.80 | 103.86 |
| Mar-97 | 122.05 | 115.17 | 110.27 | 111.79 | 107.80 |
| Jun-97 | 119.19 | 118.57 | 115.17 | 114.41 | 111.79 |
| Sep-97 | 119.39 | 120.21 | 118.57 | 116.82 | 114.41 |
| Dec-97 | 125.89 | 121.49 | 120.21 | 120.20 | 116.82 |

(continued on next page)

**TABLE 3.1** (continued)

| Date | Exchange Rate: Japanese Yen Against the US Dollar | Three Quarter Moving Average (MA3) | Forecast Based on MA3 | Five Quarter Moving Average (MA5) | Forecast Based on MA5 |
|------|------|------|------|------|------|
| Mar-98 | 129.06 | 124.78 | 121.49 | 123.12 | 120.20 |
| Jun-98 | 137.03 | 130.66 | 124.78 | 126.11 | 123.12 |
| Sep-98 | 140.36 | 135.49 | 130.66 | 130.35 | 126.11 |
| Dec-98 | 118.01 | 131.80 | 135.49 | 130.07 | 130.35 |
| Mar-99 | 119.03 | 125.80 | 131.80 | 128.70 | 130.07 |
| Jun-99 | 120.47 | 119.17 | 125.80 | 126.98 | 128.70 |
| Sep-99 | 110.75 | 116.75 | 119.17 | 121.73 | 126.98 |
| Dec-99 | 103.07 | 111.43 | 116.75 | 114.27 | 121.73 |
| Mar-00 | 107.47 | 107.10 | 111.43 | 112.16 | 114.27 |
| Jun-00 | 106.23 | 105.59 | 107.10 | 109.60 | 112.16 |
| Sep-00 | 107.88 | 107.19 | 105.59 | 107.08 | 109.60 |
| Dec-00 | 111.65 | 108.58 | 107.19 | 107.26 | 107.08 |
| Mar-01 | 119.19 | 112.91 | 108.58 | 110.48 | 107.26 |
| Jun-01 | 122.34 | 117.73 | 112.91 | 113.46 | 110.48 |
| Sep-01 | 120.95 | 120.83 | 117.73 | 116.40 | 113.46 |
| Dec-01 | 125.74 | 123.01 | 120.83 | 119.97 | 116.40 |
| Mar-02 | 133.10 | 126.60 | 123.01 | 124.26 | 119.97 |
| Jun-02 | 123.78 | 127.54 | 126.60 | 125.18 | 124.26 |
| Sep-02 | 119.65 | 125.51 | 127.54 | 124.64 | 125.18 |
| Dec-02 | 121.16 | 121.53 | 125.51 | 124.68 | 124.64 |
| Mar-03 | 118.65 | 119.82 | 121.53 | 123.27 | 124.68 |
| Jun-03 | 119.19 | 119.67 | 119.82 | 120.49 | 123.27 |
| Sep-03 | 115.99 | 117.94 | 119.67 | 118.93 | 120.49 |
| Dec-03 | 108.49 | 114.55 | 117.94 | 116.70 | 118.93 |
| Mar-04 | 106.56 | 110.35 | 114.55 | 113.78 | 116.70 |
| Jun-04 | 109.41 | 108.15 | 110.35 | 111.93 | 113.78 |
| Sep-04 | 110.77 | 108.91 | 108.15 | 110.24 | 111.93 |
| Dec-04 | 103.98 | 108.05 | 108.91 | 107.84 | 110.24 |
| Mar-05 | 105.12 | 106.62 | 108.05 | 107.17 | 107.84 |
| Jun-05 | 107.95 | 105.68 | 106.62 | 107.45 | 107.17 |
| Sep-05 | 112.16 | 108.41 | 105.68 | 108.00 | 107.45 |
| Dec-05 | 117.48 | 112.53 | 108.41 | 109.34 | 108.00 |
| Mar-06 | 117.13 | 115.59 | 112.53 | 111.97 | 109.34 |
| Jun-06 | 113.58 | 116.06 | 115.59 | 113.66 | 111.97 |
| Sep-06 | 116.51 | 115.74 | 116.06 | 115.37 | 113.66 |
| Dec-06 | 117.55 | 115.88 | 115.74 | 116.45 | 115.37 |
| Mar-07 | 119.22 | 117.76 | 115.88 | 116.80 | 116.45 |
| Jun-07 | 121.49 | 119.42 | 117.76 | 117.67 | 116.80 |
| Sep-07 | 116.72 | 119.14 | 119.42 | 118.30 | 117.67 |
| Dec-07 | 112.37 | 116.86 | 119.14 | 117.47 | 118.30 |

**TABLE 3.1** (continued)

| Date | Exchange Rate: Japanese Yen Against the US Dollar | Three Quarter Moving Average (MA3) | Forecast Based on MA3 | Five Quarter Moving Average (MA5) | Forecast Based on MA5 |
|---|---|---|---|---|---|
| Mar-08 | 103.71 | 110.93 | 116.86 | 114.70 | 117.47 |
| Jun-08 | 105.04 | 107.04 | 110.93 | 111.87 | 114.70 |
| Sep-08 | 107.10 | 105.28 | 107.04 | 108.99 | 111.87 |
| Dec-08 | 94.41 | 102.18 | 105.28 | 104.53 | 108.99 |
| Mar-09 | 95.05 | 98.85 | 102.18 | 101.06 | 104.53 |
| Jun-09 | 96.57 | 95.34 | 98.85 | 99.63 | 101.06 |
| Sep-09 | 92.56 | 94.73 | 95.34 | 97.14 | 99.63 |
| Dec-09 | 89.94 | 93.03 | 94.73 | 93.71 | 97.14 |
| Mar-10 | 90.86 | 91.12 | 93.03 | 93.00 | 93.71 |
| Jun-10 | 91.38 | 90.73 | 91.12 | 92.26 | 93.00 |
| Sep-10 | 84.66 | 88.97 | 90.73 | 89.88 | 92.26 |
| Dec-10 | 82.06 | 86.03 | 88.97 | 87.78 | 89.88 |
| Mar-11 | 82.18 | 82.97 | 86.03 | 86.23 | 87.78 |
| Jun-11 | 81.11 | 81.79 | 82.97 | 84.28 | 86.23 |
| Sep-11 | 76.88 | 80.06 | 81.79 | 81.38 | 84.28 |
| Dec-11 | 78.20 | 78.73 | 80.06 | 80.09 | 81.38 |
| Mar-12 | 79.53 | 78.20 | 78.73 | 79.58 | 80.09 |
| Jun-12 | 79.43 | 79.05 | 78.20 | 79.03 | 79.58 |
| Sep-12 | 78.05 | 79.00 | 79.05 | 78.42 | 79.03 |
| Dec-12 | 82.74 | 80.08 | 79.00 | 79.59 | 78.42 |
| Mar-13 | 92.38 | 84.39 | 80.08 | 82.43 | 79.59 |
| Jun-13 | 99.16 | 91.43 | 84.39 | 86.35 | 82.43 |
| Sep-13 | 97.99 | 96.51 | 91.43 | 90.07 | 86.35 |
| Dec-13 | 101.90 | 99.68 | 96.51 | 94.83 | 90.07 |
| Mar-14 | 102.29 | 100.73 | 99.68 | 98.74 | 94.83 |
| Jun-14 | 101.76 | 101.98 | 100.73 | 100.62 | 98.74 |
| Sep-14 | 105.32 | 103.12 | 101.98 | 101.85 | 100.62 |
| Dec-14 | 116.00 | 107.69 | 103.12 | 105.45 | 101.85 |
| Mar-15 | 119.10 | 113.47 | 107.69 | 108.89 | 105.45 |
| Jun-15 | 121.59 | 118.90 | 113.47 | 112.75 | 108.89 |
| Sep-15 | 121.69 | 120.80 | 118.90 | 116.74 | 112.75 |
| Dec-15 | 121.48 | 121.59 | 120.80 | 119.97 | 116.74 |
| Mar-16 | 115.12 | 119.43 | 121.59 | 119.80 | 119.97 |
| Jun-16 | 107.08 | 114.56 | 119.43 | 117.39 | 119.80 |
| Sep-16 | 102.60 | 108.27 | 114.56 | 113.60 | 117.39 |
| Dec-16 | 111.41 | 107.03 | 108.27 | 111.54 | 113.60 |
| Mar-17 | **112.73** | | 107.03 | | 111.54 |
| | | MAPE = 5.79% | | MAPE = 7.57% | |

that we sum the first three observations (245.52, 227.27, and 219.17). This three-quarter total is then divided by 3 to obtain 230.65, which is the first number in the "Three-Quarter Moving Average (MA3)" column. This "smoothed" number, 230.65, becomes the forecast for 1980Q4, which is designated as Dec-80. Often when using quarterly data, we select one month in the quarter to represent the quarter. In this example, we are using the end month of each quarter to represent the quarter. Thus, March (Mar) represents the first quarter, June (Jun) represents the second quarter, September (Sep) represents the third quarter, and December (Dec) represents the fourth quarter.

The final value in the "Three-Quarter Moving Average MA3" column (107.03) is the forecast for 2017Q1, designated as Mar-17. It was calculated by summing the final three values in the "Actual" column and then dividing by 3 (321.10/3 = 107.03).

The five-quarter moving averages displayed in the same table are calculated in like manner: the first moving average of 221.89 is calculated by summing the first five actual values and dividing by 5:

$$\frac{245.52 + 227.27 + 219.17 + 209.79 + 207.73}{5} = \frac{1,109.47}{5} = 221.89$$

Thus, 221.89 becomes the forecast for the next period (Jun-81).

The five entries from Dec-15 through Dec-16 in the "Actual" column are averaged to give the final five-quarter moving average:

$$\frac{121.48 + 115.12 + 107.08 + 102.60 + 111.41}{5} = \frac{557.70}{5} = 111.54$$

This final moving average serves as the forecast for Mar-17.

*The choice of the interval for the moving average depends on the length of the underlying cycle or pattern in the original data.*

Obviously, three- and five-quarter moving averages are not the only kinds of moving averages. We could calculate seven- or nine-quarter moving averages if we wished or eight- or ten-quarter averages and so on. The choice of the interval for the moving average depends on the length of the underlying cycle or pattern in the original data. If we believe the actual data to be exhibiting a cycle that recurs every four periods, we would choose a four-period moving average in order to best dampen the short-run fluctuation. The simplest naive model of Chapter 1 used each period's actual value as the forecast for the next period; you could correctly think of this model as a one-period moving average, that is, a special case of the model we are examining here.

In order to compute whether the three-quarter or five-quarter moving average is the better forecasting model, it is useful to compute the mean absolute percentage error (MAPE) as we calculated it in Chapter 1. Table 3.1 shows the MAPE for both forecasts at the bottom of the table. The MAPE of 5.79 percent for the three-quarter moving average is less than the MAPE of 7.57 percent calculated for the five-quarter case, and so we conclude that the better forecast in this particular case is generated by the three-quarter model.

**FIGURE 3.2**   **Three-Quarter Moving-Average Forecast of the U.S. Exchange Rate with Japan**   (c3t1)

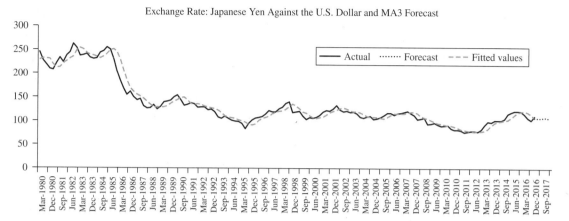

Exchange Rate: Japanese Yen Against the U.S. Dollar and MA3 Forecast

In preparing the forecasts for Mar-17, it was assumed that the actual value for that quarter was unknown. However, the actual value for that quarter is known in this situation and is shown in Table 3.1. Thus, we can see which of the two moving-average forecasts developed above was really the best for Mar-17. The forecast for the single quarter (Mar-17) shows that the five-quarter moving average was more accurate for this one quarter, even though for the entire time span the three-quarter moving average had the lower MAPE.

The three- and five-quarter moving averages are shown graphically in Figures 3.2 and 3.3, respectively. Notice in Figures 3.2 and 3.3 that the peaks and troughs of the actual series are different from those for either moving average. This failure of the moving averages to predict peaks and troughs is one of the shortcomings of moving-average models.

Moving averages are most likely to be successful in forecasting when the data are stationary. That is, when there is little, if any, positive or negative trend in the series.

*The moving-average forecasting method has fooled more than one forecaster by appearing to identify a cycle.*

One final and important observation: The moving-average forecasting method has fooled more than one forecaster by appearing to identify a cycle when, in fact, no cycle was present in the actual data. Such an occurrence can be understood if you think of an actual data series as being simply a series of random numbers. Since any moving average is serially correlated, because a number of contiguous periods have been averaged, *any* sequence of random numbers could appear to exhibit cyclical fluctuation.[1]

[1] This incorrect conclusion is sometimes called the *Slutsky-Yule* effect, named after Eugen Slutsky and G. Udny Yule, who first pointed out the possibility of making a mistake in this manner. See Eugen E. Slutsky, "The Summation of Random Causes as the Source of Cyclic Processes," *Econometrica* 5 (1937), pp. 105–46; and G. Udny Yule, "On a Method of Investigating Periodicities in Disturbed Series, with Special Reference to Wolfer's Sunspot Numbers," Royal Society of London, *Philosophical Transactions* (1927), pp. 267–98.

**FIGURE 3.3** **Five-Quarter Moving-Average Forecast of the U.S. Exchange Rate with Japan** (c3t1)

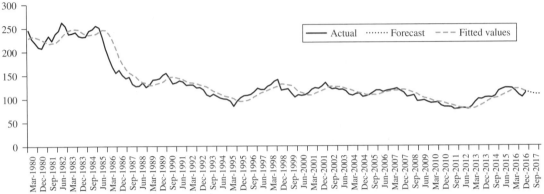

Exchange Rate: Japanese Yen Against the U.S. Dollar and MA5 Forecast

# SIMPLE EXPONENTIAL SMOOTHING

With exponential smoothing, the forecast value at any time is a weighted average of all the available previous values.

Simple exponential smoothing, like moving averages, uses only past values of a time series to forecast future values of the same series and is properly employed when there is no trend or seasonality present in the data. With exponential smoothing, the forecast value at any time is a weighted average of all the available previous values; the weights decline exponentially as you go back in time.

Moving-average forecasting gives equal weights to the past values included in each average. However, exponential smoothing gives more weight to the recent observations and less to the older observations. The weights are made to decline exponentially with the age of the observation to conform to the argument that the most recent observations contain the most relevant information. As a result, more recent values are accorded proportionately more influence than older observations.

The number we choose for $\alpha$ is called the *level smoothing constant.*

Exponential smoothing proceeds by smoothing past values of the series but in a different manner than moving averages. The calculations for producing exponentially smoothed forecasts can be expressed as an equation. The weight of the most recent observation is assigned by multiplying the observed value by $\alpha$, the next most recent observation by $(1 - \alpha)\alpha$, the next observation by $(1 - \alpha)^2\alpha$, and so on. The number we choose for $\alpha$ is called the *level smoothing constant.*[2]

---

[2] Our notation throughout the chapter for exponential smoothing follows approximately the notation found in Everette S. Gardner, "Exponential Smoothing: The State of the Art," *Journal of Forecasting* 4, no. 1 (1985), pp. 1–28. This article contains a very complete description of different forms of smoothing that are in common use and explains (with advanced mathematics) that there may be theoretical advantages for employing smoothing in situations where it can be shown that certain assumptions concerning the probability distribution of the series are met.

The simple exponential smoothing model can be written in the following manner:

$$F_{t+1} = \alpha X_t + (1 - \alpha)F_t \qquad \textbf{(3.1)}$$

where:

$F_{t+1}$ = Forecast value for period $t + 1$

$\alpha$ = Smoothing constant $(0 < \alpha < 1)$

$X_t$ = Actual value now (in period $t$)

$F_t$ = Forecast (i.e., smoothed) value for period $t$

In using this equation, the forecaster does not need to deal with every actual past value at every step; only the exponentially smoothed value for the last period and the actual value for this period are necessary. However, you will see that in practice all previous actual and forecast values play a role in the simple exponential smoothing forecast.

An alternative way of writing Equation 3.1 results from rearranging the terms as follows:

$$\begin{aligned} F_{t+1} &= \alpha X_t + (1 - \alpha)F_t \\ &= \alpha X_t + F_t - \alpha F_t \\ &= F_t + \alpha(X_t - F_t) \end{aligned} \qquad \textbf{(3.2)}$$

From this form we can see that the exponential smoothing model "learns" from past errors. The forecast value at period $t + 1$ is increased if the actual value for period $t$ is greater than it was forecast to be, and it is decreased if $X_t$ is less than $F_t$.

We can show how all historical observations are included in a simple exponential smoothing forecast as follows:

$$F_{t+1} = \alpha X_t + (1 - \alpha)F_t \qquad \textbf{(3.3)}$$

and $\qquad F_t = \alpha X_{t-1} + (1 - \alpha)F_{t-1}$

therefore $\quad F_{t+1} = \alpha X_t + (1 - \alpha)\alpha X_{t-1} + (1 - \alpha)^2 F_{t-1}$

and $\qquad F_{t-1} = \alpha X_{t-2} + (1 - \alpha)F_{t-2}$

thus, $\qquad F_{t+1} = \alpha X_t + (1 - \alpha)\alpha X_{t-1} + (1 - \alpha)^2 \alpha X_{t-2} + (1 - \alpha)^3 F_{t-2}$

We could continue this expansion to include $X$ terms as far back as we have data, but this is probably far enough to help you see how the weights for previous time periods become smaller and smaller at a rate that depends on the value of $\alpha$, as will be shown in the following tables for two alternative values of $\alpha$.

The value of the level smoothing constant $\alpha$ is constrained to be in the range of zero to one. If a value close to 1 is chosen, recent values of the time series are weighted heavily relative to those of the distant past when the smoothed values are calculated. Likewise, if the value of $\alpha$ is chosen close to 0, then the values of the time series in the distant past are given weights comparable to those given the recent values. The rate at which the weights decrease can be seen from their values for an $\alpha$ of 0.1:

| Time | $\alpha = 0.1$ Calculation | Weight |
|------|---------------------------|--------|
| $t$ | | 0.1 |
| $t-1$ | $0.9 \times 0.1$ | 0.090 |
| $t-2$ | $0.9 \times 0.9 \times 0.1$ | 0.081 |
| $t-3$ | $0.9 \times 0.9 \times 0.9 \times 0.1$ | 0.073 |
| $\vdots$ | | $\vdots$ |
| Total | | 1.000 |

Regardless of the smoothing constant chosen, the weights will eventually sum to 1. Whether the sum of the weights converges on 1 quickly or slowly depends on the smoothing constant chosen. If, for example, we choose a smoothing constant of 0.9, the sum of the weights will approach 1 much more rapidly than when the level smoothing constant is 0.1:

| Time | $\alpha = 0.9$ Calculation | Weight |
|------|---------------------------|--------|
| $t$ | | 0.9 |
| $t-1$ | $0.1 \times 0.9$ | 0.09 |
| $t-2$ | $0.1 \times 0.1 \times 0.9$ | 0.009 |
| $t-3$ | $0.1 \times 0.1 \times 0.1 \times 0.9$ | 0.0009 |
| $\vdots$ | | $\vdots$ |
| Total | | 1.000 |

In practice, relatively small values of alpha ($\alpha$) generally work best when simple exponential smoothing is the most appropriate model.

As a guide in choosing $\alpha$, select values close to 0 if the series has a great deal of random variation; select values close to 1 if you wish the forecast values to depend strongly on recent changes in the actual values. The mean absolute percentage error (MAPE) is often used as the criterion for assigning an appropriate smoothing constant; the smoothing constant giving the smallest MAPE would be selected as the model likely to produce the smallest error in generating additional forecasts. In practice, relatively small values of alpha ($\alpha$) generally work best when simple exponential smoothing is the most appropriate model.

The following example will demonstrate the technique. Suppose we wish to forecast the University of Michigan Index of Consumer Sentiment for January 2017 based on monthly data from January 2016 through December 2016. These values are shown in the "$X_t$" column of Tables 3.2A and 3.2B for January 2016 through December 2016. Since no previous forecast is available for the first period (January 2016), we have to select a value. This value is called a seed value because it allows the process to begin, just as a plant seed allows the plant to begin growth. In the A part of Table 3.2, we use a seed value equal to that month's actual index value of 92. That is, we are assuming that the forecast for January 2016 was perfect. This process of choosing an initial value for the smoothed (forecast) series is called *initializing* the model, or *warming up* the model.[3] All the other values in the "Forecast" column were calculated by using Equation 3.1

**TABLE 3.2A** **Simple Exponential Smoothing Forecast of the University of Michigan Index of Consumer Sentiment** (c3t2A&B)

| Date | UMICS = $X_t$ | Forecast = $F_t =$ $\alpha X_{t-1} + (1-\alpha)F_{t-1}$ | Error $(X - F)$ | Absolute Error | Absolute % Error (Absolute Error/X)*100 |
|---|---|---|---|---|---|
| Jan-2016 | 92 | 92.00 | 0.00 | 0.00 | 0.00 |
| Feb-2016 | 91.7 | 92.00 | −0.30 | 0.30 | 0.33 |
| Mar-2016 | 91 | 91.88 | −0.88 | 0.88 | 0.97 |
| Apr-2016 | 89 | 91.53 | −2.53 | 2.53 | 2.84 |
| May-2016 | 94.7 | 90.52 | 4.18 | 4.18 | 4.42 |
| Jun-2016 | 93.5 | 92.19 | 1.31 | 1.31 | 1.40 |
| Jul-2016 | 90 | 92.71 | −2.71 | 2.71 | 3.02 |
| Aug-2016 | 89.8 | 91.63 | −1.83 | 1.83 | 2.04 |
| Sep-2016 | 91.2 | 90.90 | 0.30 | 0.30 | 0.33 |
| Oct-2016 | 87.2 | 91.02 | −3.82 | 3.82 | 4.38 |
| Nov-2016 | 93.8 | 89.49 | 4.31 | 4.31 | 4.59 |
| Dec-2016 | 98.2 | 91.21 | 6.99 | 6.99 | 7.11 |
| Jan-2017 | NA | 94.01 | | | |
| | | | | MAPE = | 2.86 |

Table 3.2A. Simple Exponential Smoothing Forecast of the University of Michigan Index of Consumer Sentiment and calculation of the MAPE (c3t2). A seed value of 92 has been used and an alpha of 0.4 has been arbitrarily selected.

(continued on next page)

[3] The choice of a starting value in exponential smoothing models has been a matter of some discussion, with little empirical evidence favoring any particular approach. R. G. Brown first suggested using the mean of the data for the starting value, and this suggestion has been quite popular in actual practice. A linear regression (like that described in Chapter 4) is sometimes used when selecting starting values for seasonal factors, and time-series decomposition (as discussed in Chapter 6) has also been used. If the data include a trend, backcasting is sometimes used to select a starting value; but if the trend is erratic, this sometimes leads to negative starting values, which make little sense. A discussion of the various alternatives (including using the first value in the series or using the mean of the series, which are both popular in practice) appears in the Gardner article (footnote 2).

**TABLE 3.2B**

| Date | UMICS = $X_t$ | Forecast = $F_t$ = $\alpha X_{t-1} + (1 - \alpha)F_{t-1}$ | Error $(X - F)$ | Absolute Error | Absolute % Error (Absolute Error/X)*100 |
|---|---|---|---|---|---|
| Jan-2016 | 92 | 0.00 | 92.00 | 92.00 | 100.00 |
| Feb-2016 | 91.7 | 36.80 | 54.90 | 54.90 | 59.87 |
| Mar-2016 | 91 | 58.76 | 32.24 | 32.24 | 35.43 |
| Apr-2016 | 89 | 71.66 | 17.34 | 17.34 | 19.49 |
| May-2016 | 94.7 | 78.59 | 16.11 | 16.11 | 17.01 |
| Jun-2016 | 93.5 | 85.04 | 8.46 | 8.46 | 9.05 |
| Jul-2016 | 90 | 88.42 | 1.58 | 1.58 | 1.75 |
| Aug-2016 | 89.8 | 89.05 | 0.75 | 0.75 | 0.83 |
| Sep-2016 | 91.2 | 89.35 | 1.85 | 1.85 | 2.03 |
| Oct-2016 | 87.2 | 90.09 | −2.89 | 2.89 | 3.32 |
| Nov-2016 | 93.8 | 88.93 | 4.87 | 4.87 | 5.19 |
| Dec-2016 | 98.2 | 90.88 | 7.32 | 7.32 | 7.45 |
| Jan-2017 | NA | 93.81 | | | |
| | | | | MAPE = | 14.67 |

Table 3.2B. Here a seed value of 0 has been used and alpha has been kept at 0.4. Note how little the forecast for January 2017 has changed.

with a level smoothing constant ($\alpha$) of 0.4. The actual and forecast values are shown in Figure 3.4.

In part B of Table 3.2, we have changed the seed value to zero. This is certainly a dramatic difference from the perfect forecast of 92 assumed in part A of that table. Notice that, even with a fairly short data series of 12 observations, the

**FIGURE 3.4**

**A Simple Exponential Smoothing Forecast of the University of Michigan Index of Consumer Sentiment (c3t2A&B)**

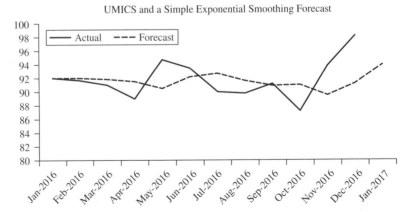

UMICS and a Simple Exponential Smoothing Forecast

affect on the January 2017 forecast is quite small. The difference is only 0.20. The MAPE for the model in Table 3.2B is 14.67 percent compared to a MAPE of 2.86 percent for the model in Table 3.2A. You can see that this is strongly influenced by the very low early errors when the first forecast was assumed to be perfect compared to the large early errors when the first forecast was assumed to be zero.

Let us illustrate the calculation of the forecast value for February 2016 by using Equation 3.1 as follows:

$$F_{t+1} = \alpha X_t + (1 - \alpha) F_t$$
$$F_2 = \alpha X_1 + (1 - \alpha) F_1$$
$$F_2 = 0.4(92) + (1 - 0.4)(92) = 92$$

This smoothed value of 92 is the forecast for February 2016 ($t = 2$). Once actual data for February become available, the model is used to forecast March, and so on.

The error for February 2016 forecast (rounded) is calculated as:

$$e_2 = X_2 - F_2 = 91.7 - 92 = -0.30$$

The predominant reason for using simple smoothing is that it requires a limited quantity of data and it is simpler than most other forecasting methods. Its limitations, however, are that its forecasts lag behind the actual data, and it has no ability to adjust for any trend or seasonality in the data. Like moving averages, simple exponential smoothing is best used when the data have little or no positive or negative trend. That is, simple exponential smoothing is best applied for data that are stationary. In the following section, you will see that a modification to the simple exponential smoothing model allows for the use of data that does have a significant trend.

# HOLT'S EXPONENTIAL SMOOTHING

Holt's two-parameter exponential smoothing method (called "Double Exponential Smoothing Holt" in ForecastX™) is an extension of simple exponential smoothing; it adds a growth factor (or trend factor) to the smoothing equation as a way of adjusting for the trend.

Two further extensions of the smoothing model can be used in order to bring the forecast values closer to the values observed if the data series exhibits a trend and/or seasonality (the first extension is discussed in this section, and the second in the following section). In real-world situations, one or both of these techniques are often used because real-world data often are not stationary and often include a seasonal pattern.

The first extension is to adjust the smoothing model for a trend in the data; with a trend in the data, the simple smoothing model will have large errors that often move from positive to negative or vice versa. When a trend exists, the forecast may be improved by adjusting for the trend by using a form of smoothing named after its originator, C. C. Holt. Holt's two-parameter exponential smoothing method is an extension of simple exponential smoothing; it adds a growth factor (or trend factor) to the smoothing equation as a way of adjusting for the trend. Three equations and two smoothing constants are used in the model.

$$F_{t+1} = \alpha X_t + (1 - \alpha)(F_t + T_t) \qquad \textbf{(3.4)}$$

$$T_{t+1} = \gamma(F_{t+1} - F_t) + (1 - \gamma)T_t \qquad \textbf{(3.5)}$$

$$H_{t+m} = F_{t+1} + m T_{t+1} \qquad \textbf{(3.6)}$$

where:

$F_{t+1}$ = Smoothed value for period $t + 1$

$\alpha$ = Smoothing constant for the level $(0 < \alpha < 1)$

$X_t$ = Actual value now (in period $t$)

$F_t$ = Forecast (i.e., smoothed) value for time period $t$

$T_{t+1}$ = Trend estimate

$\gamma$ = Smoothing constant for the trend estimate $(0 < \gamma < 1)$

$m$ = Number of periods ahead to be forecast

$H_{t+m}$ = Holt's forecast value for period $t + m$

Equation 3.4 adjusts $F_{t+1}$ for the growth of the previous period, $T_t$, by adding $T_t$ to the smoothed value of the previous period, $F_t$. The trend estimate is calculated in Equation 3.5, where the difference of the last two smoothed values is calculated. Because these two values have already been smoothed, the difference between them is assumed to be an estimate of trend in the data. The second smoothing constant, $\gamma$ in Equation 3.5, is arrived at by using the same principle employed in simple exponential smoothing. The most recent trend $(F_{t+1} - F_t)$, is weighted by $\gamma$, and the last previous smoothed trend, $T_t$, is weighted by $(1 - \gamma)$. The sum of the weighted values is the new smoothed trend value $T_{t+1}$.

Equation 3.6 is used to forecast $m$ periods into the future by adding the product of the trend component, $T_{t+1}$, times the number of periods to forecast, $m$, to the current value of the smoothed data $F_{t+1}$.

Holt's method accounts for any linear trend in the data.[4] As an example, consider personal consumption expenditures (PCE) in the United States. A graph of

---

[4] All trends, of course, do not have to be linear, and there are smoothing models that can account for nonlinear trends. In this chapter, we are examining only a subset of the number of possible smoothing models. For a listing of smoothing models, see Carl C. Pegels, "Exponential Forecasting: Some New Variations," *Management Science* 15, no. 12 (1969), pp. 311–15, or the Gardner article (1985). Both of these articles cover many smoothing models, including some that are very rarely used in actual practice.

**FIGURE 3.5**  **Personal Consumption Expeditures in the United States. Quarterly Data in Millions of Constant 2009 Dollars**   (c3t3)

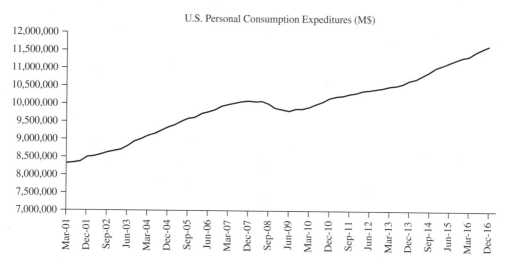

PCE (in millions of constant dollars) is shown in Figure 3.5. In this graph, it is clear that over time PCE have been rising. That is, the data have a clear positive trend (they are not stationary). The downturn in the U.S. economy is evident in 2008, when PCE dropped for a short period. Note that in Figure 3.5, the vertical axis has been adjusted to start at 7,000,000 million rather than at zero. This has been done to better illustrate the drop during 2008.

Table 3.3 illustrates the application of Holt's model to U.S. personal consumption expenditures, using the ForecastX$^{TM}$ software. The two smoothing constants are $\alpha = 0.88$ and $\gamma = 0.68$. Two starting values are needed: one for the first smoothed value and another for the first trend value. The initial smoothed value is often a recent actual value available; the initial trend value is often 0.00 if no past data are available (see footnote 3). The following naming conventions for model constants are used by ForecastX$^{TM}$ for all smoothing models (simple, Holt's, and Winters'):

### ForecastX$^{TM}$ Naming Conventions for Smoothing Constants

| Alpha ($\alpha$) | = | the level smoothing constant |
|---|---|---|
| Gamma ($\gamma$) | = | the trend smoothing constant |
| Beta ($\beta$) | = | the seasonal smoothing constant (Winters' only) |

For the personal consumption data, Equations 3.4 through 3.6 can be used to calculate the Holt's forecast for June 2001. To do so, we will arbitrarily select the first actual value as our initial smoothed value ($F_1 = 8,319,403$) and 53,000 as our

**TABLE 3.3**  Personal Consumption Expenditures in Millions of Dollars (SA)  (c3t3)

| Date | U.S. Personal Consumption Expenditures (M$) | Fitted and Forecast Values | Error (Actual - Predicted) |
|---|---|---|---|
| Mar-01 | 8,319,403 | 8,347,587 | −28,184 |
| Jun-01 | 8,340,761 | 8,339,189 | 1,572 |
| Sep-01 | 8,371,247 | 8,357,981 | 13,266 |
| Dec-01 | 8,499,132 | 8,395,073 | 104,059 |
| Mar-02 | 8,524,579 | 8,574,887 | −50,307 |
| Jun-02 | 8,568,126 | 8,588,268 | −20,142 |
| Sep-02 | 8,628,043 | 8,616,129 | 11,915 |
| Dec-02 | 8,674,353 | 8,679,435 | −5,082 |
| Mar-03 | 8,712,527 | 8,724,691 | −12,165 |
| Jun-03 | 8,809,507 | 8,756,378 | 53,129 |
| Sep-03 | 8,939,387 | 8,877,635 | 61,751 |
| Dec-03 | 9,008,814 | 9,043,673 | −34,858 |
| Mar-04 | 9,096,415 | 9,103,518 | −7,103 |
| Jun-04 | 9,155,468 | 9,183,567 | −28,099 |
| Sep-04 | 9,243,001 | 9,228,182 | 14,820 |
| Dec-04 | 9,337,837 | 9,319,571 | 18,266 |
| Mar-05 | 9,409,222 | 9,424,996 | −15,774 |
| Jun-05 | 9,511,451 | 9,490,903 | 20,548 |
| Sep-05 | 9,585,233 | 9,601,215 | −15,982 |
| Dec-05 | 9,621,339 | 9,669,688 | −48,349 |
| Mar-06 | 9,729,225 | 9,680,507 | 48,718 |
| Jun-06 | 9,781,025 | 9,806,265 | −25,240 |
| Sep-06 | 9,838,106 | 9,851,600 | −13,493 |
| Dec-06 | 9,938,409 | 9,899,171 | 39,237 |
| Mar-07 | 9,990,656 | 10,016,871 | −26,215 |
| Jun-07 | 10,024,604 | 10,061,063 | −36,459 |
| Sep-07 | 10,069,158 | 10,074,270 | −5,113 |
| Dec-07 | 10,081,798 | 10,112,047 | −30,249 |
| Mar-08 | 10,060,966 | 10,109,444 | −48,477 |
| Jun-08 | 10,077,941 | 10,061,580 | 16,361 |
| Sep-08 | 10,005,097 | 10,080,750 | −75,654 |
| Dec-08 | 9,884,724 | 9,973,223 | −88,499 |
| Mar-09 | 9,850,832 | 9,801,088 | 49,744 |
| Jun-09 | 9,806,377 | 9,780,826 | 25,552 |
| Sep-09 | 9,865,864 | 9,754,609 | 111,255 |
| Dec-09 | 9,864,805 | 9,870,956 | −6,152 |
| Mar-10 | 9,917,689 | 9,880,052 | 37,637 |
| Jun-10 | 9,998,389 | 9,950,425 | 47,964 |
| Sep-10 | 10,063,083 | 10,058,782 | 4,301 |
| Dec-10 | 10,166,127 | 10,131,219 | 34,909 |
| Mar-11 | 10,217,123 | 10,251,666 | −34,543 |
| Jun-11 | 10,237,676 | 10,290,064 | −52,387 |
| Sep-11 | 10,282,234 | 10,281,185 | 1,049 |

**TABLE 3.3** (continued)

| Date | U.S. Personal Consumption Expenditures (M$) | Fitted and Forecast Values | Error (Actual - Predicted) |
|---|---|---|---|
| Dec-11 | 10,316,776 | 10,320,067 | −3,291 |
| Mar-12 | 10,379,022 | 10,353,141 | 25,881 |
| Jun-12 | 10,396,630 | 10,427,523 | −30,893 |
| Sep-12 | 10,424,119 | 10,433,235 | −9,117 |
| Dec-12 | 10,453,205 | 10,452,665 | 540 |
| Mar-13 | 10,502,300 | 10,480,936 | 21,364 |
| Jun-13 | 10,523,928 | 10,540,435 | −16,507 |
| Sep-13 | 10,573,135 | 10,556,596 | 16,539 |
| Dec-13 | 10,662,222 | 10,611,859 | 50,362 |
| Mar-14 | 10,712,811 | 10,727,272 | −14,461 |
| Jun-14 | 10,813,346 | 10,776,807 | 36,539 |
| Sep-14 | 10,912,871 | 10,893,319 | 19,553 |
| Dec-14 | 11,036,376 | 11,006,620 | 29,755 |
| Mar-15 | 11,102,370 | 11,146,833 | −44,463 |
| Jun-15 | 11,181,347 | 11,194,821 | −13,474 |
| Sep-15 | 11,255,893 | 11,262,028 | −6,135 |
| Dec-15 | 11,319,286 | 11,332,015 | −12,729 |
| Mar-16 | 11,365,214 | 11,388,523 | −23,309 |
| Jun-16 | 11,484,859 | 11,421,667 | 63,192 |
| Sep-16 | 11,569,014 | 11,569,145 | −130 |
| Dec-16 | 11,655,004 | 11,660,696 | −5,692 |
| Mar-17 | | 11,743,915 | |
| Jun-17 | | 11,832,155 | |
| Sep-17 | | 11,920,394 | |
| Dec-17 | | 12,008,634 | |
| Mar-18 | | 12,096,873 | |
| Jun-18 | | 12,185,113 | |
| Sep-18 | | 12,273,352 | |
| Dec-18 | | 12,361,592 | |

Alpha = 0.88
Gamma = 0.68
MAPE = 0.30%

initial trend ($T_1 = 53,000$). The initial trend estimate of 53,000 was determined by calculating the average quarter to quarter change for the entire series. The smoothed value for period 2 (June 2001) is calculated by:

$$F_{t+1} = \alpha X_t + (1 - \alpha)(F_t + T_1)$$
$$F_2 = 0.88(8,319,403) + (1 - 0.88)(8,319,403 + 53,000)$$
$$= 7,321,075 + 1,004,688$$
$$= 8,325,763$$

The trend estimate for period 2 is calculated as:

$$T_{t+1} = \gamma(F_{t+1} - F_t) + (1 - \gamma)T_t$$
$$T_2 = 0.68(8,325,763 - 8,319,403) + (1 - 0.68)(53,000)$$
$$= 0.68(6,360) + (0.32)(53,000)$$
$$= 4,325 + 16,960$$
$$= 21,285$$

The forecast for period 2 is calculated as:

$$H_{t+m} = F_{t+1} + mT_{t+1}$$
$$H_2 = F_2 + 1T_2$$
$$= 8,325,763 + (1)(21,285)$$
$$= 8,347,048$$

Our calculated forecast for June 2001 differs from what you see in Table 3.3. This is because our arbitrary selection of seed values differs from those selected by ForecastX™. Over the course of many quarters, the effect of differing seed values would diminish to almost nothing, and if we continued the hand calculations, our final forecasts would be virtually identical to those in Table 3.3. In Table c3t2A&B, the affect of changing the seed value for a simple exponential smoothing problem was demonstrated to have little affect on the final forecast. The same result is true for all exponential smoothing models. In the example for simple exponential smoothing, we had only 12 observations, while in the current situation, we have 64 observations. The more observations one has, the less the affect of the seed value on the final forecast.

Figure 3.6 shows a plot of the actual values, the fitted values, and the forecast values generated by this model. For 2001 through 2016 (the period for which data exist), the calculated values are called the "fitted" data. For 2017 through 2018 (the forecast period), the values are called "forecast" values.

**FIGURE 3.6**   **Personal Consumption Expenditures and Holt's Forecast**   In this case, alpha (the level constant) was 0.88 and gamma (the trend constant) was 0.68.   (c3t3)

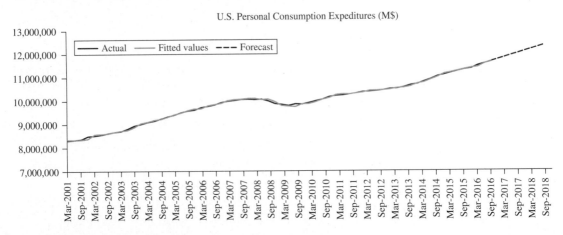

U.S. Personal Consumption Expeditures (M$)

Some commercially available forecasting packages allow the forecaster to minimize the value of the MAPE (or some similar summary statistic) by automatically adjusting the smoothing constants (ForecastX™ automatically adjusts). This, of course, is preferable to making numerous adjustments by hand. In this example, the smoothing constants were determined by ForecastX™.

Holt's form of exponential smoothing is tedious to calculate by hand, or even using Excel. For Holt's exponential smoothing and other advanced smoothing methods, specialized forecasting software (such as ForecastX™) should be used. Holt's exponential smoothing is appropriate when the data show some linear trend but little or no seasonality. A descriptive name for Holt's smoothing might be *linear-trend smoothing.*

# WINTERS' EXPONENTIAL SMOOTHING

Winters' exponential smoothing model is the second extension of the basic smoothing model; it is used for data that exhibit both trend and seasonality.

Winters' exponential smoothing model is the second extension of the basic smoothing model; it is used for data that exhibit both trend and seasonality. It is a three-parameter model that is an extension of Holt's model. Winters was a student of professor Holt and developed this modification as part of his graduate work. For this reason, the same model is referred to by two names: Winters' exponential smoothing and Holt-Winters' exponential smoothing.

In the Winters' model, an additional equation adjusts the model for the seasonal component. The four equations necessary for Winters' model are:

$$F_t = \alpha X_t / S_{t-p} + (1 - \alpha)(F_{t-1} + T_{t-1}) \tag{3.7}$$

$$S_t = \beta X_t / F_t + (1 - \beta) S_{t-p} \tag{3.8}$$

$$T_t = \gamma(F_t - F_{t-1}) + (1 - \gamma) T_{t-1} \tag{3.9}$$

$$W_{t+m} = (F_t + m T_t) S_{t+m-p} \tag{3.10}$$

where:

$F_t$ = Smoothed value for period $t$

$\alpha$ = Smoothing constant for the level $(0 < \alpha < 1)$

$X_t$ = Actual value now (in period $t$)

$F_{t-1}$ = Average experience of series smoothed to period $t - 1$

$T_{t+1}$ = Trend estimate

$S_t$ = Seasonality estimate

$\beta$ = Smoothing constant for seasonality estimate $(0 < \beta < 1)$

$\gamma$ = Smoothing constant for trend estimate $(0 < \gamma < 1)$

$m$ = Number of periods in the forecast lead period

$p$ = Number of periods in the seasonal cycle

$W_{t+m}$ = Winters' forecast for $m$ periods into the future

Equation 3.7 updates the smoothed series for both trend and seasonality; note that the equation is only slightly different from Equation 3.4 in Holt's model. In Equation 3.7, $X_t$ is divided by $S_{t-p}$ to adjust for seasonality; this operation deseasonalizes the data or removes any seasonal effects left in the data. It is easy to see how this deseasonalizes the data if you consider what happens when $S_{t-p}$ is greater than 1, as it would be when the value in period $t - p$ is greater than the average in its seasonality. Dividing $X_t$ by $S_{t-p}$ reduces the original value by a percentage equal to the percentage that the seasonality of the period was above the average. An opposite adjustment would take place if the period were below the average in terms of seasonality.

The seasonality estimate itself is smoothed in Equation 3.8, and the trend estimate is smoothed in Equation 3.9; each of these processes is exactly the same as in simple exponential smoothing. The final equation, 3.10, is used to compute the forecast for $m$ periods into the future; the procedure is almost identical to that in Holt's model (Equation 3.6).

To illustrate Winters' exponential smoothing, we will use data for U.S. sales by new car dealers, in millions of dollars. The data are quarterly starting with the first quarter of 2001 and extending through the last quarter of 2016. The last month of each quarter is used to represent the quarter.

Sales by new car dealers are typically highest in the second and third quarters of the year. This would include the months of April, May, and June for the second quarter, then July, August, and September for the third quarter. As you can see by the dotted trend line in Figure 3.7., there has been an overall upward trend in the data since our 2001Q1 (Mar-01) starting point.

You have seen already how to apply the equations to do a few of the calculations for simple and Holt's exponential smoothing. We will not repeat that process for the Winters' model. Doing the calculations for a model like Winters' by hand

**FIGURE 3.7**  **U.S. Retail Sales: New Car Dealers: NAICS 44111: NSA: Millions of Dollars**  (c3t4)

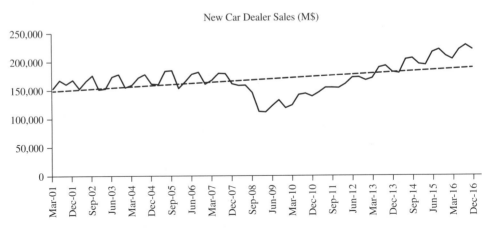

or in Excel is tedious. Professional forecasters use specialized forecasting software for such calculations.

Having ForecastX™ determine the parameters that would minimize the MAPE results in an alpha (level) constant of 0.86, a beta (seasonal) constant of 1.00, and a gamma (trend) constant of 0.06. The MAPE for the model is 3.65 percent.

As with simple and Holt's exponential smoothing, initial values must be selected to *initialize* or *warm up* the model. Over a long time period, such as in this example, the particular values selected have little effect on the forecast of sales by new car dealers for 2017 and 2018. These initial values are also determined within the software.

The results of the Winters' exponential smoothing forecast of sales by new car dealers are shown in Table 3.4 and in Figure 3.8. You can see, especially in the graph, that the model works quite well. The mean absolute percentage error (MAPE) of 3.65 percent suggests that one could have confidence in the Winters' forecast.

**TABLE 3.4**  Winters' Three-Parameter Exponential Smoothing for New Car Dealer Sales   (c3t4)

| Dates | Actual Sales (M$) | Fitted and Forecast Sales | Error | Dates | Actual Sales (M$) | Fitted and Forecast Sales | Error |
|---|---|---|---|---|---|---|---|
| Mar-2001 | 153,232 | 153,384 | −152 | Mar-2007 | 167,528 | 163,453 | 4,075 |
| Jun-2001 | 167,504 | 169,134 | −1,630 | Jun-2007 | 180,006 | 182,930 | −2,924 |
| Sep-2001 | 160,865 | 169,026 | −8,161 | Sep-2007 | 179,216 | 182,976 | −3,760 |
| Dec-2001 | 167,812 | 146,934 | 20,878 | Dec-2007 | 160,957 | 160,405 | 552 |
| Mar-2002 | 152,641 | 164,119 | −11,478 | Mar-2008 | 158,360 | 164,023 | −5,663 |
| Jun-2002 | 166,036 | 170,007 | −3,971 | Jun-2008 | 158,742 | 172,743 | −14,001 |
| Sep-2002 | 175,863 | 166,830 | 9,033 | Sep-2008 | 145,973 | 161,599 | −15,626 |
| Dec-2002 | 151,219 | 163,066 | −11,847 | Dec-2008 | 112,431 | 130,926 | −18,495 |
| Mar-2003 | 152,843 | 147,028 | 5,815 | Mar-2009 | 111,787 | 113,834 | −2,047 |
| Jun-2003 | 173,360 | 168,732 | 4,628 | Jun-2009 | 122,914 | 117,947 | 4,967 |
| Sep-2003 | 178,086 | 175,191 | 2,895 | Sep-2009 | 132,665 | 120,640 | 12,025 |
| Dec-2003 | 154,916 | 163,076 | −8,160 | Dec-2009 | 119,052 | 114,509 | 4,543 |
| Mar-2004 | 159,086 | 152,759 | 6,327 | Mar-2010 | 124,075 | 120,746 | 3,329 |
| Jun-2004 | 172,174 | 175,615 | −3,441 | Jun-2010 | 142,226 | 132,870 | 9,356 |
| Sep-2004 | 178,077 | 174,724 | 3,353 | Sep-2010 | 144,107 | 142,139 | 1,968 |
| Dec-2004 | 161,216 | 161,390 | −174 | Dec-2010 | 138,852 | 125,933 | 12,919 |
| Mar-2005 | 160,070 | 160,194 | −124 | Mar-2011 | 145,940 | 141,270 | 4,670 |
| Jun-2005 | 183,594 | 176,212 | 7,382 | Jun-2011 | 154,269 | 158,973 | −4,704 |
| Sep-2005 | 184,878 | 186,328 | −1,450 | Sep-2011 | 154,364 | 156,131 | −1,767 |
| Dec-2005 | 153,405 | 167,976 | −14,571 | Dec-2011 | 153,993 | 137,555 | 16,438 |
| Mar-2006 | 164,864 | 153,908 | 10,956 | Mar-2012 | 160,738 | 155,929 | 4,809 |
| Jun-2006 | 178,363 | 180,943 | −2,580 | Jun-2012 | 172,010 | 174,567 | −2,557 |
| Sep-2006 | 181,615 | 180,771 | 844 | Sep-2012 | 172,592 | 175,235 | −2,643 |
| Dec-2006 | 160,780 | 162,530 | −1,750 | Dec-2012 | 167,210 | 157,336 | 9,874 |

(continued on next page)

**TABLE 3.4** (continued)

| Dates | Actual Sales (M$) | Fitted and Forecast Sales | Error | Dates | Actual Sales (M$) | Fitted and Forecast Sales | Error |
|---|---|---|---|---|---|---|---|
| Mar-2013 | 171,170 | 169,126 | 2,044 | Sep-2016 | 228,487 | 223,641 | 4,846 |
| Jun-2013 | 189,758 | 185,575 | 4,183 | Dec-2016 | 220,871 | 212,233 | 8,638 |
| Sep-2013 | 192,435 | 193,039 | −604 | Mar-2017 | | 219,465 | |
| Dec-2013 | 181,771 | 177,678 | 4,093 | Jun-2017 | | 242,499 | |
| Mar-2014 | 179,891 | 183,998 | −4,107 | Sep-2017 | | 247,349 | |
| Jun-2014 | 203,920 | 196,344 | 7,576 | Dec-2017 | | 231,285 | |
| Sep-2014 | 205,787 | 206,568 | −781 | Mar-2018 | | 229,692 | |
| Dec-2014 | 195,460 | 190,925 | 4,535 | Jun-2018 | | 253,670 | |
| Mar-2015 | 193,971 | 196,852 | −2,881 | Sep-2018 | | 258,613 | |
| Jun-2015 | 216,030 | 213,557 | 2,473 | Dec-2018 | | 241,699 | |
| Sep-2015 | 221,044 | 218,448 | 2,596 | | Alpha = 0.86 | | |
| Dec-2015 | 209,566 | 205,608 | 3,958 | | Beta = 1.00 | | |
| Mar-2016 | 204,015 | 210,249 | −6,234 | | Gamma = 0.06 | | |
| Jun-2016 | 220,405 | 225,923 | −5,518 | | MAPE = 3.65% | | |

**FIGURE 3.8** New Car Dealer Sales. The Graph Shows the Actual Historic Values, the Fitted Values and an Eight Quarter Forecast

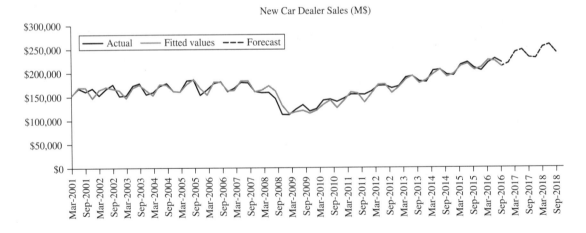

## The Seasonal Indices

Winters' exponential smoothing provides forecasters with one additional piece of information that can be of significant value to a manager. As part of the calculation with an adjustment for seasonality, seasonal indices are calculated and displayed in most forecasting software. ForecastX™ produces seasonal indices with each Winters' model. For the new car dealer sales model, the seasonal indices were calculated as:

| Seasonal Indices | Value |
|---|---|
| Index 1 | 0.95 |
| Index 2 | 1.04 |
| Index 3 | 1.05 |
| Index 4 | 0.96 |

Since our data set began with the first quarter of the year 2001 (i.e., January, February, and March), index 1 above refers to this first quarter of the year as well. The remaining three quarters also match the calendar quarters. These indices may be easily interpreted as percentages. Index 1 (0.95) is interpreted as indicating that quarter one sales are usually about 5 percent below an "average quarter." On the other hand, the second quarter index of 1.04 indicates that typically second-quarter sales are 4 percent higher than an "average quarter." An average quarter is the result of adding all four quarters together and dividing by four.

With this interpretation in mind, it becomes easy to see that new car dealer sales are relatively high in quarters two and three. Some products and services will exhibit very strong seasonality, while others may be affected only to a minor degree. When working with business and economic data, it is usually a good assumption to expect the data to be seasonal. Computing a Winters' model for the data will help the researcher determine the magnitude of the seasonality and identify precisely when above-average and below-average occurrences take place.

# ADAPTIVE–RESPONSE-RATE SINGLE EXPONENTIAL SMOOTHING

An interesting variant on simple smoothing called *adaptive–response-rate single exponential smoothing (ADRES)* has an important advantage over normal smoothing models because of the manner in which the smoothing constant is chosen. In ADRES smoothing, there is no requirement to actually choose an $\alpha$ value! This is an attractive feature if what you need is a very low-cost method of forecasting requiring no sophisticated knowledge of the technique. Real-world situations requiring the frequent forecasting of many items (perhaps thousands) would be ideal candidates for ADRES smoothing forecasts.

Adaptive-response smoothing does not use one single $\alpha$ value like the simple exponential smoothing model does. The word *adaptive* in its name gives a clue to how the model works. The $\alpha$ value in the ADRES model is not just a single number, but rather *adapts* to the data. When there is a change in the basic pattern of the data, the $\alpha$ value adapts.

For instance, suppose that some data to be forecast fluctuate around a mean value of $m$. The best estimate of the next observation of the data might then be that mean value ($m$). But suppose further that after some time an outside force changes the mean value of $m$ and the new value is now $m'$. The data then fluctuate

Adaptive-response smoothing does not use one single $\alpha$ value like the simple exponential smoothing model does.

around the new mean value of $m'$. If we had a way of adapting to the new mean of $m'$, we could then use that adapted estimate as the forecast for future values of the data. In fact, we would like to be able to adapt each time the mean value of the data changed; sometimes we would adapt very often, if the mean changed frequently, and at other times we would adapt very rarely, if the data changed only infrequently.

Because of the simplicity of the ADRES smoothing model and its ability to adapt to changing circumstances, it is quite often used in actual practice. Keep in mind, however, that it is a variant of the simple smoothing model and so assumes that the data to be forecast have little trend or seasonality (or that the trend or seasonality in the data has been removed).

The ADRES model looks very much like the simple smoothing model presented earlier:

$$F_{t+1} = \alpha_t X_t + (1 - \alpha_t) F_t \quad \text{(ADRES equation)} \tag{3.11}$$

where:

$$\alpha_t = \left| \frac{S_t}{A_t} \right| \tag{3.12}$$

$$S_t = \beta e_t + (1 - \beta) S_{t-1} \quad \text{(Smoothed error)} \tag{3.13}$$

$$A_t = \beta |e_t| + (1 - \beta) A_{t-1} \quad \text{(Absolute smoothed error)} \tag{3.14}$$

$$e_t = X_t - F_t \quad \text{(Error)} \tag{3.15}$$

Note carefully the subscripts on the $\alpha$ term! There may now be a different $\alpha$ value for each period.

The ADRES equation is the same as the one for simple exponential smoothing with the exception of the manner in which the $\alpha$ value is chosen. In the simple exponential smoothing model, we chose the $\alpha$ value by selecting the value that minimized the mean absolute percentage error associated with the model. But in simple smoothing, we were allowed to choose only a single value for $\alpha$. In the ADRES smoothing model, we may allow the $\alpha$ value to adapt as the data change.

The smoothing value ($\alpha$) is now given as the absolute value of the smoothed error divided by the absolute smoothed error. The smoothed error is itself a smoothed value, with a smoothing factor of $\beta$. The absolute smoothed error is also a smoothed value, again using the smoothing constant $\beta$. In most cases, $\beta$ is assigned a value of either 0.1 or 0.2. Thus, the first term of both the smoothed error and absolute smoothed error equations has a lighter weight than the second term.

To explain ADRES smoothing, consider Table 3.5, which lists 12 values of an observed data series. We would like to model the series using an adaptive–response-rate smoothing model. Note that the first six values of the series average about 100; the last six values in the series average about 125. This is a situation similar to that described in the preceding paragraphs and one conducive to the use of this technique. An adaptive–response-rate model should do quite well in modeling these data.

**TABLE 3.5**   **Adaptive-Response Example**   (c3t5)

| Period | Observed | Forecast | Error | Smoothed Error | Absolute Smoothed Error | $\alpha$ |
|--------|----------|----------|-------|----------------|-------------------------|----------|
| 1 | 100 | | | | | |
| 2 | 96 | 100.000 | −4.00 | −0.800 | 0.800 | 1.000 |
| 3 | 107 | 96.000 | 11.00 | 1.560 | 2.840 | 0.549 |
| 4 | 98 | 102.042 | −4.04 | 0.440 | 3.080 | 0.143 |
| 5 | 103 | 101.464 | 1.53 | 0.659 | 2.771 | 0.238 |
| 6 | 99 | 101.830 | −2.83 | −0.039 | 2.783 | 0.014 |
| 7 | 126 | 101.790 | 24.21 | 4.811 | 7.068 | 0.681 |
| 8 | 128 | 118.267 | 9.73 | 5.795 | 7.601 | 0.762 |
| 9 | 122 | 125.687 | −3.69 | 3.899 | 6.818 | 0.572 |
| 10 | 130 | 123.579 | 6.42 | 4.403 | 6.739 | 0.653 |
| 11 | 125 | 127.774 | −2.77 | 2.968 | 5.946 | 0.499 |
| 12 | 124 | 126.390 | −2.39 | 1.896 | 5.235 | 0.362 |

For period 5, the computations are as follows (with some rounding difference in the third decimal place):

$$F_5 = \alpha_4 X_4 + (1 - \alpha_4) F_4$$
$$= (0.143)(98) + (1 - 0.143)(102.042)$$
$$= 14.014 + 87.450$$
$$= 101.464$$

Once the observed value of 103 becomes available for period 5, it is possible to make the following computations (assuming $\beta = .2$):

$$e_5 = 103 - 101.464 = 1.536$$
$$S_5 = (0.2)(1.536) + (1 - 0.2)(0.440) = 0.659$$
$$A_5 = (0.2)(|1.536|) + (1 - 0.2)(3.080) = 2.771$$

and finally

$$\alpha_5 = \left|\frac{0.659}{2.771}\right| = 0.238$$

The process continues iteratively for all the remaining values in the example. In ForecastX$^{TM}$, you will get somewhat different results due to its use of a somewhat different algorithm.

Perhaps the most important consideration in adaptive–response-rate single exponential smoothing is the selection of the appropriate $\beta$ factor. The $\beta$ factor is usually set near 0.1 or 0.2 because these values reduce the effects of previous errors (i.e., they allow adaptation) but the values are small enough that the adaptation takes place gradually.

The ADRES model has no explicit way to handle seasonality. There are ways of using the ADRES model, however, with seasonal data. In fact, simple smoothing, Holt's smoothing, and the ADRES smoothing model may all be used with seasonal data. An example follows in the next section.

## USING SINGLE, HOLT'S, OR ADRES SMOOTHING TO FORECAST A SEASONAL DATA SERIES

When data have a seasonal pattern, the Winters' model provides an easy way to incorporate the seasonality *explicitly* into the model. An alternative method, however, is widely practiced. This alternative consists of first "deseasonalizing" the data. Deseasonalizing is a process that removes the effects of seasonality from the raw data before the forecasting model is employed. The forecasting model is then applied to the deseasonalized data, and finally, the results are "reseasonalized" to provide accurate forecasts. The process consists of the following steps:

1. Calculate seasonal indices for the series. This can be done in different ways, one of which is to use the **Winters'** exponential smoothing routine in ForecastX$^{TM}$. As you have seen, part of the output from Winters' (Holt Winters' in ForecastX$^{TM}$) includes seasonal indices.

2. **Deseasonalize** the original data by **dividing** each value by its corresponding seasonal index.

3. Apply a forecasting method (such as simple, Holt's, or adaptive-response exponential smoothing) to the deseasonalized series to produce an intermediate forecast of the deseasonalized data.

4. Reseasonalize the series by **multiplying** each deseasonalized forecast by its corresponding seasonal index.

Many forecasters have found this method more accurate than using Winters' smoothing to incorporate seasonality.

Many forecasters have found this method more accurate than using Winters' smoothing to incorporate seasonality. This method is more flexible than the Winters' method alone because it allows for the use of simple smoothing in situations without any trend whatsoever while allowing Holt's smoothing to be used if a trend is present. (Recall that Winters' model assumes that a trend is present.) Further, the ADRES model could be used in situations where some adaptation of the $\alpha$ factor is desirable.

To illustrate this approach to forecasting a seasonal series, let us use data on new houses sold in the United States between January 2011 and December 2016. Table 3.6 shows a complete Excel sheet to illustrate the process. Note

**TABLE 3.6**  New Houses Sold (NHS), Seasonally Adjusted or Deseasonalized Total New Houses Sold (DSNHS), Holt's Exponential Smoothing Forecast of Seasonally Adjusted New Houses Sold, the Seasonal Indices (SI), and the Reseasonalized New Houses Sold Forecast   (c3t6)

| Date | Total New Houses Sold in the United States: Thousands: NSA (NHS) | Seasonally Adjusted or Deseasonalized NHS (DSNHS | Holt's Forecast of DSNHS | Reseasonalized Forecast for NHS | SI |
|---|---|---|---|---|---|
| Jan-11 | 21 | 24 | 24 | 21.10 | 0.88 |
| Feb-11 | 22 | 23 | 24 | 23.28 | 0.96 |
| Mar-11 | 28 | 25 | 24 | 25.99 | 1.10 |
| Apr-11 | 30 | 26 | 25 | 28.49 | 1.15 |
| May-11 | 28 | 25 | 26 | 29.10 | 1.13 |
| Jun-11 | 28 | 25 | 25 | 28.35 | 1.12 |
| Jul-11 | 27 | 26 | 25 | 26.58 | 1.05 |
| Aug-11 | 25 | 25 | 26 | 25.33 | 0.98 |
| Sep-11 | 24 | 26 | 26 | 24.24 | 0.94 |
| Oct-11 | 25 | 26 | 26 | 24.88 | 0.96 |
| Nov-11 | 23 | 27 | 26 | 22.67 | 0.87 |
| Dec-11 | 24 | 28 | 27 | 23.02 | 0.87 |
| Jan-12 | 23 | 26 | 27 | 24.08 | 0.88 |
| Feb-12 | 30 | 31 | 27 | 25.98 | 0.96 |
| Mar-12 | 34 | 31 | 29 | 32.36 | 1.10 |
| Apr-12 | 34 | 30 | 30 | 34.98 | 1.15 |
| May-12 | 35 | 31 | 30 | 34.21 | 1.13 |
| Jun-12 | 34 | 30 | 31 | 34.43 | 1.12 |
| Jul-12 | 33 | 32 | 31 | 32.27 | 1.05 |
| Aug-12 | 31 | 32 | 31 | 30.86 | 0.98 |
| Sep-12 | 30 | 32 | 32 | 29.81 | 0.94 |
| Oct-12 | 29 | 30 | 32 | 30.86 | 0.96 |
| Nov-12 | 28 | 32 | 31 | 27.13 | 0.87 |
| Dec-12 | 28 | 32 | 32 | 27.80 | 0.87 |
| Jan-13 | 32 | 36 | 32 | 28.53 | 0.88 |
| Feb-13 | 36 | 37 | 35 | 33.60 | 0.96 |
| Mar-13 | 41 | 37 | 36 | 40.13 | 1.10 |
| Apr-13 | 43 | 37 | 37 | 42.71 | 1.15 |
| May-13 | 40 | 35 | 38 | 42.56 | 1.13 |
| Jun-13 | 43 | 39 | 37 | 40.93 | 1.12 |
| Jul-13 | 33 | 32 | 38 | 39.67 | 1.05 |
| Aug-13 | 31 | 32 | 35 | 34.08 | 0.98 |
| Sep-13 | 31 | 33 | 33 | 31.23 | 0.94 |
| Oct-13 | 36 | 37 | 33 | 32.06 | 0.96 |
| Nov-13 | 32 | 37 | 36 | 31.03 | 0.87 |
| Dec-13 | 31 | 36 | 37 | 31.77 | 0.87 |
| Jan-14 | 33 | 38 | 36 | 32.05 | 0.88 |
| Feb-14 | 35 | 36 | 37 | 35.97 | 0.96 |

(continued on next page)

**TABLE 3.6**   (continued)

| Date | Total New Houses Sold in the United States: Thousands: NSA (NHS) | Seasonally Adjusted or Deseasonalized NHS (DSNHS | Holt's Forecast of DSNHS | Reseasonalized Forecast for NHS | SI |
|---|---|---|---|---|---|
| Mar-14 | 39 | 35 | 37 | 40.74 | 1.10 |
| Apr-14 | 39 | 34 | 36 | 41.83 | 1.15 |
| May-14 | 43 | 38 | 35 | 39.97 | 1.13 |
| Jun-14 | 38 | 34 | 37 | 41.29 | 1.12 |
| Jul-14 | 35 | 33 | 36 | 37.25 | 1.05 |
| Aug-14 | 36 | 37 | 35 | 34.00 | 0.98 |
| Sep-14 | 37 | 39 | 36 | 33.75 | 0.94 |
| Oct-14 | 38 | 40 | 38 | 36.57 | 0.96 |
| Nov-14 | 31 | 36 | 39 | 33.89 | 0.87 |
| Dec-14 | 35 | 40 | 38 | 32.54 | 0.87 |
| Jan-15 | 39 | 44 | 39 | 34.58 | 0.88 |
| Feb-15 | 45 | 47 | 42 | 40.82 | 0.96 |
| Mar-15 | 46 | 42 | 45 | 49.50 | 1.10 |
| Apr-15 | 48 | 42 | 44 | 50.05 | 1.15 |
| May-15 | 47 | 42 | 43 | 48.54 | 1.13 |
| Jun-15 | 44 | 39 | 42 | 47.37 | 1.12 |
| Jul-15 | 43 | 41 | 41 | 42.93 | 1.05 |
| Aug-15 | 41 | 42 | 41 | 40.54 | 0.98 |
| Sep-15 | 35 | 37 | 42 | 39.24 | 0.94 |
| Oct-15 | 39 | 41 | 40 | 38.06 | 0.96 |
| Nov-15 | 36 | 42 | 40 | 34.98 | 0.87 |
| Dec-15 | 38 | 44 | 41 | 35.74 | 0.87 |
| Jan-16 | 39 | 44 | 43 | 37.72 | 0.88 |
| Feb-16 | 45 | 47 | 44 | 42.40 | 0.96 |
| Mar-16 | 50 | 45 | 46 | 50.30 | 1.10 |
| Apr-16 | 55 | 48 | 46 | 52.67 | 1.15 |
| May-16 | 53 | 47 | 47 | 53.45 | 1.13 |
| Jun-16 | 50 | 45 | 47 | 52.82 | 1.12 |
| Jul-16 | 54 | 52 | 46 | 48.34 | 1.05 |
| Aug-16 | 46 | 47 | 49 | 48.48 | 0.98 |
| Sep-16 | 44 | 47 | 48 | 45.37 | 0.94 |
| Oct-16 | 46 | 48 | 48 | 45.98 | 0.96 |
| Nov-16 | 40 | 46 | 48 | 41.73 | 0.87 |
| Dec-16 | 39 | 45 | 47 | 41.04 | 0.87 |
| Jan-17 | | | 46.38 | 40.77 | 0.88 |
| Feb-17 | | | 46.63 | 44.98 | 0.96 |
| Mar-17 | | | 46.89 | 51.62 | 1.10 |
| Apr-17 | | | 47.15 | 54.19 | 1.15 |
| May-17 | | | 47.40 | 53.67 | 1.13 |
| Jun-17 | | | 47.66 | 53.23 | 1.12 |

**FIGURE 3.9**
**New House Sales and
the Deseasonalized
New House Sales**

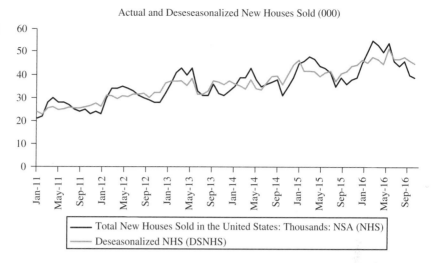

that in this example we are using monthly data. The first column contains the
dates, as is always the case. The second column has the raw data for new houses
sold (NHS). The third column has the data for NHS after the original data has
been deseasonalized (DSNHS). To deseasonalize the NHS data, each value was
divided by the seasonal index (SI) for the corresponding month. The seasonal
indices are shown in the last column. Look at the seasonal indices to note that
they repeat year after year; that is, all the January indices are the same. All the
February indices are the same, and so on for all months. There are two good
ways to get the seasonal indices. One is from the results of a Winters' exponential smoothing. Another way will be discussed in Chapter 6, which deals with
time series decomposition. The raw NHS data and the deseasonalized values
(DSNHS) are shown in Figure 3.9.

To forecast the deseasonalized data (DSNHS), we used a Holt's exponential
smoothing model. The resulting forecast of DSNHS is shown in the fourth column
of Table 3.6 and in Figure 3.10.

The seasonality was put back in the data by multiplying each value in the fourth
column by the corresponding seasonal index from the last column. The results are
in the fifth column and represent the forecast for new houses sold. The original
values for new houses sold and the forecast are shown in the second and fifth of
Table 3.6, as well as in Figure 3.11.

## NEW-PRODUCT FORECASTING (GROWTH CURVE FITTING)

For new products, because they typically lack historical data, most forecasting
techniques cannot produce satisfying results. For example, it is typically impossible for Holt's exponential smoothing to determine the trend since the data set

**FIGURE 3.10**
**Deseasonalized NHS and a Holt's Forecast**

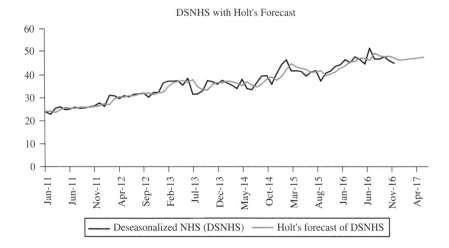

**FIGURE 3.11**
**Actual New Houses Sold and the Forecast of NHS**

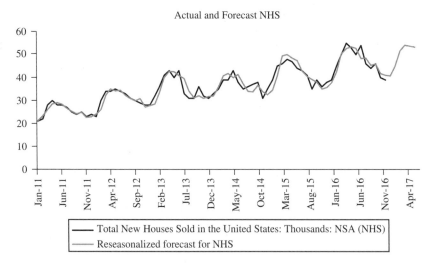

is too small. Alternatively, it may only predict a strong trend despite the fact that the new product has a growth limitation. To overcome this difficulty, forecasters use a number of models that generally fall in the category called *diffusion models* (probably because they described the manner in which technological innovations and new products "diffused" through an industry). These models are alternatively called S-curves, growth models, saturation models, or substitution curves. We have already seen one of these diffusion models in Chapter 1: the Bass model. An understanding of how to correctly use these models in the forecasting process can make them important tools for managerial decisions. These models as a group allow the forecaster to model the characteristic patterns that economists have identified for a number of processes (most importantly including the introduction of new products).

In this section, we present two new product models. The two diffusion models are the Gompertz curve and the logistic curve. There are two main differences between these models. The first difference is in the shapes of the product curve (i.e., amount of time that lapses before a product's growth curve stabilizes). The second difference lies in the fact that these new-product models may use different lower and upper limits for the same forecast data.

These models are most commonly used to forecast the sales of new products and technology life cycles. Just as new products have life cycles, technologies also have life cycles that follow a common pattern:

1. A period of slow growth just after introduction during an embryonic stage.
2. A period of rapid growth.
3. Slowing growth in a mature phase.
4. Decline.

The forecaster's task is to identify and estimate the parameters of such a pattern of growth using the same set of diagnostic statistics we have already learned to use with smoothing models in general.

Each new-product model has its own lower and upper limit. Expert opinion is needed to determine the correct upper and lower limits on the growth curves. In most instances, the lower limitation is 0 (e.g., sales cannot be below zero). Determining the upper limit is a more complicated undertaking. Regardless of the complication, diffusion models provide an important technique to use for forecasting when new products or technologies will replace existing products or technologies.

A significant benefit of using diffusion models in new-product forecasting is to identify and predict the timing of the four phases of the life cycle. In the late 1990s, the U.S. government decided to adopt a national standard for high-definition television (HDTV) and set a timetable for the changeover from analog to HDTV. The original plan called for broadcasters to begin broadcasting digital signals by 2002 and to turn off their analog transmitters altogether in 2006. This was a very ambitious plan and assumed that the adoption of HDTV by consumers would take place very quickly. Realizing that the elimination of analog transmissions would cause hardship if it occurred too early, another provision set forth by the Federal Communications Commission was that a market needed 85 percent penetration by HDTV before the analog signal could be eliminated.

Being able to forecast the growth and maturity of HDTV technology would allow broadcasters the opportunity to see if the 2006 "drop dead" date for analog television was reasonable. If 85 percent penetration was not reasonably achieved by this date, then broadcasters would be in the unenviable position of having to

**FIGURE 3.12**
Characteristic
S-Curve

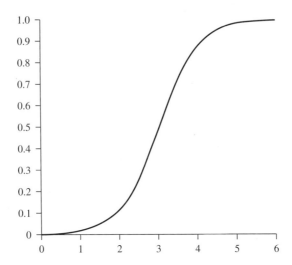

keep two transmitters functioning with, perhaps, two different and costly sets of programming. The costs in extra electricity, tower rental, and insurance would be substantial.

Analyses of many technology introductions (like HDTV) have shown that technology develops initially at a very slow growth rate. But it is also the case that these same technologies soon begin to grow in predictable patterns such as the S-curve shown in Figure 3.12.

The usual reason for the transition from very slow initial growth to rapid growth is often the result of solutions to technical difficulties and the market's acceptance of the new technology. But such growth curves also have their limits; the rapid growth cannot be sustained indefinitely. There are upper limits on the adoptions of new technology or the sales of new products. As the upper limit is reached, a maturity phase occurs in which growth slows and finally ceases. The economic law of diminishing marginal returns is usually at work in these processes.

Figure 3.13 contains information on the early years of HDTV shipments in the United States. During the entire time represented in the graph, there were very few broadcast stations operating in HDTV mode, but in each year, the number of HDTV broadcasters increased and the hours of HDTV programming available also increased. This entire four years of data represent the period of experimentation and slow growth characteristic of all new products and technologies.

When a new technology like HDTV enters the marketplace, we can expect an S-curve to accurately predict future shipments or sales. There is, however, more than one technique that could be used to model this S-curve.

Fortunately, ForecastX$^{TM}$ provides flexible settings for a multitude of situations. If you do not know what the upper limit should be, you can use ForecastX$^{TM}$ to

**FIGURE 3.13**
**Shipments and**
**Cumulative**
**Shipments of HDTV**
**Units**   (c3t7)

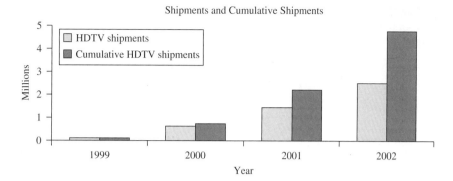

Shipments and Cumulative Shipments

determine the best upper limit to fit your data. Of course, if you know the exact upper limit, ForecastX$^{TM}$ can use it to determine an optimal model.

The two most common forms of S-curves used in forecasting are the Gompertz curve and the logistics curve (also called the Pearl curve). A third useful model called the Bass model was discussed in Chapter 1; we will again cover that model and provide an example of its use.

## Gompertz Curve

The Gompertz curve is named after its developer, Benjamin Gompertz, an English actuary. Gompertz applied calculus to actuarial questions and is most well known for *Gompertz's Law of Mortality*. Gompertz's law showed that the mortality rate increases in a geometric progression. Thus, when death rates are plotted on a logarithmic scale, a straight line known as the *Gompertz function* is obtained. The Gompertz curve is the most used actuarial function for investigating the process of aging. The slope of this function is known as the rate of actuarial aging, and differences in the longevity between species are the result in large part of differences in this rate of aging.

The Gompertz function is given as

$$Y_t = L e^{-ae^{-bt}}$$

where:

$L$ = Upper limit of Y

$e$ = Natural number 2.718282 . . .

$a$ and $b$ = coefficients describing the curve (estimated by ForecastX$^{TM}$)

The Gompertz curve will range in value from zero to $L$ as $t$ varies from $-\infty$ to $\infty$. The curve is widely used in the fields of biology and demography to model (i.e., forecast) the level of populations at a given point in time for plants and animals as well as many organisms. The Gompertz curve is an elegant way to summarize the growth of a population with just a few parameters.

**TABLE 3.7**

**Data on HDTV Shipments** (c3t7)

| Date | Cumulative HDTV Shipments (millions) |
|------|--------------------------------------|
| 12/31/1999 | 0.12 |
| 12/31/2000 | 0.77 |
| 12/31/2001 | 2.23 |
| 12/31/2002 | 4.76 |

Consider the HDTV shipments charted in Figure 3.13; the actual figures are given in Table 3.7.

The Gompertz curve estimated from this data (with the assumption that 248 million televisions is the upper limit) is shown in Figure 3.14. The assumption of 248 million television sets is used as the upper limit because in the year 2002 this was the total number of televisions of all types in use. This rather generous assumption reflects the opportunity for every existing television to be converted to an HDTV. An actual forecaster might choose a different upper limit if another rationale seemed more plausible.

Note the characteristic S-shape to the curve in Figure 3.14. In fitting the curve, we have used the first few data points and the known maximum value for television shipments to estimate a forecast of how HDTV shipments will progress through time. We have ample evidence that this Gompertz function will model the situation well; when color televisions were introduced in the 1960s, their adoption followed a very similar pattern. This form of curve fitting is often used, as it is here, to make forecasts far into the future. Unlike the moving-average and exponential smoothing models, growth curves are routinely used to make mid- to long-range forecasts.

In order to use ForecastX$^{TM}$ to make the estimate shown in Figure 3.14, the Method Selection dialog box would be filled out as shown in Figure 3.15.

**FIGURE 3.14**

**An Estimate of HDTV Shipments Using Four Years of Data** (c3t7)

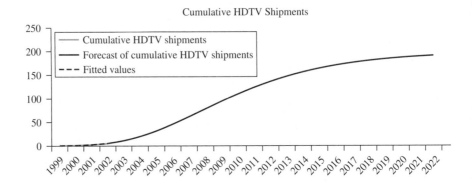

Cumulative HDTV Shipments

**FIGURE 3.15**
ForecastX™ Method
Selection Dialog
Box for a Gompertz
Model

Source: John Galt Solutions

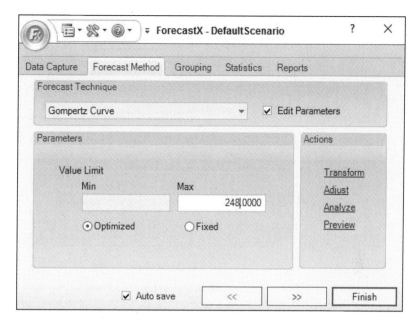

The Edit Parameters box is checked in Figure 3.15 and the maximum value of 248 is entered; this, along with the information on the first four years of actual shipments, allows the estimation of the best-fit Gompertz curve.

The Gompertz curve is best used in situations where it becomes more difficult to achieve an increase in the growth rate as the maximum value is approached. We will see that this is the exact opposite of the recommendation for the best situation in which to use the logistics function. Consider the adoption of color televisions shown in Table 3.8.

**TABLE 3.8**
**Color Television
Adoption in
Percentages**   (c3t8)

| Year | Percent Adoptions | Year | Percent Adoptions |
|------|-------------------|------|-------------------|
| *Dec-65* | *0* | Dec-78 | 79.37021852 |
| *Dec-66* | *6.145835684* | Dec-79 | 82.72351665 |
| *Dec-67* | *12.72965645* | Dec-80 | 85.59728784 |
| *Dec-68* | *19.64872441* | Dec-81 | 88.03946805 |
| *Dec-69* | *26.77512032* | Dec-82 | 90.10007711 |
| Dec-70 | 33.96440431 | Dec-83 | 91.82826105 |
| Dec-71 | 41.06698245 | Dec-84 | 93.27031978 |
| Dec-72 | 47.94034951 | Dec-85 | 94.46854445 |
| Dec-73 | 54.46013052 | Dec-86 | 95.46066873 |
| Dec-74 | 60.52818203 | Dec-87 | 96.27975333 |
| Dec-75 | 66.07679819 | Dec-88 | 96.95435387 |
| Dec-76 | 71.06899248 | Dec-89 | 97.50885698 |
| Dec-77 | 75.49558333 | Dec-90 | 97.96390133 |

**FIGURE 3.16**    **Actual and Predicted Adoptions of Color Televisions Obtained by Using the First Five Years of Adoptions and a Gompertz Estimate**    (c3t8)

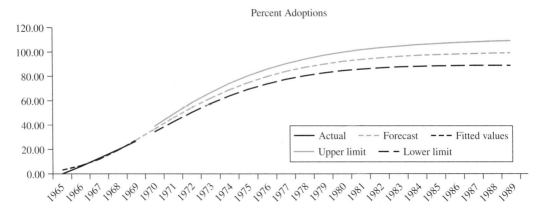

Using only the first five years of data on color television adoptions (and the assumption of a maximum of 100 percent), it is possible to very closely approximate the future growth pattern with a Gompertz function. Figure 3.16 shows the actual and predicted shipments obtained using only the first five data points from Table 3.8.

Had you been asked in late 1969 to forecast color television adoptions with only the first five years of annual data, you would have produced very accurate forecasts if you had used a Gompertz model. The assumption regarding the increased difficulty of obtaining the maximum value as it is approached probably describes color television adoptions quite well. The same assumption might also apply to HDTV adoptions and sales since the situation is similar.

### Logistics Curve

The logistics curve is a second way of forecasting with sparse data and is also used frequently to forecast new-product sales. The logistics curve has the following form:

$$Y_t = \frac{L}{1 + ae^{-bt}}$$

where:

$L$ = Upper limit of Y
$e$ = Natural number 2.718282 . . .
$a$ and $b$ = coefficients describing the curve (estimated by ForecastX™)

Just as in the Gompertz function, there is an upper limit to $Y$ called $L$, and $e$ is the base of natural logarithms. The logistics curve is symmetric about its point of inflection (the upper half of the curve is a reflection of the lower half); the Gompertz curve is not necessarily symmetric about its points of inflection. Why would you use the logistics curve rather than the Gompertz curve?

The answer lies in whether, in a particular situation, it is easier to achieve the maximum value the closer you get to it, or whether it becomes more difficult to attain the maximum value the closer you get to it. The question of which function to use in a particular estimate comes down to whether there are factors assisting the attainment of the maximum value once you get close to it, or whether there are factors preventing the attainment of the maximum value once it is nearly attained. If there is an offsetting factor such that growth is more difficult to maintain as the maximum is approached, then the Gompertz curve will be the best choice. If there are no such offsetting factors hindering the attainment of the maximum value, the logistics curve will be the best choice.

A clear case of the appropriate use of a logistics function might be the prediction of U.S. households with telephones. There is a "network effect" at work here such that, as more people have a telephone, telephones become more useful to everyone (since you are now able to call a larger number of people). The larger the network, the greater the advantage to being a member of the network. The more recent case of the adoption of cellular telephones would likely progress in much the same manner as the original telephone adoption. The adoption data for cellular telephones in the United States is presented in Table 3.9.

**TABLE 3.9**
**Percentage of Cellular Telephone Adoption in the United States** (c3t9)

| Year | Cellular Telephone Adoption Percentage |
|---|---|
| *12/31/1986* | *0* |
| *12/31/1987* | *0.989132021* |
| *12/31/1988* | *2.47063319* |
| *12/31/1989* | *4.661420125* |
| *12/31/1990* | *7.840611381* |
| 12/31/1991 | 12.33023714 |
| 12/31/1992 | 18.43261935 |
| 12/31/1993 | 26.3098137 |
| 12/31/1994 | 35.82721276 |
| 12/31/1995 | 46.4488152 |
| 12/31/1996 | 57.30203601 |
| 12/31/1997 | 67.43707273 |
| 12/31/1998 | 76.13611792 |
| 12/31/1999 | 83.07839603 |
| 12/31/2000 | 88.3037847 |
| 12/31/2001 | 92.06622305 |
| 12/31/2002 | 94.68961176 |
| 12/31/2003 | 96.47806155 |
| 12/31/2004 | 97.6786669 |

**FIGURE 3.17**  Actual and Predicted Adoptions of Cellular Telephones in the United States  (c3t9)

| Year | Cellular Telephone Adoption Percentage | Logistics |
|---|---|---|
| 31-12-1986 | 0 | 0.54 |
| 31-12-1987 | 0.989132021 | 1.09 |
| 31-12-1988 | 2.47063319 | 2.20 |
| 31-12-1989 | 4.661420125 | 4.37 |
| 31-12-1990 | 7.840611381 | 8.48 |
| 31-12-1991 | | 15.84 |
| 31-12-1992 | | 27.65 |
| 31-12-1993 | | 43.70 |
| 31-12-1994 | | 61.18 |
| 31-12-1995 | | 76.19 |
| 31-12-1996 | | 86.66 |
| 31-12-1997 | | 92.96 |
| 31-12-1998 | | 96.40 |
| 31-12-1999 | | 98.20 |
| 31-12-2000 | | 99.10 |
| 31-12-2001 | | 99.56 |
| 31-12-2002 | | 99.78 |
| 31-12-2003 | | 99.89 |
| 31-12-2004 | | 99.95 |
| 31-12-2005 | | 99.97 |

By fitting a logistics curve to the first five years of cellular telephone data, the results in Figure 3.17 are calculated.

It is not surprising that a logistics estimate of cellular telephone adoption works so well; as more individuals have cellular telephones, it becomes more advantageous to have one yourself. Thus, there is a factor assisting the attainment of the maximum value the closer you get to the maximum value (i.e., the network effect).

Note that there should be some theoretical reason for choosing a logistics function for your forecast estimate before estimating the model. In the case of cellular phones, the hypothesized existence of a network effect would lead a researcher to choose a logistics model. The ForecastX™ Method Selection dialog box used to select the cellular telephone model appears in Figure 3.18.

Let's generalize our suggestions for employing the Gompertz and logistics models. Use a Gompertz model when you expect it to be more difficult to attain constant improvement as the maximum value is approached. On the other hand, select a logistics model when there are factors that help maintain improvements as the maximum value is approached. At times it will not be easy to predict which of the two models may work best; in those instances ForecastX™ allows the choice of "New Product Forecasting" as a selection in the Method Selection dialog box.

**FIGURE 3.18**
**ForecastX™ Method**
**Selection Dialog Box**
**for a Logistics Model**

Source: John Galt Solutions

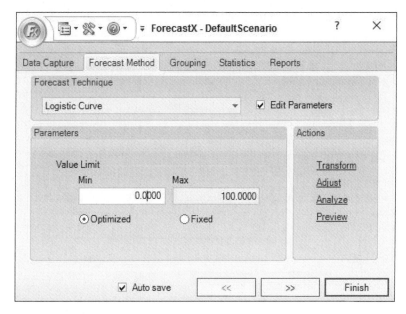

Choosing New Product Forecasting allows ForecastX™ to choose the optimal model from among three contenders: the logistics model, the Gompertz model, and a Probit curve.

## Bass Model

Named after Professor Frank M. Bass, this model has been used for over 30 years to forecast the diffusion of innovations, to forecast the penetration of new products in a market, and in a variety of biological, medical, and scientific forecasts. This is a relatively simple model in which only three parameters are chosen by the researcher.

As they are used in ForecastX™, the three parameters are $p$, $r$, and qbar, where:

$p$ = The innovation rate
$r$ = The imitation rate (called $q$ in the forecasting literature)
qbar = The cumulative value of all the historical values

The Bass model could be called a model of social contagion where the $p$ (the innovation rate) refers to the probability of initial purchase of a new good independent of the influence of previous buyers (i.e., with no network effect considered). The $r$ (the imitation rate) refers to the pressure of imitation on previous purchasers. The Bass model would appear most often in a graph like the S-curves we have been examining. As we indicated in Chapter 1, getting the estimates of the three parameters of the model is the difficult part. We can be helped significantly here by using past studies to suggest parameters that may place us in the ballpark for our own estimates.

# The Bass Model in Action

**1**

## CHRISTOPHE VAN DEN BULTE

The U.S. Department of Energy (DOE) in 1980 used the Bass model to forecast the adoption of solar batteries. The DOE used a survey of home builders to aid in its initial choices for p and q values. Using these empirically suggested values, the DOE concluded that solar battery technology was not sufficiently robust to encourage word-of-mouth propagation. Because of their finding, they postponed their proposed wide-scale introduction of the technology until solar battery technology had improved to the point that new users would be satisfied with the technology and thus the higher q value would predict faster sales growth.

A decade later in the 1990s, DirecTV had planned a launch of its subscription satellite television delivery service. Prudently, it attempted to obtain a prelaunch forecast for five years into the future. DirecTV's forecast was again based on the Bass model, and the p and q values were also obtained from a survey of prospective users; this information was combined with histories of similar services. The forecasts produced in 1992 were quite good from the company's point of view, and after the fact, the estimates compared favorably with the actual 1994 to 1999 experience.

Numerous other firms have reported productive results using the Bass model. RCA in the mid-1980s used a modified Bass model to forecast the sales of music CDs as a function of CD player sales. The model proved quite accurate. The Bass model is also used routinely to predict box office revenues for movies and to make decisions on how many screens to use for a particular movie.

**Source:** Van den Bulte, Christophe, "Want to Know How Diffusion Speed Varies across Countries and Products? Try Using a Bass Model," *PDMA Visions* 26, no. 4 (2002), pp. 12–15.

Christopher Van den Bulte of the Wharton School has constructed a database of 1,586 sets of p and q parameters from 113 separate recent articles.[5] Some suggestions from Van den Bulte's work appear in Table 3.10.

An interesting set of patterns emerges from this large number of p and q estimations. Recall that the parameter Van den Bulte refers to as q is the r parameter (the imitation rate) in ForecastX$^{TM}$ What estimates for p and q would be best for your product? Van den Bulte took as a baseline durable goods launched in the United States in 1976. The p factor measures the intrinsic tendency for an individual to adopt a new product, while the q measures the "word of mouth" or "social contagion" effect on purchases. Van den Bulte recommends that when a forecaster tries to set the values of p and q in a Bass model, you should use a range of values within his estimated confidence interval (given in Table 3.10). For countries with a collectivist mentality (like Japan) as opposed to an individualistic mentality (like the United States), a higher q value is better. People in collectivist cultures care more about what others think of them, according to Van den Bulte's study. In countries with higher purchasing power, the p tends to be higher. More disposable income makes it easier to adopt innovations. Finally, products that exhibit significant network effects or require heavy investment in complementary infrastructure (like television and the cellular telephone) will have higher values for q. Van den Bulte has summarized these results in a set of conclusions presented in Table 3.11.

[5] Christophe Van den Bulte, "Want to Know How Diffusion Speed Varies across Countries and Products? Try Using a Bass Model," *PDMA Visions* 26, no. 4 (2002), pp. 12–15.

**TABLE 3.10**
Van den Bulte's *p* and *q* Estimates from Selected Articles

| p Estimates | Best Guess | 90% Confidence Interval | |
|---|---|---|---|
| Baseline case: U.S. consumer, durable, launch in 1976 | 0.409 | 0.355 $(t^0)$ | 0.471 |
| For other cases, multiply by the following factors: | | | |
| Cellular telephone | 0.635 | 0.465 | 0.868 |
| Nondurable product | 0.931 | 0.713 | 1.216 |
| Industrial | 1.149 | 0.909 | 1.451 |
| Noncommercial innovation | 2.406 | 1.488 | 3.891 |
| Western Europe | 0.949 | 0.748 | 1.203 |
| Asia | 0.743 | 0.571 | 0.966 |
| Other regions | 0.699 | 0.429 | 1.137 |
| For each year after 1976, multiply by | 1.028 | 1.018 | 1.039 |
| **q Estimates (labeled r in ForecastX)** | | | |
| Baseline case: U.S. consumer, durable, launch in 1976 | 0.016 | 0.012 | 0.021 |
| For other cases, multiply by the following factors: | | | |
| Cellular telephone | 0.226 | 0.125 | 0.409 |
| Nondurable product | 0.689 | 0.415 | 1.143 |
| Industrial | 1.058 | 0.679 | 1.650 |
| Noncommercial innovation | 0.365 | 0.146 | 0.910 |
| Western Europe | 0.464 | 0.296 | 0.729 |
| Asia | 0.595 | 0.360 | 0.981 |
| Other regions | 0.796 | 0.315 | 2.008 |
| For each year after 1976, multiply by | 1.021 | 1.002 | 1.041 |

**TABLE 3.11**
Van den Bulte's Conclusions Regarding *p* and *q* Values

- There are systematic regional differences in diffusion patterns.
- The average coefficient of innovation p (speed of takeoff) in Europe and Asia is roughly half of that in the United States.
- The average coefficient of imitation q (speed of late growth) in Asia is roughly a quarter less than that in the United States and Europe.
- Also, economic differences explain national variations in speed better than cultural differences do.
- There are systematic product differences in diffusion patterns. For instance, takeoff is slower for nondurables and products with competing standards that require heavy investments in infrastructure, while late growth is faster for industrial products and products with competing standards, which require heavy investments in infrastructure.

Table 3.12 presents data for the adoption of telephone-answering devices in the United States.

Using only the first five observations in Table 3.12, it is possible to accurately represent the entire adoption cycle for telephone-answering devices. After some

**TABLE 3.12**
**Adoption of**
**Telephone-Answering**
**Devices in the United**
**States** (c3t12)

| Year | Adoption |
|------|----------|
| Dec-84 | 0 |
| Dec-85 | 3.030551 |
| Dec-86 | 7.351138 |
| Dec-87 | 13.29582 |
| Dec-88 | 21.08724 |
| Dec-89 | 30.67365 |
| Dec-90 | 41.59211 |
| Dec-91 | 52.98598 |
| Dec-92 | 63.84035 |
| Dec-93 | 73.31923 |
| Dec-94 | 80.98819 |
| Dec-95 | 86.81843 |
| Dec-96 | 91.04448 |
| Dec-97 | 94.00304 |
| Dec-98 | 96.02418 |
| Dec-99 | 97.38195 |
| Dec-00 | 98.28381 |
| Dec-01 | 98.87837 |
| Dec-02 | 99.26839 |
| Dec-03 | 99.52341 |
| Dec-04 | 99.6898 |

trial and error, the researcher has selected a $p$ value of 0.035 and an $r$ value of 0.406. Note that the $r$ value in ForecastX$^{TM}$ is the same as the $q$ value used for explaining the imitation rate in the Bass model, as shown in Figure 3.19. The qbar value is 100 because we are working with percentages.

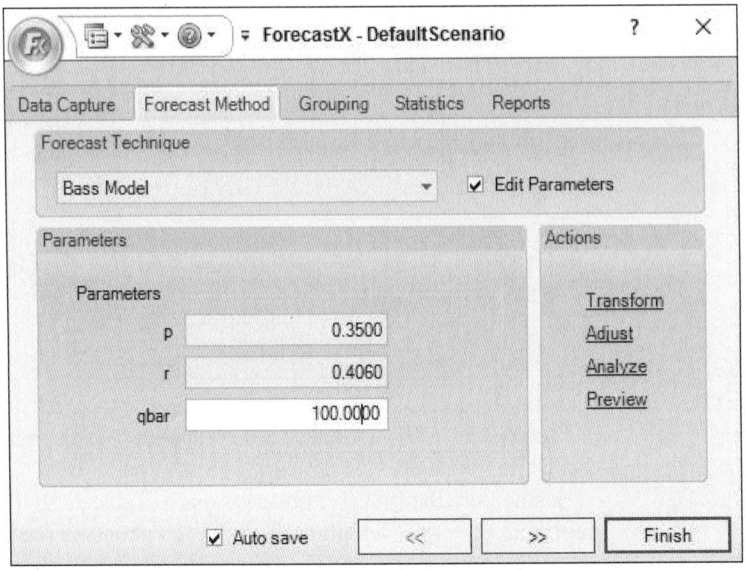

**FIGURE 3.19**
**ForecastX$^{TM}$ Method**
**Selection Dialog for**
**the Bass Model**

Source: John Galt Solutions

**FIGURE 3.20**
**Bass Model of Telephone-Answering Machine Adoptions in the United States** (c3t12)

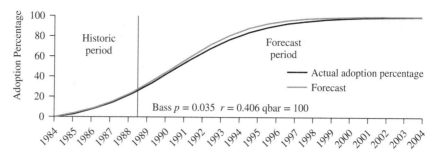

The resulting plot of actual and predicted values in Figure 3.20 shows a model that closely approximates the actual occurrence in the United States for answering-machine adoptions.

# EVENT MODELING

Event modeling is a feature of some exponential smoothing programs such as ForecastX™. This feature allows the user to specify the time of one or more special events, such as irregular promotions and natural disasters, in the calibration data. For each type of special event, the effect is estimated and the data adjusted so that the events do not distort the trend and seasonal patterns of the time series.

*When forecasting sales or demand in a highly promoted market, using the smoothing technique of event modeling will significantly improve forecast accuracy.*

When forecasting sales or demand in a highly promoted market, using this smoothing technique will significantly improve forecast accuracy. Consider the case of a manufacturer of a popular condiment (e.g., ketchup, mustard, steak sauce, and so on). This type of product tends to be highly seasonal and also tends to be aggressively promoted by marketers. Is there a method for modeling the effect of future promotions on the sales or demand for such a product?

The answer to this dilemma is *event modeling.* By using the basic smoothing models already developed earlier in the chapter as a base, an event model may be generated to replicate the effects of various promotions and combinations of promotions.

The method of event modeling follows in the same pattern for the smoothing models already examined: after the systematic patterns are identified in the historical data, the exponential smoothing method uses smoothing equations for each component in the series to estimate and build up structural patterns. The event model adds a smoothing equation for each of the "events" identified as being important. The weights for each smoothing equation are represented by a parameter.

*Event models are analogous to seasonal models.*

Event models are analogous to seasonal models: just as each month is assigned its own index for seasonality, so, too, each event type is assigned its own index for a specific promotional activity. For example, when monthly data are used, the seasonal index for a particular month is updated at regular intervals, each time that month recurs. However, event adjustments are created through the use of an indicator variable that assigns an integer for each event type to the period during which it recurs. Thus, one example of integer value assignment would be that 0 indicates a period where no event has occurred, 1 indicates a period where a free-standing insert (FSI) was circulated, 8 indicates a period where thematic advertising was used, and so on. The event indicator variable must be defined for each historic period *and* future period in the forecast horizon. In this way, the event smoothing equation is used to calculate the historical lift in sales above baseline that occurred as a result of a particular type of promotion and applies that lift to the baseline forecast in the future period where the same promotion is planned.

To illustrate how this method is used in actual practice, we examine some actual demand data. The product, mustard, is a condiment commonly used in American households and found at every picnic. The company that produces and sells mustard uses a number of marketing promotions to enhance sales and maintain market share. Free-standing inserts are perhaps the most common of the promotions for this type of product; these are the familiar coupons found in Sunday newspapers or in online promotions and redeemable when the item is purchased. These FSIs are often used in conjunction with themed advertising campaigns, especially during particular seasons of the year. Our condiment manufacturer uses a separate event value, 7, to stand for the combination of FSIs and an advertising campaign. On-pack coupons are a separate type of coupon usually attached to the product packaging itself and redeemed at the cash register at checkout.

In addition to adjusting the price to the consumer through coupons, the mustard manufacturer also adjusts the price to the jobber by reducing case prices for a short period of time. When this takes place, it is common for jobbers to stock up on the reduced-price item and delay future purchases. Because of this, the manufacturer uses two event values called *load* and *deload* to signify periods of reduced prices and the periods immediately following such a promotion; these are actually two separate events.

The event values for this particular condiment manufacturer are listed in the following table.

---

**Event Indices Legend:**

0 = Nothing
1 = FSI
2 = Thematics
3 = Big Load
4 = After Load
5 = Deload
6 = Light Load
7 = FSI / Act Media
8 = Cross Cpn

FSI = free standing inserts. These are cents-off coupons distributed in newspapers
Thematics = Themed ad campaign
Big Load = Large trade promotion—often a deep drop in the case price for the retailer
Deload = Month after effect of a "load"
Act Media = Radio, television, print ad campaign
Cross Coupons = Cents-off coupons placed directly on the packaging of other goods

---

Figure 3.21 shows monthly historical demand of mustard over time. Table 3.13 shows the events related to each of these historical months and the company's planned promotions for the next six months.

**FIGURE 3.21**
**Mustard Demand**
(c3t13)

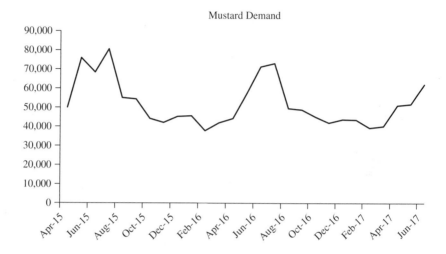

**TABLE 3.13**
**An Event Model**
**Example** (c3t13)

| Date | Mustard | Event Index |
|---|---|---|
| Apr-15 | 50,137 | 7 |
| May-15 | 76,030 | 7 |
| Jun-15 | 68,590 | 3 |
| Jul-15 | 80,681 | 4 |
| Aug-15 | 55,228 | 5 |
| Sep-15 | 54,577 | 0 |
| Oct-15 | 44,384 | 8 |
| Nov-15 | 42,337 | 0 |
| Dec-15 | 45,512 | 6 |
| Jan-16 | 45,798 | 4 |
| Feb-16 | 38,045 | 5 |
| Mar-16 | 42,127 | 0 |
| Apr-16 | 44,422 | 2 |
| May-16 | 57,662 | 1 |
| Jun-16 | 71,427 | 6 |
| Jul-16 | 73,269 | 5 |
| Aug-16 | 49,695 | 8 |
| Sep-16 | 49,021 | 1 |
| Oct-16 | 45,263 | 0 |
| Nov-16 | 42,210 | 1 |
| Dec-16 | 43,968 | 6 |
| Jan-17 | 43,778 | 4 |

(continued on next page)

**TABLE 3.13** (continued)

| Date | Mustard | Event Index |
|---|---|---|
| Feb-17 | 39,524 | 0 |
| Mar-17 | 40,476 | 0 |
| Apr-17 | 51,167 | 2 |
| May-17 | 51,916 | 1 |
| Jun-17 | 62,274 | 6 |
| Jul-17 | | 4 |
| Aug-17 | | 5 |
| Sep-17 | | 0 |
| Oct-17 | | 2 |
| Nov-17 | | 1 |
| Dec-17 | | 6 |

**Legend:**

**0 = Nothing**
**1 = FSI**
**2 = Thematics**
**3 = Big Load**
**4 = After Load**
**5 = Deload**
**6 = Light Load**
**7 = FSI / Act Media**
**8 = Cross Cpn**

FSI = free standing inserts. These are off-cents coupons distributed in newspapers
Thematics = Themed add campaign
Big Load = Large trade promotion − often a deep drop in the case price for the retailer
Deload = Month after effect of a "load"
Act Media = Radio, television, print add campaign
Cross Coupons = Cents off coupons placed directly on the packaging of other goods

Using a Winters' smoothing model on these data picks up the implied seasonality and trend quite well; the calculated level, seasonal, and trend are 0.05, 0.88, and 0.26, respectively. This indicates that there is very little trend in the data but a high degree of seasonality. Actually, some of the apparent seasonality is not seasonality at all; instead, it is "induced seasonality" caused by the company's various promotions. The MAPE for the Winters' model without including events is 5.18 percent. This result is shown in Figure 3.22.

Using the Winters' smoothing model again, but with eight event smoothing factors added in, the level, seasonal, and trend factors are 0.2, 0.92, and 0.26. By examining these factors, we see that there is definitely little trend, but now the seasonality has also apparently changed. The seasonality has not disappeared; it is changed by the eight event indices. When the eight events are included, the MAPE improves to 2.62 percent. This result is shown in Figure 3.23.

**FIGURE 3.22** **Mustard Demand Forecast Using Winters' Exponential Smoothing. No Events Are Included. MAPE = 5.18%**

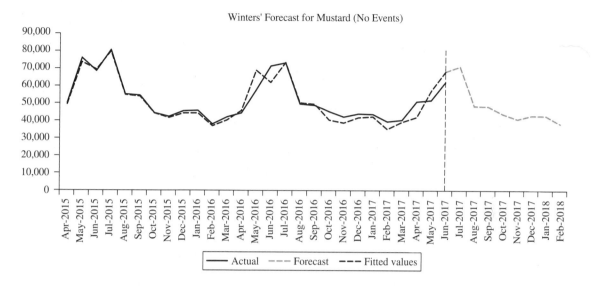

**FIGURE 3.23** **Mustard Demand Forecast Using Winters' Exponential Smoothing; Including Eight Events. MAPE = 2.62%**

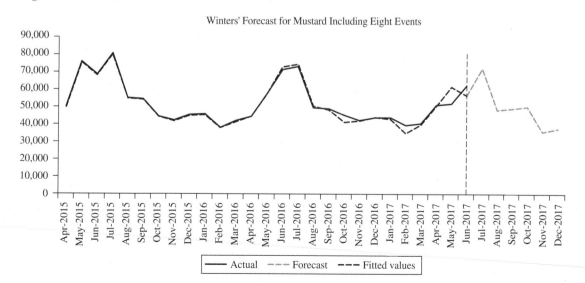

**TABLE 3.14**
**Summary of Results of a Winters' Model for Mustard Demand Without and with Eight Events**

| | Winters' Model | Winters' Model with Event Indices |
|---|---|---|
| Historical MAPE | 5.18% | 2.62% |
| Level Smoothing Factor (alpha) | 0.05 | 0.20 |
| Seasonal Smoothing Factor (beta) | 0.88 | 0.92 |
| Trend Smoothing Factor (gamma) | 0.26 | 0.26 |
| Event Index 1 | NA | 0.94 |
| Event Index 2 | NA | 1.16 |
| Event Index 3 | NA | 0.99 |
| Event Index 4 | NA | 1.03 |
| Event Index 5 | NA | 1.00 |
| Event Index 6 | NA | 0.94 |
| Event Index 7 | NA | 1.03 |
| Event Index 8 | NA | 0.99 |

The addition of the events to the historical period caused a tighter fit between the actual mustard demand and predicted mustard demand. Using the knowledge of the planned company promotions for the next six months allows the forecaster to calculate a much better picture of predicted demand than the Winters' model alone.

In this particular case, we used the Winters' model as a base because we believed the original data had both trend and seasonality. If the data had lacked trend or seasonality, we could have used simple smoothing as the base model. ForecastX™ allows a number of models to be used as the underlying basis for event forecasting.

Ignoring events (usually promotions) that a company has scheduled in advance will likely lead to poorer forecasts when those events have significant impacts. However, an event may be any occurrence that has taken place in the historical period that you believe will either be replicated in the forecast period (such as advertising promotions) or require adjustment to the parameters because of its large effect (such as a natural disaster).

# FORECASTING JEWELRY SALES WITH EXPONENTIAL SMOOTHING

Let us now look at quarterly data on jewelry sales in the United States (in millions of dollars), which show a great deal of seasonality and a slight trend as shown in Figure 3.24.

In this chapter, Winters' exponential smoothing is the only method we have used so far in which seasonality was explicitly taken into account. Thus, a Winters' model would appear to be an excellent candidate as a forecasting technique for jewelry sales. You might want to go back to Table 2.1, which provided a guide

**FIGURE 3.24**   **Jewelry Sales (M$)**

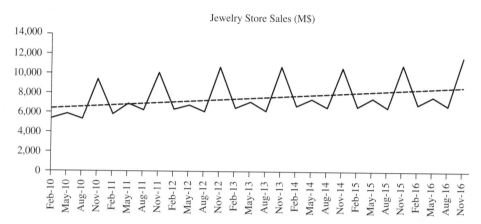

Jewelry Store Sales (M$)

to model selection, to see how this handy table would help you select Winters' model for this series. You will note that we do not apply simple or Holt's exponential smoothing to the jewelry sales data because neither of those methods would be an appropriate model, given the guidelines in Table 2.1.

Applying the Winters' model, ForecastX™ finds the optimum values for the weights to be level, 0.38; seasonal, 0.49; trend, 0.02. The historic MAPE for this Winters' model is 2.25 percent. The seasonal value shows that we indeed do have a rather high degree of seasonality, and the trend value indicates trend is also present. The resulting forecast is shown graphically in Figure 3.25.

**FIGURE 3.25**   **Jewelry Sales with a Winters' Forecast. MAPE = 2.25%**

Jewelry Store Sales (M$)

As shown in Table 3.15, the seasonal indices for this model are quite revealing:

**TABLE 3.15**  Jewelry Sales Seasonal Indices

| Seasonal Indices | Value |
|---|---|
| Index 1 (Quarter 1 = February) | 0.87 |
| Index 2 (Quarter 2 = May) | 0.93 |
| Index 3 (Quarter 3 = August) | 0.82 |
| Index 4 (Quarter 4 = November) | 1.38 |

Months are the middle month of each calendar quarter.

The dramatic seasonal index of 1.38 for the the fourth quarter is likely due to the gift giving that takes place during the holiday season. This degree of seasonality shows up clearly in the plot of actual and predicted values in Figure 3.24.

## Summary

If the time series you are forecasting is a stationary one, the moving-average method of forecasting may accurately predict future values. The moving-average method calculates the average of the past observations, and this average becomes the forecast for the next period.

When recent-past observations are thought to contain more information than distant-past observations, some form of exponential smoothing may be appropriate. Exponential smoothing provides self-correcting forecasts that adjust so as to regulate the forecast values by changing them in the opposite direction from recent errors. It is a characteristic of smoothing models in general, however, that their forecasts lag behind movements in the original time-series data. Exponential smoothing requires the specification of a smoothing constant, which determines the relative weights accorded to recent as opposed to more distant historical observations.

A suggested method for choosing an optimal smoothing constant is to minimize the mean absolute percentage error (MAPE).

When some trend is observed in the original time series, simple exponential smoothing becomes less able to perform accurate prediction; adding a procedure to adjust for the trend results in Holt's two-parameter exponential smoothing. Holt's smoothing adds a growth factor to the smoothing model to account for trend; in a sense, the growth or trend factor itself is smoothed in the same manner as the original data.

When seasonality is also present in the original data, Winters' three-parameter exponential smoothing adds a correction factor to Holt's smoothing model to correct for the seasonality. The correction factor is provided by an additional equation. Winters' method can also be used with data that are stationary but that have seasonality.

Adaptive–response-rate single exponential smoothing provides another technique that can be useful when the "level" of the forecasted variable changes infrequently. Adaptive-response models adjust the smoothing factor for changing conditions rather than choosing a constant smoothing factor.

In addition to trying Winters' exponential smoothing for seasonal data, you might also deseasonalize the data and then use another forecasting tool to forecast the deseasonalized series. The deseasonalized forecast can then be reseasonalized by multiplying the deseasonalized forecast by the corresponding seasonal indices.

Event models are very useful for many business applications. The events may be planned and implemented by a business, or they may be caused by forces outside of the business. Examples of the latter type could be a strike, a natural disaster, or some action by another business.

## Integrative Case:

# The Gap

## FORECASTING THE GAP SALES DATA WITH EXPONENTIAL SMOOTHING

The sales of The Gap stores for the 44 quarters covering April 2006 through January 2017 are once again shown below. From this graph, it is clear that The Gap sales are quite seasonal and are increasing over time. Recall that the 2004 data are used as a holdout period.

(c3Gap Sales Data)

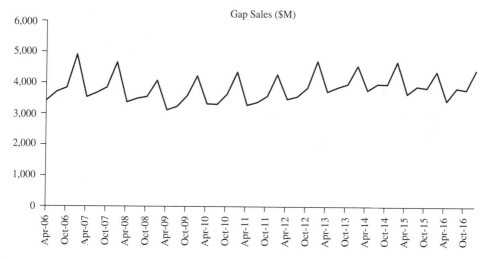

**Gap Sales for Chapter 3 Case.**

**Case Questions**

1. Using The Gap data for April 2006 through January 2016, what exponential smoothing model do you think would be the most appropriate if you want to develop a quarterly forecast for April 2016 through January 2017 (Gap's 2016 fiscal year) sales? Explain why.

2. Make a one-year (four-quarter) forecast for The Gap sales using the method you selected. What is the MAPE for this period of historic data?

3. To evaluate your forecast accuracy for the four quarters of the 2016 fiscal year, calculate the MAPE for those four months that were not used in developing the forecast. Compare the historic period MAPE with the forecast period MAPE.

4. What are the seasonal indices for the The Gap sales, and what do they tell you about this company's sales pattern?

## Solutions to Case Questions

1. Of the exponential smoothing models discussed in the text, the one that is most appropriate for The Gap sales data is Winters' exponential smoothing. This model takes both trend and seasonality into account. Allowing ForecastX™ to determine the optimal smoothing weights, we obtain level = 0.57, seasonal = 1.00, and trend = 0.00.

2. The forecast graph is shown below. The MAPE using the historic period is 2.60 percent,

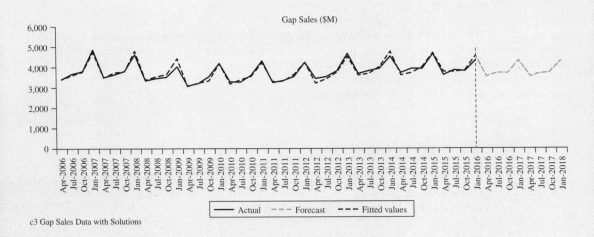

c3 Gap Sales Data with Solutions

| End Month of The Gap's Quarters | The Gap Sales | Forecast |
|---|---|---|
| April-16 | 3,438 | 3,573 |
| July-16 | 3,851 | 3,763 |
| October-16 | 3,798 | 3,747 |
| January 17 | 4,429 | 4,385 |

3. Using The Gap sales data and the forecast values (both are shown in the above table), the MAPE for the 2016 fiscal year is calculated as shown in the following table:

| Date | Actual Sales | Forecast | Error | Absolute Error | Absolute % Error |
|---|---|---|---|---|---|
| Apr-16 | 3,438 | 3,573 | −135 | 135 | 3.93 |
| Jul-16 | 3,851 | 3,763 | 88 | 88 | 2.29 |
| Oct-16 | 3,798 | 3,747 | 51 | 51 | 1.34 |
| Jan-17 | 4,429 | 4,385 | 44 | 44 | 0.99 |
| | | | | MAPE = 2.14% | |

In this case, it turns out that the forecast period MAPE (2.14 percent) is slightly lower than the historic MAPE (2.60 percent). Typically, a forecast period MAPE will be larger than the historic MAPE.

4. The seasonal indices are:

| Seasonal Indexes | Value |
| --- | --- |
| Index 1April | 0.88 |
| Index 2 July | 0.94 |
| Index 3 October | 0.97 |
| Index 4 January | 1.21 |

These indices suggest The Gap has strong holiday season sales since the fourth quarter (ending in January) would include the months when holiday shopping peaks.

# USING FORECASTX™ TO MAKE EXPONENTIAL SMOOTHING FORECASTS

What follows is a brief discussion of how to use ForecastX™ for preparing an exponential smoothing forecast. This also serves as a further introduction to the ease of use of ForecastX™. The illustration used here is for a forecast of The Gap data that has trend and seasonality.

First, put your data into an Excel spreadsheet in column format, such as the The Gap data shown in the table below. Once you have your data in this format, while in Excel put your cursor in any cell with sales data. For example, put the cursor in cell B4 in the Excel file. See the Excel file c3 Gap Sales Data with Solutions.

| Date | Gap Sales ($M) | Date | Gap Sales ($M) |
| --- | --- | --- | --- |
| Apr-06 | 3441 | Jul-09 | 3,245 |
| Jul-06 | 3,714 | Oct-09 | 3,589 |
| Oct-06 | **3,851** Example cell | Jan-10 | 4,236 |
|  | in which to place your | Apr-10 | 3,329 |
|  | cursor (cell B4). | Jul 10 | 3,317 |
| Jan-07 | 4,919 | Oct-10 | 3,654 |
| Apr-07 | 3,549 | Jan-11 | 4,364 |
| Jul-07 | 3,685 | Apr-11 | 3,295 |
| Oct-07 | 3,854 | Jul-11 | 3,386 |
| Jan-08 | 4,675 | Oct-11 | 3,585 |
| Apr-08 | 3,384 | Jan-12 | 4,283 |
| Jul-08 | 3,499 | Apr-12 | 3,487 |
| Oct-08 | 3,561 | Jul-12 | 3,575 |
| Jan-09 | 4,082 | Oct-12 | 3,864 |
| Apr-09 | 3,127 | Jan-13 | 4,725 |

(continued on next page)

(continued)

| Date | Gap Sales ($M) | Date | Gap Sales ($M) |
|------|----------------|------|----------------|
| Apr-13 | 3,729 | Apr-15 | 3,657 |
| Jul-13 | 3,868 | Jul-15 | 3,898 |
| Oct-13 | 3,976 | Oct-15 | 3,857 |
| Jan-14 | 4,575 | Jan-16 | 4,385 |
| Apr-14 | 3,774 | Apr-16 | 3,438 |
| Jul-14 | 3,981 | Jul-16 | 3,851 |
| Oct-14 | 3,972 | Oct-16 | 3,798 |
| Jan-15 | 4,708 | Jan-17 | 4,429 |

Then select Add-Ins from the top of your Excel sheet. In Add-Ins, select "Forecast" as shown below:

This will start ForecastX™. The following dialog box will appear.

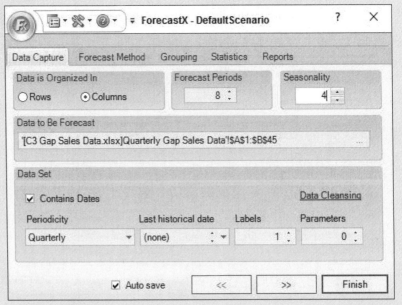

Source: John Galt Solutions

Check the items in this box to be sure ForecastX has correctly identified your data for periodicity, number of lines with labels (usually 1), whether your data are in rows or columns (typically columns), and the number of periods you want to forecast (8 in this example). Here we have set the seasonality to 4 since we know The Gap data have a four-period seasonality. Note that "Auto save" is also checked. This saves all selections, which makes it easier when repeating the same process for more than on Excel sheet. Once you have verified the selections, click the **Forecast Method** tab at the top. The following screen appears.

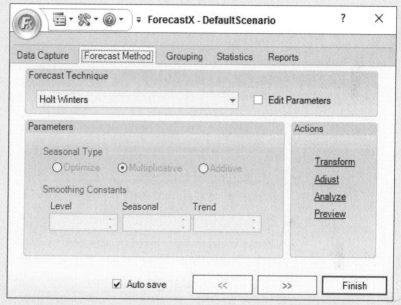

Source: John Galt Solutions

Click the down arrow in the **Forecasting Technique** window and select **Holt Winters,** which is what ForecastX™ calls Winters' exponential smoothing. This would be an appropriate method for data such as The Gap series. You can enter your own values for the constants, or you can leave those spaces blank and let ForecastX™ select the best set of values. Letting the software pick optimal values for the constants is most common.

We will not be using the "Grouping" tab, so now click on the "Statistics" tab. The following will appear:

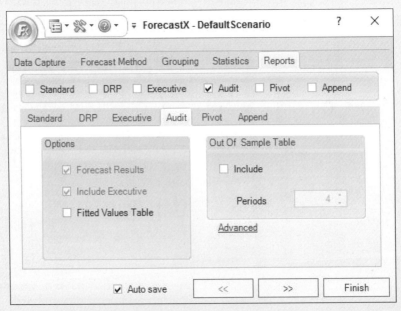

Source: John Galt Solutions

For this example, the only thing we want is the MAPE, which you see is checked above. Many other measures are available, so you might want to explore this box to familiarize yourself with the wide variety of options available.

Nest click on the "Reports" tab and the following will appear:

Source: John Galt Solutions

For this example, we only want what is called the "Audit" report, so that is what is checked. You will want to explore the other options. The "Standard" report is often useful.

Near the lower right of this box you see the word *Advanced* in dark blue. You may find it useful to click on *Advanced*. The following appears:

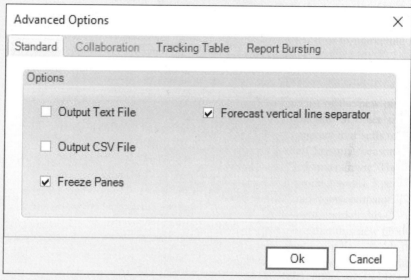

Source: John Galt Solutions

The two options most students find useful are the "Freeze Panes" and the "Forecast vertical line separator" options. You see those are checked above. Once you click on Ok, you will return to the "Reports" tab. Now click on "Finish." Your results will be calculated and displayed in a new Excel book. You may first need to click "View Output" in the following box.

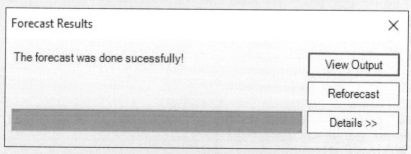

Source: John Galt Solutions

## Suggested Readings

Armstrong, J. Scott, ed. *Principles of Forecasting: A Handbook for Researchers and Practitioners.* Boston: Kluwer Academic Publishers, 2001.

Bass, Frank M. "A New Product Growth Model for Consumer Durables." *Management Science* 15 (January 1969), pp. 215–27. (Web site: http://www.basseconomics.com.)

Gardner, Everette S. "Exponential Smoothing: The State of the Art." *Journal of Forecasting* 4, no. 1 (1985), pp. 1–28.

Holt, C. C. "Forecasting Seasonal and Trends by Exponentially Weighted Moving Averages." Office of Naval Research, Memorandum No. 52, 1957.

Lilien, Gary L.; and Arvind Rangaswamy. *Marketing Engineering: Computer-Assisted Marketing Analysis and Planning.* 2nd ed. Upper Saddle River, NJ: Prentice-Hall, 2003. (Web site: http://www.mktgeng.com.)

Lilien, Gary L.; Arvind Rangaswamy; and Christophe Van den Bulte, "Diffusion Models: Managerial Applications and Software." In *New-Product Diffusion Models,* edited by Vijay Mahajan, Eitan Muller, and Jerry Wind. Boston: Kluwer Academic Publishers, 2000, pp. 295–336.

Makridakis, Spyros; and Steven C. Wheelwright. *Forecasting Methods for Management.* 5th ed. New York: John Wiley & Sons, 1989.

Makridakis, Spyros, et al. "The M2-Competition: A Real-Time Judgmentally Based Forecasting Study." *International Journal of Forecasting* 9, no. 1 (April 1993), pp. 5–22.

Makridakis, Spyros; Steven C. Wheelwright; and Victor E. McGee. *Forecasting: Methods and Applications.* 2nd ed. New York: John Wiley & Sons, 1983.

Pegels, Carl C. "Exponential Forecasting: Some New Variations." *Management Science* 15, no. 12 (January 1969), pp. 311–15.

West, Douglas C. "Number of Sales Forecast Methods and Marketing Management." *Journal of Forecasting* 13, no. 4 (August 1994), pp. 395–407.

Winters, P. R. "Forecasting Sales by Exponentially Weighted Moving Averages." *Management Science* 6 (1960), pp. 324–42.

## Exercises

1. Assume you were to use $\alpha$ values of 0.1, 0.5, and 0.9 in a separate simple exponential smoothing models. How would these different $\alpha$ values weight past observations of the variable to be forecast? How would you know which of these $\alpha$ values provided the best forecasting model? If the $\alpha = 0.9$ value provided the best forecast for your data, would this imply that you should do anything else? Does exponential smoothing place more or less weight on the most recent data when compared with the moving-average method? What weight is applied to each observation in a moving-average model? Why is smoothing (simple, Holt's, and Winters') also called *exponential* smoothing?

2. Under what conditions would you choose to use simple exponential smoothing, Holt's exponential smoothing, or Winters' exponential smoothing? Are these the only smoothing models possible to construct? If there are other possible models, suggest one that might be useful.

3. Exponential smoothing is meant to be used with time-series data when the data are made up of some or all of the basic components of level, trend, seasonality, and error. If the data series only fluctuates about an average with no trend and no seasonality, which form of smoothing would you employ? If the data include all of these

components, which form of smoothing would you employ? How should the smoothing constants be chosen?

4. The smoothing constant chosen in simple exponential smoothing determines the weight to be placed on different terms of time-series data. If the smoothing factor is high rather than low, is more or less weight placed on recent observations? If $\alpha$ is .3, what weight is applied to the observation four periods ago?

5. Consider the following rates offered on certificates of deposit at a large metropolitan bank during a recent year (c3p5):

| Month | Rate (%) |
| --- | --- |
| Jan-16 | 1.025 |
| Feb-16 | 2.047 |
| Mar-16 | 2.28 |
| Apr-16 | 2.65 |
| May-16 | 2.714 |
| Jun-16 | 2.963 |
| Jul-16 | 1.575 |
| Aug-16 | 2.612 |
| Sep-16 | 2.985 |
| Oct-16 | 2.298 |
| Nov-16 | 1.454 |
| Dec-16 | 2.461 |

Use a three-month average to forecast the rate for the following January.

6. The following inventory pattern has been observed in the Zahm Corporation over 12 months (c3p6):

| Month | Inventory |
| --- | --- |
| Apr-16 | 1,544 |
| May-16 | 1,913 |
| Jun-16 | 2,028 |
| Jul-16 | 1,178 |
| Aug-16 | 1,554 |
| Sep-16 | 1,910 |
| Oct-16 | 1,208 |
| Nov-16 | 2,467 |
| Dec-16 | 2,101 |
| Jan-17 | 1,662 |
| Feb-17 | 2,432 |
| Mar-17 | 2,443 |

Use both three-month and five-month moving-average models to forecast the inventory for the next January. Use mean absolute percentage error (MAPE) to evaluate these two forecasts.

7. Consider the following data on full-service restaurant sales. Calculate both the three-month and five-month moving averages for these data, and compare the forecasts by calculating the mean absolute percentage errors and MAPEs. The data are in millions of dollars. (c3p7)

| Date | Sales (000,000) | Date | Sales (000,000) |
|---|---|---|---|
| Jan-02 | 6910 | Jun-05 | 8549 |
| Feb-02 | 6959 | Jul-05 | 8902 |
| Mar-02 | 7268 | Aug-05 | 9035 |
| Apr-02 | 7023 | Sep-05 | 8271 |
| May-02 | 7555 | Oct-05 | 8328 |
| Jun-02 | 7021 | Nov-05 | 7987 |
| Jul-02 | 7297 | Dec-05 | 8383 |
| Aug-02 | 7558 | Jan-06 | 7532 |
| Sep-02 | 6945 | Feb-06 | 7943 |
| Oct-02 | 7464 | Mar-06 | 8685 |
| Nov-02 | 7138 | Apr-06 | 8502 |
| Dec-02 | 7355 | May-06 | 8977 |
| Jan-03 | 6854 | Jun-06 | 8716 |
| Feb-03 | 6699 | Jul-06 | 8978 |
| Mar-03 | 7324 | Aug-06 | 9548 |
| Apr-03 | 7514 | Sep-06 | 8675 |
| May-03 | 7898 | Oct-06 | 9032 |
| Jun-03 | 7814 | Nov-06 | 9005 |
| Jul-03 | 8049 | Dec-06 | 8921 |
| Aug-03 | 8322 | Jan-07 | 8688 |
| Sep-03 | 7730 | Feb-07 | 8640 |
| Oct-03 | 8049 | Mar-07 | 9592 |
| Nov-03 | 7449 | Apr-07 | 9332 |
| Dec-03 | 7774 | May-07 | 9976 |
| Jan-04 | 6998 | Jun-07 | 9460 |
| Feb-04 | 7275 | Jul-07 | 10071 |
| Mar-04 | 8177 | Aug-07 | 10517 |
| Apr-04 | 8143 | Sep-07 | 9539 |
| May-04 | 8364 | Oct-07 | 9850 |
| Jun-04 | 8292 | Nov-07 | 9227 |
| Jul-04 | 8689 | Dec-07 | 9699 |
| Aug-04 | 8661 | Jan-08 | 9147 |
| Sep-04 | 8080 | Feb-08 | 9114 |
| Oct-04 | 8264 | Mar-08 | 9972 |
| Nov-04 | 7822 | Apr-08 | 9825 |
| Dec-04 | 8352 | May-08 | 10423 |
| Jan-05 | 7507 | Jun-08 | 10203 |
| Feb-05 | 7341 | Jul-08 | 10458 |
| Mar-05 | 8243 | Aug-08 | 10541 |
| Apr-05 | 8269 | Sep-08 | 9844 |
| May-05 | 8615 | Oct-08 | 10455 |

(continued on next page)

(continued)

| Date | Sales (000,000) | Date | Sales (000,000) |
|---|---|---|---|
| Nov-08 | 9715 | Jun-12 | 12685 |
| Dec-08 | 10338 | Jul-12 | 12873 |
| Jan-09 | 9583 | Aug-12 | 13357 |
| Feb-09 | 9515 | Sep-12 | 11743 |
| Mar-09 | 10385 | Oct-12 | 12129 |
| Apr-09 | 10571 | Nov-12 | 12003 |
| May-09 | 10792 | Dec-12 | 12794 |
| Jun-09 | 10553 | Jan-13 | 11811 |
| Jul-09 | 11083 | Feb-13 | 11523 |
| Aug-09 | 10939 | Mar-13 | 12957 |
| Sep-09 | 10297 | Apr-13 | 12423 |
| Oct-09 | 11056 | May-13 | 13741 |
| Nov-09 | 10229 | Jun-13 | 13250 |
| Dec-09 | 10703 | Jul-13 | 13673 |
| Jan-10 | 10092 | Aug-13 | 14329 |
| Feb-10 | 10532 | Sep-13 | 12465 |
| Mar-10 | 11464 | Oct-13 | 13026 |
| Apr-10 | 11240 | Nov-13 | 12606 |
| May-10 | 11393 | Dec-13 | 13281 |
| Jun-10 | 11332 | Jan-14 | 12953 |
| Jul-10 | 11752 | Feb-14 | 12926 |
| Aug-10 | 11581 | Mar-14 | 13709 |
| Sep-10 | 11257 | Apr-14 | 13324 |
| Oct-10 | 11447 | May-14 | 14042 |
| Nov-10 | 10742 | Jun-14 | 13669 |
| Dec-10 | 11372 | Jul-14 | 14572 |
| Jan-11 | 10726 | Aug-14 | 14149 |
| Feb-11 | 10691 | Sep-14 | 13268 |
| Mar-11 | 11919 | Oct-14 | 13918 |
| Apr-11 | 11312 | Nov-14 | 12992 |
| May-11 | 12002 | Dec-14 | 14312 |
| Jun-11 | 12191 | Jan-15 | 13202 |
| Jul-11 | 12374 | Feb-15 | 13260 |
| Aug-11 | 12797 | Mar-15 | 14359 |
| Sep-11 | 11292 | Apr-15 | 14368 |
| Oct-11 | 11523 | May-15 | 14687 |
| Nov-11 | 11259 | Jun-15 | 14445 |
| Dec-11 | 12596 | Jul-15 | 15142 |
| Jan-12 | 11520 | Aug-15 | 14905 |
| Feb-12 | 11414 | Sep-15 | 13982 |
| Mar-12 | 12696 | Oct-15 | 14575 |
| Apr-12 | 12140 | Nov-15 | 13838 |
| May-12 | 12857 | Dec-15 | 15478 |

8. Forecasters at Siegfried Corporation are using simple exponential smoothing to forecast the sales of its major product. They are trying to decide what smoothing constant will give the best results. They have tried a number of smoothing constants with the following results:

| Smoothing Constant | MAPE |
|---|---|
| 0.10 | 12.5% |
| 0.15 | 9.7% |
| 0.20 | 13.6% |
| 0.25 | 14.1% |

Which smoothing constant appears best from these results? Why? Could you perhaps get even better results, given these outcomes? How would you go about improving the MAPE?

9. The number of tons of brake assemblies received at an auto parts distribution center last month was 670. The forecast tonnage was 720 for last month. The company uses a simple exponential smoothing model with a smoothing constant of 0.6 to develop its forecasts. What will be the company's forecast for the next month?

10. The number of service calls received at LaFortune Electric during four months is shown in the following table (c3p10):

| Month | Number of Service Calls |
|---|---|
| April | 19 |
| May | 31 |
| June | 27 |
| July | 29 |

Forecast the number of service calls in August by using a simple exponential smoothing model with a smoothing constant of 0.1. (Assume the forecast for April was 21.)

11. *a.* Plot the data presented in Exercise 7 to examine the possible existence of trend and seasonality in the data. (c3p11)

   *b.* Prepare three separate exponential smoothing models to forecast the full-service restaurant sales data using the monthly data.

      1. A simple smoothing model
      2. Holt's model
      3. Winters' model

   *c.* Examine the accuracy of each model by calculating the mean absolute percentage error for each during the historical period. Explain carefully what characteristics of the original data led one of these models to have the lowest MAPE.

12. The data in the table below represent warehouse club and superstore sales in the eastern and central United States on a monthly basis. The data are in millions of dollars. (c3p12)

| Date | Sales | Date | Sales |
|---|---|---|---|
| Jan-02 | 2,580 | Jan-06 | 4,758 |
| Feb-02 | 2,616 | Feb-06 | 4,914 |
| Mar-02 | 2,838 | Mar-06 | 5,431 |
| Apr-02 | 2,985 | Apr-06 | 5,474 |
| May-02 | 3,258 | May-06 | 6,124 |
| Jun-02 | 3,107 | Jun-06 | 6,027 |
| Jul-02 | 3,097 | Jul-06 | 5,914 |
| Aug-02 | 3,288 | Aug-06 | 6,244 |
| Sep-02 | 3,077 | Sep-06 | 5,808 |
| Oct-02 | 3,429 | Oct-06 | 6,373 |
| Nov-02 | 4,011 | Nov-06 | 6,994 |
| Dec-02 | 5,739 | Dec-06 | 9,018 |
| Jan-03 | 2,877 | Jan-07 | 5,694 |
| Feb-03 | 2,885 | Feb-07 | 5,431 |
| Mar-03 | 3,259 | Mar-07 | 6,240 |
| Apr-03 | 3,454 | Apr-07 | 6,101 |
| May-03 | 3,771 | May-07 | 6,849 |
| Jun-03 | 3,667 | Jun-07 | 6,694 |
| Jul-03 | 3,743 | Jul-07 | 6,815 |
| Aug-03 | 3,792 | Aug-07 | 6,948 |
| Sep-03 | 3,699 | Sep-07 | 6,450 |
| Oct-03 | 4,082 | Oct-07 | 7,190 |
| Nov-03 | 4,727 | Nov-07 | 7,738 |
| Dec-03 | 6,672 | Dec-07 | 9,769 |
| Jan-04 | 3,560 | Jan-08 | 6,665 |
| Feb-04 | 3,575 | Feb-08 | 6,400 |
| Mar-04 | 4,220 | Mar-08 | 7,277 |
| Apr-04 | 4,282 | Apr-08 | 7,584 |
| May-04 | 4,594 | May-08 | 8,169 |
| Jun-04 | 4,691 | Jun-08 | 8,179 |
| Jul-04 | 4,629 | Jul-08 | 8,118 |
| Aug-04 | 4,795 | Aug-08 | 8,284 |
| Sep-04 | 4,632 | Sep-08 | 7,962 |
| Oct-04 | 5,067 | Oct-08 | 8,636 |
| Nov-04 | 5,746 | Nov-08 | 9,433 |
| Dec-04 | 7,965 | Dec-08 | 11,786 |
| Jan-05 | 4,317 | Jan-09 | 8,082 |
| Feb-05 | 4,118 | Feb-09 | 7,761 |
| Mar-05 | 4,855 | Mar-09 | 8,994 |
| Apr-05 | 4,999 | Apr-09 | 8,803 |
| May-05 | 5,343 | May-09 | 9,712 |
| Jun-05 | 5,392 | Jun-09 | 9,843 |
| Jul-05 | 5,274 | Jul-09 | 9,769 |
| Aug-05 | 5,435 | Aug-09 | 9,944 |
| Sep-05 | 5,217 | Sep-09 | 9,582 |
| Oct-05 | 5,460 | Oct-09 | 10,209 |
| Nov-05 | 6,288 | Nov-09 | 11,115 |
| Dec-05 | 8,403 | Dec-09 | 14,995 |

(continued on next page)

(continued)

| Date | Sales | Date | Sales |
|---|---|---|---|
| Jan-10 | 9,183 | Nov-13 | 20,336 |
| Feb-10 | 9,478 | Dec-13 | 24,665 |
| Mar-10 | 10,751 | Jan-14 | 17,686 |
| Apr-10 | 10,518 | Feb-14 | 17,908 |
| May-10 | 11,349 | Mar-14 | 18,691 |
| Jun-10 | 11,728 | Apr-14 | 19,030 |
| Jul-10 | 11,590 | May-14 | 20,623 |
| Aug-10 | 11,871 | Jun-14 | 19,596 |
| Sep-10 | 11,336 | Jul-14 | 20,122 |
| Oct-10 | 11,986 | Aug-14 | 20,029 |
| Nov-10 | 13,130 | Sep-14 | 18,669 |
| Dec-10 | 16,694 | Oct-14 | 20,518 |
| Jan-11 | 11,195 | Nov-14 | 21,967 |
| Feb-11 | 10,919 | Dec-14 | 27,584 |
| Mar-11 | 12,389 | Jan-15 | 19,315 |
| Apr-11 | 12,619 | Feb-15 | 19,186 |
| May-11 | 13,489 | Mar-15 | 21,211 |
| Jun-11 | 13,620 | Apr-15 | 20,985 |
| Jul-11 | 13,438 | May-15 | 22,385 |
| Aug-11 | 14,084 | Jun-15 | 22,223 |
| Sep-11 | 13,172 | Jul-15 | 22,602 |
| Oct-11 | 14,040 | Aug-15 | 22,456 |
| Nov-11 | 15,759 | Sep-15 | 21,418 |
| Dec-11 | 19,992 | Oct-15 | 23,092 |
| Jan-12 | 13,162 | Nov-15 | 24,598 |
| Feb-12 | 13,394 | Dec-15 | 30,706 |
| Mar-12 | 15,285 | Jan-16 | 21,692 |
| Apr-12 | 14,467 | Feb-16 | 21,699 |
| May-12 | 16,086 | Mar-16 | 23,402 |
| Jun-12 | 16,027 | Apr-16 | 24,046 |
| Jul-12 | 15,622 | May-16 | 24,881 |
| Aug-12 | 16,360 | Jun-16 | 24,602 |
| Sep-12 | 14,714 | Jul-16 | 24,631 |
| Oct-12 | 15,894 | Aug-16 | 24,831 |
| Nov-12 | 18,152 | Sep-16 | 23,603 |
| Dec-12 | 22,089 | Oct-16 | 24,608 |
| Jan-13 | 15,161 | Nov-16 | 26,705 |
| Feb-13 | 15,342 | Dec-16 | 34,023 |
| Mar-13 | 16,997 | Jan-17 | 23,837 |
| Apr-13 | 16,623 | Feb-17 | 23,438 |
| May-13 | 18,064 | Mar-17 | 26,305 |
| Jun-13 | 17,605 | Apr-17 | 25,429 |
| Jul-13 | 17,746 | May-17 | 27,152 |
| Aug-13 | 18,907 | Jun-17 | 27,218 |
| Sep-13 | 16,735 | Jul-17 | 26,722 |
| Oct-13 | 18,146 | | |

*a.* Prepare a time-series plot of the data, and visually inspect that plot to determine the characteristics you see in this series.

*b.* Use an exponential smoothing model to develop a forecast of sales for the next 12 months, and explain why you selected that model. Plot the actual and forecast values. Determine the MAPE for your model during the historical period.

13. The data in the table below are for retail sales in book stores by quarter. (c3p13)

**U.S. Retail Book Sales (in Millions of Dollars, NSA)**

| Date | Sales | Date | Sales |
|---|---|---|---|
| Mar-02 | 1,866 | Mar-09 | 3,480 |
| Jun-02 | 1,666 | Jun-09 | 2,943 |
| Sep-02 | 2,351 | Sep-09 | 3,654 |
| Dec-02 | 2,455 | Dec-09 | 4,108 |
| Mar-03 | 2,169 | Mar-10 | 3,628 |
| Jun-03 | 1,815 | Jun-10 | 3,203 |
| Sep-03 | 2,498 | Sep-10 | 4,051 |
| Dec-03 | 2,637 | Dec-10 | 4,010 |
| Mar-04 | 2,326 | Mar-11 | 3,719 |
| Jun-04 | 2,020 | Jun-11 | 3,084 |
| Sep-04 | 2,858 | Sep-11 | 4,234 |
| Dec-04 | 2,915 | Dec-11 | 4,073 |
| Mar-05 | 2,725 | Mar-12 | 3,983 |
| Jun-05 | 2,283 | Jun-12 | 3,132 |
| Sep-05 | 3,134 | Sep-12 | 4,328 |
| Dec-05 | 3,066 | Dec-12 | 4,007 |
| Mar-06 | 2,876 | Mar-13 | 3,969 |
| Jun-06 | 2,445 | Jun-13 | 3,257 |
| Sep-06 | 3,190 | Sep-13 | 4,824 |
| Dec-06 | 3,407 | Dec-13 | 4,129 |
| Mar-07 | 3,197 | Mar-14 | 4,298 |
| Jun-07 | 2,575 | Jun-14 | 3,312 |
| Sep-07 | 3,290 | Sep-14 | 4,811 |
| Dec-07 | 3,693 | Dec-14 | 4,336 |
| Mar-08 | 3,273 | Mar-15 | 4,261 |
| Jun-08 | 2,713 | Jun-15 | 3,278 |
| Sep-08 | 3,514 | Sep-15 | 4,991 |
| Dec-08 | 3,794 | Dec-15 | 4,447 |

*a.* Plot these data and examine the plot. Does this view of the data suggest a particular smoothing model? Do the data appear to be seasonal? Explain.

*b.* Use an exponential smoothing method to forecast the next four quarters. Plot the actual and forecast values.

14. Monthly data from March 2014 through September 2017 are provided below for the number of lunches served in public schools. You are charged with making a 12-month forecast of the meals to be served. Begin by plotting the data and examining it for the patterns of trend and seasonality. Choose an appropriate model for the data and forecast for the next 12 months. (c3p14)

| Month | Meals Served | Month | Meals Served |
|---|---|---|---|
| Mar-14 | 108,371,749 | Jan-16 | 98,887,496 |
| Apr-14 | 99,199,094 | Feb-16 | 96,477,065 |
| May-14 | 92,195,689 | Mar-16 | 114,094,756 |
| Jun-14 | 81,447,374 | Apr-16 | 96,093,092 |
| Jul-14 | 72,792,981 | May-16 | 107,527,897 |
| Aug-14 | 78,931,911 | Jun-16 | 87,135,336 |
| Sep-14 | 89,982,843 | Jul-16 | 72,397,374 |
| Oct-14 | 96,761,533 | Aug-16 | 88,657,480 |
| Nov-14 | 92,772,827 | Sep-16 | 94,566,627 |
| Dec-14 | 83,103,478 | Oct-16 | 106,889,806 |
| Jan-15 | 93,109,115 | Nov-16 | 97,638,605 |
| Feb-15 | 93,267,674 | Dec-16 | 83,280,944 |
| Mar-15 | 105,290,897 | Jan-17 | 102,522,133 |
| Apr-15 | 103,625,467 | Feb-17 | 95,537,211 |
| May-15 | 100,549,323 | Mar-17 | 111,462,237 |
| Jun-15 | 85,155,854 | Apr-17 | 103,542,365 |
| Jul-15 | 71,406,448 | May-17 | 111,242,080 |
| Aug-15 | 85,623,392 | Jun-17 | 85,765,747 |
| Sep-15 | 94,828,432 | Jul-17 | 78,943,762 |
| Oct-15 | 97,917,922 | Aug-17 | 89,965,185 |
| Nov-15 | 95,753,418 | Sep-17 | 92,934,809 |
| Dec-15 | 83,145,194 | | |

15. Describe what is meant by the term *moving average*? When would a moving average be an appropriate forecast method?

16. How are simple moving averages models different from exponential smoothing models?

17. Why is the term *exponential* used when describing exponential smoothing forecast models?

18. For what type of data pattern would a simple exponential smoothing model be good as a forecast method?

19. When is a Holt's exponential smoothing model most appropriate?

20. What data pattern would suggest the use of a Winters' exponential smoothing model?

21. What are some methods that might be useful to forecast "new products" for which there are few historical observations?

22. What is an "event model?" Give some examples of when such a model might be useful.

# Chapter **Four**

# Extrapolation 2. Introduction to Forecasting with Regression Trend Models

In this chapter, the fundamentals of bivariate regression analysis are presented in the context of forecasting applications. A bivariate regression model has just two variables (it is **bi**variate). The variables are commonly designated as $Y$ and $X$. The $Y$ variable is called the **dependent variable**. The $X$ variable is called the **independent** variable. So, $Y$ **depends on the value of** $X$. Or, $Y$ is a function of $X$.

In this chapter, regression models are developed for jewelry store sales and disposable personal income), based on quarterly data. These regression models are then used to make forecasts of each series. As you might expect, jewelry store sales are quite seasonal. You will see how seasonal data can be forecast with a bivariate regression.

At the end of the chapter, we return to our continuing examples of forecasting total new houses sold and to the continuing The Gap case study. In both these situations, the variables being forecast have a seasonal pattern. You will see again how the seasonal pattern can be handled in a bivariate regression. In Chapter 5, you will learn another way to deal with seasonality using regression analysis.

## LEARNING OBJECTIVES

After studying this chapter, you should be able to:

1. Explain why it is important to look at data in a graph rather than only in a table.
2. Describe the type of data patterns for which a linear regression trend forecast would be appropriate.

3. Explain how a seasonal data set can be forecast with a linear regression trend.

4. Discuss the four steps that should be used to evaluate a linear regression model.

5. Explain the difference between a trend model and a causal model..

6. Explain the difference between the most common kind of correlation (the Pearson product moment correlation) and serial correlation.

7. Explain what is meant by heteroscedasticity.

# THE BIVARIATE REGRESSION MODEL

Bivariate regression analysis (also called *simple linear least-squares regression*) is a statistical tool that gives us the ability to estimate the mathematical relationship between a dependent variable (usually called $Y$) and a single independent variable (usually called $X$).[1] The dependent variable is the variable for which we want to develop a forecast. While various nonlinear forms may be used, simple linear regression models are the most common. Nonlinear models will be discussed in Chapter 5.

In using regression analyses, we begin by supposing that $Y$ is a function of $X$. That is:

$$Y = f(X)$$

Since we most often begin by using linear functions, we may write the population regression model as:

$$Y = \beta_0 + \beta_1 X + \varepsilon$$

where $\beta_0$ represents the intercept of the regression line on the vertical (or $Y$) axis and $\beta_1$ is the slope of the regression line. Thus, $\beta_1$ tells us the rate of change in $Y$ per unit change in $X$. The intercept ($\beta_0$) is the value that the dependent variable would have if $X = 0$. While this is a correct interpretation from an algebraic perspective, such an interpretation is often not valid in applications, since a value of $X = 0$ is frequently not in the relevant range of observations on $X$. The $\varepsilon$ in this model represents an error term. That is, every $Y$ is not likely to be predicted exactly from the values of $\beta_0$ and $\beta_1 X$. The resulting error is $\varepsilon$.

We would like to estimate values of $\beta_0$ and $\beta_1$ such that the resulting equation best fits the data. To do so, we need to decide on a criterion against which the fit of the estimated model can be evaluated. The most common such rule is called the *ordinary least-squares* (OLS) criterion. This rule says that the best model is the one that minimizes the sum of the squared error terms.

The unobserved model that describes the whole population of data is expressed as

$$Y = \beta_0 + \beta_1 X + \varepsilon$$

[1] For a more detailed discussion of the regression model, including underlying assumptions, see Bruce Bowerman, Richard T. O'Connell, and Emily Murphree, *Business Statistics* in *Practice*, 8th ed. (New York, NY. McGraw-Hill Education, 2017).

These values of the intercept ($\beta_0$) and slope ($\beta_1$) are population parameters that are typically estimated using sample data. The corresponding sample statistics are $b_0$ and $b_1$. The estimated regression model is expressed as

$$\hat{Y} = b_0 + b_1 X$$

Deviations of predicted values ($\hat{Y}$) from the actual values of $Y$ are called *residuals* or *errors* and are denoted by $e$, where

$$e = Y - \hat{Y}$$

or,

$$e = Y - b_0 - b_1 X$$

The ordinary least-squares method seeks to find estimates of the slope and intercept parameters that minimize the sum of squared residuals:

$$Minimize \, \Sigma e^2 = \Sigma (Y - b_0 - b_1 X)^2$$

By taking partial derivatives of the sum of squared residuals with respect to $b_0$ and $b_1$, setting the partial derivatives equal to zero, and solving the two equations simultaneously, we obtain estimating formulas:

$$b_1 = \left( \Sigma XY - n\bar{X}\bar{Y} \right) / \left( \Sigma X^2 - n\bar{X}^2 \right)$$
$$b_0 = \bar{Y} - b_1\bar{X}$$

These formulas could be used to calculate $b_0$ and $b_1$ by hand. However, even for simple regression, a computer program is normally used for such calculations.

# VISUALIZATION OF DATA: AN IMPORTANT STEP IN REGRESSION ANALYSIS

There was a time when regression lines were estimated in a rather *ad hoc* manner, based solely on an analyst's visual interpretation of the data. The analyst would plot the data by hand and would "eyeball" the resulting scatter of points to determine the position of a straight line that was believed to "best" represent the general relationship between $Y$ and $X$. Such a straight line was then drawn through the scatterplot, and by selecting two points from the line, its algebraic equation was calculated (i.e., values for $b_0$ and $b_1$ were estimated). One obvious problem with such a procedure is that different analysts would almost surely come up with differing estimates of $b_0$ and $b_1$.

Today, it is doubtful that anyone would take this approach to estimating a regression equation. Modern computer technology makes it very easy to obtain the OLS equation without ever looking at the data. This equation is best, according to the ordinary least-squares criterion, and numerous evaluative statistics can be simultaneously determined. Every analyst obtains precisely the same results, and those results are easily replicated. Thus, it may appear that computer-based regression analysis is a clearly superior method. However, something is lost. Analysts may

Source: Anscombe, F. J. "Graphs in Statistical Analysis," *American Statistician* 27, February 1973, 17–21, as reported in Edward R. Tufte, *The Visual Display of Quantitative Information,* Cheshire, CT: Graphics Press, 1983, 13.

**TABLE 4.1** Four Dissimilar Data Sets with Similar Regression Results (c4t1)

| Set A | | Set B | | Set C | | Set D | |
|---|---|---|---|---|---|---|---|
| X | Y | X | Y | X | Y | X | Y |
| 10 | 8.04 | 10 | 9.14 | 10 | 7.46 | 8 | 6.58 |
| 8 | 6.95 | 8 | 8.14 | 8 | 6.77 | 8 | 5.76 |
| 13 | 7.58 | 13 | 8.74 | 13 | 12.74 | 8 | 7.71 |
| 9 | 8.81 | 9 | 8.77 | 9 | 7.11 | 8 | 8.84 |
| 11 | 8.33 | 11 | 9.26 | 11 | 7.81 | 8 | 8.47 |
| 14 | 9.96 | 14 | 8.10 | 14 | 8.84 | 8 | 7.04 |
| 6 | 7.24 | 6 | 6.13 | 6 | 6.08 | 8 | 5.25 |
| 4 | 4.26 | 4 | 3.10 | 4 | 5.39 | 19 | 12.50 |
| 12 | 10.84 | 12 | 9.13 | 12 | 8.15 | 8 | 5.56 |
| 7 | 4.82 | 7 | 7.26 | 7 | 6.42 | 8 | 7.91 |
| 5 | 5.68 | 5 | 4.74 | 5 | 5.73 | 8 | 6.89 |

just enter data into Excel or some statistical software, issue appropriate commands, get the corresponding statistical results, and run off to apply the model in some decision-based context such as forecasting. In the process, they would never have *looked* at the data. Such blind attention to statistical estimates can be dangerous.

To illustrate this point, consider the four data sets in Table 4.1. For all four of the data sets in Table 4.1, the calculated regression results show an OLS equation of:

$$\hat{Y} = 3 + 0.5X$$

It might also be noted that the mean of the $X$'s is 9.0 and the mean of the $Y$'s is 7.5 in all four cases. The standard deviation is 3.32 for all of the $X$ variables and 2.03 for all of the $Y$ variables. Similarly, the correlation for each pair of $X$ and $Y$ variables is 0.82.[2]

From these results, an analyst who looks only at these summary statistics would likely conclude that the four data sets are identical or, at the very least, quite similar. But, oh, how wrong this conclusion would be. If you take the time to prepare a scattergram of each of the four data sets, dramatic differences become apparent. In Figure 4.1, we have plotted each $XY$ pair in a separate plot, along with the corresponding OLS regression lines (all four of the regression lines have the same equation: $\hat{Y} = 3 + 0.5X$).

It is important to *look* at the data before plunging into data analysis and the selection of an appropriate set of forecasting techniques.

Visualization of these data allows us to see stark differences that would not be apparent from the descriptive statistics we have reviewed. The regression line is most clearly inappropriate for the data in the lower-right plot. The lower-left plot has, with the exception of one outlier, a perfectly linear relationship between $Y$ and $X$, which is not so clear without visual inspection of the data. The upper-right plot of data suggests that a nonlinear model would fit the data better than a linear

[2] Many statistical diagnostics on the regression equations, which we will cover later in this chapter, are also equal. These include standard errors of the regression, $t$-ratios for the coefficients, $R$-squared, and the regression sum of squares. Statistics related to the evaluation of residuals, such as the Durbin-Watson statistic, show some differences.

**FIGURE 4.1**
**Scatterplots of**
**Four *XY* Data Sets**
**That Have Very**
**Similar Statistical**
**Properties but Are**
**Visually Quite**
**Different** (c4f1)
For Each of the
Data Sets, the
OLS Regression
Equation Is
$Y = 3 + 0.5X.$

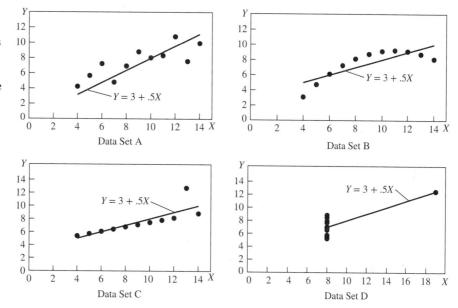

function. Only the upper-left plot suggests a data set that is a good candidate for a linear regression model. Visually, these data sets are quite dissimilar, even though they have some very similar statistical properties.

Forecasters can benefit from this example.

## A PROCESS FOR REGRESSION FORECASTING

It is useful to have a plan at hand when approaching any task. And so it is with developing a regression-based forecast. In this section, we suggest one such plan, or process, that helps to organize the task of preparing a regression forecast. What we say here is not separate from the forecast process discussed in Chapter 2. Rather, it complements that process, especially data considerations, model selection, model evaluation, and forecast preparation.

We begin with data considerations, which become somewhat more complex for regression models. Not only do we need to pay attention to the dependent variable, the series to be forecasted, but we must also consider the independent variable(s) that will drive the regression forecast. We should utilize graphic techniques to inspect the data, looking especially for trend, seasonal, and cyclical components, as well as for outliers. This will help in determining what type of regression model may be most appropriate (e.g., linear versus nonlinear, or trend versus causal).

Next we must make a forecast of the independent variable(s). This becomes a separate, yet related, forecasting effort. Each potential independent variable should be forecast using a method that is appropriate to that particular series,

*The forecaster should utilize graphic techniques to inspect the data, looking especially for trend, seasonal, and cyclical components, as well as for outliers.*

taking into account the model-selection guidelines discussed in Chapter 2 and summarized in Table 2.1.

Once the data have been thoroughly reviewed and the type of regression model has been selected, it is time to specify the model. By model specification, we mean the statistical process of estimating the regression coefficients ($b_0$ and $b_1$, in simple bivariate regression models). In doing so, we recommend using a holdout period for evaluation. Thus, if you have 10 years of quarterly data ($n = 40$), you might use 9 years of data ($n = 36$) to estimate the regression coefficients. Initial evaluation of regression models (based on diagnostic statistics we will discuss shortly) can be done on this subsample of the historical data. However, the real test of a forecasting model is in the actual forecast. Thus, if you have set aside a holdout period of data, you can then test the model in this period to get a truer feel for how well the model meets your needs.

This relates to our discussion of fit versus accuracy in Chapter 2. When the model is evaluated in comparison with the data used in specifying the model, we are determining how well the model **"fits"** the data. This is a retrospective approach, often called an *in-sample* evaluation. By using a holdout period, we have an opportunity to evaluate the model **"out of sample."** That is, we can determine how **"accurate"** the model is for an actual forecast horizon. After an evaluation of fit and accuracy, a forecaster should respecify the best of the models using the entire span of data that are available. The newly specified model is then used to forecast beyond the frontier of what is known at the time of the forecast.

# FORECASTING WITH A SIMPLE LINEAR TREND[3]

It is sometimes possible to make reasonably good forecasts on the basis of a simple linear time trend. To do so, we set up a time index ($T$) to use as the independent or $X$ variable in the basic regression model, where $T$ is usually set equal to 1 for the first observation and increased by 1 for each subsequent observation. The regression model is then:

$$\hat{Y} = b_0 + b_1(T)$$

where $Y$ is the series we wish to forecast.

To illustrate this process, consider the data in Table 4.2. DPI is disposable personal income in billions of dollars on a quarterly basis. In the "Date" column, the months represent the end month of each calendar quarter. The data are for 2010 through 2016. Only data though December 2015 will be used to develop a forecast so that we can evaluate it against actual data for the four quarters of 2016.

---

[3] Throughout this chapter, you may find some situations in which the standard calculations that we show do not match exactly with the ForecastX results. This is because, at times, they invoke proprietary alterations from the standard calculations. The results are usually very close but may not match perfectly with "hand" calculations or those done in Excel.

**TABLE 4.2**
**Disposable Personal Income In Billions Of Dollars. Quarterly From 2010 Through 2016** (c4t2&f2)

| Date | DPI (B$) | Time Index |
|---|---|---|
| Mar-10 | 11,041 | 1 |
| Jun-10 | 11,198 | 2 |
| Sep-10 | 11,287 | 3 |
| Dec-10 | 11,426 | 4 |
| Mar-11 | 11,652 | 5 |
| Jun-11 | 11,752 | 6 |
| Sep-11 | 11,877 | 7 |
| Dec-11 | 11,925 | 8 |
| Mar-12 | 12,190 | 9 |
| Jun-12 | 12,321 | 10 |
| Sep-12 | 12,355 | 11 |
| Dec-12 | 12,748 | 12 |
| Mar-13 | 12,259 | 13 |
| Jun-13 | 12,336 | 14 |
| Sep-13 | 12,454 | 15 |
| Dec-13 | 12,534 | 16 |
| Mar-14 | 12,736 | 17 |
| Jun-14 | 12,962 | 18 |
| Sep-14 | 13,127 | 19 |
| Dec-14 | 13,265 | 20 |
| Mar-15 | 13,277 | 21 |
| Jun-15 | 13,465 | 22 |
| Sep-15 | 13,612 | 23 |
| Dec-15 | 13,726 | 24 |
| Mar-16 | 13,807 | 25 |
| Jun-16 | 13,977 | 26 |
| Sep-16 | 14,129 | 27 |
| Dec-16 | 14,270 | 28 |

Disposable personal income is an important economic series, since income is an important determinant for many kinds of sales. The linear time-trend model for DPI is:

$$\widehat{DPI} = b_0 + b_1(T)$$

You see in Table 4.2 that $T$ (time) equals 1 for the first quarter of 2010 and 28 for the fourth quarter of 2016.

It is usually a good idea to look at data such as those given in Table 4.2 in graphic form before beginning to do any regression analysis. A visual inspection of the data can be helpful in deciding whether a linear or nonlinear model would be most appropriate. A graph of DPI versus $T$ is shown in Figure 4.2. From this graph, you can get a good feel for how this important measure of income has increased over the period presented. All observations do not fall on a single straight line. However, it does appear that a linear trend line would fit the data well. The positive trend to DPI is more easily seen in the graphic form of Figure 4.2 than in the tabular form of Table 4.2.

**FIGURE 4.2**

**Graph of Disposable Personal Income (DPI) Over Time**

While DPI Does not Follow A Perfectly Linear Path, it Does Follow a Trend That is Very Close to Linear.   (c4t2&f2)

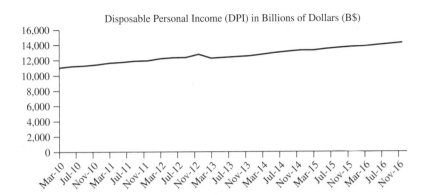

Disposable Personal Income (DPI) in Billions of Dollars (B$)

Suppose that you are asked to forecast DPI for the four quarters of 2016, using a simple linear trend, based only on data from 2010 through 2015. The first thing you would do is to use the linear regression part of your regression software to provide the estimates of $b_0$ and $b_1$ for the following model:

$$\text{DPI} = b_0 + b_1(T)$$

The regression results from ForecastX and from Excel are shown at the bottom of Figure 4.3. From those results we see that the intercept ($b_0$) is 11,042.86 and that the coefficient for $T$ ($b_1$, or the slope) is 108.32. Thus, the regression forecast model may be written as:

$$\widehat{\text{DPI}} = 11,042.86 + 108.32\left(T\right)$$

The slope term in this model tells us that, on average, disposable personal income increased by \$108.32 billion per quarter. The other statistical results shown Table 4.3 are helpful in evaluating the usefulness of the model. Most of these will

**FIGURE 4.3   Disposable personal income (DPI) with a linear trend line forecast**   The linear trend follows the actual DPI quite well and provides a forecast for 2016 that looks very reasonable. The trend equation is: DPI = 11,042.86 + 108.32(*T*)   (c4f3)

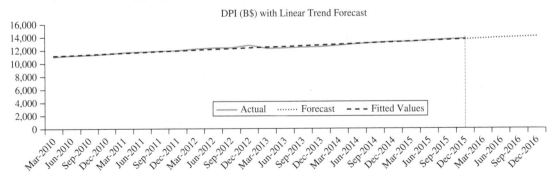

DPI (B$) with Linear Trend Forecast

**TABLE 4.3**
**Regression Trend Statistical Results from ForecastX (Audit Report).**

Audit Trail—ANOVA Table (Trend (Linear) Regression Selected)

| Source of variation | SS | df | MS | SEE | Overall F-test |
|---|---|---|---|---|---|
| Regression | 1,34,93,902.63 | 1 | 1,34,93,902.63 | | 571.28 |
| Error | 5,19,653.32 | 22 | 23,620.61 | 153.69 | |
| Total | 1,40,13,555.95 | 23 | | | |

Audit Trail—Coefficient Table (Trend (Linear) Regression Selected)

| Name | Value | Standard Error | T-test | P-value |
|---|---|---|---|---|
| Intercept | 11,042.86 | 64.76 | 170.53 | 0.00 |
| Slope | 108.32 | 4.53 | 23.90 | 0.00 |

Audit Trail—Statistics

| Accuracy Measures | Value | | Forecast Statistics | Value |
|---|---|---|---|---|
| MAPE | 0.94% | | Durbin Watson (1) | 1.03 |
| R-Square | 96.29% | | | |

| Method Statistics | Value |
|---|---|
| Method Selected | Trend (Linear) Regression |

be discussed in detail in the section "Statistical Evaluation of Regression Models" in this chapter. Our discussion of others will be held in abeyance until Chapter 5. For now, we will just comment that statistical evaluation suggests that this linear equation provides a very good fit to the data.

The results in Table 4.3 are from the ForecastX™ Audit Report (the F value has been added) when "Trend (Linear) Regression" is selected as the forecast method.

The results in Table 4.4 are from Excel. You should look carefully at Tables 4.3 and 4.4. Notice that while the organization of information is different, the results are the same.

To use this equation to make a forecast for the four quarters of 2016, we need only substitute the appropriate values for time (*T*). These are 25 through 28, as seen in Table 4.2. The trend estimates of DPI for four representative quarters follow:

$$2016 \text{ Quarter 1: DPI} = 11{,}042.86 + 108.32(25) = 13{,}750.86$$
$$2016 \text{ Quarter 2: DPI} = 11{,}042.86 + 108.32(26) = 13{,}859.18$$
$$2016 \text{ Quarter 3: DPI} = 11{,}042.86 + 108.32(27) = 13{,}967.50$$
$$2016 \text{ Quarter 4: DPI} = 11{,}042.86 + 108.32(28) = 14{,}075.82$$

**TABLE 4.4**
**Regression Trend Statistical Results from Excel.**

Regression Statistics

| | |
|---|---|
| R Square | 0.96 |
| Standard Error | 153.69 |
| Observations | 24 |

ANOVA

| | df | SS | MS | F | Significance F |
|---|---|---|---|---|---|
| Regression | 1 | 1,34,93,902.63 | 1,34,93,902.63 | 571.28 | 0.00 |
| Residual | 22 | 5,19,653.32 | 23,620.61 | | |
| Total | 23 | 1,40,13,555.95 | | | |

| | Coefficients | Standard Error | t Stat | P-value |
|---|---|---|---|---|
| Intercept | 11,042.86 | 64.76 | 170.53 | 0.00 |
| Time Index | 108.32 | 4.53 | 23.90 | 0.00 |

You can see in Figure 4.3 that the simple linear trend line does fit the actual data quite well and provides a reasonable forecast for the first four quarters of 2016. It is useful to provide a metric to evaluate the goodness of fit and accuracy of a forecast model. Goodness of fit refers to how well the model predicts values in sample (within the historic data set). Accuracy refers to how well the model works in the forecast period (here, the four quarters of 2016). We will use the MAPE as the metric.

In Table 4.3, you can see that the historic MAPE is 0.94 percent, indicating very low errors in the historic period (a measure of fit). This is consistent with the visual evaluation we see in Figure 4.3. The calculation of the MAPE for the holdout quarters of 2016 is shown in Table 4.5. The fit and accuracy MAPEs are the same, and less than 1 percent, suggesting that this linear regression trend forecast is quite good.

Trend models such as this can sometimes be very helpful in forecasting, and, as you see, they are easy to develop and to implement. In such models, we simply

**TABLE 4.5**
**Calculation of the MAPE for the 2016 Forecast of DPI.**

| Date | Actual | Forecast | Error | Absolute Error | Absolute % Error |
|---|---|---|---|---|---|
| Mar-2016 | 13,807.40 | 13,750.93 | 56.47 | 56.47 | 0.41 |
| Jun-2016 | 13,977.30 | 13,859.25 | 118.05 | 118.05 | 0.84 |
| Sep-2016 | 14,128.70 | 13,967.57 | 161.13 | 161.13 | 1.14 |
| Dec-2016 | 14,270.30 | 14,075.89 | 194.41 | 194.41 | 1.36 |
| | | | | MAPE = | 0.94 |

track the past time trend and project it forward for the forecast horizon of interest. Note that we do not imply any sense of causality in such a model. Time does not cause income to rise. Income has increased over time at a reasonably steady rate for reasons not explained by our model.

# USING A CAUSAL REGRESSION MODEL TO FORECAST

Trend models, such as the one we looked at in the previous section for disposable personal income, use the power of regression analysis to determine the best linear trend line. However, such uses do not exploit the full potential of this powerful statistical tool. Regression analysis is especially useful for developing causal models.

In a causal model, expressed as $Y = f(X)$, a change in the independent variable ($X$) is assumed to cause a change in the dependent variable ($Y$). The selection of an appropriate causal variable ($X$) should be based on some insight that suggests that a causal relationship is reasonable. A forecaster does not arbitrarily select an $X$ variable but rather looks to past experience and understanding to identify potential causal factors. For example, suppose that you were attempting to develop a bivariate regression model that might be helpful in explaining and predicting the level of jewelry sales in the United States. What factors do you think might have an impact on jewelry sales? Some potential causal variables that might come to mind could include income, some measure of the level of interest rates, and the unemployment rate, among others.

Discussions with knowledgeable people in the jewelry industry would help you determine other variables and would be helpful in prioritizing those that are identified. Library research in areas related to jewelry sales and to consumer behavior may turn up yet other potential $X$ variables. One thing you would learn quickly is that there is a substantial seasonal aspect to jewelry sales.

It is important that the independent variable be selected on the basis of a logical construct that relates it to the dependent variable. Otherwise, you might find a variable through an arbitrary search process that works well enough in a given historical period, more or less by accident, but then breaks down severely out of sample. Consider, for example, William Stanley Jevons' sunspot theory of business cycles. For a certain historical period, a reasonably strong correlation appeared to support such a notion. Outside that period, however, the relationship was quite weak. In this case, it is difficult to develop a strong conceptual theory tying business cycles to sunspot activity.

To illustrate the use of a causal model, we will consider how well jewelry sales (JS) can be forecast on the basis of disposable personal income, as a measure of overall purchasing power.

Before we start to develop a forecast of jewelry sales, we should take a look at a time-series plot of the series. In this example, we will use quarterly data for jewelry sales from February 2010 through November 2015, and we want to forecast JS for each of the four quarters of 2016. A time-series plot of JS is found in Figure 4.4, and the raw data are in Table 4.6.

**FIGURE 4.4**

**Jewelry Store Sales in Millions of Dollars** Here We See Clearly the Seasonality of Jewelry Sales in the Raw Data (Solid Line). the Deseasonalized Data (Dashed Line) Help us See the Upward Trend More Clearly. (c4t6&f4)

Jewelry Store Sales and Deseasonalized Values (M$)

**TABLE 4.6**

**Jewelry Store Sales in Millions of Dollars with the Deseasonalized Values and the Seasonal Indices**

| Date | Jewelry Store Sales (M$) | Deseasonalized Sales (M$) | Seasonal Indices |
|---|---|---|---|
| Feb-10 | 5,372 | 6,304.7 | 0.85 |
| May-10 | 5,841 | 6,201.2 | **0.94** |
| Aug-10 | 5,311 | 6,434.3 | 0.83 |
| Nov-10 | 9,385 | 6,797.8 | 1.38 |
| Feb-11 | 5,823 | 6,834.0 | 0.85 |
| May-11 | 6,911 | 7,337.2 | **0.94** |
| Aug-11 | 6,243 | 7,563.4 | 0.83 |
| Nov-11 | 10,073 | 7,296.1 | 1.38 |
| Feb-12 | 6,337 | 7,437.2 | 0.85 |
| May-12 | 6,772 | 7,189.6 | **0.94** |
| Aug-12 | 6,102 | 7,392.6 | 0.83 |
| Nov-12 | 10,651 | 7,714.8 | 1.38 |
| Feb-13 | 6,484 | 7,609.8 | 0.85 |
| May-13 | 7,106 | 7,544.2 | **0.94** |
| Aug-13 | 6,175 | 7,481.0 | 0.83 |
| Nov-13 | 10,686 | 7,740.1 | 1.38 |
| Feb-14 | 6,681 | 7,841.0 | 0.85 |
| May-14 | 7,397 | 7,853.2 | **0.94** |
| Aug-14 | 6,548 | 7,932.9 | 0.83 |
| Nov-14 | 10,586 | 7,667.7 | 1.38 |
| Feb-15 | 6,617 | 7,765.9 | 0.85 |
| May-15 | 7,477 | 7,938.1 | **0.94** |
| Aug-15 | 6,529 | 7,909.9 | 0.83 |
| Nov-15 | 10,882 | 7,882.1 | 1.38 |
| Feb-16 | 6,851 | 8,040.5 | 0.85 |
| May-16 | 7,648 | 8,119.6 | **0.94** |
| Aug-16 | 6,735 | 8,159.4 | 0.83 |
| Nov-16 | 11,684 | 8,463.0 | 1.38 |

In Table 4.6, the values for the four quarters of 2016 are separated. We will hold these four quarters out when we make forecasts and use them to evaluate accuracy using the MAPE for just those four quarters.

Note also that the seasonal indices repeat year after year. The May (second quarter) seasonal indices have been put in bold type to help illustrate this. For this example, the seasonal indices were calculated using time series decomposition. This method will be covered in detail in Chapter 6.

# A JEWELRY SALES FORECAST BASED ON DISPOSABLE PERSONAL INCOME

If we hypothesize that disposable personal income (DPI) is influential in determining jewelry store sales (JS), we might initially want to look at a scattergram of these two variables. This is shown in Figure 4.5, where JS is plotted on the vertical axis and DPI is on the horizontal axis. Note that the horizontal axis does not start at zero. This helps us see the data more clearly. You can see that higher values of JS appear to be associated with higher incomes.

In the top graph, you can see the effect of seasonality in a dramatic way. Look at the six values that are circled. These six points are all fourth-quarter data points due to high holiday season sales.

In the lower graph, the JS data are shown after the seasonality has been removed. In Chapter 6, you will learn how to deseasonalize data and how to find

**FIGURE 4.5**
**Scatterplots of Jewelry Store Sales (Top Graph) and Deseasonalized Jewelry Store Sales (Bottom Graph) with Disposable Personal Income.** (c4f5)

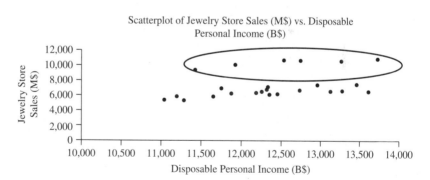

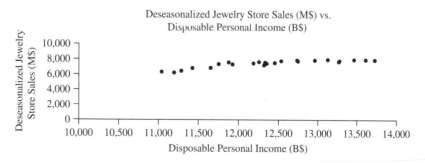

seasonal indices. In the bottom graph, you can see that a straight line through those points could provide a reasonably good fit to the data. You also can see that all of these observations are well away from the origin. If you do not look closely in the graph, you might think the observations are not so far from the vertical axis. But note that again in this case, the horizontal axis starts at 10,000, not at zero. This was done to better display the deseasonalized data points. It is important to look at graphs carefully.

The bivariate regression model for seasonally adjusted jewelry sales (which we will call SAJS) as a function of DPI may be written as:

$$SAJS = b_0 + b_1(DPI)$$

The JS data used to estimate values for $b_0$ and $b_1$ are given in Table 4.7, along with the data for DPI.

The basic regression results are shown in Figure 4.6, along with a graph of the actual and predicted values based on this model. To use this model to forecast for 2016, a Holt's exponential smoothing forecast of DPI was used. On the basis of these results, the forecast model (equation) for jewelry sales as a function of disposable personal income per capita is:

$$JS = -3,812.18 + 0.91(DPI)$$

**TABLE 4.7**
**Jewelry Sales and Disposable Personal Income**   (c4t7f6)

| Date | Jewelry Store Sales (M$) | DPI |
|---|---|---|
| Feb-10 | 5,372 | 11041.47 |
| May-10 | 5,841 | 11197.63 |
| Aug-10 | 5,311 | 11286.63 |
| Nov-10 | 9,385 | 11425.73 |
| Feb-11 | 5,823 | 11652.23 |
| May-11 | 6,911 | 11751.63 |
| Aug-11 | 6,243 | 11876.67 |
| Nov-11 | 10,073 | 11924.93 |
| Feb-12 | 6,337 | 12189.97 |
| May-12 | 6,772 | 12321.33 |
| Aug-12 | 6,102 | 12355.43 |
| Nov-12 | 10,651 | 12748.13 |
| Feb-13 | 6,484 | 12259.27 |
| May-13 | 7,106 | 12335.9 |
| Aug-13 | 6,175 | 12453.83 |
| Nov-13 | 10,686 | 12534.33 |
| Feb-14 | 6,681 | 12735.83 |
| May-14 | 7,397 | 12962.43 |
| Aug-14 | 6,548 | 13127.43 |
| Nov-14 | 10,586 | 13265.27 |
| Feb-15 | 6,617 | 13276.5 |
| May-15 | 7,477 | 13464.7 |
| Aug-15 | 6,529 | 13611.7 |
| Nov-15 | 10,882 | 13726.37 |

**FIGURE 4.6** **Jewelry Sales Forecast as a Function of DPI we See That the Upward Trend in Jewelry Sales is Accounted for by the Regression Model but the Seasonality is not Taken Into Account. Thus, for Any Given Quarter the Forecast is Likely to be Substantially Incorrect. The Quarter Represented by the December 2016 Forecast is Surely Much Too Low.** (c4t7&f6)

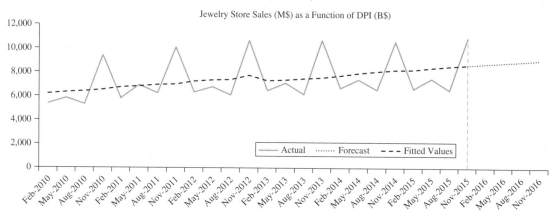

Jewelry Store Sales (M$) as a Function of DPI (B$)

### Audit Trail—Coefficient Table (Multiple Regression Selected)

|           | Coefficient | Standard error | T-test | P-value |
|-----------|-------------|----------------|--------|---------|
| Intercept | −3,812.18   | 5,766.40       | −0.66  | 0.52    |
| DPI       | 0.91        | 0.46           | 1.95   | 0.06    |

### Audit Trail - Statistics

| Accuracy  | Value   | Forecast Statistics | Value |
|-----------|---------|---------------------|-------|
| MAPE      | 17.78%  | Durbin Watson (4)   | 0.04  |
| R-Square  | 14.75%  |                     |       |

Data for 2010–2015 were used to estimate this model. The positive slope (0.91) indicates that, on average, JS increases by $0.91 million for each additional $1 billion increase in disposable personal income. A major problem with this model is apparent in Figure 4.6. It is clear from the graph of actual and predicted retail sales that this model fails to deal with the seasonality in JS.

The failure of this model to deal well with the seasonal nature of jewelry sales suggests that either we should use a model that can account for seasonality directly or we should deseasonalize the data before developing the regression forecasting model. In Chapter 3, you learned how to forecast a seasonal series with Winters' exponential smoothing. In Chapter 5, you will see how regression methods can also incorporate seasonality, and in Chapter 6, you will see how a seasonal pattern can be modeled using time-series decomposition.

We will now develop a model based on seasonally adjusted jewelry sales data (SAJS) and then reintroduce the seasonality to the forecast. To seasonally adjust jewelry sales, the following seasonal indices were used:

| | |
|---|---|
| Quarter 1 (February) | 0.85 |
| Quarter 2 (May) | 0.94 |
| Quarter 3 (August) | 0.82 |
| Quarter 4 (November) | 1.38 |

Note that the seasonal index is highest during the holiday shopping period. The index of 1.38 for quarter four indicates that sales are typically 1.38 times the quarterly average for the year. There are several ways to calculate seasonal indices. The method used here is described in Chapter 6 using time-series decomposition.[4]

The deseasonalized jewelry store sales data (SAJS) are in Table 4.8 along with DPI and the seasonal indices. (c4t8&f7)

**TABLE 4.8.**
**Deseasonalized Jewelry Sales, Disposable Personal Income, and the Seasonal Indices**

| Date | Deseasonalized Sales (M$) | DPI (B$) | Seasonal Indices |
|---|---|---|---|
| Feb-10 | 6,313.6 | 11,041.5 | 0.85 |
| May-10 | 6,202.7 | 11,197.6 | 0.94 |
| Aug-10 | 6,438.1 | 11,286.6 | 0.82 |
| Nov-10 | 6,788.4 | 11,425.7 | 1.38 |
| Feb-11 | 6,843.6 | 11,652.2 | 0.85 |
| May-11 | 7,339.0 | 11,751.6 | 0.94 |
| Aug-11 | 7,567.8 | 11,876.7 | 0.82 |
| Nov-11 | 7,286.0 | 11,924.9 | 1.38 |
| Feb-12 | 7,447.7 | 12,190.0 | 0.85 |
| May-12 | 7,191.3 | 12,321.3 | 0.94 |
| Aug-12 | 7,396.9 | 12,355.4 | 0.82 |
| Nov-12 | 7,704.1 | 12,748.1 | 1.38 |
| Feb-13 | 7,620.5 | 12,259.3 | 0.85 |
| May-13 | 7,546.0 | 12,335.9 | 0.94 |
| Aug-13 | 7,485.4 | 12,453.8 | 0.82 |
| Nov-13 | 7,729.4 | 12,534.3 | 1.38 |
| Feb-14 | 7,852.0 | 12,735.8 | 0.85 |
| May-14 | 7,855.1 | 12,962.4 | 0.94 |
| Aug-14 | 7,937.6 | 13,127.4 | 0.82 |
| Nov-14 | 7,657.1 | 13,265.3 | 1.38 |
| Feb-15 | 7,776.8 | 13,276.5 | 0.85 |
| May-15 | 7,940.0 | 13,464.7 | 0.94 |
| Aug-15 | 7,914.5 | 13,611.7 | 0.82 |
| Nov-15 | 7,871.2 | 13,726.4 | 1.38 |

[4] In ForecastX™, use the "Decomposition" forecast method. Then for "Type" select "Multiplicative" and for "Decomposed Data" select "Trend (Linear) Regression."

When we regress the seasonally adjusted values of jewelry sales (SAJS) as a function of disposable personal income using data for 2010–2015, we get the results shown at the bottom of Figure 4.7 and summarized by the following equation:

$$SAJS = 61.53 + 0.59(DPI)$$

We can substitute values of DPI into this equation to get predictions for seasonally adjusted jewelry sales (SAJS). To get DPI values for 2016, a Holt's exponential smoothing forecast was used. The results for 2016 DPI are:

| Date | DPI Forecast for 2016 |
|------|------------------------|
| Feb-16 | 13,832.2 |
| May-16 | 13,943.8 |
| Aug-16 | 14,055.5 |
| Nov-16 | 14,167.1 |

The values calculated for SAJS in 2016 from the regression equation (SAJS = 61.53 + 0.59*DPI) are plotted in Figure 4.7, along with the actual data for 2010 through 2015. During the historical period, actual values of DPI were used to calculate SAJS, while in the forecast period (2016), forecast values of DPI using Holt's exponential smoothing were used.

Multiplying SAJS by the seasonal index for each quarter, we obtain a prediction of the unadjusted jewelry sales for each quarter. This process is illustrated in Table 4.9 and graphed in Figure 4.8.

Let's summarize how this forecast was done.

1. We first found the seasonal indices using a process you will learn in Chapter 6 (although you already know a way to get seasonal indices using Winters' method).

2. We then calculated the deseasonalized (sometimes called seasonally adjusted) jewelry store sales (SAJS) by dividing the actual values by the seasonal indices.

3. The deseasonalized values were forecast using a simple regression with SAJS as a function of disposable personal income. In Figure 4.7, you see that the model fit fairly well.

4. The final forecast was found by multiplying the SAJS fitted and forecast values by the seasonal indices. This put the seasonality back into the final forecast. In Figure 4.8, you see that the process appears to have worked well.

We do have the real data for 2016, so let's use that to calculate the MAPE for the four quarters of 2016.

| Date | Actual Jewelry Store Sales | Forecast Jewelry Store Sales | Error | Absolute Error | Absolute % Error |
|------|------|------|------|------|------|
| Feb-16 | 6,851 | 7,023.49 | -172.49 | 172.49 | 2.52 |
| May-16 | 7,648 | 7,835.44 | -187.44 | 187.44 | 2.45 |
| Aug-16 | 6,735 | 6,918.56 | -183.56 | 183.56 | 2.73 |
| Nov-16 | 11,684 | 11,686.17 | -2.17 | 2.17 | 0.02 |
| | | | | MAPE = | 1.93 |

**FIGURE 4.7**   **Seasonally Adjusted Jewelry Sales as a Function of DPI**   The Upward Trend in SAJS is
Seen Clearly in This Graph. The Forecast Values Now Need to be Readjusted to Put the Seasonality Back into the
Forecast. This is Done in Table 4.8.   (C4t8&f7)

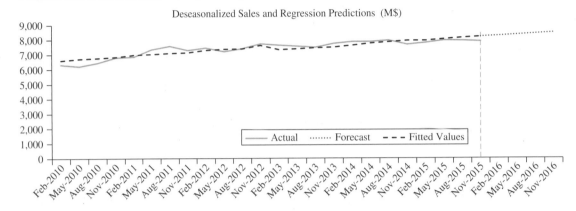

| Date | Forecast |
|------|----------|
| Feb-2016 | 8,254.53 |
| May-2016 | 8,320.64 |
| Aug-2016 | 8,386.76 |
| Nov-2016 | 8,452.88 |

**Audit Trail—ANOVA Table (Multiple Regression Selected)**

| Source | SS | df | MS | SEE | F-ratio |
|--------|-----|-----|-----|-----|---------|
| Regression | 49,16,436.99 | 1 | 49,16,436.99 | | 79.43 |
| Error | 13,61,670.56 | 22 | 61,894.12 | 248.79 | |
| Total | 62,78,107.55 | 23 | | | |

**Audit Trail—Coefficient Table (Multiple Regression Selected)**

| Series Description | Coefficient | Standard error | T-test | P-value |
|--------------------|-------------|----------------|--------|---------|
| Intercept | 61.53 | 825.44 | 0.07 | 0.94 |
| DPI (B$) | 0.59 | 0.07 | 8.91 | 0.00 |

**Audit Trail - Statistics**

| Accuracy Measures | Value | Forecast Statistics | Value |
|-------------------|-------|---------------------|-------|
| MAPE | 2.82% | Durbin Watson (1) | 0.67 |
| R-Square | 78.31% | | |

**TABLE 4.9**

**Calculation of a Final Forecast for Jewelry Store Sales** (c4t9&f8)

| Date | Fitted and Forecast SAJS | Seasonal Indices | Fitted and Forecast JS |
|---|---|---|---|
| Feb-10 | 6,601.53 | 0.85 | 5,617.02 |
| May-10 | 6,694.03 | 0.94 | 6,303.68 |
| Aug-10 | 6,746.75 | 0.82 | 5,565.65 |
| Nov-10 | 6,829.14 | 1.38 | 9,441.34 |
| Feb-11 | 6,963.30 | 0.85 | 5,924.83 |
| May-11 | 7,022.17 | 0.94 | 6,612.69 |
| Aug-11 | 7,096.23 | 0.82 | 5,853.96 |
| Nov-11 | 7,124.82 | 1.38 | 9,850.12 |
| Feb-12 | 7,281.80 | 0.85 | 6,195.84 |
| May-12 | 7,359.61 | 0.94 | 6,930.45 |
| Aug-12 | 7,379.81 | 0.82 | 6,087.89 |
| Nov-12 | 7,612.41 | 1.38 | 10,524.22 |
| Feb-13 | 7,322.85 | 0.85 | 6,230.76 |
| May-13 | 7,368.24 | 0.94 | 6,938.58 |
| Aug-13 | 7,438.09 | 0.82 | 6,135.97 |
| Nov-13 | 7,485.78 | 1.38 | 10,349.15 |
| Feb-14 | 7,605.13 | 0.85 | 6,470.94 |
| May-14 | 7,739.34 | 0.94 | 7,288.04 |
| Aug-14 | 7,837.08 | 0.82 | 6,465.11 |
| Nov-14 | 7,918.72 | 1.38 | 10,947.69 |
| Feb-15 | 7,925.37 | 0.85 | 6,743.43 |
| May-15 | 8,036.84 | 0.94 | 7,568.19 |
| Aug-15 | 8,123.91 | 0.82 | 6,701.73 |
| Nov-15 | 8,191.83 | 1.38 | 11,325.28 |
| Feb-16 | 8,254.53 | 0.85 | 7,023.49 |
| May-16 | 8,320.64 | 0.94 | 7,835.44 |
| Aug-16 | 8,386.76 | 0.82 | 6,918.56 |
| Nov-16 | 8,452.88 | 1.38 | 11,686.17 |

**FIGURE 4.8** **Jewelry Sales Final Forecast** Actual and Forecast Values are Shown in the Graph for Each Quarter from 2010 Through 2015. The Forecast Values for 2016 are Shown by the Dotted Line. (c4t9&f8)

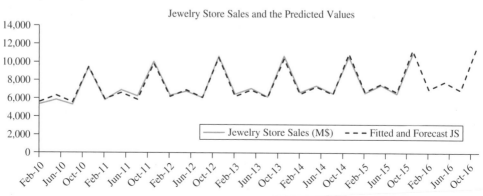

We see that the MAPE is 1.93 percent. This confirms our visual inspection of Figure 4.8, which suggests that this model does a good job of forecasting jewelry store sales.

# STATISTICAL EVALUATION OF REGRESSION MODELS

Now that you have a basic understanding of how simple bivariate regression models ($Y = fX$) can be applied to forecasting, let us look more closely at some things that should be considered in evaluating regression models. The regression model developed for the deseasonalized jewelry store sales (SAJS) as a function of disposable personal income (DPI) will be used as an example. Parts of the ForecastX Audit Report are shown in Table 4.10. The graphic result is also shown to help you remember the nature of the original SAJS data and the values predicted by the regression model.

## Basic Diagnostic Checks for Evaluating Regression Results

First, ask yourself whether the sign on the slope term makes sense.

As we progress, we will develop a five-step process for evaluating a regression model. Right now, we will consider just the first three steps, then in the "Serial Correlation" section of this chapter, we will introduce the fourth step. The fifth step will not become relevant until we get to Chapter 5.

To start with, there are several things you should consider when you look at regression results. **First**, ask yourself whether the model you estimate is **logical**. The answer to this question depends on you business/economic knowledge about the situation. There is no statistical test involved. You need to have a basic understanding of the data being analyzed. For example, if you were trying to model automobile sales in units and were asked whether you would expect sales to go up or down if the interest rate were to decline, you would surely say sales would increase. There is certainly an abundance of evidence that this is the belief within the auto industry. Otherwise, car companies would not offer zero- or low-interest financing from time to time. But consider the affect of a decline in personal income. Again your answer would be obvious: sales would decline if people have less money to spend.

We can evaluate the logic of a model by looking at the sign(s) for regression coefficient(s). If a coefficient has a negative sign, there is an inverse relationship, such as between automotive sales and the interest rate. On the other hand, a direct relationship will result in a positive coefficient, such as between auto sales and income. There is almost always an economic or business logic that indicates whether the relationship between the dependent variable ($Y$) and an independent variable ($X$) should be positive or negative.

In the example shown in Table 4.10, where seasonally adjusted jewelry sales (SAJS) are modeled as a function of disposable personal income (DPI), a positive sign is certainly logical. For *most* goods and services, sales can be expected to increase as income increases.

**TABLE 4.10**  **Basic Regression Results. Seasonally adjusted jewelry store sales as a function of disposable personal income.**

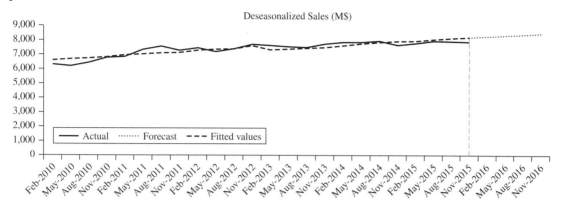

Deseasonalized Sales (M$)

Actual ······· Forecast --- Fitted values

---

Multiple Regression—Result Formula

Deseasonalized Sales (M$) = 61.53 + ((DPI (B$)) * 0.592313)

Audit Trail—ANOVA Table (Multiple Regression Selected)

| Source of variation | SS | df | MS | SEE | F-test |
|---|---|---|---|---|---|
| Regression | 49,16,436.99 | 1 | 49,16,436.99 | | 79.43 |
| Error | 13,61,670.56 | 22 | 61,894.12 | 248.79 | |
| Total | 62,78,107.55 | 23 | | | |

Audit Trail—Coefficient Table (Multiple Regression Selected)

| Series Description | Coefficient | Standard error | T-test | P-value |
|---|---|---|---|---|
| Intercept | 61.53 | 825.44 | 0.07 | 0.94 |
| DPI (B$) | 0.59 | 0.07 | 8.91 | 0.00 |

Audit Trail - Statistics

| Accuracy Measures | Value | Forecast Statistics | Value |
|---|---|---|---|
| MAPE | 2.82% | Durbin Watson (1) | 0.67 |
| R-Square | 78.31% | | |

It would not be wise to use regression models that have coefficients with signs that are not logical.

What if the signs do not make sense? This is a clear indication that something is wrong with the regression model. It may be that the model is incomplete and that more than one independent variable is needed. In such a case, the model is said to be **_underspecified_**. If so, a multiple-regression model may be appropriate. (Such models will be discussed in Chapter 5.) It would not be wise to use regression models that have coefficients with signs that are not logical.

The second thing that should be considered in an initial evaluation of a model is whether or not the slope term is significantly positive or negative.

The **second** thing that should be considered in an initial evaluation of a regression model is **whether or not the slope term is significantly positive or negative**. If not, then there is probably no statistical relationship between the dependent and independent variables. If the slope is zero, the regression line is perfectly horizontal, indicating that the value of $Y$ is independent of the value of $X$ (i.e., there is probably no relationship between $X$ and $Y$).

But how far from zero need the slope term be? If $Y = 100 + 25X$, is the slope (25) significantly positive? What if $Y = 10 + 0.025X$? Is the slope (0.025) significantly positive? Actually. there is no way to tell from just that information. The size of the slope is dependent on how the data are scaled. In our jewelry store sales examples, we used disposable personal income in billions of dollars. If we had used the income data in trillions of dollars, the slope term in the regression would have been larger. Because 1,500 billion is 1.5 trillion, the slope using billions would be smaller than the slope using trillions. The resulting predictions, however, would be the same either way income is measured. To determine if the slope is significantly greater or less than zero, we must test a hypothesis concerning the true slope. Remember that our basic regression model is:

$$Y = \beta_0 + \beta_1 X + \varepsilon$$

If $\beta_1 = 0$, then $Y = \beta_0$ regardless of the value of $X$.

When we have a predisposition about whether the coefficient should be positive or negative based on our knowledge of the relationship, a one-tailed hypothesis test is appropriate. If our belief suggests a positive coefficient, the hypothesis would be set up as follows:

$$H_0 : \beta \leq 0$$
$$H_1 : \beta > 0$$

This form would be correct for the case in Table 4.10, since a direct (positive) relationship is expected.

When our belief suggests a negative coefficient, the hypothesis would be set up as follows:

$$H_0 : \beta \geq 0$$
$$H_1 : \beta < 0$$

This form would be correct when an inverse (negative) relationship is expected.

In some situations, we may not have a specific expectation about the direction of causality, in which case a two-tailed hypothesis test is used. The hypothesis would be set up as follows:

$$H_0 : \beta = 0$$
$$H_1 : \beta = 0$$

The appropriate statistical test is a *t*-test, where the calculated value of *t* ($t_{calc}$) is equal to the slope term minus zero, divided by the standard error of the slope.[5] That is:

$$t_{calc} = (b_1 - 0) / (s.e. \ of b_1)$$

It is typical to use a 95 percent confidence level (an $\alpha$, or significance level, of 5 percent) in testing this type of hypothesis. The appropriate number of degrees of freedom in bivariate regression is always $n - 2$, where $n$ is the number of observations used in estimating the model. As described above, when we have a greater-than or less-than sign in the alternative hypothesis, a one-tailed test is appropriate.

For our present example, there are 22 degrees of freedom (24 − 2). From the *t*-table on page 66, we find the critical value of *t* (such that 0.05 is in one tail) to be 1.717. The calculated value of *t* is:

---

**For the SAJS = *f*(DPI)**
**Causal Model**

$t_{calc} = (0.59 - 0)/0.07$

$= 8.91$

---

The *t*-value shown here is from Table 4.10. If you do this calculation by hand, the results may differ from the value shown here and in Table 4.10 due to rounding.

For our example, the calculated value is larger (more positive) than the critical, or table, value, so we can reject $H_0$ and conclude that the regression coefficient is significantly greater than zero. If this statistical evaluation of the coefficients in a regression analysis results in failure to reject the null hypothesis, then it is probably not wise to use the model as a forecasting tool.[6] However, it is not uncommon to relax the criterion for evaluation of the hypothesis test to a 90 percent confidence level (a 10 percent significance level).

In determining whether or not to reject $H_0$, an alternative to comparing *t*-values is to consider the significance level (often called the *P*-value) given in most computer output. Let us assume that we desire a 95 percent confidence level. This is the equivalent of saying that we desire a 5 percent significance level.[7]

---

[5] The standard error of the estimated regression coefficient measures the sampling variability of $b_1$ about its expected value $\beta_1$, the true population parameter.

[6] A phenomenon known as *serial correlation* (which we will discuss shortly) may cause coefficients to appear significantly different from zero (as measured by the t-test) when in fact they are not.

[7] Remember that the confidence level and the significance level add to 1. Thus, if we know one of these, we can easily determine the other.

The third check of regression results is to evaluate what percent of the variation (i.e., up-and-down movement) in the dependent variable is explained by variation in the independent variable.

For a two-tailed hypothesis test ($H_1$: $\beta_1 \neq 0$), we can then reject $H_0$ if the reported two-tailed significance level[8] in the output is less than 0.05. For a one-tailed hypothesis test ($H_1$: $\beta_1 < 0$ or $H_1$: $\beta_1 > 0$), we can reject $H_0$ if one-half of the reported two-tailed significance level is less than 0.05.

In our example in Table 4.10, the two-tailed significance level associated with the calculated $t$-ratio is 0.00. Clearly, one-half of 0.00 is less than 0.05, so it is appropriate to reject $H_0$. Note that we reach the same conclusion whether we evaluate a hypotheses by comparing the calculated and table $t$-ratios or by looking at the significance level.

The **third** check of regression results is to evaluate **what percent of the variation** (i.e., up-and-down movement) **in the dependent variable is explained by variation in the independent variable.** This is evaluated by interpreting the $R$-squared value that is reported in regression output. $R$-squared is the **coefficient of determination,** which tells us the fraction of the variation in the dependent variable that is explained by variation in the independent variable. Thus, $R$-squared can range between zero and one. Zero would indicate no explanatory power, while one would indicate that all of the variation in $Y$ is explained by the variation in $X$. (A related statistic, adjusted $R$-squared, will be discussed in Chapter 5.)

The model for seasonally adjusted jewelry sales as a function of DPI has an $R$-squared of .7831. Thus, variations in the DPI explain 78.31 percent of the variation in seasonally adjusted jewelry sales.

It is possible to perform a statistical test to determine whether the coefficient of determination ($R^2$) is significantly different from zero. The hypothesis test may be stated as:

$$H_0 : R^2 = 0$$
$$H_1 : R^2 \neq 0$$

The appropriate statistical test is an $F$-test, which will be presented in Chapter 5. With bivariate regression, it turns out that the $t$-test for the slope term in the regression equation is equivalent to the $F$-test for $R$-squared. Thus, we will wait until we explore multiple-regression models to discuss the application of the $F$-test. But you might note that if you square the t-ratio in our example, you get the $F$-ratio that is reported (you may get a slightly different answer due to rounding).

Before considering other statistical diagnostics, let us summarize these three initial evaluative steps for bivariate regression models:

1. **Logic**: Ask whether the sign for the slope term makes sense.

2. **Statistical significance**: Check to see whether the slope term is statistically positive or negative at the desired significance level by using a $t$-test.

3. **Explanatory power**: Evaluate how much of the variation in the dependent variable is explained by the regression model using the $R$-squared ($R^2$) value.

These three items can be evaluated from the results presented in standard computer output, such as shown in Table 4.10.

[8] In ForecastX™, as well as most other statistical packages, two-tailed significance levels are reported. These are frequently referred to as *P-values*, as is the case in ForecastX™.

# USING THE STANDARD ERROR OF THE ESTIMATE

The forecasts we made in the preceding pages—using a simple linear trend model and the two causal regression models—were point estimates. In each case, we substituted a value for the independent variable into the regression equation to obtain a single number representing our best estimate (forecast) of the dependent variable. It is sometimes useful to provide an interval estimate rather than a point estimate.

The standard error of the estimate (SEE) can be used to generate *approximate* confidence intervals with relative ease. The SEE is often also called the *standard error of the regression.* The confidence intervals we present here are approximate because the true confidence band is not parallel to the regression line but rather bows away from the regression line at values of *Y* and *X* far from the means. This is illustrated in Figure 4.9. The approximate 95 percent confidence interval can be calculated as follows:[9]

$$\text{Point estimate} \pm 2 \text{ (standard error of the estimate)}$$

The value of 2 is used as an easy approximation for the correct *t*-value. Recall that if there are a large number of degrees of freedom, $t = 1.96$.

Representative calculations of approximate 95 percent confidence bands for the regression forecasts developed for seasonally adjusted jewelry sales (SAJS)

**FIGURE 4.9    Confidence Bands Around a Regression Line**    The true Confidence Band Bows away From the Regression Line. An Approximate 95 Percent Confidence Band can be Calculated by Taking the Point Estimate for Each *X*, Plus or Minus 2 Times the Standard Error of the Estimate.

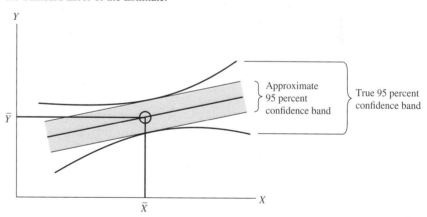

[9] The true 95 percent confidence band for predicting *Y* for a given value of *X* ($X_0$) can be found as follows:

$$\hat{Y} \pm t(\text{SEE}) \sqrt{1 + (1/n) + [(X_0 + \overline{X})^2/\Sigma(X - \overline{X})^2]}$$

where *t* is the appropriate value from the *t*-distribution at $n - 2$ degrees of freedom and the desired significance level, SEE is the standard error of the estimate, and $\hat{Y}$ is the point estimate determined from the estimated regression equation.

**TABLE 4.11**
Representative
Calculations of
Approximate 95
Percent Confidence
Intervals: Point
Estimate ±2 ×
Standard Error of
the Estimate (SEE).
The SEE is taken
from the ANOVA
part of Figure 4.7.

| | For SAJS: 2 × SEE = 2 × 248.79 = 497.58 | |
|---|---|---|
| **Period** | **95 Percent Confidence Interval** | **Actual SAJS†** |
| February 2015 | 7,925.37 ± 497.58 = 7,427.79 to 8,422.95 | 7,776.8 |
| May 2015 | 8,036.84 ± 497.58 = 7,539.26 to 8,534.42 | 7,940.0 |
| August 2015 | 8,123.91 ± 497.58 = 7,626.33 to 8,621.49 | 7,914.5 |
| November 2015 | 8,191.83 ± 497.58 = 7,694.25 to 8,689.41 | 7,871.2 |

† Note that this is for jewelry sales seasonally adjusted.

are shown in Table 4.11. The standard errors of the regressions are taken from Table 4.10, while the point estimates for each model and each quarter are those that were found in the "Using a Causal Regression Model to Forecast" section. Figure 4.10 shows the original SAJS along with the point estimates and the upper and lower bounds of the approximate 95 percent confidence interval. All of the actual SAJS data happen to fall within 95 percent confidence bounds in this case, although the May 2010 and August 2011 values are close to the lower and upper bounds, respectively. It would not be uncommon for a few actual values to fall outside of the 95 percent confidence bands. A 90 percent confidence band would be more narrow, and there would be a higher likelihood of values falling outside.

**FIGURE 4.10** The 95% Confidnce Interval for SAJS. Seasonally Adjusted Jewelry Store Sales, Predicted Values from the Regression Model and 95% Confidence Bands.

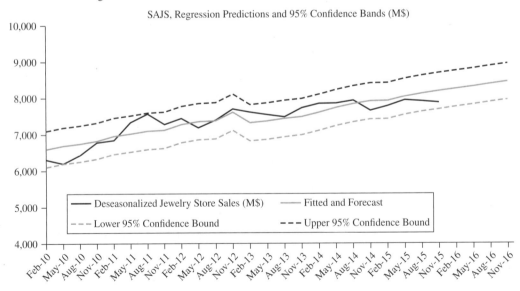

# SERIAL CORRELATION

Business and economic data used in forecasting are most often time-series data. The disposable personal income data and the jewelry store sales data used in this chapter are typical of such time series. In using regression analysis with time-series data, the problem known as *serial correlation* can cause some difficulty.

One of the assumptions of the ordinary least-squares regression model is that the error terms are independent and normally distributed, with a mean of zero and a constant variance. If this is true for a particular case, we would not expect to find any regular pattern in the error terms. When a significant time pattern in the error terms occurs, it violates the independence assumption, and therefore serial correlation is a potential problem.

Figure 4.11 illustrates the two possible cases of serial correlation. In the left-hand graph, the case of negative serial correlation is apparent. Negative serial correlation exists when a negative error is followed by a positive error, then another negative error, and so on. The error terms alternate in sign. Positive serial correlation is shown in the right-hand graph in Figure 4.11. In positive serial correlation, positive errors tend to be followed by other positive errors, while negative errors are followed by other negative errors.

When serial correlation exists, problems can develop in using and interpreting the OLS regression function. The existence of **serial correlation does not bias the coefficients** that are estimated, but it **does make the estimates of the standard errors smaller** than the true standard errors. This means that the *t*-ratios **calculated for each coefficient will be overstated**, which in turn may lead to the rejection of null hypotheses that should not have been rejected. That is, regression coefficients may be deemed statistically significant when indeed they are not. In addition, the existence of serial correlation causes the $R$-squared and $F$-statistics

**FIGURE 4.11** **Negative and Positive Serial Correlation**  The Left-Hand Graph Shows an Example of Negative Serial Correlation; the Right-Hand Graph Illustrates Positive Serial Correlation. The Latter is Common When Dealing with Business Data.

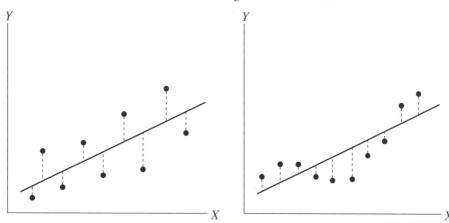

to be unreliable in evaluating the overall significance of the regression function (the *F*-statistic will be discussed in Chapter 5).

There are a number of ways to test statistically for the existence of serial correlation. The method most frequently used is the evaluation of the Durbin-Watson statistic (DW). This statistic is calculated as follows:

$$DW = \frac{\Sigma(e_t - e_{t-1})^2}{\Sigma e_t^2}$$

where $e_t$ is the residual for the time period *t*, and $e_{t-1}$ is the residual for the preceding time period ($t - 1$). Almost all computer programs for regression analysis include the Durbin-Watson statistic, so you are not likely to have to calculate it directly. Excel is an exception to this. Therefore, in Excel one needs to do the calculations from the residuals that are provided when requested.

The DW statistic will always be in the range of 0 to 4. As a rule of thumb, a value close to 2 (e.g., between 1.50 and 2.50) indicates that there is no serial correlation. When the DW statistic approaches 4, the degree of negative serial correlation increases. When positive serial correlation exists, the value of DW approaches 0.

To be more precise in evaluating the significance and meaning of the calculated DW statistic, we must refer to a Durbin-Watson table, such as Table 4.12. Note that for each number of independent variables (*k*), two columns of values labeled $d_l$ and $d_u$ are given. The values in these columns for the appropriate number of observations (*N*) are used in evaluating the calculated value of DW according to the criteria shown in Figure 4.12.

To illustrate, let us consider the simple regression for seasonally adjusted jewelry sales as a function of disposable personal income (DPI). From Table 4.10 (see page 179), you see that the calculated Durbin-Watson statistic is 0.67. This value is well below 2 and relatively close to zero. Therefore, without doing a formal evaluation, we would suspect positive serial correlation could be a problem. However, it is always wise to do the formal DW test.

Using Table 4.12, we find for $k = 1$ and $N = 24$ that:

$$d_l = 1.27$$
$$d_u = 1.45$$

Using these values and our calculated value, we can evaluate the criteria in Figure 4.12:

| Region | Comparison | Result |
|--------|-----------|--------|
| A | 4 > 0.67 > (4 − 1.27) | False |
| B | (4 − 1.27) > 0.67 > (4 − 1.45) | False |
| C | (4 − 1.69) > 0.67 > 1.69 | False |
| D | 1.69 > 0.67 > 1.45 | False |
| E | 1.27 > 0.67 > 0 | True |

**TABLE 4.12**
**The Durbin-Watson Statistic**

| N | $k=1$ $d_l$ | $d_u$ | $k=2$ $d_l$ | $d_u$ | $k=3$ $d_l$ | $d_u$ | $k=4$ $d_l$ | $d_u$ | $k=5$ $d_l$ | $d_u$ |
|---|---|---|---|---|---|---|---|---|---|---|
| 15 | 1.08 | 1.36 | 0.95 | 1.54 | 0.82 | 1.75 | 0.69 | 1.97 | 0.56 | 2.21 |
| 16 | 1.10 | 1.37 | 0.98 | 1.54 | 0.86 | 1.73 | 0.74 | 1.93 | 0.62 | 2.15 |
| 17 | 1.13 | 1.38 | 1.02 | 1.54 | 0.90 | 1.71 | 0.78 | 1.90 | 0.67 | 2.10 |
| 18 | 1.16 | 1.39 | 1.05 | 1.53 | 0.93 | 1.69 | 0.82 | 1.87 | 0.71 | 2.06 |
| 19 | 1.18 | 1.40 | 1.08 | 1.53 | 0.97 | 1.68 | 0.86 | 1.85 | 0.75 | 2.02 |
| 20 | 1.20 | 1.41 | 1.10 | 1.54 | 1.00 | 1.68 | 0.90 | 1.83 | 0.79 | 1.99 |
| 21 | 1.22 | 1.42 | 1.13 | 1.54 | 1.03 | 1.67 | 0.93 | 1.81 | 0.83 | 1.96 |
| 22 | 1.24 | 1.43 | 1.15 | 1.54 | 1.05 | 1.66 | 0.96 | 1.80 | 0.86 | 1.94 |
| 23 | 1.26 | 1.44 | 1.17 | 1.54 | 1.08 | 1.66 | 0.99 | 1.79 | 0.90 | 1.92 |
| 24 | 1.27 | 1.45 | 1.19 | 1.55 | 1.10 | 1.66 | 1.01 | 1.78 | 0.93 | 1.90 |
| 25 | 1.29 | 1.45 | 1.21 | 1.55 | 1.12 | 1.66 | 1.04 | 1.77 | 0.95 | 1.89 |
| 26 | 1.30 | 1.46 | 1.22 | 1.55 | 1.14 | 1.65 | 1.06 | 1.76 | 0.98 | 1.88 |
| 27 | 1.32 | 1.47 | 1.24 | 1.56 | 1.16 | 1.65 | 1.08 | 1.76 | 1.01 | 1.86 |
| 28 | 1.33 | 1.48 | 1.26 | 1.56 | 1.18 | 1.65 | 1.10 | 1.75 | 1.03 | 1.85 |
| 29 | 1.34 | 1.48 | 1.27 | 1.56 | 1.20 | 1.65 | 1.12 | 1.74 | 1.05 | 1.84 |
| 30 | 1.35 | 1.49 | 1.28 | 1.57 | 1.21 | 1.65 | 1.14 | 1.74 | 1.07 | 1.83 |
| 31 | 1.36 | 1.50 | 1.30 | 1.57 | 1.23 | 1.65 | 1.16 | 1.74 | 1.09 | 1.83 |
| 32 | 1.37 | 1.50 | 1.31 | 1.57 | 1.24 | 1.65 | 1.18 | 1.73 | 1.11 | 1.82 |
| 33 | 1.38 | 1.51 | 1.32 | 1.58 | 1.26 | 1.65 | 1.19 | 1.73 | 1.13 | 1.81 |
| 34 | 1.39 | 1.51 | 1.33 | 1.58 | 1.27 | 1.65 | 1.21 | 1.73 | 1.15 | 1.81 |
| 35 | 1.40 | 1.52 | 1.34 | 1.53 | 1.28 | 1.65 | 1.22 | 1.73 | 1.16 | 1.80 |
| 36 | 1.41 | 1.52 | 1.35 | 1.59 | 1.29 | 1.65 | 1.24 | 1.73 | 1.18 | 1.80 |
| 37 | 1.42 | 1.53 | 1.36 | 1.59 | 1.31 | 1.66 | 1.25 | 1.72 | 1.19 | 1.80 |
| 38 | 1.43 | 1.54 | 1.37 | 1.59 | 1.32 | 1.66 | 1.26 | 1.72 | 1.21 | 1.79 |
| 39 | 1.43 | 1.54 | 1.38 | 1.60 | 1.33 | 1.66 | 1.27 | 1.72 | 1.22 | 1.79 |
| 40 | 1.44 | 1.54 | 1.39 | 1.60 | 1.34 | 1.66 | 1.29 | 1.72 | 1.23 | 1.79 |
| 45 | 1.48 | 1.57 | 1.43 | 1.62 | 1.38 | 1.67 | 1.34 | 1.72 | 1.29 | 1.78 |
| 50 | 1.50 | 1.59 | 1.46 | 1.63 | 1.42 | 1.67 | 1.38 | 1.72 | 1.34 | 1.77 |
| 55 | 1.53 | 1.60 | 1.49 | 1.64 | 1.45 | 1.68 | 1.41 | 1.72 | 1.38 | 1.77 |
| 60 | 1.55 | 1.62 | 1.51 | 1.65 | 1.48 | 1.69 | 1.44 | 1.73 | 1.41 | 1.77 |
| 65 | 1.57 | 1.63 | 1.54 | 1.66 | 1.50 | 1.70 | 1.47 | 1.73 | 1.44 | 1.77 |
| 70 | 1.58 | 1.64 | 1.55 | 1.67 | 1.52 | 1.70 | 1.49 | 1.74 | 1.46 | 1.77 |
| 75 | 1.60 | 1.65 | 1.57 | 1.68 | 1.54 | 1.71 | 1.51 | 1.74 | 1.49 | 1.77 |
| 80 | 1.61 | 1.66 | 1.59 | 1.69 | 1.56 | 1.72 | 1.53 | 1.74 | 1.51 | 1.77 |
| 85 | 1.62 | 1.67 | 1.60 | 1.70 | 1.57 | 1.72 | 1.55 | 1.75 | 1.52 | 1.77 |
| 90 | 1.63 | 1.68 | 1.61 | 1.70 | 1.59 | 1.73 | 1.57 | 1.75 | 1.54 | 1.78 |
| 95 | 1.64 | 1.69 | 1.62 | 1.71 | 1.60 | 1.73 | 1.58 | 1.75 | 1.56 | 1.78 |
| 100 | 1.65 | 1.69 | 1.63 | 1.72 | 1.61 | 1.74 | 1.59 | 1.76 | 1.57 | 1.78 |

$k$ = the number of independent variables; $N$ = the number of observations used in the regression.

Source: Durbin, J. and Watson, G. S., "Testing for Serial Correlation in Least Squares Regression," *Biometrika* 38, June 1951, 173.

**FIGURE 4.12** A
Schematic for
Evaluating Serial
Correlation Using
the Durbin-Watson
Statistic

$d_u$ = Upper value
of Durbin-
Watson from
Table 4.12

$d_l$ = Lower value
of Durbin-
Watson from
Table 4.12

$H_0: \rho = 0$ (i.e., no serial
correlation)

$H_1: \rho \neq 0$ (i.e., serial
correlation
exists)

| Value of Calculated Durbin-Watson | Result | Region Designator |
|---|---|---|
| 4 | | |
| | Negative serial correlation (reject $H_0$) | A |
| $4 - d_l$ | | |
| | Indeterminate | B |
| $4 - d_u$ | | |
| 2 | No serial correlation (do not reject $H_0$) | C |
| $d_u$ | | |
| | Indeterminate | D |
| $d_l$ | | |
| | Positive serial correlation (reject $H_0$) | E |
| 0 | | |

Since our result is in region E, we can conclude that positive serial correlation exists in this case. You can see evidence of this positive serial correlation if you look at Figure 4.10 (page 184) at how the regression line (fitted) is at first above, then below, then above, then below, and finally above the actual data in a recurring pattern. This is a classic case of positive serial correlation. Positive serial correlation is more common with business/economic data than is negative serial correlation.

A primary cause
of positive serial
correlation is the
existence of long-
term cycles and trends
in economic and
business data.

You might well ask: What causes positive serial correlation and what can be done about it? A primary cause of serial correlation is the existence of long-term cycles and trends in economic and business data. Such trends and cycles are likely to produce positive serial correlation. Serial correlation can also be caused by a misspecification of the model. Either leaving out one or more important variables or failing to include a nonlinear term when one is called for can be a cause.

We can try several relatively simple things to reduce serial correlation. One is to first use differences of the variables rather than the actual values when performing the regression analysis. That is, use the change in each variable from period to period in the regression. For example, we could try the following:

$$\Delta Y = b_0 + b_1(\Delta X)$$

where $\Delta$ means "change in" and is calculated as follows:

$$\Delta Y_t = Y_t - Y_{t-1}$$
$$\Delta X_t = X_t - X_{t-1}$$

This process of "first-differencing" will be seen again in Chapter 7, when we discuss ARIMA forecasting models.

Other approaches to solving the serial correlation problem often involve moving into the realm of multiple regression, where there is more than one independent variable in the regression model. For example, it may be that other causal factors account for the differences between the actual and predicted values. For example, in the jewelry sales regression, we might add the interest rate and the unemployment rate as additional independent variables.

A third, and somewhat related, approach to dealing with serial correlation is to introduce the square of an existing causal variable as another independent variable. The model might look as follows:

$$Y_t = b_0 + b_1 X_t + b_2 Y^2$$

Also, we might introduce a lag of the dependent variable as an independent variable. Such a model might look as follows:

$$Y_t = b_0 + b_1 X_t + b_2 Y_{t-1}$$

where $t$ represents the current time period and $t - 1$ represents the previous time period.

There are other procedures, based on more sophisticated statistical models, that are helpful in dealing with the problems created by serial correlation. These are typically based on an extension of the use of first differences in that they involve the use of generalized differencing to alter the basic linear regression model into one for which the error terms are independent of one another (i.e., $\rho = 0$, where $\rho$ [rho] is the correlation between successive error terms).

The basic regression model is:

$$Y_t = \beta_0 + \beta_1 X_t + \varepsilon_t$$

and since this is true for all time periods, it follows that:

$$Y_{t-1} = \beta_0 + \beta_1 X_{t-1} + \varepsilon_{t-1}$$

Multiplying the second of these equations by $\rho$ and subtracting the result from the first yields the following generalized-differencing transformed equation:

$$Y_t^* = (1 - \rho)\beta_0 + \beta_1 X_t^* + v_t$$

where:

$$Y_t^* = Y_t - \rho Y_{t-1}$$
$$X_t^* = X_t - \rho X_{t-1}$$
$$v_t = \varepsilon_t - \rho \varepsilon_{t-1}$$

It can be shown that the resulting error term, $v_t$, is independently distributed with a mean of zero and a constant variance.[10] The problem with this generalized-differencing model is that we do not know the correct value for $\rho$. Two common methods for estimating $\rho$ and the corresponding regression model are the Cochrane-Orcutt procedure and the Hildreth-Lu procedures.[11]

---

[10] Most econometrics books describe the underlying statistical theory as well as the two correction procedures we include herein. For example, see Robert S. Pindyck and Daniel L. Rubinfeld, *Econometric Models and Economic Forecasts*, 3rd ed. (New York: McGraw-Hill, 1991), pp. 137–47.

[11] While these methods help solve the serial-correlation problem, they are not often used in practice for forecasting, largely due to their added complexity and inability to produce forecasts beyond a very short time frame.

# HETEROSCEDASTICITY

One of the assumptions of regression analysis is that the error terms in the population regression ($\varepsilon i$) have a constant variance across all values of the independent variable ($X$). When this is true, the model is said to be *homoscedastic,* and if this assumption is violated, the model is termed *heteroscedastic.* With heteroscedasticity, the standard errors of the regression coefficients may be underestimated, causing the calculated $t$-ratios to be larger than they should be, which may lead us to conclude incorrectly that a variable is statistically significant. Heteroscedasticity is more common with cross-sectional data than with time-series data.

We can evaluate a regression model for heteroscedasticity by looking at a scatterplot of the residuals (on the vertical axis) versus the independent variable (on the horizontal axis). In an ideal model, the plot of the residuals would fall within a horizontal band, as shown in the top graph of Figure 4.13. This graph illustrates a residual pattern representative of homoscedasticity. A typical heteroscedastic situation is shown by the funnel-shaped pattern of residuals in the lower graph of Figure 4.13.

**FIGURE 4.13**
**Residual Patterns Indicative of Homoscedasticity (Top Graph) and Heteroscedasticity (Bottom Graph).**

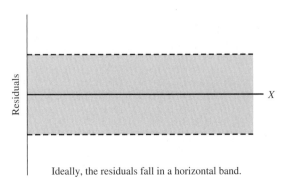

Ideally, the residuals fall in a horizontal band.

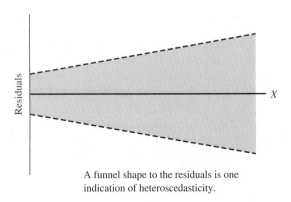

A funnel shape to the residuals is one indication of heteroscedasticity.

One common way to reduce or eliminate a problem of heteroscedasticity is to use the logarithm of the dependent variable in the estimation of the regression model. This often works because the logarithms will have less overall variability than the raw data. A second possible solution would be to use a form of regression analysis other than the ordinary least-squares method. Discussion of such methods is beyond the scope of this text but can be found in many econometric texts.

# CROSS-SECTIONAL FORECASTING

While most forecasting is based on time-series data, there are situations in which cross-sectional analysis is useful. In cross-sectional analysis, the data all pertain to one time period rather than a sequence of periods. Suppose, for example, that you are the sales manager for a firm that sells small specialty sandwiches through convenience stores. You currently operate in eight cities and are considering expanding into another. You have the data shown at the top of Table 4.13 for the most recent year's sales and the population of each city. You may try to predict sales based on population by using a bivariate regression model. The model may be written as:

$$\text{Sales} = b_0 + b_1(\text{POP})$$

Regression results for this model, given the eight data points just shown, are presented in the lower part of Table 4.13.

**TABLE 4.13**
**Regression Results for Sales as a Function of Population**

| Population (000) | Sales (000) |
| --- | --- |
| 505 | 372 |
| 351 | 275 |
| 186 | 214 |
| 175 | 135 |
| 132 | 81 |
| 115 | 144 |
| 108 | 90 |
| 79 | 97 |

| Regression Statistic | |
| --- | --- |
| $R$-Square | 0.914 |
| Standard error | 32.72 |
| Observations | 8 |

| | Coefficient | Standard Error | $T$-test | $P$-value |
| --- | --- | --- | --- | --- |
| Intercept | 37.02 | 20.86 | 1.77 | 0.126 |
| Population (000) | 0.67 | 0.08 | 8.00 | 0.000 |

The Durbin-Watson statistic is not shown because it is not relevant for cross-sectional data. Indeed, the order in which the data are placed will change the Durbin-Watson statistics.

While most forecasting is based on time-series data, there are situations in which cross-sectional analysis is useful. In cross-sectional analysis, the data all pertain to one time period rather than a sequence of periods.

The statistical results show the expected positive sign for the coefficient of population. The critical value of $t$ from the $t$-table at six degrees of freedom $(n - 2 = 6)$ and a 5 percent significance level (one-tailed test) is 1.943. Since the calculated value for population is greater $(8.005 > 1.943)$, we conclude that there is a statistically significant positive relationship between sales and population. The coefficient of determination ($R$-squared) is 0.914, which tells us that 91.4 percent of the variation in sales is explained by the variation in population.

The actual and predicted sales for each city are shown in the top graph of Figure 4.14. Visually, this graph helps you see that population size is a pretty good predictor of sales. In the lower graph of Figure 4.14, you see a scatter-gram depicting the relationship between sales (vertical axis) and population (horizontal axis).

**FIGURE 4.14**

**Sandwich Sales in Eight Cities** The Upper Graph Shows How Well Population can Help Predict Sales. In the Lower Graph You See the Relationship Between Sales and Population in a Scatter-Gram.

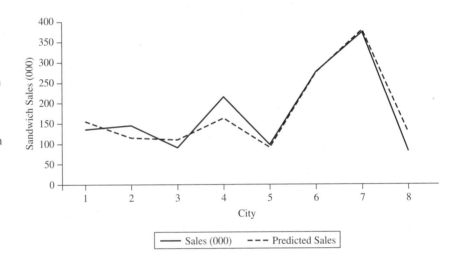

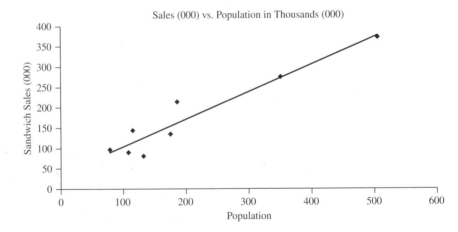

Now, suppose that the city that you are considering expanding into has a population of 155,000. You can use the regression results to forecast sales as follows:

$$\text{Sales} = 37.02 + 0.67(\text{POP})$$
$$= 37.02 + 0.67(155)$$
$$= 140.87$$

Remember that sales are in thousands, so this is a point estimate of 140,870 sandwiches. An approximate 95 percent confidence interval estimate could be constructed as follows:

$$\text{Point estimate} \pm 2(\text{standard error of regression}) = 140.870 \pm 2(32.72)$$
$$= 140.870 \pm 65.44$$
$$= 75.43 \text{ to } 206.31$$

That is, about 75,430 to 206,310 sandwiches.

# FORECASTING TOTAL HOUSES SOLD WITH TWO BIVARIATE REGRESSION MODELS

You may recall that the total houses sold (THS) series that we forecast in Chapters 1 and 3 showed quite a bit of variability, including a substantial seasonal component. Therefore, you might expect that it would be difficult to forecast such a series based on a simple regression equation with one causal variable. One thing that would make the process more workable would be to deseasonalize the THS data prior to attempting to build a regression model. In this section, we will look at THS data and on a quarterly basis using quarterly seasonal indices. The seasonal indices are shown in Table 4.14 along with the data.

In this section, we will first prepare a forecast of THS based solely on a simple linear trend; then we will do a second forecast using disposable personal income as a causal variable.

When seasonally adjusted monthly data for total houses sold (SATHS) are regressed as a function of a time index, where $t = 1$ for the first quater of 2010, the results are as shown in Figure 4.15. Data used to develop the model and forecast were from 2010 through 2015. The forecast was made 2016 on a quarterly basis. The equation for seasonally adjusted total houses sold is:

$$\text{SATHS} = 68.69 + 2.40(\text{Time})$$

The positive slope for time of 2.40 is logical, and from the $t$-ratio (11.21), we see that the slope is quite statistically significant in this model (the significance level, or $p$-value, is .000—even at a two-tailed level). The $R$-squared ($R^2$) tells us that 85.10 percent of the variation in seasonally adjusted total houses sold is explained by this model. We see that the Durbin-Watson test for serial correlation indicates positive serial correlation (DW = 1.11, where 1.11 < 1.27).

To make a forecast of SATHS for 2016 with this model, we use time index values of 25, 26. 27, and 28. Doing so gives us the the dotted portion of the straight

**TABLE 4.14** Data and Seasonal Indices for Forecasting Total Houses Sold in Thousands and the Corresponding Seasonally Adjusted Total Houses Sold (SATHS). Data for 2010 through 2015 are used to make a forecast for 2016. The trend regression results for seasonally adjusted THS are shown in Figure 4.15 along with the forecast for 2016. (c4t14&f15)

| Date | THS (000) | Seasonal Indices | SATHS (000) |
|---|---|---|---|
| Feb-10 | 87 | 0.999 | 87.091 |
| May-10 | 95 | 1.128 | 84.229 |
| Aug-10 | 74 | 0.994 | 74.477 |
| Nov-10 | 66 | 0.880 | 75.035 |
| Feb-11 | 71 | 0.999 | 71.075 |
| May-11 | 86 | 1.128 | 76.250 |
| Aug-11 | 76 | 0.994 | 76.490 |
| Nov-11 | 72 | 0.880 | 81.857 |
| Feb-12 | 87 | 0.999 | 87.091 |
| May-12 | 103 | 1.128 | 91.322 |
| Aug-12 | 94 | 0.994 | 94.606 |
| Nov-12 | 85 | 0.880 | 96.637 |
| Feb-13 | 109 | 0.999 | 109.114 |
| May-13 | 126 | 1.128 | 111.715 |
| Aug-13 | 95 | 0.994 | 95.613 |
| Nov-13 | 99 | 0.880 | 112.553 |
| Feb-14 | 107 | 0.999 | 107.112 |
| May-14 | 120 | 1.128 | 106.395 |
| Aug-14 | 108 | 0.994 | 108.696 |
| Nov-14 | 104 | 0.880 | 118.238 |
| Feb-15 | 130 | 0.999 | 130.137 |
| May-15 | 139 | 1.128 | 123.241 |
| Aug-15 | 119 | 0.994 | 119.767 |
| Nov-15 | 113 | 0.880 | 128.470 |
| | | | |
| Feb-16 | 134 | 0.999 | 134.141 |
| May-16 | 158 | 1.128 | 140.087 |
| Aug-16 | 144 | 0.994 | 144.929 |
| Nov-16 | 125 | 0.880 | 142.113 |

**FIGURE 4.15** Trend Forecast for Seasonally Adjusted Total Houses Sold (000) The Straight Line in This Graph Represents the Forecast Values. It is Dotted in the 2016 Forecast Horizon and Dashed in the Historic Period. Data From 2010 Through 2015 Were Used to Develop the Forecast. (c4t14&f15)

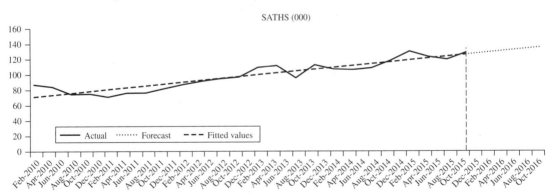

**TABLE 4.15**
**Statistical Results for the Regression Time Trend for SATHS**
(c4t14&f15)

Audit Trail—ANOVA Table (Multiple Regression Selected)

| Source of variation | SS | df | MS | SEE | F-test |
|---|---|---|---|---|---|
| Regression | 6,600.56 | 1 | 6,600.56 | | 125.60 |
| Error | 1,156.11 | 22 | 52.55 | 7.25 | |
| Total | 7,756.67 | 23 | | | |

Audit Trail— Coefficient Table (Multiple Regression Selected)

| Series Description | Coefficient | Standard error | T-test | P-value |
|---|---|---|---|---|
| Intercept | 68.69 | 3.05 | 22.49 | 0.00 |
| Time Index (T) | 2.40 | 0.21 | 11.21 | 0.00 |

Audit Trail—Statistics

| Accuracy Measures | Value | Forecast Statistics | Value |
|---|---|---|---|
| MAPE | 6.06% | Durbin Watson (1) | 1.11 |
| R-Square | 85.10% | | |

line in Figure 4.15. Below are values for the seasonally adjusted total houses sold in the four quarters of 2016.

| | |
|---|---|
| Feb-2016 | 128.54 |
| May-2016 | 130.89 |
| Aug-2016 | 133.24 |
| Nov-2016 | 135.59 |

To get the forecast of nonseasonally adjusted values we multiply the seasonally adjusted forecast values by the corresponding seasonal index for each quarter.[12] This is shown below:

| Date | SATHS Forecast | SI | THS Forecast |
|---|---|---|---|
| Feb-2016 | 128.54 | 0.999 | 128.402 |
| May-2016 | 130.89 | 1.128 | 147.625 |
| Aug-2016 | 133.24 | 0.994 | 132.386 |
| Nov-2016 | 135.59 | 0.880 | 119.264 |

[12] The seasonal indices used are from a time-series decomposition of the data using ForecastX™. This will be discussed in Chapter 6.

The MAPE for the forecast period is:

| Date | Actual 2016 THS | THS Forecast | Error | Absolute Error | Absolute % Error |
|---|---|---|---|---|---|
| Feb-2016 | 134 | 128.40 | 5.60 | 5.60 | 4.18 |
| May-2016 | 158 | 147.63 | 10.37 | 10.37 | 6.57 |
| Aug-2016 | 144 | 132.39 | 11.61 | 11.61 | 8.06 |
| Nov-2016 | 125 | 119.26 | 5.74 | 5.74 | 4.59 |
| | | | | MAPE = | 5.85% |

What are the causal factors that you think would influence the sales of houses? You might come up with a fairly long list. Some of the variables that might be on such a list are:

Income

Unemployment rate

Interest or mortgage rates

Consumer attitudes[13]

Housing prices

To develop a forecast of THS as a function of disposable personal income (DPI), the THS data were again deseasonalized; then those values were regressed as a function of DPI. These results are shown in Figure 4.16. The slope of 0.02 is logical since you would expect that more new houses would be sold as income increases. The $t$-value of 8.66 is very significant, as indicated by the two-tailed

---

[13] Consumer attitudes are often measured by the University of Michigan's Index of Consumer Sentiment. This is an index that is released each month by the University of Michigan Survey Research Center. Each month, 500 respondents in a national survey are interviewed about a variety of topics. There are five specific questions in the survey that go into the calculation of the Index of Consumer Sentiment, which has been adjusted to a base of 100 for 1966. Those five questions are:

1. We are interested in how people are getting along financially these days. Would you say that you (and your family living there) are better off or worse off financially than you were a year ago?
2. Now looking ahead—do you think that a year from now you (and your family living there) will be better off financially, or worse off, or about the same as now?
3. Now turning to business conditions in the country as a whole—do you think that during the next 12 months we'll have good times financially, or bad times, or what?
4. Looking ahead, which would you say is more likely—that in the country as a whole we'll have continuous good times during the next five years or so, or that we will have periods of widespread unemployment or depression, or what?
5. About the big things people buy for their homes—such as furniture, a refrigerator, stove, television, and things like that. Generally speaking, do you think now is a good or bad time for people to buy major household items?

The way in which the index is computed makes it higher when people's responses to these questions are more positive.

**FIGURE 4.16**  **Forecast of Seasonally Adjusted Total Houses Sold as a Function of Disposable Personal Income (DPI)**  Data for 2010 Through 2015 Were Used to Develop the Forecast. For 2016, Holt's Exponential Smoothing was Used to Forecast DPI.  (c4t16&f16)

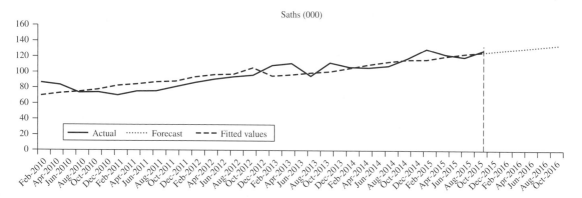

*P*-value of 0.00. The $R^2$ indicates that 77.33 percent of the variation in new houses sold is explained by this model. The equation for SATHS is:

$$\text{Seasonally adjusted total houses sold (000)} = 6.29 + 0.01(\text{DPI})$$

as shown in Figure 4.16.

The regression equation is: SATHS = $-157.85 + 0.02*(\text{DPI})$. The statistical results are in Table 4.16. In this case, the MAPE is 7.72 percent, and the explanatory

**TABLE 4.16**
**Statistical Results for the Regression of SATHS as a Function of Disposable personal Income (DPI).**  (c4t15)

Audit Trail—ANOVA Table (Multiple Regression Selected)

| Source of variation | SS | df | MS | SEE | F-test |
|---|---|---|---|---|---|
| Regression | 5,998.47 | 1 | 5,998.47 | | 75.06 |
| Error | 1,758.20 | 22 | 79.92 | 8.94 | |
| Total | 7,756.67 | 23 | | | |

Audit Trail—Coefficient Table (Multiple Regression Selected)

| Series Description | Coefficient | Standard error | T-test | P-value |
|---|---|---|---|---|
| Intercept | −157.85 | 29.66 | −5.32 | 0.00 |
| DPI (B$) | 0.02 | 0.00 | 8.66 | 0.00 |

Audit Trail—Statistics

| Accuracy Measures | Value | Forecast Statistics | Value |
|---|---|---|---|
| MAPE | 7.72% | Durbin Watson (1) | 1.09 |
| *R*-Square | 77.33% | | |

power (R2) is 77.33 percent. Again, there is positive serial correlation, as evidenced by the DW of 1.09. However, since the *t*-ratio (8.66) is so large, any bias may not be too bad.

The seasonally adjusted forecast for 2016 was then multiplied by each quarter's seasonal index to get nonseasonally adjusted forecasts. This is shown below:

| Date | 2016 SATHS Forecast | Seasonal Indices | 2016 Forecast for THS |
|---|---|---|---|
| Feb-2016 | 128.33 | 0.999 | 128.20 |
| May-2016 | 130.64 | 1.128 | 147.34 |
| Aug-2016 | 132.95 | 0.994 | 132.10 |
| Nov-2016 | 135.26 | 0.880 | 118.97 |

The MAPE for this forecast is shown below:

| Date | Actual 2016 THS | THS Forecast | Error | Absolute Error | Absolute % Error |
|---|---|---|---|---|---|
| Feb-2016 | 134 | 128.200 | 5.800 | 5.800 | 4.328 |
| May-2016 | 158 | 147.340 | 10.660 | 10.660 | 6.747 |
| Aug-2016 | 144 | 132.100 | 11.900 | 11.900 | 8.264 |
| Nov-2016 | 125 | 118.970 | 6.030 | 6.030 | 4.824 |
| | | | | MAPE = | 6.04 |

# Comments from the Field 1

While working for Dow Plastics, a business group of the Dow Chemical Company, Jan Neuenfeldt received on-the-job training while assisting others in developing forecasts. This led her to enroll in an MBA forecasting class in which she obtained formal training in quantitative forecasting methods.

The methodology that Jan uses most is regression analysis. On occasion, she also uses exponential smoothing models, such as Winters'. However, the marketing and product managers who use the forecasts usually are interested in *why* as well as in the forecast values. Most of the forecasts Jan prepares are on a quarterly basis. It is fairly typical for annual forecasts one year out to be within a 5 percent margin of error. For large-volume items in mature market segments, the annual margin for error is frequently only about 2 percent.

Each quarter, Jan reports forecast results to management, using a newsletter format. She begins with an exposition of the results, followed by the supporting statistical information and a graphic presentation of the forecast. She finds that graphics are extremely useful as she prepares forecasts, as well as when she communicates results to end users.

**Source:** This comment is based on an interview with Jan Neuenfeldt.

## Integrative Case

# The Gap

## FORECASTING THE GAP SALES DATA WITH A SIMPLE REGRESSION TREND MODEL

The sales of The Gap stores for the period covering quarter 1 of 2006 through quarter 4 of fiscal 2015 are shown in the graph below. From this graph, it is clear that The Gap sales are quite seasonal and have been reasonably flat during this period. The dashed line represents actual sales, while the solid line shows the deseasonalized sales for each quarter. April is the end month of The Gap's first quarter of its fiscal year.

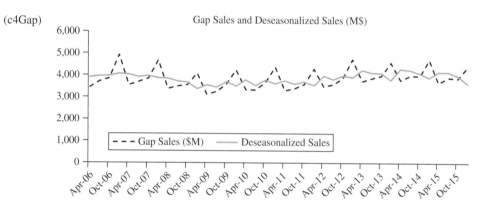

(c4Gap)

Gap Sales and Deseasonalized Sales (M$)

| Case Questions | |
|---|---|

1. Do you think that the general growth path of The Gap sales has followed a linear path over the period shown? As part of your answer, show a graph of the deseasonalized The Gap sales along with a linear trend line. What does this graph suggest to you about the results you might expect from using a linear trend as the basis of a forecast of The Gap sales for 2017? The deseasonalized sales can be calculated using the following seasonal indices:

| Seasonal Indexes | |
|---|---|
| Index 1 April | 0.88 |
| Index 2 July | 0.94 |
| Index 3 October | 0.97 |
| Index 4 January | 1.21 |

2. Use a regression of deseasonalized The Gap sales as a function of a linear regression time trend as the basis for a forecast of The Gap sales for 2017. Be sure to reseasonalize your forecast; then graph the actual The Gap sales along with your forecast. What do you think about this forecast based on your graph?

3. Calculate the MAPE for both the 2016 fiscal year using the quarterly data.

# Solutions to Case Questions

1. When The Gap sales data are deseasonalized and a linear trend is plotted through the deseasonalized series, it becomes clear that the trend in sales was essentailly stationary. This can be seen in the graph below, in which actual sales (seasonally adjusted) are graphed along with the trend line.

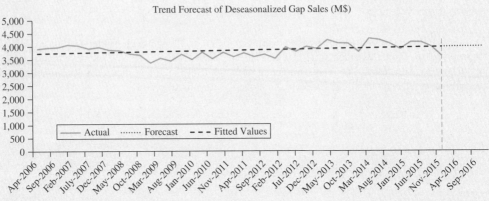

Trend Forecast of Deseasonalized Gap Sales (M$)

2. The Gap sales data were deseasonalized using the following seasonal indices: Q1 = 0.88, Q2 = 0.94, Q3 = 0.97, and Q4 = 1.21. The deseasonalized sales data for 2006Q1 through 2015Q4 were then regressed against a time index. The seasonality was then put back into the forecast. The results are shown in the following graph.

(c4Gap)

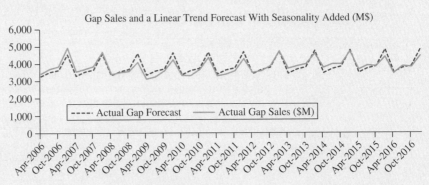

Gap Sales and a Linear Trend Forecast With Seasonality Added (M$)

3. The MAPE calculation for the forecast year (for quarters) is as follows:

| Date | Actual Gap Sales ($M) | Actual Gap Forecast (M$) | Error | Absolute Error | Absolute % Error |
|---|---|---|---|---|---|
| Apr-2016 | 3438 | 3,496.29 | -58.29 | 58.29 | 1.70 |
| Jul-2016 | 3851 | 3,740.19 | 110.81 | 110.81 | 2.88 |
| Oct-2016 | 3798 | 3,865.25 | -67.25 | 67.25 | 1.77 |
| Jan-2017 | 4429 | 4,828.69 | -399.69 | 399.69 | 9.02 |
| | | | | MAPE = | 3.84 |

# USING FORECASTX™ TO MAKE REGRESSION FORECASTS

What follows is a brief discussion of how to use ForecastX™ for making a forecast based on a regression model. This will increase your familiarity with the of use of ForecastX™. The illustration used here is for a trend forecast.

First, put your data into an Excel spreadsheet in column format, such as the sample of The Gap data shown in the table below. Once you have your data in this format, while in Excel place your cursor in any data cell such as B6. Then go to Add-ins to open ForecastX™. The following dialog box appears.

**A Sample of The Gap Data in Column Format**

| Date | Gap Sales ($M) |
|---|---|
| Apr-06 | 3441 |
| Jul-06 | 3,714 |
| Oct-06 | 3,851 |
| Jan-07 | 4,919 |
| Apr-07 | 3,549 |
| Jul-07 | 3,685 |
| Oct-07 | 3,854 |
| Jan-08 | 4,675 |
| Apr-08 | 3,384 |
| Jul-08 | 3,499 |
| Oct-08 | 3,561 |
| Jan-09 | 4,082 |
| Apr-09 | 3,127 |
| Jul-09 | 3,245 |
| Oct-09 | 3,589 |
| Jan-10 | 4,236 |
| Apr-10 | 3,329 |
| Jul-10 | 3,317 |
| Oct-10 | 3,654 |
| Jan-11 | 4,364 |
| Apr-11 | 3,295 |
| Jul-11 | 3,386 |
| Oct-11 | 3,585 |
| Jan-12 | 4,283 |
| Apr-12 | 3,487 |
| Jul-12 | 3,575 |
| Oct-12 | 3,864 |

Source: John Galt Solutions

Verify the periodicity of your data (**Quarterly** for this example); then click the **Forecast Method** tab at the top. Click the down arrow in the **Forecasting Technique** window, and select **Trend (Linear) Regression.** The following window will result. In the terminology used by ForecastX™, *linear regression* refers to a method that makes a regression trend forecast. If you want to develop a causal regression model, select **Multiple Regression.** (See the "Further Comments on Regression Models" section on page 210.)

After selecting **Trend (Linear) Regression,** the dialog box will then look like the one below.

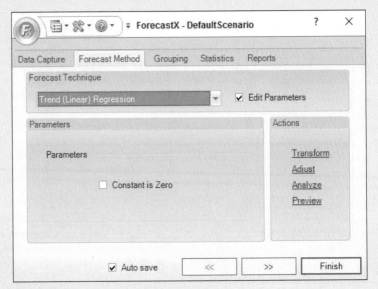

Source: John Galt Solutions

Now you are ready to click the **Statistics** tab, which will take you to the next dialog box.

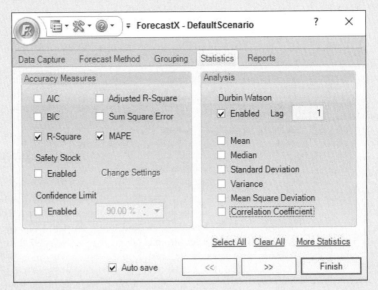

Source: John Galt Solutions

Here you want to select the desired statistics. Often the ones selected in this example would be what you would want for simple regression models.

In addition, you will want to click the **More Statistics** button at the bottom and check the box for **P-value** (in **Coeff table**) under the **Regression** tab. Look at the other tabs in this box and select desired statistics. Then click **OK** and you return to the **Statistics** box.

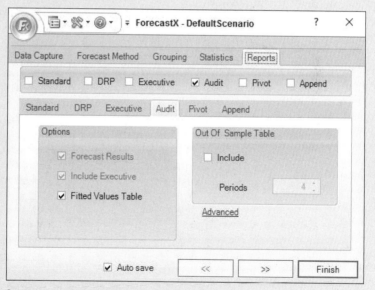

Source: John Galt Solutions

Next click the **Reports** tab to get the **Reports** dialog box. This is where you select the particular reports and report contents that you want. Some exploration and experimentation with these options will help you see what each option leads to in terms of results. Clicking on the Audit report yields the following:

Source: John Galt Solutions

After you click **Finish** in the lower right corner, reports will be put in new Excel workbooks—Book 2, Book 3, and so forth. The book numbers will vary depending on what you have been doing in Excel up to that point.

# FURTHER COMMENTS ON USING FORECASTX™ TO DEVELOP REGRESSION MODELS

## Causal Models

To do a *causal regression model* and forecast, select the data sheet with dates in column A, the dependent variable in column B, and independent variables in columns C, D, E, etc. In our example here, we will use jewelry store sales as a function of only one independent variable, disposable personal income (DPI). In Chapter 5, we will expand to more independent variables.

Place your cursor in a cell with data for the dependent variable, such as cell B4. Then go to Add-ins to open ForecastX™. You will get the following dialog box:

**A sample of jewelry store sales data and DPI follows:**

| Date | Jewelry Store Sales (M$) | DPI |
|------|------|------|
| Feb-10 | 5,372 | 11041.47 |
| May-10 | 5,841 | 11197.63 |
| Aug-10 | 5,311 | 11286.63 |
| Nov-10 | 9,385 | 11425.73 |
| Feb-11 | 5,823 | 11652.23 |
| May-11 | 6,911 | 11751.63 |
| Aug-11 | 6,243 | 11876.67 |
| Nov-11 | 10,073 | 11924.93 |
| Feb-12 | 6,337 | 12189.97 |
| May-12 | 6,772 | 12321.33 |
| Aug-12 | 6,102 | 12355.43 |
| Nov-12 | 10,651 | 12748.13 |
| Feb-13 | 6,484 | 12259.27 |
| May-13 | 7,106 | 12335.9 |
| Aug-13 | 6,175 | 12453.83 |
| Nov-13 | 10,686 | 12534.33 |
| Feb-14 | 6,681 | 12735.83 |
| May-14 | 7,397 | 12962.43 |
| Aug-14 | 6,548 | 13127.43 |
| Nov-14 | 10,586 | 13265.27 |

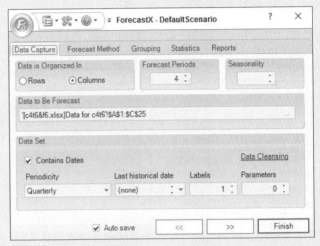

Source: John Galt Solutions

In the **Data Capture** tab of the **Data Capture** window, look at the default selection. If it is not what you want, click inside the **Data To Be Forecast** window to the right of the **Data to Be Forecast** box. In the following window, select the data columns you want, then click **OK**.

Source: John Galt Solutions

Next click the **Forecast Method** tab and select **Multiple Regression** in the **Forecasting Technique** window. Under parameters, in the **Dependent Series** window select the variable you want to forecast (**Jewelry Store Sales** in this example).

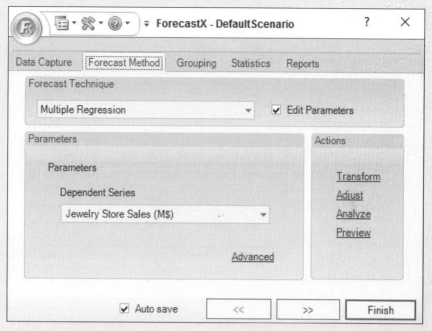

Source: John Galt Solutions

From this point on, you follow the same selections as described above for regression trend forecasts.

You are probably wondering how you forecast the independent variable into the future and unknown forecast horizon. You can use any acceptable method to do this, but ForecastX[TM] makes it easy by doing an automated forecast using a procedure called ProCast[TM].

## Deseasonalizing Data

The following is a summary of how to deseasonalize data in ForecastX[TM]. We use a method called *decomposition* (this method of forecasting will be discussed in detail in Chapter 6). For now, we will simply look at the portion of the method and results that we need to take the seasonality out of a data series.

Begin by opening your data file in Excel with dates in column A and the data to be deseasonalized in column B. Place your curor in a data cell such as B5. Then start the ForecastX[TM] software. The Data Capture screen will look like the following (just check to be sure everything is correct; it is almost always correct):

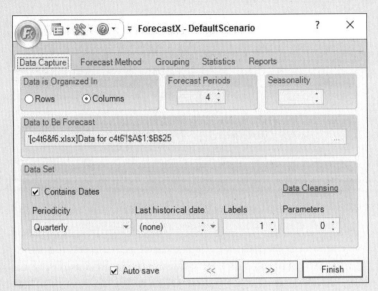

Source: John Galt Solutions

In the **Forecast Method** dialog box, select **Decomposition** as the **Forecasting Technique,** check **Multiplicative,** and select **Trend (Linear) Regression** as the **Forecast Method for Decomposed Data.**

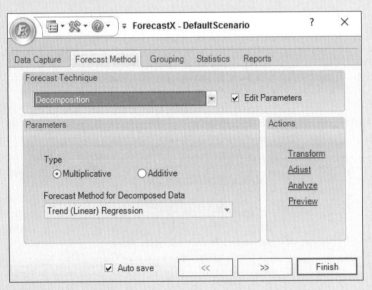

Source: John Galt Solutions

For this application, we do not care about statistics, so skip that tab. Click the **Reports** tab, and select only the **Audit** report. There is no need now to ask for the Fitted Values Table.

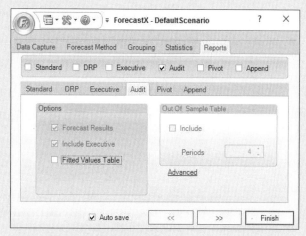

Source: John Galt Solutions

Now click **Finish,** and you will get results that will include the following near the bottom of the page:

## Components of Decomposition

| Date | Original Data | Forecasted Data | Centered Moving Average | CMA Trend | Seasonal Indices | Cycle Factors |
|------|---------------|-----------------|-------------------------|-----------|------------------|---------------|
| Feb-2010 | 5,372.00 | | | | 0.85 | |
| May-2010 | 5,841.00 | | | | 0.94 | |
| Aug-2010 | 5,311.00 | 5,389.84 | 6,533.63 | 6,913.58 | 0.82 | 0.95 |
| Nov-2010 | 9,385.00 | 9,295.64 | 6,723.75 | 6,971.31 | 1.38 | 0.96 |
| Feb-2011 | 5,823.00 | 5,933.94 | 6,974.00 | 7,029.04 | 0.85 | 0.99 |
| May-2011 | 6,911.00 | 6,758.02 | 7,176.50 | 7,086.76 | 0.94 | 1.01 |
| Aug-2011 | 6,243.00 | 6,044.12 | 7,326.75 | 7,144.49 | 0.82 | 1.03 |
| Nov-2011 | 10,073.00 | 10,194.10 | 7,373.63 | 7,202.22 | 1.38 | 1.02 |
| Feb-2012 | 6,337.00 | 6,244.19 | 7,338.63 | 7,259.94 | 0.85 | 1.01 |
| May-2012 | 6,772.00 | 6,962.13 | 7,393.25 | 7,317.67 | 0.94 | 1.01 |
| Aug-2012 | 6,102.00 | 6,173.74 | 7,483.88 | 7,375.40 | 0.82 | 1.01 |
| Nov-2012 | 10,651.00 | 10,429.64 | 7,544.00 | 7,433.12 | 1.38 | 1.01 |
| Feb-2013 | 6,484.00 | 6,462.22 | 7,594.88 | 7,490.85 | 0.85 | 1.01 |
| May-2013 | 7,106.00 | 7,164.71 | 7,608.38 | 7,548.58 | 0.94 | 1.01 |
| Aug-2013 | 6,175.00 | 6,300.37 | 7,637.38 | 7,606.30 | 0.82 | 1.00 |
| Nov-2013 | 10,686.00 | 10,643.07 | 7,698.38 | 7,664.03 | 1.38 | 1.00 |
| Feb-2014 | 6,681.00 | 6,620.91 | 7,781.38 | 7,721.76 | 0.85 | 1.01 |
| May-2014 | 7,397.00 | 7,359.75 | 7,815.50 | 7,779.48 | 0.94 | 1.00 |
| Aug-2014 | 6,548.00 | 6,430.40 | 7,795.00 | 7,837.21 | 0.82 | 0.99 |
| Nov-2014 | 10,586.00 | 10,779.42 | 7,797.00 | 7,894.94 | 1.38 | 0.99 |
| Feb-2015 | 6,617.00 | 6,640.69 | 7,804.63 | 7,952.66 | 0.85 | 0.98 |
| May-2015 | 7,477.00 | 7,382.12 | 7,839.25 | 8,010.39 | 0.94 | 0.98 |
| Aug-2015 | 6,529.00 | 6,559.58 | | 8,068.12 | 0.82 | 0.99 |
| Nov-2015 | 10,882.00 | 11,046.36 | | 8,125.84 | 1.38 | 0.98 |

The "Seasonal Indices" column heading is in bold here but will not be in bold in your output. These are the indices that you will use to deseasonalize the original data and to reseasonalize results. You should copy this column of seasonal indices and paste it into your Excel workbook along with your original data.

You can now calculate a deseasonalized series by dividing the original data by the seasonal indices.

$$\text{Deseasonalized series} = \text{Original series} \div \text{Seasonal indices}$$

To reseasonalize results, reverse the process.

$$\text{Reseasonalized results} = \text{Deseasonalized results} \times \text{Seasonal indices}$$

## Suggested Readings

Bassin, William M. "How to Anticipate the Accuracy of a Regression Based Model." *Journal of Business Forecasting* 6, no. 4 (Winter 1987–88), pp. 26–28.

Bowerman, Bruce L.; and Richard T. O' Connell. *Applied Statistics: Improving Business Processes.* Chicago: Irwin, 1997.

Bowerman, Bruce L.; Richard T. O' Connell; and J. B. Orris. *Essentials of Business Statistics.* Boston: Irwin/McGraw-Hill, 2004.

Dalrymple, Douglas J.; William M. Strahle; and Douglas B. Bock. "How Many Observations Should Be Used in Trend Regression Forecasts?" *Journal of Business Forecasting* 8, no. 1 (Spring 1989), pp. 7–9.

Harris, John L.; and Lon-Mu Liu. "GNP as a Predictor of Electricity Consumption." *Journal of Business Forecasting,* Winter 1990–91, pp. 24–27.

Lapide, Larry. "Do You Need to Use Causal Forecasting?" *Journal of Business Forecasting,* Summer 1999, pp. 13–14.

Lind, Douglas A.; Robert D. Mason; and William G. Marchal. *Basic Statistics for Business and Economics,* 3rd ed. New York: Irwin/McGraw-Hill, 2000.

Meade, Nigel; and Towhidul Islam. "Forecasting with Growth Curves: An Empirical Comparison." *International Journal of Forecasting* 11, no. 2 (June 1995), pp. 199–215.

Monaco, Ralph M. "MEXVAL: A Simple Regression Diagnostic Tool." *Journal of Business Forecasting,* Winter 1989–90, pp. 23–27.

Morrison, Jeffrey S. "Target Marketing with Logit Regression." *Journal of Business Forecasting* 14, no. 4 (Winter 1995–96), pp. 10–12.

Pindyck, Robert S.; and Daniel L. Rubinfeld. *Econometric Models and Economic Forecasts.* 3rd ed. New York: McGraw-Hill, 1991.

Wang, George C. S.; and Charles K. Akabay. "Heteroscedasticity: How to Handle in Regression Modeling." *Journal of Business Forecasting* 13, no. 2 (Summer 1992), pp. 11–17.

West, Kenneth D.; et al. "Regression-Based Tests of Predictive Ability." *International Economic Review* 39, no. 4 (November 1998), pp. 817–40.

Wooldridge, Jeffrey M. *Introductory Econometrics.* 2nd ed. Mason, OH: Thompson/South-Western, 2003.

## Exercises

1. Why is it useful to look at data in a graph as well as in a table? What is the main advantage of seeing a graph of the data?

2. For what kind of data pattern is a linear regression model most applicable? Give an example based on data used in this chapter.

3. How can seasonal data be forecast with a simple bivariate linear regression model? Explain the deseasonalize-forecast-reseasonalize process. How does the material in this chapter suggest that you find seasonal indices?

4. In this chapter, you learned four steps that should be used to evaluate a regression model. What is the first step and why is it so important? Explain the other three steps, indicating what you learn from each of those three steps.

5. Explain the difference between a simple trend model and a causal model.

6. Explain the difference between the most common kind of correlation (the Pearson product moment correlation, discussed in Chapter 2) and serial correlation.

7. Explain what is meant by heteroscedasticity.

8. The following regression results relate to a study of the salaries of public school teachers in a midwestern city (the sample size was 450 teachers):

| Variable | Coefficient | Standard Error | t-ratio |
|---|---|---|---|
| Constant | 20,720 | 6,820 | 3.04 |
| EXP | 805 | 258 | |

$R$-squared = 0.684; $n$ = 105.
Standard error of the estimate = 2,000.
EXP is the experience of teachers in years of full-time teaching.

   *a.* What is the *t*-ratio for EXP? Does it indicate that experience is a statistically significant determinant of salary if a 95 percent confidence level is desired?

   *b.* What percentage of the variation in salary is explained by this model?

   *c.* Determine the point estimate of a salary for a teacher with 20 years of experience.

   *d.* What is the approximate 95 percent confidence interval for your point estimate from part (*c*)?

9. Nelson Industries manufactures a part for a type of aircraft engine that is becoming obsolete. The sales history for the last 10 years is as follows:

| (c4p9) Year | Sales |
|---|---|
| 2008 | 945 |
| 2009 | 875 |
| 2010 | 760 |
| 2011 | 690 |
| 2012 | 545 |
| 2033 | 420 |
| 2014 | 305 |
| 2015 | 285 |
| 2016 | 250 |
| 2017 | 210 |

   *a.* Plot sales versus time.

   *b.* Estimate the regression model for a linear time trend of sales.

   *c.* What is the mean absolute percent error of the linear regression estimates for these 10 years?

   *d.* Using this model, estimate sales for year 11.

10. Mid-Valley Travel Agency (MVTA) has offices in 12 cities. The company believes that its monthly airline bookings are related to the mean income in those cities and has collected the following data:

| (c4p10) | Location | Bookings | Income |
|---|---|---|---|
| | 1 | 1,098 | $43,299 |
| | 2 | 1,131 | 45,021 |
| | 3 | 1,120 | 40,290 |
| | 4 | 1,142 | 41,893 |
| | 5 | 971 | 30,620 |
| | 6 | 1,403 | 48,105 |
| | 7 | 855 | 27,482 |
| | 8 | 1,054 | 33,025 |
| | 9 | 1,081 | 34,687 |
| | 10 | 982 | 28,725 |
| | 11 | 1,098 | 37,892 |
| | 12 | 1,387 | 46,198 |

*a.* Develop a linear regression model of monthly airline bookings as a function of income.

*b.* Use the process described in the chapter to evaluate your results.

*c.* Make the point and approximate 95 percent confidence interval estimates of monthly airline bookings for another city in which MVTA is considering opening a branch, given that income in that city is $39,020.

11. Barbara Lynch is the product manager for a line of skiwear produced by HeathCo Industries and privately branded for sale under several different names, including Northern Slopes and Jacque Monri. A new part of Ms. Lynch's job is to provide a quarterly forecast of sales for the northern United States, a region composed of 27 states stretching from Maine to Washington. A 10-year sales history is shown:

| (c4p11) | Sales ($000) | | | |
|---|---|---|---|---|
| Year | 1st Quarter | 2nd Quarter | 3rd Quarter | 4th Quarter |
| 2007 | $ 72,962 | $ 81,921 | $ 97,729 | $ 142,161 |
| 2008 | 145,592 | 117,129 | 114,159 | 151,402 |
| 2009 | 153,907 | 100,144 | 123,242 | 128,497 |
| 2010 | 176,076 | 180,440 | 162,665 | 220,818 |
| 2011 | 202,415 | 211,780 | 163,710 | 200,135 |
| 2012 | 174,200 | 182,556 | 198,990 | 243,700 |
| 2013 | 253,142 | 218,755 | 225,422 | 253,653 |
| 2014 | 257,156 | 202,568 | 224,482 | 229,879 |
| 2015 | 289,321 | 266,095 | 262,938 | 322,052 |
| 2016 | 313,769 | 315,011 | 264,939 | 301,479 |

*a.* Because Ms. Lynch has so many other job responsibilities, she has hired you to help with the forecasting effort. First, she would like you to prepare a time-series plot of the data and to write her a memo indicating what the plot appears to show and whether it seems likely that a simple linear trend would be useful in preparing forecasts.

*b.* In addition to plotting the data over time, you should estimate the least-squares trend line in the form:

$$SALES = a + b(TIME)$$

Set TIME = 1 for 2007Q1 through TIME = 40 for 2016Q4. Write the trend equation:

$$SALES = \underline{\hspace{1.5cm}} +/- \underline{\hspace{1.5cm}}(TIME)$$

(Circle + or − as appropriate)

*c.* Do your regression results indicate to you that there is a significant trend to the data? Explain why or why not.

*d.* On the basis of your results, prepare a forecast for the four quarters of 2017.

| Period | TIME | Sales Forecast (F1) |
|--------|------|---------------------|
| 2017Q1 | 41 | |
| 2017Q2 | 42 | |
| 2017Q3 | 43 | |
| 2017Q4 | 44 | |

*e.* A year later, Barbara gives you a call and tells you that the actual sales for the four quarters of 2017 were: Q1 = 334,271, Q2 = 328,982, Q3 = 317,921, and Q4 = 350,118. How accurate was your model? What was the mean absolute percentage error (MAPE)?

12. Dick Staples, another product manager with HeathCo (see Exercise 11), has mentioned to Barbara Lynch that he has found both the unemployment rate and the level of income to be useful predictors for some of the products under his responsibility.

*a.* Suppose that Ms. Lynch provides you with the following unemployment data for the northern region she is concerned with:

(c4p12)

| Year | Unemployment Rate (%) 1st Quarter | 2nd Quarter | 3rd Quarter | 4th Quarter |
|------|------|------|------|------|
| 2007 | 8.4% | 8.2% | 8.4% | 8.4% |
| 2008 | 8.1 | 7.7 | 7.5 | 7.2 |
| 2009 | 6.9 | 6.5 | 6.5 | 6.4 |
| 2010 | 6.3 | 6.2 | 6.3 | 6.5 |
| 2011 | 6.8 | 7.9 | 8.3 | 8.0 |
| 2012 | 8.0 | 8.0 | 8.0 | 8.9 |
| 2013 | 9.6 | 10.2 | 10.7 | 11.5 |
| 2014 | 11.2 | 11.0 | 10.1 | 9.2 |
| 2015 | 8.5 | 8.0 | 8.0 | 7.9 |
| 2016 | 7.9 | 7.9 | 7.8 | 7.6 |

*b.* Using Excel, plot a scattergram of SALES versus northern-region unemployment rate (NRUR). Does there appear to be a relationship? Explain.

c. Prepare a bivariate regression model of sales as a function of NRUR in the following form:

$$\text{SALES} = a + b(\text{NRUR})$$

Write your answer in the following equation:

$$\text{SALES} = \underline{\hspace{1.5cm}} +/- \underline{\hspace{1.5cm}} (\text{NRUR})$$

(Circle + or − as appropriate)

d. Write a memo to Ms. Lynch in which you evaluate these results and indicate how well you think this model would work in forecasting her sales series.

e. Use the model to make a forecast of sales for each quarter of 2017, given the forecast for unemployment (FNRUR) that HeathCo has purchased from a macroeconomic consulting firm (MacroCast):

| Period | FNRUR | Sales Forecast (F2) |
|---|---|---|
| 2017Q1 | 7.6% | _____ |
| 2017Q2 | 7.7 | _____ |
| 2017Q3 | 7.5 | _____ |
| 2017Q4 | 7.4 | _____ |

f. For the actual sales given in Exercise 11(c), calculate the MAPE for this model. How does it compare with what you found in Exercise 11(c)?

g. Barbara Lynch also has data on income (INC), in billions of dollars, for the region as follows:

| | Income ($ Billions) | | | |
|---|---|---|---|---|
| (c4p12) | | | | |
| Year | 1st Quarter | 2nd Quarter | 3rd Quarter | 4th Quarter |
| 2007 | $ 218 | $ 237 | $ 263 | $ 293 |
| 2008 | 318 | 359 | 404 | 436 |
| 2009 | 475 | 534 | 574 | 622 |
| 2010 | 667 | 702 | 753 | 796 |
| 2011 | 858 | 870 | 934 | 1,010 |
| 2012 | 1,066 | 1,096 | 1,162 | 1,187 |
| 2013 | 1,207 | 1,242 | 1,279 | 1,318 |
| 2014 | 1,346 | 1,395 | 1,443 | 1,528 |
| 2015 | 1,613 | 1,646 | 1,694 | 1,730 |
| 2016 | 1,755 | 1,842 | 1,832 | 1,882 |

Using Excel, plot a scattergram of SALES with INC. Does there appear to be a relationship? Explain.

h. Prepare a bivariate regression model of SALES as a function of income (INC) and write your results in the equation:

$$\text{SALES} = a + b(\text{INC})$$

$$\text{SALES} = \underline{\hspace{1.5cm}} +/- \underline{\hspace{1.5cm}} (\text{INC})$$

(Circle + or − as appropriate)

i. Write a memo to Ms. Lynch in which you explain and evaluate this model, indicating how well you think it would work in forecasting sales.

j. HeathCo has also purchased a forecast of income from MacroCast. Use the following income forecast (INCF) to make your own forecast of SALES for 2017:

| Period | INCF | Sales Forecast (F3) |
|--------|------|---------------------|
| 2017Q1 | $ 1,928 | _____ |
| 2017Q2 | 1,972 | _____ |
| 2017Q3 | 2,017 | _____ |
| 2017Q4 | 2,062 | _____ |

k. On the basis of the actual sales given in Exercise 11(c), calculate the MAPE for this model. How does it compare with the other two models you have used to forecast sales?

l. Prepare a time-series plot with actual sales for 2007Q1 through 2016Q4 along with the sales forecast you found in part (j) of this exercise. To accompany this plot, write a brief memo to Ms. Lynch in which you comment on the strengths and weaknesses of the forecasting model.

13. Carolina Wood Products, Inc., a major manufacturer of household furniture, is interested in predicting expenditures on furniture (FURN) for the entire United States. It has the following data by quarter for 2007 through 2016:

(c4p13)

| Year | FURN (in $ Billions) | | | |
|------|------------|------------|------------|------------|
| | 1st Quarter | 2nd Quarter | 3rd Quarter | 4th Quarter |
| 2007 | $ 98.1 | $ 96.8 | $ 96.0 | $ 95.0 |
| 2008 | 93.2 | 95.1 | 96.2 | 98.4 |
| 2009 | 100.7 | 104.4 | 108.1 | 111.1 |
| 2010 | 114.3 | 117.2 | 119.4 | 122.7 |
| 2011 | 125.9 | 129.3 | 132.2 | 136.6 |
| 2012 | 137.4 | 141.4 | 145.3 | 147.7 |
| 2013 | 148.8 | 150.2 | 153.4 | 154.2 |
| 2014 | 159.8 | 164.4 | 166.2 | 169.7 |
| 2015 | 173.7 | 175.5 | 175.0 | 175.7 |
| 2016 | 181.4 | 180.0 | 179.7 | 176.3 |

a. Prepare a naive forecast for 2017Q1 based on the following model (see Chapter 1):

$$NFURN_t = FURN_{t-1}$$

| Period | Naive Forecast |
|--------|----------------|
| 2017Q1 | |

b. Estimate the bivariate linear trend model for the data where TIME = 1 for 2007Q1 through TIME = 40 for 2016Q4.

$$FURN = a + b(TIME)$$

$$FURN = \underline{\hspace{1.5cm}} +/- \underline{\hspace{1.5cm}} (TIME)$$

(Circle + or − as appropriate)

c. Write a paragraph in which you evaluate this model, with particular emphasis on its usefulness in forecasting.

d. Prepare a time-trend forecast of furniture and household equipment expenditures for 2017 based on the model in part (b).

| Period | TIME | Trend Forecast |
|--------|------|----------------|
| 2017Q1 | 41 | _____ |
| 2017Q2 | 42 | _____ |
| 2017Q3 | 43 | _____ |
| 2017Q4 | 44 | _____ |

e. Suppose that the actual values of FURN for 2017 were as shown in the following table. Calculate the MAPE for both of your forecasts and interpret the results. (For the naive forecast, there will be only one observation, for 2017Q1.)

| Period | Actual FURN ($ Billions) |
|--------|--------------------------|
| 2017Q1 | 177.6 |
| 2017Q2 | 180.5 |
| 2017Q3 | 182.8 |
| 2017Q4 | 178.7 |

14. Fifteen midwestern and mountain states have united in an effort to promote and forecast tourism. One aspect of their work has been related to the dollar amount spent per year on domestic travel (DTE) in each state. They have the following estimates for disposable personal income per capita (DPI) and DTE:

| State | DPI | DTE ($ Millions) |
|-------|-----|------------------|
| Minnesota | $ 17,907 | $ 4,933 |
| Iowa | 15,782 | 1,766 |
| Missouri | 17,158 | 4,692 |
| North Dakota | 15,688 | 628 |
| South Dakota | 15,981 | 551 |
| Nebraska | 17,416 | 1,250 |
| Kansas | 17,635 | 1,729 |
| Montana | 15,128 | 725 |
| Idaho | 15,974 | 934 |
| Wyoming | 17,504 | 778 |
| Colorado | 18,628 | 4,628 |
| New Mexico | 14,587 | 1,724 |
| Arizona | 15,921 | 3,836 |
| Utah | 14,066 | 1,757 |
| Nevada | 19,781 | 6,455 |

(c4p14)

a. From these data, estimate a bivariate linear regression equation for domestic travel expenditures (DTE) as a function of disposable income per capita (DPI):

$$DTE = a + b(DPI)$$

DTE = _____ +/− _____ (DPI)

(Circle + or − as appropriate)

Evaluate the statistical significance of this model.

*b.* Illinois, a bordering state, has asked that this model be used to forecast DTE for Illinois under the assumption that DPI will be $19,648.

*c.* Given that actual DTE turned out to be $7,754 (million), calculate the percentage error in your forecast.

15. Collect data on population for your state (http://www.economagic.com may be a good source for these data) over the past 20 years and use a bivariate regression trend line to forecast population for the next five years. Prepare a time-series plot that shows both actual and forecast values. Do you think the model looks as though it will provide reasonably accurate forecasts for the five-year horizon? (c4p15)

16. AmerPlas, Inc., produces 16-ounce plastic drinking cups that are embossed with the names of prominent beers and soft drinks. It has been observed that sales of the cups match closely the seasonal pattern associated with beer production but that, unlike beer production, there has been a positive trend over time. The sales data, by month, for 2013 through 2016 are as follows:

(c4p16)

| Period | T | Sales | Period | T | Sales |
|---|---|---|---|---|---|
| 2013M01 | 1 | 857 | 2015M01 | 25 | 1,604 |
| 2013M02 | 2 | 921 | 2015M02 | 26 | 1,643 |
| 2013M03 | 3 | 1,071 | 2015M03 | 27 | 1,795 |
| 2013M04 | 4 | 1,133 | 2015M04 | 28 | 1,868 |
| 2013M05 | 5 | 1,209 | 2015M05 | 29 | 1,920 |
| 2013M06 | 6 | 1,234 | 2015M06 | 30 | 1,953 |
| 2013M07 | 7 | 1,262 | 2015M07 | 31 | 1,980 |
| 2013M08 | 8 | 1,258 | 2015M08 | 32 | 1,989 |
| 2013M09 | 9 | 1,175 | 2015M09 | 33 | 1,897 |
| 2013M10 | 10 | 1,174 | 2015M10 | 34 | 1,910 |
| 2013M11 | 11 | 1,123 | 2015M11 | 35 | 1,854 |
| 2013M12 | 12 | 1,159 | 2015M12 | 36 | 1,957 |
| 2014M01 | 13 | 1,250 | 2016M01 | 37 | 1,955 |
| 2014M02 | 14 | 1,289 | 2016M02 | 38 | 2,008 |
| 2014M03 | 15 | 1,448 | 2016M03 | 39 | 2,171 |
| 2014M04 | 16 | 1,497 | 2016M04 | 40 | 2,202 |
| 2014M05 | 17 | 1,560 | 2016M05 | 41 | 2,288 |
| 2014M06 | 18 | 1,586 | 2016M06 | 42 | 2,314 |
| 2014M07 | 19 | 1,597 | 2016M07 | 43 | 2,343 |
| 2014M08 | 20 | 1,615 | 2016M08 | 44 | 2,339 |
| 2014M09 | 21 | 1,535 | 2016M09 | 45 | 2,239 |
| 2014M10 | 22 | 1,543 | 2016M10 | 46 | 2,267 |
| 2014M11 | 23 | 1,493 | 2016M11 | 47 | 2,206 |
| 2014M12 | 24 | 1,510 | 2016M12 | 48 | 2,226 |

*a.* Use these data to estimate a linear time trend as follows:

$$SALES = a + b(T)$$

$$SALES = \underline{\hspace{2cm}} +/- \underline{\hspace{2cm}} (T)$$

(Circle + or − as appropriate)

Do your regression results support the notion that there has been a positive time trend in the SALES data? Explain.

*b.* Use your equation to forecast SALES for the 12 months of 2017:

| Period | SALES Forecast |
|---|---|
| 2017M01 | _____ |
| M02 | _____ |
| M03 | _____ |
| M04 | _____ |
| M05 | _____ |
| M06 | _____ |
| M07 | _____ |
| M08 | _____ |
| M09 | _____ |
| M10 | _____ |
| M11 | _____ |
| M12 | _____ |

*c.* Actual SALES for 2017 are:

| Period | Actual SALES |
|---|---|
| 2017M01 | 2,318 |
| M02 | 2,367 |
| M03 | 2,523 |
| M04 | 2,577 |
| M05 | 2,646 |
| M06 | 2,674 |
| M07 | 2,697 |
| M08 | 2,702 |
| M09 | 2,613 |
| M10 | 2,626 |
| M11 | 2,570 |
| M12 | 2,590 |

On the basis of your results in part (*b*) in comparison with these actual sales, how well do you think your model works? What is the MAPE for 2017?

*d.* Prepare a time-series plot of the actual sales and the forecast of sales for 2013M01 through 2017M12. Do the same for just the last two years (2016M01 to 2017M12). Do your plots show any evidence of seasonality in the data? If so, how might you account for it in preparing a forecast?

17. Alexander Enterprises manufactures plastic parts for the automotive industry. Its sales (in thousands of dollars) for 2012Q1 through 2016Q4 are as follows:

| (c4p17) | Period | Sales | Period | Sales |
|---|---|---|---|---|
| | 2012Q1 | 3,816.5 | Q2 | 4,169.4 |
| | Q2 | 3,816.7 | Q3 | 4,193.0 |
| | Q3 | 3,978.8 | Q4 | 4,216.4 |
| | Q4 | 4,046.6 | 2014Q1 | 4,238.1 |
| | 2013Q1 | 4,119.1 | Q2 | 4,270.5 |

(continued on next page)

(continued)

| (c4p17) | Period | Sales | Period | Sales |
|---|---|---|---|---|
| | Q3 | 4,321.8 | Q2 | 4,517.8 |
| | Q4 | 4,349.5 | Q3 | 4,563.6 |
| | 2015Q1 | 4,406.4 | Q4 | 4,633.0 |
| | Q2 | 4,394.6 | 2017Q1 | NA |
| | Q3 | 4,422.3 | Q2 | NA |
| | Q4 | 4,430.8 | Q3 | NA |
| | 2016Q1 | 4,463.9 | Q4 | NA |

*a.* Begin by preparing a time-series plot of sales. Does it appear from this plot that a linear trend model might be appropriate? Explain.

*b.* Use a bivariate linear regression trend model to estimate the following trend equation:

$$SALES = a + b(TIME)$$

Is the sign for *b* what you would expect? Is *b* significantly different from zero? What is the coefficient of determination for this model? Is there a potential problem with serial correlation? Explain.

*c.* Based on this model, make a trend forecast of sales for the four quarters of 2017.

*d.* Given that actual sales for the four quarters of 2017 are:

| 2017Q1 | 4,667.1 |
|---|---|
| 2017Q2 | 4,710.3 |
| 2017Q3 | 4,738.7 |
| 2017Q4 | 4,789.0 |

calculate the MAPE for this forecast model in the historical period (2012Q1–2016Q4) as well as for the forecast horizon (2017Q1–2017Q4). Which of these measures accuracy and which measures fit?

18. The following data are for shoe store sales in the United States in millions of dollars after being seasonally adjusted (SASSS). (c4p18)

| Date | SASSS | Date | SASSS | Date | SASSS | Date | SASSS |
|---|---|---|---|---|---|---|---|
| Jan-02 | 1627 | Mar-03 | 1524 | May-04 | 1623 | Jul-05 | 1692 |
| Feb-02 | 1588 | Apr-03 | 1560 | Jun-04 | 1619 | Aug-05 | 1695 |
| Mar-02 | 1567 | May-03 | 1575 | Jul-04 | 1667 | Sep-05 | 1721 |
| Apr-02 | 1578 | Jun-03 | 1588 | Aug-04 | 1660 | Oct-05 | 1698 |
| May-02 | 1515 | Jul-03 | 1567 | Sep-04 | 1681 | Nov-05 | 1770 |
| Jun-02 | 1520 | Aug-03 | 1602 | Oct-04 | 1690 | Dec-05 | 1703 |
| Jul-02 | 1498 | Sep-03 | 1624 | Nov-04 | 1710 | Jan-06 | 1745 |
| Aug-02 | 1522 | Oct-03 | 1597 | Dec-04 | 1694 | Feb-06 | 1728 |
| Sep-02 | 1560 | Nov-03 | 1614 | Jan-05 | 1663 | Mar-06 | 1776 |
| Oct-02 | 1569 | Dec-03 | 1644 | Feb-05 | 1531 | Apr-06 | 1807 |
| Nov-02 | 1528 | Jan-04 | 1637 | Mar-05 | 1707 | May-06 | 1800 |
| Dec-02 | 1556 | Feb-04 | 1617 | Apr-05 | 1707 | Jun-06 | 1758 |
| Jan-03 | 1593 | Mar-04 | 1679 | May-05 | 1715 | Jul-06 | 1784 |
| Feb-03 | 1527 | Apr-04 | 1607 | Jun-05 | 1735 | Aug-06 | 1791 |

(continued on next page)

(continued)

| Date | SASSS | Date | SASSS | Date | SASSS | Date | SASSS |
|------|-------|------|-------|------|-------|------|-------|
| Sep-06 | 1743 | Jul-09 | 1905 | May-12 | 1940 | Mar-15 | 2002 |
| Oct-06 | 1785 | Aug-09 | 1892 | Jun-12 | 1963 | Apr-15 | 2090 |
| Nov-06 | 1765 | Sep-09 | 1893 | Jul-12 | 1920 | May-15 | 2104 |
| Dec-06 | 1753 | Oct-09 | 1869 | Aug-12 | 1937 | Jun-15 | 2114 |
| Jan-07 | 1753 | Nov-09 | 1867 | Sep-12 | 1867 | Jul-15 | 2124 |
| Feb-07 | 1790 | Dec-09 | 1887 | Oct-12 | 1918 | Aug-15 | 2098 |
| Mar-07 | 1830 | Jan-10 | 1885 | Nov-12 | 1914 | Sep-15 | 2105 |
| Apr-07 | 1702 | Feb-10 | 1885 | Dec-12 | 1931 | Oct-15 | 2206 |
| May-07 | 1769 | Mar-10 | 1925 | Jan-13 | 1867 | Nov-15 | 2232 |
| Jun-07 | 1793 | Apr-10 | 1891 | Feb-13 | 1887 | Dec-15 | 2194 |
| Jul-07 | 1801 | May-10 | 1900 | Mar-13 | 1939 | Jan-16 | 2218 |
| Aug-07 | 1789 | Jun-10 | 1888 | Apr-13 | 1860 | Feb-16 | 2271 |
| Sep-07 | 1791 | Jul-10 | 1865 | May-13 | 1898 | Mar-16 | 2165 |
| Oct-07 | 1799 | Aug-10 | 1921 | Jun-13 | 1924 | Apr-16 | 2253 |
| Nov-07 | 1811 | Sep-10 | 1949 | Jul-13 | 1967 | May-16 | 2232 |
| Dec-07 | 1849 | Oct-10 | 1923 | Aug-13 | 1994 | Jun-16 | 2237 |
| Jan-08 | 1824 | Nov-10 | 1922 | Sep-13 | 1966 | Jul-16 | 2231 |
| Feb-08 | 1882 | Dec-10 | 1894 | Oct-13 | 1943 | Aug-16 | 2278 |
| Mar-08 | 1859 | Jan-11 | 1908 | Nov-13 | 1973 | Sep-16 | 2259 |
| Apr-08 | 1831 | Feb-11 | 1855 | Dec-13 | 1976 | Oct-16 | 2231 |
| May-08 | 1832 | Mar-11 | 1858 | Jan-14 | 1969 | Nov-16 | 2217 |
| Jun-08 | 1842 | Apr-11 | 1941 | Feb-14 | 1989 | Dec-16 | 2197 |
| Jul-08 | 1874 | May-11 | 1938 | Mar-14 | 2040 | Jan-17 | |
| Aug-08 | 1845 | Jun-11 | 1901 | Apr-14 | 1976 | Feb-17 | |
| Sep-08 | 1811 | Jul-11 | 1964 | May-14 | 1964 | Mar-17 | |
| Oct-08 | 1898 | Aug-11 | 1963 | Jun-14 | 1947 | Apr-17 | |
| Nov-08 | 1878 | Sep-11 | 1838 | Jul-14 | 1961 | May-17 | |
| Dec-08 | 1901 | Oct-11 | 1877 | Aug-14 | 1931 | Jun-17 | |
| Jan-09 | 1916 | Nov-11 | 1927 | Sep-14 | 1960 | Jul-17 | |
| Feb-09 | 1894 | Dec-11 | 1911 | Oct-14 | 1980 | | |
| Mar-09 | 1883 | Jan-12 | 1962 | Nov-14 | 1944 | | |
| Apr-09 | 1871 | Feb-12 | 1980 | Dec-14 | 2014 | | |
| May-09 | 1918 | Mar-12 | 1955 | Jan-15 | 2013 | | |
| Jun-09 | 1943 | Apr-12 | 1967 | Feb-15 | 2143 | | |

*a.* Make a linear trend forecast for SASSS though the first seven months of 2017. Given that the actual seasonally adjusted values for 2017 were as shown below, calculate the MAPE for those seven months of 2017.

| Date | SASSS |
|------|-------|
| Jan-17 | 2,422 |
| Feb-17 | 2,112 |
| Mar-17 | 2,290 |
| Apr-17 | 2,354 |
| May-17 | 2,013 |
| Jun-17 | 2,156 |
| Jul-17 | 2,425 |

*b.* Reseasonalize the 2017 forecast and the 2017 actual sales using the following seasonal indices:

| Month | SI |
|-------|------|
| Jan | 0.74 |
| Feb | 0.81 |
| Mar | 1.00 |
| Apr | 1.03 |
| May | 1.04 |
| Jun | 0.98 |
| Jul | 0.98 |
| Aug | 1.23 |
| Sep | 0.96 |
| Oct | 0.94 |
| Nov | 0.98 |
| Dec | 1.31 |

*c.* Plot the final forecast along with the actual sales data. Does the forecast appear reasonable? Explain.

*d.* Why do you think the April, May, August, and December seasonal indices are greater than 1?

# Chapter **Five**

# Explanatory Models 1. Forecasting with Multiple Regression Causal Models

©VLADGRIN/Getty Images

In this chapter, we will build on the introduction to the use of regression in forecasting developed in Chapter 4. We will model new car sales (NCS) with multiple independent variables. One of the variables we introduce in this chapter provides a way in which we can take into account consumer attitudes. To do so, we will use the University of Michigan Index of Consumer Sentiment. We also introduce a new type of independent variable called a "dummy variable." These variables will be used to help account for seasonality in data as well as other events that can influence sales. We will continue with our ongoing example of forecasting The Gap sales at the end of this chapter. These extensions of the bivariate regression model take us into the realm of multiple regression. We will begin by looking at the general multiple-regression model.

## LEARNING OBJECTIVES

After studying this chapter, you should be able to:
1. Explain the difference between bivariate (simple) regression and multiple regression.
2. Explain the new (fifth) step for evaluating a multiple regression model.
3. Describe how a regression plane differs from a regression line.
4. Explain what is meant by a "dummy variable."

5. Describe some ways "dummy variables" can be useful in regression models.

6. Explain things that should be considered when selecting independent variables for a multiple regression model that will be used to make a forecast.

# THE MULTIPLE-REGRESSION MODEL

Multiple regression is a statistical procedure in which a dependent variable ($Y$) is modeled as a function of more than one independent variable ($X_1, X_2, X_3, \ldots, X_n$).[1] The population multiple-regression model may be written as:

$$Y = f(X_1, X_2, X_3, \ldots, X_n)$$
$$= \beta_0 + \beta_1 X_1 + \beta_2 X_2 + \beta_3 X_3 + \cdots + \beta_k X_k + \varepsilon$$

where $\beta_0$ is the intercept and the other $\beta_i$'s are the slope terms associated with the respective independent variables (i.e., the $X_i$'s). In this model, $\varepsilon$ represents the population error term, which is the difference between the actual $Y$ and that predicted by the regression model ($\hat{Y}$).

The ordinary least-squares (OLS) criterion for the best multiple-regression model is that the sum of the squares of all the error terms is minimized. That is, we want to minimize $\Sigma\varepsilon^2$, where

$$\Sigma\varepsilon^2 = \Sigma(Y - \hat{Y})^2$$

Thus, the ordinary least-squares criterion for multiple regression is to minimize:

$$\Sigma(Y - \beta_0 - \beta_1 X_1 - \beta_2 X_2 - \beta_3 X_3 - \cdots - \beta_k X_k)^2$$

The process of achieving this is more complicated than in the bivariate regression case and involves the use of matrix algebra.

Values of the true regression parameters ($\beta_i$) are typically estimated from sample data. The resulting sample regression model is:

$$\hat{Y} = b_0 + b_1 X_1 + b_2 X_2 + b_3 X_3 + \cdots + b_k X_k$$

where $b_0$, $b_1$, $b_2$, $b_3$, and so on, are sample statistics that are estimates of the corresponding population parameters $\beta_0, \beta_1, \beta_2, \beta_3$, and so on. Deviations between the predicted values based on the sample regression ($\hat{Y}$) and the actual values ($Y$) of the dependent variable for each observation are called *residuals* (or they are called *errors*) and are equal to ($Y - \hat{Y}$). The values of the sample statistics $b_0$, $b_1$, $b_2$, $b_3$, and so on, are almost always determined for us by a computer software package. Standard errors, $t$-ratios, the multiple coefficient of determination, the Durbin-Watson statistic, and other evaluative statistics, as well as a table of residuals, are also found in most regression output.

---

[1] For more detailed discussions of the multiple-regression model, see the following: John Neter, William Wasserman, and Michael H. Kutner, *Applied Linear Regression Models* (New York: McGraw-Hill, 1996), and Damodar N. Gujarati, *Basic Econometrics* (New York: McGraw-Hill, 2003). The latter is particularly recommended.

# INITIAL CONSIDERATIONS WHEN SELECTING INDEPENDENT VARIABLES

As with bivariate regression, the process of building a multiple-regression model begins by identifying the dependent variable.

As with bivariate regression, the process of building a multiple-regression model begins by identifying the dependent variable. In our context, that is the variable that we are most interested in forecasting. It may be some "prime mover" such as disposable personal income or another macroeconomic variable, or it may be total company sales, or sales of a particular product line, or the number of patient-days for a hospital, or state tax revenues.

Once the dependent variable is determined, we begin to think about what factors contribute to its changes. In this chapter, as we will use new car sales (NCS) as the dependent variable we wish to forecast. We will use a measure of income as well as other independent (causal) variables that might improve the model. We want to think of other things that influence NCS but that do not measure the same basic relationship that is being measured by disposable personal income per capita (DPIPC). Think, for example, of the possibility of adding the gross domestic product (GDP) to the model. Both GDP and DPIPC are measures of income in the economy, so there would be a lot of overlap in the part of the variation in NCS they explain. In fact, the correlation between GDP and DPIPC is +0.99. A similar overlap would result if population and DPIPC were used in the same model. There is a high correlation between population size and real disposable personal income per capita (approximately + 0.95), and so they would have a lot of overlap in their ability to explain variations in NCS. Such overlaps can cause a problem known as *multicollinearity,* which we will discuss later in this chapter.[2]

In considering the set of independent variables to use, we should find ones that are not highly correlated with one another.

Thus, in considering the set of independent variables to use, we should find ones that are not highly correlated with one another. For example, suppose that we hypothesize that at least some portion of NCS may be influenced by the unemployment rate. It seems less likely that there would be a stronger correlation between personal income and the unemployment rate than between personal income and either GDP or population size. The correlation between the unemployment rate and disposable personal income turns out to be just 0.15, so there is less overlap between those two variables.

Sometimes it is difficult or even impossible to find a variable that measures exactly what we want to have in our model. For example, in the NCS model, we might like to have as a measure of the interest rate a national average of the rate charged on installment loans. However, a more readily available series, the prime interest rate (PR), may be a reasonable proxy for what we want to measure since all interest rates tend to be closely related.

As we build a model of new car sales (NCS), we will also begin looking at the relationship between NCS and other possible causal variables. In Figure 5.1, you see a plot of NCS. You see a seasonal pattern in the data. Thus, we will want

---

[2] Note that multicollinearity in regression analysis is really just strong correlation between two or more independent variables. Correlation here is measured, just as we did in Chapter 2 with the Pearson product-moment correlation coefficient.

**FIGURE 5.1**
**New Car Sales (NCS) in Millions of Dollars (c5f1)**

Source: economagic.com.

to consider adding another variable (or set of variables) to account for the seasonality in NCS. But how do we measure spring, or fall, or summer, or winter? The seasons are qualitative attributes that have no direct quantitative counterpart. We will see (in the section "Accounting for Seasonality in a Multiple-Regression Model") that a special kind of variable, known as a *dummy variable,* can be used to measure such a qualitative attribute as spring.

Something to consider when developing a multiple regression model to use in forecasting is that you must be able to forecast all the independent variables. This suggests that one may want to follow the KIS principle (**K**eep **I**t **S**imple). There may be a trade-off between explanatory power and the number of independent variables used.

# DEVELOPING MULTIPLE-REGRESSION MODELS

We will develop several models for NCS building in complexity as we go. When we think about car sales, we are likely to first think about the available purchasing power consumers have at their disposal. For this, we use disposable personal income per capita (DPIPC). Before we consider this and other models for NCS, look carefully at the data in the time series graph in Figure 5.1. The data are quarterly for NCS from 2002Q1 through 2016Q4. You see some seasonality and a big drop during the recession that started in 2008.

Our beginning bivariate regression model is:

$$NCS = b_0 + b_1(DPIPC)$$
$$NCS = 66,396.257 + 2.866(DPIPC)$$

where NCS stands for new car sales and DPIPC is disposable personal income per capita (per person). The coefficient for DPIPC is logical, significantly positive at a 95 percent confidence level (t = 4.144), but the coefficient of determination ($R^2$) in this case is low (22.8 percent). Also, the DW is 0.283, showing positive serial correlation. So, we must ask what else might affect car sales. We will consider a measure of how people feel about the economy, the unemployment rate, and the prime interest rate.

We will expand the model to include a measure of consumer attitudes, the unemployment rate (UR), and the bank prime rate (PR) as a proxy for all the types of car financing. To capture consumer attitudes about the economy and their place in the economy, we will use the University of Michigan Index of Consumer Sentiment (UMICS). The multiple regression model is:

$$NCS = b_0 + b_1(DPIPC) + b_2(UMICS) + b_3(UR) + b_4(PR)$$

Before running the regression, think about what signs should be expected for $b_1$, $b_2$, $b_3$, and $b_4$. Business and economic logic would suggest that $b_1$ should be positive ($b_1 > 0$) because the more income people have, the more likely they are to purchase a car. For $b_2$, we also expect a positive sign since the UMICS increases when people feel better about the state of the economy and are, therefore, more likely to make a major purchase ($b_2 > 0$). When there is high unemployment, we would expect fewer people to be in the market to buy a car, so $b_3$ should be negative ($b_3 < 0$). If the cost of borrowing decreases, we expect more car sales, and thus, we expect $b_4$ to be negative ($b_4 < 0$). As shown in Table 5.1, the regression results support this notion. The model is:

$$NCS = 25,304.35 + 3.227(DPIPC) + 1,123.363(UMICS) \\ - 7,659.605(UR) - 3,216.777(PR)$$

Statistical evaluation of this model, based on the results in Table 5.1, will be considered in the next section. The data are in the c5t1&f2 Excel file. For now, we can see that at least the signs for the coefficients are consistent with our expectations. The predicted values from this model are plotted in Figure 5.2.

**TABLE 5.1**
**Regression Results for New Car Sales (NCS) as a Function of Disposable Income per Capita (DPIPC), the University of Michigan Index of Consumer Sentiment (UMICS), the Unemployment Rate (UR), and the Prime Interest Rate (PR)** (c5t1&f2)

| Regression Statistics | | | | | |
|---|---|---|---|---|---|
| Adjusted R Square | 0.816 | | | | |
| Standard Error | 11,690.644 | | | | |
| Observations | 60 | | | DW = | 1.376 |
| | | | | | |
| | Coefficients | Std Error | t Stat | P-value | P/2 |
| Intercept | 25,304.350 | 37,454.530 | 0.676 | 0.502 | 0.251 |
| DPIPC | 3.227 | 0.392 | 8.240 | 0.000 | 0.000 |
| UMICS | 1,123.363 | 210.582 | 5.335 | 0.000 | 0.000 |
| UR | −7,659.605 | 1,661.586 | −4.610 | 0.000 | 0.000 |
| PR | −3,216.777 | 1,412.449 | −2.277 | 0.027 | 0.013 |

**FIGURE 5.2**
**New Car Sales**
**and Predicted**
**Values (M$) Based**
**on The Model in**
**Table 5.1** (c5t1&f2)

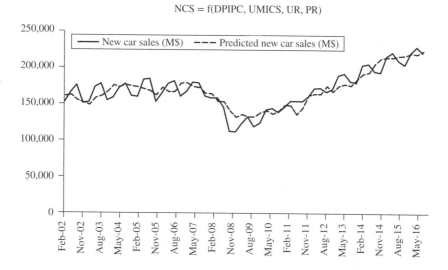

In Figure 5.2, the solid line shows actual values of new car sales (NCS) for 20022Q1 through 2016Q4. The dotted line shows the values predicted by this model for 2002Q1 through 2016Q4. Based on the results in Table 5.1, we will do a statistical analysis of the model. This model is in a five-dimensional space that we cannot visualize. A bivariate regression model is two dimensional, so it is easy to visualize as a line in a graph. If we used only two independent variables, we could construct a three-dimensional graph. Let us briefly look at such a graph for NCS.

## A Three-Dimensional Scattergram

Suppose we model NCS as a function of only DPIPC and the UR. The model would be:

$$NCS = 113,524.568 + 3.469(DPIPC) - 10,636.670(UR)$$

We see that the signs for the two independent variables are consistent with business/economic logic.

In our three-variable case (with NCS as the dependent variable and with DPIPC and UR as independent variables), three measured values are made for each sample point (i.e., for each quarter). These observations can be depicted in a scatter diagram like those in Chapter 2, but the scatter diagram must be three-dimensional. Figure 5.3 shows the new car sales (NCS) of any observation as measured vertically from the DPIPC/UR plane. The value of UR is measured along the "UR" axis, and the value of DPIPC is measured along the "DPIPC" axis. All 60 observations are represented as points in the upper diagram. The regression plane is added in the lower panel of Figure 5.3.

In a multiple-regression analysis, our task is to suspend a linear three-dimensional plane (called the *regression plane*) among the observations in such a way that the plane best represents the observations. The multiple-regression analysis estimates an equation ($Y = a + b_1X + b_2Z$) in such a manner that all the estimates of $Y$ made with the equation fall on or close to the surface of the linear plane.

If all the actual data points were to lie very close to the regression plane, the adjusted $R$-squared of the equation would be very high. If on the other hand, most of the actual points were far above or below the regression plane, the adjusted $R$-squared would be lower than it otherwise would be. Normally, regression packages do not have a provision for the graphing of output in three-dimensional form. This is because relatively few of the problems faced in the real world involve exactly three variables. Sometimes you are working with only two variables, while at other times you will be working with more than three. Thus, a three-dimensional diagram will

*If all the actual data points were to lie very close to the regression plane, the adjusted R-squared of the equation would be very high.*

**FIGURE 5.3** **New Car Sales (NCS) in Millions of Dollars with DPIPC and UR Viewed in Three Dimensions** The Three Dimensional Scattergram Below Shows how Car sales Vary as Both the UR and DPIPC Vary. In Figure 5.3, continued on the next page, you will see the Regression Plane in this Three Dimensional Space. (c5t1&f2)

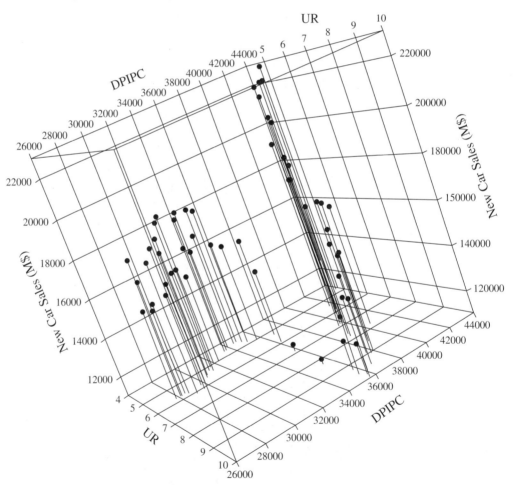

**FIGURE 5.3**   (continued)

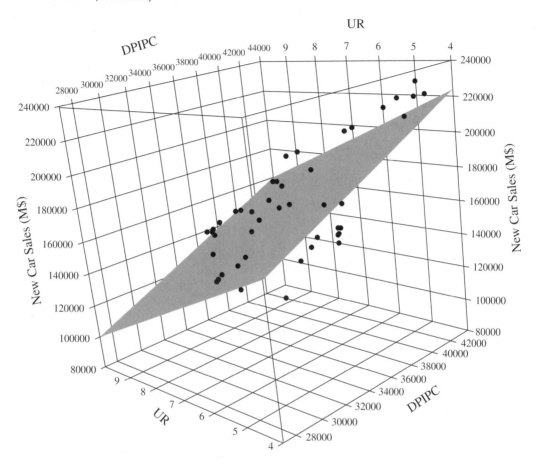

be useful only in a few cases. The plane is a normal plane when there are two independent variables, and it is called a *hyperplane* (more than three-dimensional) when there are more than two independent variables, as in the model shown in Table 5.1.

# STATISTICAL EVALUATION OF MULTIPLE-REGRESSION MODELS

The statistical evaluation of multiple-regression models is similar to that discussed in Chapter 4 for simple bivariate regression models. However, some important differences will be brought out in this section. In addition to evaluating the multiple-regression model, we will be comparing these results with a corresponding bivariate model. Thus, in Table 5.2, you see the regression results for both models. The multiple-regression results appear at the bottom of the table.

**TABLE 5.2**   **Regression Results for Multiple and Bivariate Regression Models of New Car Sales (NCS)**   (c5t2&f4)

### The Bivariate Regression Model for New Car Sales

Regression Statistics

| | | | | | |
|---|---|---|---|---|---|
| R Square | 0.228 | | | | |
| Adjusted R Square | 0.215 | | | | |
| Standard Error | 24,121.582 | | | | |
| Observations | 60 | | | DW = | 0.283 |

| | Coefficients | Std Error | t Stat | P-value | P/2 |
|---|---|---|---|---|---|
| Intercept | 66,396.257 | 25,045.655 | 2.651 | 0.010 | 0.005 |
| DPIPC | 2.866 | 0.692 | 4.144 | 0.000 | 0.000 |

| ANOVA | df | SS | MS | F | Sig F |
|---|---|---|---|---|---|
| Regression | 1 | 9,991,526,948.715 | 9,991,526,948.715 | 17.172 | 0.000 |
| Residual | 58 | 33,747,342,641.469 | 581,850,735.198 | | |
| Total | 59 | 43,738,869,590.183 | | | |

### The Multiple Regression Model for New Car Sales

Regression Statistics

| | | | | | |
|---|---|---|---|---|---|
| Adjusted R Square | 0.816 | | | | |
| Standard Error | 11,690.644 | | | | |
| Observations | 60 | | | DW = | 1.376 |

| | Coefficients | Std Error | t Stat | P-value | P/2 |
|---|---|---|---|---|---|
| Intercept | 25,304.350 | 37,454.530 | 0.676 | 0.502 | 0.251 |
| DPIPC | 3.227 | 0.392 | 8.240 | 0.000 | 0.000 |
| UMICS | 1,123.363 | 210.582 | 5.335 | 0.000 | 0.000 |
| UR | −7,659.605 | 1,661.586 | −4.610 | 0.000 | 0.000 |
| PR | −3,216.777 | 1,412.449 | −2.277 | 0.027 | 0.013 |

| ANOVA | df | SS | MS | F | Sig F |
|---|---|---|---|---|---|
| Regression | 4 | 36,221,956,000.002 | 9,055,489,000.000 | 66.257 | 0.000 |
| Residual | 55 | 7,516,913,590.181 | 136,671,156.185 | | |
| Total | 59 | 43,738,869,590.183 | | | |

## The First Four Quick Checks in Evaluating Multiple-Regression Models

The first thing you should do in reviewing regression results is to see whether the signs on the coefficients make sense.

As discussed in Chapter 4, the **first** thing you should do in reviewing regression results is to see whether the signs on the coefficients make sense. Let's start with the simple bivariate model, that is:

$$NCS = b_0 + b_1(DPIPC)$$

We have said that we expect a positive relationship between NCS and disposable personal income. Our expectation is confirmed, since:

$$b_1 = +2.866 > 0$$

The second thing to consider is whether these results are statistically significant at our desired level of confidence.

The **second** thing to consider is whether these results are statistically significant at our desired level of confidence. We will follow the convention of using a 95 percent confidence level and thus a 0.05 significance level. The hypothesis to be tested is as follows:

> **For DPIPC**
>
> $H_0: \beta_1 \leq 0$
>
> $H_1: \beta_1 > 0$

This hypothesis is evaluated using a $t$-test where the calculated $t$-ratio is found by dividing the estimated regression coefficient by its standard error (i.e., $t_{calc} = b_i/\text{s.e. of } b_i$). The table value of $t(t_T)$ can be found from Table 2.5 at $n - (K + 1)$ degrees of freedom, where $n$ = the number of observations and $K$ = the number of independent variables. For our current problem $n = 60$ and $K = 1$, so df = $60 - (1 + 1) = 58$. We will follow the rule that if df $\geq 30$, the infinity row of the $t$-table will be used. Thus, the table value is 1.645. Note that we have used the 0.05 column, since we have one-tailed tests, and in such cases, the entire significance level (0.05) goes in one tail.

Remember that since the $t$-distribution is symmetrical, we compare the absolute value of $t_{calc}$ with the table value. For our hypothesis test, the results can be summarized as follows:

> **For DPIPC**
>
> $t_{calc} = 4.144$
>
> $|t_{calc}| > t_T$
>
> $4.144 > 1.645$
>
> $\therefore$ Reject $H_0$

Because the absolute value of $t_{calc}$ is greater than the table value at $\alpha = 0.05$ and df = 58, we reject the null hypothesis at the 0.05 level for the DPIPC coefficient. Thus, we have statistical support for the notion that there is a positive effect of DPIPC on NCS.

By setting the 95 percent confidence level as our criterion, we are at the same time saying that we are willing to accept a 5 percent chance of error or, alternatively, that we set a 5 percent desired significance level.

The third part of our quick check of regression results involves an evaluation of the coefficient of determination.

The **third** part of our quick check of regression results involves an evaluation of the coefficient of determination, which, you may recall, measures the percentage of the variation in the dependent variable that is explained by the regression model. In Chapter 4, we designated the coefficient of determination as $R$-squared. If you look at the output in Table 5.2, you will see that $R^2$ is 0.228. This means that the bivariate model (or variations in DPIPC) explains 22.8 percent of the variation in NCS.

The **fourth** thing to consider is the Durbin-Watson test for serial correlation. For this model, we see in Table 5.2 that DW = 0.283. From Table 4.11 with n = 60 and k = 1, we find $D_l$ and $D_u$ to be 1.55 and 1.62, respectively. Since our DW of 0.283 < 1.55, we find that this model has positive serial correlation. Thus, the standard errors may be biased downward, making the *t*-ratio larger than it should be. It is then possible that we rejected the null hypothesis in error. This positive serial correlation is obvious in the top graph of Figure 5.4, where you see a series

**FIGURE 5.4**

**Two Models for New Car Sales (NCS)** (c5t2&f4)

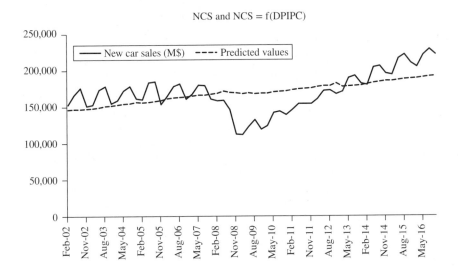

NCS and NCS = f(DPIPC)

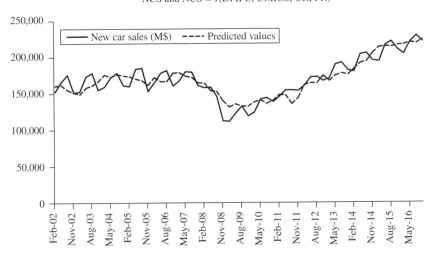

NCS and NCS = f(DPIPC, UMICS, UR, PR)

of positive errors followed by a series of negative errors followed by more positive errors. Remember that the errors are calculated as the actual value minus the predicted value for each observation.

Now let us consider the multiple regression model. The process is the same. **First**, are the coefficients logical? That is, do they have the expected signs based on business/economic logic? The results of interest are:

| Variable | Coefficient |
|---|---|
| DPIPC | 3.227 |
| UMICS | 1,123.363 |
| UR | −7,659.605 |
| PR | −3,216.777 |

For income (DPIPC), we expect a positive relationship, which we find. The same is true for the University of Michigan Index of Consumer Sentiment (UMICS). For the unemployment rate (UR) and the prime interest rate (PR), we expect and find a negative relationship with sales. So the model is logical. Note that we have said nothing about the intercept (or constant). This is because, for the present purpose, this value has no particular importance for us. It simply places the function at some height in hyperspace and has nothing to do with the causality we are interested in evaluating.

**Second,** we want to evaluate the statistical significance. As before, we will use a 95 percent confidence level (5 percent significance level). Consider the following values from Table 5.2:

|  | Coefficients | *t* Stat | P-value | P/2 |
|---|---|---|---|---|
| DPIPC | 3.227 | 8.240 | 0.000 | 0.000 |
| UMICS | 1,123.363 | 5.335 | 0.000 | 0.000 |
| UR | −7,659.605 | −4.610 | 0.000 | 0.000 |
| PR | −3,216.777 | −2.277 | 0.027 | 0.013 |

Each *t*-statistic is calculated by dividing the coefficient by its standard error. (If you do this by hand, you may get slightly different *t*-statistics due to rounding.) The table *t*-statistic at n-(k + 1) = 60 − (4 + 1) = 55 degrees of freedom is 1.654 using the infinity row of the *t*-table for a one tailed test and a 0.05 significance level. All of our calculated *t*-statistics are larger than 1.645 in absolute terms, so we can conclude that we have statistical support for the hypotheses that DPIPC and the UMICS have a positive relationship with new car sales and that the UR and PR have an inverse (negative) relationship with new car sales.

Let's think about this in a slightly different way: as the *t*-value gets bigger (in absolute value), we move toward a tail of the *t*-distribution, and as we move into the tails of the distribution, the remaining area gets smaller. That remaining area is called a P-value. All statistical software provides a two tailed P-value (although they rarely tell you that explicitly). In business/economics, we often (maybe usually) have a directional or one-tailed hypothesis such as for DPIPC, UMICS, UR, and PR in our present example. If we divide the two-tailed P-value by two, we get the P-value for a one-tailed test. If P/2 is smaller than our desired significance level, the calculated $t$-statistic must be larger than the corresponding table value of $t$. This means that if P/2 is smaller than 0.05 (for our 95 percent confidence level), we can reject the null hypothesis and conclude that the independent variable has a statistically significant influence on the dependent variable. Looking at P-values is what most analysts do. It is quicker and in some cases actually more accurate. In our present example, we see that all of the P/2 values are less than 0.05. Thus, all four independent variables are found to have a significant influence on NCS at a 95 percent level of confidence.

**Third,** we are interested in the explanatory power of our model. We still want to use the coefficient of determination. But with multiple regression, this is measured by something known as the adjusted $R$-square. This is a normal part of the output from statistical software. You see in Table 5.2 for the current model the adjusted $R^2 = 0.816$. Thus, this model explains 81.6 percent of the variation in NCS.

In evaluating multiple-regression equations, you should always consider the adjusted $R$-squared value. The reason for the adjustment is that adding another independent variable will always increase $R$-squared, even if the variable has no meaningful relation to the dependent variable. Indeed, if we added enough independent variables, we could get very close to an $R$-squared of 1.00—a perfect fit for the historical period. However, the model would probably work very poorly for values of the independent variables other than those used in estimation. To get around this and to show only meaningful changes in $R$-squared, an adjustment is made to account for a decrease in the number of degrees of freedom.[3] The adjusted $R$-squared is often denoted $\bar{R}^2$ (called $R$-bar-squared or the multiple coefficient of determination).

For our multiple-regression model of new car sales (NCS), we see, in Table 5.2, that the adjusted $R$-squared is 81.6 percent. Thus, this model explains 81.6 percent of the variation in new car sales. This compares with an $R$-squared of 22.8 percent for the bivariate model (using only DPIPC as an independent variable).

In looking at regression output, you often see an $F$-statistic. This statistic can be used to test the following joint hypothesis:

$$H_0 : \beta_1 = \beta_2 = \beta_3 = \cdots = \beta_k = 0 \quad \text{or } H_0 : R^2 = 0$$

(i.e., all slope terms are simultaneously equal to zero);

$$H_1 : \text{All slope terms are not simultaneously equal to zero or } H_1 : R^2 \neq 0$$

If the null hypothesis is true, it follows that none of the variation in the dependent variable would be explained by the regression model. It follows that if $H_0$ is true, the true coefficient of determination would be zero.

---

[3] These concepts are expanded in J. Scott Armstrong, *Long-Range Forecasting* (New York: John Wiley & Sons, 1978), pp. 323–25, 466.

The *F*-statistic is calculated as follows:

$$F = \frac{\text{Explained variation}/K}{\text{Unexplained variation}/[n - (K + 1)]}$$

The *F*-test is a test of the overall significance of the estimated multiple regression. To test the hypothesis, this calculated *F*-statistic is compared with the *F*-value from Table 5.3 at *K* degrees of freedom for the numerator and $n - (K + 1)$ degrees of freedom for the denominator.[4] For our current regression, $K = 4$ and $[n - (K + 1)] = 55$, so the table value of *F* is 2.53 (taking the closest value). In using an *F*-test, the criterion for rejection of the null hypothesis is that $F_{calc} > F_T$ (the calculated *F* must be greater than the table value). In this case, the calculated value is 66.257, so we would reject $H_0$ (i.e., our equation passes the *F*-test).

**TABLE 5.3**   **Critical Values of the *F*-Distribution at a 95 Percent Confidence Level ($\alpha = .05$)**

|     | 1* | 2 | 3 | 4 | 5 | 6 | 7 | 8 | 9 |
|-----|-----|-----|-----|-----|-----|-----|-----|-----|-----|
| 1† | 161.40 | 199.50 | 215.70 | 224.60 | 230.20 | 234.00 | 236.80 | 238.90 | 240.50 |
| 2 | 18.51 | 19.00 | 19.16 | 19.25 | 19.30 | 19.33 | 19.35 | 19.37 | 19.38 |
| 3 | 10.13 | 9.55 | 9.28 | 9.12 | 9.01 | 8.94 | 8.89 | 8.85 | 8.81 |
| 4 | 7.71 | 6.94 | 6.59 | 6.39 | 6.26 | 6.16 | 6.09 | 6.04 | 6.00 |
| 5 | 6.61 | 5.79 | 5.41 | 5.19 | 5.05 | 4.95 | 4.88 | 4.82 | 4.77 |
| 6 | 5.99 | 5.14 | 4.76 | 4.53 | 4.39 | 4.28 | 4.21 | 4.15 | 4.10 |
| 7 | 5.59 | 4.74 | 4.35 | 4.12 | 3.97 | 3.87 | 3.79 | 3.73 | 3.68 |
| 8 | 5.32 | 4.46 | 4.07 | 3.84 | 3.69 | 3.58 | 3.50 | 3.44 | 3.39 |
| 9 | 5.12 | 4.26 | 3.86 | 3.63 | 3.48 | 3.37 | 3.29 | 3.23 | 3.18 |
| 10 | 4.96 | 4.10 | 3.71 | 3.48 | 3.33 | 3.22 | 3.14 | 3.07 | 3.02 |
| 11 | 4.84 | 3.98 | 3.59 | 3.36 | 3.20 | 3.09 | 3.01 | 2.95 | 2.90 |
| 12 | 4.75 | 3.89 | 3.49 | 3.26 | 3.11 | 3.00 | 2.91 | 2.85 | 2.80 |
| 13 | 4.67 | 3.81 | 3.41 | 3.18 | 3.03 | 2.92 | 2.83 | 2.77 | 2.71 |
| 14 | 4.60 | 3.74 | 3.34 | 3.11 | 2.96 | 2.85 | 2.76 | 2.70 | 2.65 |
| 15 | 4.54 | 3.68 | 3.29 | 3.06 | 2.90 | 2.79 | 2.71 | 2.64 | 2.59 |
| 16 | 4.49 | 3.63 | 3.24 | 3.01 | 2.85 | 2.74 | 2.66 | 2.59 | 2.54 |
| 17 | 4.45 | 3.59 | 3.20 | 2.96 | 2.81 | 2.70 | 2.61 | 2.55 | 2.49 |
| 18 | 4.41 | 3.55 | 3.16 | 2.93 | 2.77 | 2.66 | 2.58 | 2.51 | 2.46 |
| 19 | 4.38 | 3.52 | 3.13 | 2.90 | 2.74 | 2.63 | 2.54 | 2.48 | 2.42 |
| 20 | 4.35 | 3.49 | 3.10 | 2.87 | 2.71 | 2.60 | 2.51 | 2.45 | 2.39 |
| 21 | 4.32 | 3.47 | 3.07 | 2.84 | 2.68 | 2.57 | 2.49 | 2.42 | 2.37 |
| 22 | 4.30 | 3.44 | 3.05 | 2.82 | 2.66 | 2.55 | 2.46 | 2.40 | 2.34 |

(continued on next page)

[4] This *F*-table corresponds to a 95 percent confidence level ($\alpha = 0.05$). You could use any $\alpha$ value and the corresponding *F*-distribution.

**TABLE 5.3** (continued)

|     | 1* | 2 | 3 | 4 | 5 | 6 | 7 | 8 | 9 |
|-----|------|------|------|------|------|------|------|------|------|
| 23  | 4.28 | 3.42 | 3.03 | 2.80 | 2.64 | 2.53 | 2.44 | 2.37 | 2.32 |
| 24  | 4.26 | 3.40 | 3.01 | 2.78 | 2.62 | 2.51 | 2.42 | 2.36 | 2.30 |
| 25  | 4.24 | 3.39 | 2.99 | 2.76 | 2.60 | 2.49 | 2.40 | 2.34 | 2.28 |
| 26  | 4.23 | 3.37 | 2.98 | 2.74 | 2.59 | 2.47 | 2.39 | 2.32 | 2.27 |
| 27  | 4.21 | 3.35 | 2.96 | 2.73 | 2.57 | 2.46 | 2.37 | 2.31 | 2.25 |
| 28  | 4.20 | 3.34 | 2.95 | 2.71 | 2.56 | 2.45 | 2.36 | 2.29 | 2.24 |
| 29  | 4.18 | 3.33 | 2.93 | 2.70 | 2.55 | 2.43 | 2.35 | 2.28 | 2.22 |
| 30  | 4.17 | 3.32 | 2.92 | 2.69 | 2.53 | 2.42 | 2.33 | 2.27 | 2.21 |
| 40  | 4.08 | 3.23 | 2.84 | 2.61 | 2.45 | 2.34 | 2.25 | 2.18 | 2.12 |
| 60  | 4.00 | 3.15 | 2.76 | 2.53 | 2.37 | 2.25 | 2.17 | 2.10 | 2.04 |
| 120 | 3.92 | 3.07 | 2.68 | 2.45 | 2.29 | 2.17 | 2.09 | 2.02 | 1.96 |
| ∞   | 3.84 | 3.00 | 2.60 | 2.37 | 2.21 | 2.10 | 2.01 | 1.94 | 1.88 |

* Degrees of freedom for the numerator = $K$
† Degrees of freedom for the denominator = $n - (K + 1)$

**Fourth,** we want to consider the Durbin-Watson test for serial correlation. In this example, n = 60 and k = 4. Looking at Table 4.11, we find $D_l = 1.44$ and $D_u = 1.73$. Because of our calculated DW = 1.376 (smaller than $D_l$), we still have positive serial correlation. We will come back to the serial correlation issue again. For now, let us comment that this DW is for a lag of one period. For seasonal data, it is better to use a lag associated with the seasonality: a lag of four for quarterly data and a lag of 12 for monthly data.

The **fifth** step in evaluation for a multiple regression model is new, so we will devote a new topic to that discussion.

## Multicollinearity

In multiple-regression analysis, one of the assumptions that is made is that the independent variables are not highly linearly correlated with each other or with linear combinations of other independent variables. If this assumption is violated, a problem known as *multicollinearity* results. If your regression results show that one or more independent variables appear not to be statistically significant when theory suggests that they should be, and/or if the signs on coefficients are not logical, multicollinearity may be indicated. Sometimes it is possible to spot the cause of the multicollinearity by looking at a correlation matrix for the independent variables.

To illustrate the multicollinearity problem, suppose that we model new homes sold (NHS) as a function of disposable personal income (DPIPC), the mortgage interest rate (MR), and the gross domestic product (GDP). The model would be:

$$NHS = b_0 + b_1(DPIPC) + b_2(GDP) + b_3(MR)$$

Business and economic logic would tell us to expect a positive sign for $b_1$, a positive sign for $b_2$, and a negative sign for $b_3$. The actual regression results are:

| | Coefficient | t-Ratio |
|---|---|---|
| Constant | 1,884 | 2.09 |
| DPIPC | *-0.01* | -0.21 |
| GDP | 0.23 | 2.83 |
| IR | -147.82 | -5.25 |

We see that the coefficient for DPIPC is negative, which does not make sense. It would be difficult to argue persuasively that NHS would fall as DPIPC rises.

If we look at the correlations between these variables, we can see the source of the problem. The correlations are:

| | DPIPC | GDP | IR |
|---|---|---|---|
| DPIPC | 1 | | |
| GDP | *0.99* | 1 | |
| IR | -0.65 | -0.67 | 1 |

Clearly, there is a very strong linear association between GDP and DPIPC. In this case, both of these variables are measuring essentially the same thing. There are no firm rules in deciding how strong a correlation is too great. Two rules of thumb, however, provide some guidance. First, we might avoid correlations between independent variables that are close to 1 in absolute value. Second, we might try to avoid situations in which the correlation between independent variables is greater than the correlation of those variables with the dependent variable. One thing to do when multicollinearity exists is to drop all but one of the highly correlated variables. The use of first differences can also help when there is a common trend in the two highly correlated independent variables.

Now let us consider multicollinearity in the context of the NCS multiple regression. We have no reason to suspect a problem since the results are logical and statistically significant as business/economic concepts would suggest. The correlation matrix for the independent variables is shown below.

| | UMICS | DPIPC | PR | UR |
|---|---|---|---|---|
| UMICS | 1.00 | | | |
| DPIPC | -0.16 | 1.00 | | |
| PR | 0.25 | -0.43 | 1.00 | |
| UR | -0.68 | 0.15 | -0.62 | 1.00 |

Note that no pair of independent variables has a correlation that is close to 1.0. The correlations of 1.00 along the main diagonal are to be expected. They simply tell us that each variable is perfectly correlated with itself. No surprise there. You might ask what does "close to 1.0" mean? There is no concrete answer that we can use here. It is best not to have any correlation that is in the +/− 0.9s. The +/− 0.8s are also good to avoid, especially if you see more than one in that size range. Ideally, all the correlations would be zero, but that is unrealistic in a business/economic environment. A situation such as shown by the correlation matrix above is good enough.

## Serial Correlation: An Extended Look

*Serial correlation results when there is a significant time pattern in the error terms of a regression analysis.*

The problem known as *serial correlation* was introduced in Chapter 4, where we indicated that serial correlation results when there is a significant time pattern in the error terms of a regression analysis that violates the assumption that the errors are independent over time. Positive serial correlation, as shown in the right-hand graph of Figure 4.11 (page 185), is common with business and economic data.

A test involving comparisons between table values of the Durbin-Watson statistic and the calculated Durbin-Watson statistic is commonly used to detect serial correlation. These comparisons are repeated here, where $d_l$ and $d_u$ represent the lower and upper bounds of the Durbin-Watson statistic from Table 4.12 (page 187).

| Value of Calculated Durbin-Watson | Result | Region Designator |
|---|---|---|
| 4 | | |
| | Negative serial correlation (reject $H_0$) | A |
| $4 - d_l$ | | |
| | Indeterminate | B |
| $4 - d_u$ | | |
| 2 | No serial correlation (do not reject $H_0$) | C |
| $d_u$ | | |
| | Indeterminate | D |
| $d_l$ | | |
| | Positive serial correlation (reject $H_0$) | E |
| 0 | | |

In Table 5.2, you see that for the bivariate regression of NCS with DPIPC, the DW is 0.283, indicating positive serial correlation.

For the multiple regression of NCS with DPIPC, UMICS, UR, and PR, the calculated Durbin-Watson statistic is 1.376. (See Table 5.2, which has DW for both the bivariate and the multiple regressions.) This satisfies the region "E" test:

$$DW < d_l$$
$$1.376 < 1.44$$

where $d_l$ is found from Table 4.11 for $k = 4$ and $N = 60$. Thus, we conclude that this model also has positive serial correlation. This is an improvement in the DW test for serial correlation, but we have yet to solve the problem. When a regression fails the Durbin-Watson test, the usual interpretation is that this represents the effect of an omitted or unobservable variable (or variables) on the dependent variable. The easiest correction is to collect data on the omitted variable and include it in a new formulation of the model; if the correct variable is added, the serial correlation problem will disappear. However, it is often difficult to identify and measure the missing construct.

In practice, it is often assumed that a first-order check for serial correlation of the residuals will suffice. Remember that the normal Durbin-Watson statistic checks the error terms for serial correlation by comparing errors that are lagged a single period.

When quarterly (or monthly) data are employed, however, the presence of nonsystematic seasonal variation, or an incomplete accounting for seasonality by the included variables, will produce seasonal effects in the error terms, with the consequence that the fourth-order (or 12th order) serial correlation may be significant.

The Durbin-Watson statistic has then been generalized to test for such upper-order instances of serial correlation in the error terms. The fourth-order test statistic has a distribution that differs from that of the normal Durbin-Watson statistic and tables of its critical values as presented in Table 4.7. However, the differences are small, and the user may wish to simply use Table 4.7 to interpret the upper-order Durbin-Watson statistics.[5] When a regression with quarterly (or monthly) data fails the DW(4 or 12) test for serial correlation among the error terms, the usual culprit is that the seasonality in the data has not been fully accounted for by the variables included.

# SERIAL CORRELATION AND THE OMITTED-VARIABLE PROBLEM

*The most common reason for serial correlation is that an important explanatory variable has been omitted.*

The most common reason for serial correlation is that an important explanatory variable has been omitted. To address this situation, it will often be necessary to add an additional explanatory variable to the equation to correct for serial correlation. In Table 5.4 you see that both price and income data are available to use in the model.

In the first regression displayed in Table 5.5, price is used as the single independent variable to explain the firm's sales (the bivariate regression). The results are less than satisfactory on a number of accounts. Most importantly, the sign on the price coefficient is positive, indicating that as price increases, sales also increase. This is inconsistent with business/economic theory and reality. Second, the $R$-squared is quite low, explaining only about 39 percent of the variation in

---

[5] For a table showing the exact critical values of the Durbin-Watson statistic for quarterly data (both with and without seasonal dummy variables), see the K. F. Wallis article in the Suggested Readings list at the end of this chapter.

**TABLE 5.4**
**Quarterly Data
for a Firm's Unit
Sales, the Price the
Firm Charges for
Its Product, and the
Income of Potential
Purchasers.**   (c5t4)

| PERIOD | Unit SALES | PRICE | INCOME |
|---|---|---|---|
| Mar-13 | 80 | 5.00 | 2620 |
| Jun-13 | 86 | 4.87 | 2733 |
| Sep-13 | 93 | 4.86 | 2898 |
| Dec-13 | 99 | 4.79 | 3056 |
| Mar-14 | 106 | 4.79 | 3271 |
| Jun-14 | 107 | 4.87 | 3479 |
| Sep-14 | 109 | 5.01 | 3736 |
| Dec-14 | 110 | 5.31 | 3868 |
| Mar-15 | 111 | 5.55 | 4016 |
| Jun-15 | 113 | 5.72 | 4152 |
| Sep-15 | 110 | 5.74 | 4336 |
| Dec-15 | 112 | 5.59 | 4477 |
| Mar-16 | 131 | 5.50 | 4619 |
| Jun-16 | 136 | 5.48 | 4764 |
| Sep-16 | 137 | 5.47 | 4802 |
| Dec-16 | 139 | 5.49 | 4916 |

**TABLE 5.5**   **Statistical Regression Results Based on the Data in Table 5.4. The results shown are from ForecastX™**   (c5t4)

### The Bivariate Regression

Audit Trail--Coefficient Table (Multiple Regression Selected)

| Series Description | Included in Model | Coefficient | Standard Error | T-test | P-value | Overall F-test |
|---|---|---|---|---|---|---|
| Sales | Dependent | −51.24 | 54.32 | −0.94 | 0.36 | 8.98 |
| Price | Yes | 30.92 | 10.32 | 3.00 | 0.01 | |

Audit Trail--Statistics

| Accuracy Measures | Value | Forecast Statistics | Value |
|---|---|---|---|
| AIC | 130.02 | Durbin Watson (1) | 0.34 |
| BIC | 130.80 | | |
| Mean Absolute Percentage Error (MAPE) | 10.67% | | |
| R-Square | 39.07% | | |
| Adjusted R-Square | 39.07% | | |

### Multiple Regression

Audit Trail--Coefficient Table (Multiple Regression Selected)

| Series Description | Included in Model | Coefficient | Standard Error | T-test | P-value | Overall F-test |
|---|---|---|---|---|---|---|
| Sales | Dependent | 123.47 | 19.40 | 6.36 | 0.00 | 154.86 |
| Price | Yes | −24.84 | 4.95 | −5.02 | 0.00 | |
| Income | Yes | 0.03 | 0.00 | 13.55 | 0.00 | |

(continued on next page)

**TABLE 5.5**   (continued)

| Audit Trail--Statistics | | | | |
|---|---|---|---|---|
| Accuracy Measures | Value | | Forecast Statistics | Value |
| AIC | 86.56 | | Durbin Watson (1) | 1.67 |
| BIC | 87.34 | | | |
| Mean Absolute Percentage Error (MAPE) | 2.22% | | | |
| R-Square | 95.97% | | | |
| Adjusted R-Square | 95.97% | | | |

sales. Furthermore, the DW statistic is 0.34, indicating positive serial correlation. See the upper graph in Figure 5.5.

The problem may be that an important variable that could account for the large errors and the incorrect sign of the price coefficient has been omitted from the regression. The second regression in Table 5.5 adds income as a second explanatory variable. The results are dramatic. The adjusted $R$-squared shows that the model now accounts for about 96 percent of the variation in sales. The signs of both the explanatory variable coefficients are as expected. The price coefficient is negative, indicating that unit sales decrease as price increases, while the income coefficient is positive, indicating that sales of the good rise as incomes increase (which would be reasonable for a "normal" economic good). See the lower graph in Figure 5.5.

The Durbin-Watson statistic (1.67) is within the rule-of-thumb 1.5 to 2.5 range. There does not seem to be serial correlation (and so the $R$-squared and $t$-statistics are probably accurate). The formal test for serial correlation requires us to look for the upper and lower values in the Durbin-Watson table (Table 4.11). Note carefully that the appropriate values are 0.95 and 1.54 (i.e., $N = 15$ and column $k = 2$).

| Value of Calculated Durbin-Watson | Result | Region Designator and Result | |
|---|---|---|---|
| 4 | | | |
| | Negative serial correlation (reject $H_0$) | A | False |
| $4 - d_l$ | | | |
| | Indeterminate | B | False |
| $4 - d_u$ | | | |
| 2 | No serial correlation (do not reject $H_0$) | C | True |
| $d_u$ | | | |
| | Indeterminate | D | False |
| $d_l$ | | | |
| | Positive serial correlation (reject $H_0$) | E | False |
| 0 | | | |

**FIGURE 5.5** **Graphs for the Two Models from Table 5.5** In the Upper Graph, the Positive Serial Correlation is Clear, Errors are Negative for Early Observations, then Positive for Awhile, then Negative, then Positive. In the Lower Graph, there is Not Such a Distinctive Pattern (c5t4)

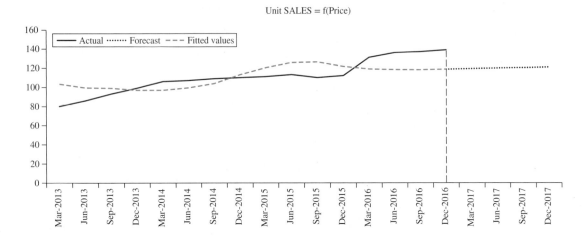

Unit SALES = f(Price)

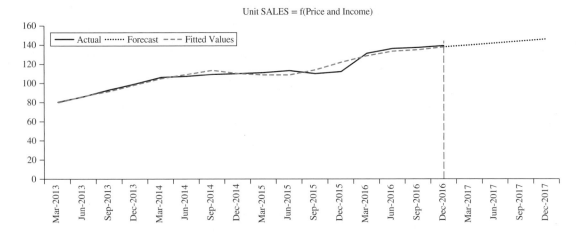

Unit SALES = f(Price and Income)

Using these Durbin-Watson (DW) values and our calculated value, we see that the following is true: $1.54 < 1.67 < 2$. Thus, we can conclude that no serial correlation is present. Since our result is true for test C, we conclude that no serial correlation is present. Apparently, the addition of the second explanatory variable explained the pattern in the residuals that the Durbin-Watson statistic identified.

## Alternative-Variable Selection Criteria

There is a strong tendency for forecasters to use a single criterion for deciding which of several variables ought to be used as independent variables in a regression. The criterion many people use appears to be the coefficient of determination, or *R*-squared. Recall that *R*-squared is a measure of the proportion of total variance accounted for by the linear influence of the explanatory variables (only *linear* influence is accounted for, since we are using linear least-squares regression). The *R*-squared measure has at least one obvious fault when used in this manner: it can be increased by simply increasing the number of independent variables. Because of this, we proposed the corrected or adjusted *R*-squared, which uses unbiased estimators of the respective variances. Most forecasters use the adjusted *R*-squared to lead them to the correct model by selecting the model that maximizes adjusted *R*-squared. The adjusted *R*-squared measure is based on selecting the correct model by using a quadratic form of the residuals or squared errors in which the true model minimizes those squared errors. But the adjusted *R*-squared measure may not be the most powerful of the measures involving the squared errors.

There are two other
model-specification
statistics reported by
ForecastX™ and other
statistical packages
that can be of use in
selecting the "correct"
independent variables.

There are two other model-specification statistics reported by ForecastX™ and other statistical packages that can be of use in selecting the "correct" independent variables. These are the Akaike information criterion (AIC) and the Bayesian information criterion (BIC).[6]

The Akaike information criterion selects the best model by considering the accuracy of the estimation and the "best" approximation to reality. The statistic (which is minimized by the best model) involves both the use of a measure of the accuracy of the estimate *and* a measure of the principle of parsimony (i.e., the concept that fewer independent variables are better than more, all other things being equal). The calculation of the AIC is detailed in Judge and coauthors.[7] We

In actual practice, a
decrease in the AIC
as a variable is added
indicates that accuracy
has increased after
adjustment for the rule
of parsimony.

can say that the statistic is constructed so that, as the number of independent variables increases, the AIC has a tendency to increase as well; this means that there is a penalty for "extra" independent variables that must be sufficiently offset by an increase in estimation accuracy to keep the AIC from increasing. In actual practice, a decrease in the AIC as a variable is added indicates that accuracy has increased after adjustment for the rule of parsimony.

The Bayesian criterion is quite similar to the AIC. The BIC uses Bayesian arguments about the prior probability of the true model to suggest the correct model. While the calculation routine for the BIC is quite different from that for the AIC, the results are usually quite consistent.[8] The BIC is also to be minimized, so that, if the BIC decreases after the addition of a new independent variable, the resulting model specification is seen as superior to the prior model specification. Often, AIC and BIC lead to the same model choice.

In a study of the model-selection process, Judge and coauthors created five independent variables that were to be used to estimate a dependent variable. Two of the five independent variables were actually related to the dependent variable,

[6] The Bayesian information criterion is also called the Schwarz information criterion, after its creator.

[7] For a complete description of the calculation routine, see George G. Judge, R. Carter Hill, William E. Griffiths, Helmut Lutkepohl, and Tsoung-Chao Lee, *Introduction to the Theory and Practice of Econometrics*, 2nd ed. (New York: John Wiley & Sons, 1988), chapter 20.

[8] Again see Judge et al. for a complete description of the calculation routine.

while the remaining three were extraneous variables. Various combinations of the five independent variables were used to estimate the dependent variable, and three measures were used to select the "best" model. The three measures used were the adjusted $R$-squared, the AIC, and the BIC.

The correct model containing only the two variables actually related to the dependent variable was chosen 27 percent of the time in repeated experiments by the adjusted $R$-squared criterion. The AIC chose the correct model in 45 percent of the cases, and the BIC chose the correct model in 46 percent of the cases. The results should make the forecaster wary of accepting only the statistical results of what constitutes the best model without some economic interpretation of why a variable is included. It should be clear, however, that the adjusted $R$-squared criterion may not always be the best measure to use in model selection; either the AIC or the BIC would usually be superior. The same study also showed that in 9 percent of the repeated trials the adjusted $R$-squared criterion chose the model with all five variables (i.e., the two "correct" ones and the three extraneous ones). The AIC and the BIC made the same incorrect choice in only 3 percent of the cases.

In Table 5.5, we added a second variable to a regression. When both price and income were included, the AIC decreased from 130.02 to 86.56, and the BIC decreased to 87.34 from 130.80. Apparently, the inclusion of income as a variable was a correct choice.

There is a clear indication of a better identified model if the two competing models differ by more than 10 in their AIC score.

How much of a decrease in the Akaike information criterion constitutes a "better" model? According to Hirotugu Akaike, there is a clear indication of a better identified model if the two competing models differ by more than 10 in their AIC score. If the difference is between 4 and 7, there is much less certainty that a clear winner has emerged. If the difference in AIC scores is 2 or less, then both candidate models have strong support. For this example, the differences in the Akaike scores between the candidate models exceeded 10, and therefore, the second model was clearly the best identified model.

The researcher should not compare the AIC or BIC of one series with the AIC or BIC of another series; the assumption is that models with identical dependent variables are being compared. There is no easy interpretation of the magnitude of the AIC and BIC, nor is one necessary. Only the relative size of the statistics is important.

# ACCOUNTING FOR SEASONALITY IN A MULTIPLE-REGRESSION MODEL

Many business and economic data series display pronounced seasonal patterns that recur with some regularity year after year. The pattern may be associated with weather conditions typical of the four seasons of the year. For example, sales of ski equipment would be expected to be greater during the fall and winter (the fourth and first quarters of the calendar year, respectively) than during the spring and summer (the second and third quarters).

Other regular patterns that would be referred to as seasonal patterns may have nothing to do with weather conditions. For example, jewelry sales in the United States tend to be high in November and December because of Christmas shopping and gift giving, and turkey sales are also highest in these months because of traditional Thanksgiving and Christmas dinners.

Patterns such as these are not easily accounted for by the typical causal variables that we use in regression analysis. However, a special type of variable known as a dummy variable can be used effectively to account for seasonality or many other qualitative attributes. The dependent variable in a regression is often influenced not only by continuous variables such as income, price, and advertising expenditures but also by variables that may be qualitative or nominally scaled (such as the season of the year). A dummy variable takes on a value of either 0 or 1. It is 0 if the condition does not exist for an observation, and it is 1 if the condition does exist.

Suppose that we were studying monthly data on turkey sales at grocery stores and we would like to include the November and December seasonality in our model. We could define a dummy variable called M11, for the eleventh month, to be equal to 1 for November observations and 0 otherwise. Another dummy variable, M12, could be defined similarly for December. Thus, for every year these variables would be as follows:

| Month | M11 | M12 | Month | M11 | M12 |
|---|---|---|---|---|---|
| January | 0 | 0 | July | 0 | 0 |
| February | 0 | 0 | August | 0 | 0 |
| March | 0 | 0 | September | 0 | 0 |
| April | 0 | 0 | October | 0 | 0 |
| May | 0 | 0 | November | 1 | 0 |
| June | 0 | 0 | December | 0 | 1 |

In the regression results, the coefficients for M11 and M12 would reveal the degree of difference in sales for November and December, respectively, compared to other months of the year. In both of these cases, we would expect the coefficients to be positive (indicating that sales in these two months were higher, on average than in the remaining months of the year).

To illustrate very specifically the use of dummy variables to account for and measure seasonality, let us use new cars sold (NCS) in the United States measured in millions of dollars (not seasonally adjusted). These data were first plotted in Figure 5.1 and again here in Figure 5.6. You see in this figure that through the five years, there are lower new car sales during the first quarter than in the other quarters of the year; in most years, there is a peak in sales sometime during the summer months (quarter 3). This pattern is reasonably consistent, although there is variability in the degree of seasonality and some deviation from the overall pattern.

**FIGURE 5.6**

**Total New Cars Sold (NCS)** (c5f6)

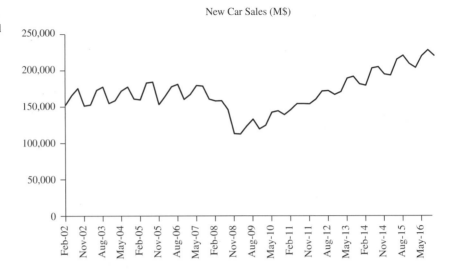

New Car Sales (M$)

To account for and measure this seasonality in the NCS regression model, we will use three dummy variables: These will be coded as follows:

$$Q2 = 1 \text{ for quarter 2 and zero otherwise}$$
$$Q3 = 1 \text{ for quarter 3 and zero otherwise}$$
$$Q4 = 1 \text{ for quarter 4 and zero otherwise}$$

Data for new cars sold (NCS), disposable personal income per capita (DPIPC), the University of Michigan Index of Consumer Sentiment (UMICS), the unemployment rate (UR), the bank prime loan rate (PR), and the three seasonal dummy variables are shown in Table 5.6. **Examine the data carefully to verify your understanding of the coding of the seasonal dummy variables.**

Since we have assigned dummy variables for each quarter except quarter 1, the first quarter is the base quarter for our regression model. Any quarter could be used as the base, with dummy variables to adjust for differences attributed to the other quarters. The number of seasonal dummy variables to use depends upon the data. There is one important rule (the Iron Rule of Dummy Variables):

If we have $P$ states of nature, we cannot use more than $P - 1$ dummy variables.

In our current example, $P = 4$, since we have quarterly data, and so we would use only 3 seasonal dummy variables at a maximum. There are 4 states of nature: the 4 quarters in the year. We could use fewer than 3 if we found that all 3 were unnecessary by evaluating their statistical significance by $t$-tests. But if we violate the rule and use 4 dummy variables to represent all the quarters, we create a situation of perfect multicollinearity (because there is more than one exact relationship among the variables).

**TABLE 5.6**   Data for New Cars Sold (NCS), Disposable Personal Income per Capita (DPIPC), the University of Michigan Index of Consumer Sentiment (UMICS), the Unemployment Rate (UR), the Bank Prime Loan Rate (PR), and Three Seasonal Dummy Variables   (c5t6&f7)

| Date | New Car Sales (M$) | DPIPC | UMICS | UR | PR | Q2 | Q3 | Q4 |
|------|--------------------|-------|-------|-----|------|-----|-----|-----|
| Feb-02 | 152,641 | 27,840 | 93.13 | 5.70 | 4.75 | 0 | 0 | 0 |
| May-02 | 166,036 | 28,134 | 94.10 | 5.83 | 4.75 | 1 | 0 | 0 |
| Aug-02 | 175,863 | 28,168 | 87.27 | 5.73 | 4.75 | 0 | 1 | 0 |
| Nov-02 | 151,219 | 28,363 | 83.83 | 5.87 | 4.45 | 0 | 0 | 1 |
| Feb-03 | 152,843 | 28,584 | 79.97 | 5.87 | 4.25 | 0 | 0 | 0 |
| May-03 | 173,360 | 28,958 | 89.27 | 6.13 | 4.24 | 1 | 0 | 0 |
| Aug-03 | 178,086 | 29,539 | 89.30 | 6.13 | 4.00 | 0 | 1 | 0 |
| Nov-03 | 154,916 | 29,708 | 91.97 | 5.83 | 4.00 | 0 | 0 | 1 |
| Feb-04 | 159,086 | 30,094 | 98.00 | 5.70 | 4.00 | 0 | 0 | 0 |
| May-04 | 172,174 | 30,537 | 93.33 | 5.60 | 4.00 | 1 | 0 | 0 |
| Aug-04 | 178,077 | 30,800 | 95.60 | 5.43 | 4.42 | 0 | 1 | 0 |
| Nov-04 | 161,216 | 31,353 | 93.87 | 5.43 | 4.94 | 0 | 0 | 1 |
| Feb-05 | 160,070 | 31,145 | 94.07 | 5.30 | 5.44 | 0 | 0 | 0 |
| May-05 | 183,594 | 31,533 | 90.20 | 5.10 | 5.91 | 1 | 0 | 0 |
| Aug-05 | 184,878 | 31,961 | 87.50 | 4.97 | 6.43 | 0 | 1 | 0 |
| Nov-05 | 153,405 | 32,396 | 82.43 | 4.97 | 6.97 | 0 | 0 | 1 |
| Feb-06 | 164,864 | 33,217 | 88.93 | 4.73 | 7.43 | 0 | 0 | 0 |
| May-06 | 178,363 | 33,448 | 83.80 | 4.63 | 7.90 | 1 | 0 | 0 |
| Aug-06 | 181,615 | 33,696 | 84.03 | 4.63 | 8.25 | 0 | 1 | 0 |
| Nov-06 | 160,780 | 33,991 | 92.47 | 4.43 | 8.25 | 0 | 0 | 1 |
| Feb-07 | 167,528 | 34,457 | 92.20 | 4.50 | 8.25 | 0 | 0 | 0 |
| May-07 | 180,006 | 34,720 | 86.90 | 4.50 | 8.25 | 1 | 0 | 0 |
| Aug-07 | 179,216 | 34,918 | 85.73 | 4.67 | 8.18 | 0 | 1 | 0 |
| Nov-07 | 160,957 | 35,209 | 77.50 | 4.80 | 7.52 | 0 | 0 | 1 |
| Feb-08 | 158,369 | 35,688 | 72.90 | 5.00 | 6.21 | 0 | 0 | 0 |
| May-08 | 158,761 | 36,742 | 59.60 | 5.33 | 5.08 | 1 | 0 | 0 |
| Aug-08 | 146,003 | 36,175 | 64.83 | 6.00 | 5.00 | 0 | 1 | 0 |
| Nov-08 | 112,460 | 35,801 | 57.67 | 6.87 | 4.06 | 0 | 0 | 1 |
| Feb-09 | 111,819 | 35,459 | 58.27 | 8.27 | 3.25 | 0 | 0 | 0 |
| May-09 | 122,950 | 35,798 | 68.20 | 9.30 | 3.25 | 1 | 0 | 0 |
| Aug-09 | 132,705 | 35,546 | 68.40 | 9.63 | 3.25 | 0 | 1 | 0 |
| Nov-09 | 119,091 | 35,658 | 70.17 | 9.93 | 3.25 | 0 | 0 | 1 |
| Feb-10 | 124,117 | 35,744 | 73.87 | 9.83 | 3.25 | 1 | 0 | 0 |
| May-10 | 142,278 | 36,183 | 73.93 | 9.63 | 3.25 | 0 | 1 | 0 |
| Aug-10 | 144,165 | 36,397 | 68.30 | 9.47 | 3.25 | 0 | 0 | 1 |
| Nov-10 | 138,913 | 36,770 | 71.27 | 9.50 | 3.25 | 0 | 0 | 0 |
| Feb-11 | 146,009 | 37,436 | 73.07 | 9.03 | 3.25 | 1 | 0 | 0 |
| May-11 | 154,335 | 37,692 | 71.87 | 9.07 | 3.25 | 0 | 1 | 0 |
| Aug-11 | 154,418 | 38,017 | 59.67 | 9.00 | 3.25 | 0 | 0 | 1 |
| Nov-11 | 154,026 | 38,097 | 64.80 | 8.63 | 3.25 | 0 | 0 | 0 |
| Feb-12 | 160,743 | 38,880 | 75.50 | 8.27 | 3.25 | 1 | 0 | 0 |
| May-12 | 172,000 | 39,234 | 76.30 | 8.20 | 3.25 | 0 | 1 | 0 |

(continued on next page)

**TABLE 5.6** (continued)

| Date | New Car Sales (M$) | DPIPC | UMICS | UR | PR | Q2 | Q3 | Q4 |
|------|--------------------|-------|-------|------|------|-----|-----|-----|
| Aug-12 | 172,584 | 39,266 | 74.97 | 8.03 | 3.25 | 0 | 0 | 1 |
| Nov-12 | 167,223 | 40,436 | 79.40 | 7.80 | 3.25 | 0 | 0 | 0 |
| Feb-13 | 171,221 | 38,828 | 76.67 | 7.73 | 3.25 | 1 | 0 | 0 |
| May-13 | 189,832 | 39,010 | 81.67 | 7.53 | 3.25 | 0 | 1 | 0 |
| Aug-13 | 192,517 | 39,306 | 81.57 | 7.27 | 3.25 | 0 | 0 | 1 |
| Nov-13 | 181,804 | 39,481 | 76.93 | 6.93 | 3.25 | 0 | 0 | 0 |
| Feb-14 | 179,902 | 40,049 | 80.93 | 6.67 | 3.25 | 1 | 0 | 0 |
| May-14 | 203,914 | 40,693 | 82.83 | 6.20 | 3.25 | 0 | 1 | 0 |
| Aug-14 | 205,791 | 41,128 | 82.97 | 6.10 | 3.25 | 0 | 0 | 1 |
| Nov-14 | 195,535 | 41,478 | 89.77 | 5.70 | 3.25 | 0 | 0 | 0 |
| Feb-15 | 194,135 | 41,447 | 95.50 | 5.53 | 3.25 | 1 | 0 | 0 |
| May-15 | 216,311 | 41,966 | 94.23 | 5.40 | 3.25 | 0 | 1 | 0 |
| Aug-15 | 221,493 | 42,343 | 90.73 | 5.10 | 3.25 | 0 | 0 | 1 |
| Nov-15 | 210,181 | 42,621 | 91.30 | 5.00 | 3.29 | 0 | 0 | 0 |
| Feb-16 | 204,681 | 42,807 | 91.57 | 4.93 | 3.50 | 1 | 0 | 0 |
| May-16 | 221,073 | 43,265 | 92.40 | 4.87 | 3.50 | 0 | 1 | 0 |
| Aug-16 | 229,123 | 43,651 | 90.33 | 4.90 | 3.50 | 0 | 0 | 1 |
| Nov-16 | 221,392 | 43,759 | 93.07 | 4.70 | 3.55 | 1 | 0 | 0 |

Let us now add these dummy variables to the regression model for new cars sold (NCS). Our regression model will include the following independent variables: DPIPC, UMICS, UR, PR, Q2, Q3, and Q4. The model is:

$$NCS = b_0 + b_1(DPIPC) + b_2(UMICS) + b_3(UR) + b_4(PR) + b_5(Q2) + b_6(Q3) + b_7(Q4)$$

In this model, we would expect $b_1$ to have a positive sign (because sales should increase the more disposable income people have), and we would expect $b_2$ (for the University of Michigan Index of Consumer Sentiment) to have a positive sign because when people feel good about the economy, they are more likely to make a major purchase. We should expect $b_3$ to have a negative sign (as the unemployment rate rises, fewer people are likely to be in the market for a car). We would expect $b_4$ to also be negative (as the interest rate rises, cars essentially become more expensive). For $b_5$ through $b_7$ (the seasonal dummy variables), we expect the coefficients to be positive since we selected the lowest quarter as the base quarter. It is advisable to pick the lowest season as the base so all other seasonal variables will have positive slopes. This makes evaluating statistical significance much easier.

Regression results for this model are shown in Table 5.7. We see that the model is logical (**evaluation 1**) since all coefficients have the expected signs for their coefficients. All coefficients are statistically significant (**evaluation 2**) at a 95 percent confidence level as indicated by the P/2 values, with the exception of Q2 and Q4, which have P/2 values greater than 0.05. In practice, for dummy variables, we often use a lower confidence level since the variables measure qualitative

**TABLE 5.7** **Regression Results for New Car Sales (NCS)** (c5t7)

### Audit Trail — ANOVA Table (Multiple Regression Selected)

| Source of variation | SS | df | MS | SEE | Overall F-test |
|---|---|---|---|---|---|
| Regression | 37,748,211,961.83 | 7 | 5,392,601,708.83 | | 46.81 |
| Error | 5,990,657,628.35 | 52 | 115,204,954.39 | 10,733.36 | |
| Total | 43,738,869,590.18 | 59 | | | |

### Audit Trail — Coefficient Table (Multiple Regression Selected)

| Series Description | Coefficient | Standard error | T-test | P-value | P/2 |
|---|---|---|---|---|---|
| Intercept | 32,398.89 | 34,589.87 | 0.94 | 0.35 | 0.18 |
| UMICS | 1,060.42 | 195.40 | 5.43 | 0.00 | 0.00 |
| DPIPC | 3.14 | 0.36 | 8.71 | 0.00 | 0.00 |
| UR | −8,232.04 | 1,535.96 | −5.36 | 0.00 | 0.00 |
| PR | −3,582.75 | 1,300.78 | −2.75 | 0.01 | 0.00 |
| Q2 | 5,880.09 | 3,944.63 | 1.49 | 0.14 | 0.07 |
| Q3 | 14,330.37 | 4,011.36 | 3.57 | 0.00 | 0.00 |
| Q4 | 5,138.04 | 4,006.04 | 1.28 | 0.21 | 0.10 |

### Audit Trail — Statistics

| Accuracy Measures | Value | Forecast Statistics | Value |
|---|---|---|---|
| AIC | 1,277.42 | Durbin-Watson (4) | 1.03 |
| BIC | 1,279.51 | Durbin-Watson (1) | 1.16 |
| MAPE | 5.05% | | |
| Adjusted R-Square | 84.46% | | |

attributes that are often "fuzzy" constructs. They are not as firm a value as measures such as DPIPC and other quantitative data. The adjusted $R^2 = 84.46$ percent (**evaluation 3**) so over 84 percent of the variation in NCS is explained by the model. Both DW(1) and DW(4) indicate positive serial correlation (**evaluation 4**).

The fifth step in an evaluation is to check for multicollinearity. From the correlations shown below, we see that this is not a problem for this model (**evaluation 5**).

| | New Car Sales (M$) | DPIPC | UMICS | UR | PR | Q2 | Q3 | Q4 |
|---|---|---|---|---|---|---|---|---|
| New Car Sales (M$) | 1.00 | | | | | | | |
| DPIPC | 0.48 | 1.00 | | | | | | |
| UMICS | 0.64 | −0.16 | 1.00 | | | | | |
| UR | −0.58 | 0.15 | −0.68 | 1.00 | | | | |
| PR | −0.02 | −0.43 | 0.25 | −0.62 | 1.00 | | | |
| Q2 | 0.04 | 0.03 | 0.06 | −0.01 | −0.03 | 1.00 | | |
| Q3 | 0.16 | 0.00 | 0.03 | 0.03 | 0.01 | −0.35 | 1.00 | |
| Q4 | −0.07 | 0.03 | −0.11 | 0.02 | −0.01 | −0.35 | −0.33 | 1.00 |

**FIGURE 5.7**

**A Seasonal Model for NCS**   Actual NCS and the predicted values based on the model shown in the figure title.   (c5t6&f7)

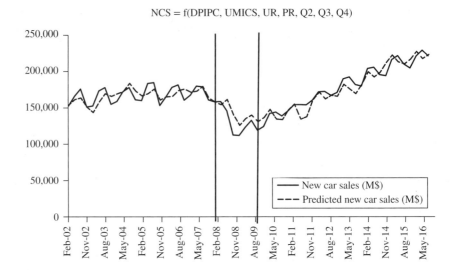

NCS = f(DPIPC, UMICS, UR, PR, Q2, Q3, Q4)

The graphic results for this model are shown in Figure 5.7. The distance between the two vertical lines is the time period usually associated with the 2008–2009 recession in the United States. This area also shows a consistent negative error between the actual and predicted value, which may contribute to the serial correlation problem.

The Federal Reserve specification of the 2008–2009 recession is shown in Figure 5.8.

## Using a Dummy Variable to Account for a Recession

We see in Figures 5.7 and 5.8 that the 2008–2009 recession seems to correspond with the lower-than-expected NCS in that period. This gives us an opportunity to

**FIGURE 5.8**   **The Federal Reserve Graphic of the 2008–2009 Recession**

Source: Federal Reserve Bank of Philadelphia

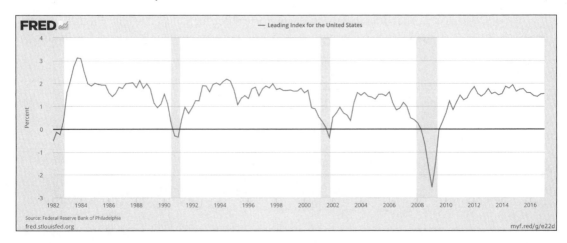

**TABLE 5.8**  **Statistical Results for NCS=f(DPIPC, UMICS, UR, PR, Q2, Q3, Q4, Recession)**  (c5t8&f9)

Audit Trail – ANOVA Table (Multiple Regression Selected)

| Source of variation | SS | df | MS | SEE | Overall F-test |
|---|---|---|---|---|---|
| Regression | 39,712,666,421.52 | 8 | 4,964,083,302.69 | | 62.88 |
| Error | 4,026,203,168.66 | 51 | 78,945,160.17 | 8,885.11 | |
| Total | 43,738,869,590.18 | 59 | | | |

Audit Trail – Coefficient Table (Multiple Regression Selected)

| Series Description | Coefficient | Standard error | T-test | P-value | P/2 |
|---|---|---|---|---|---|
| Intercept | 125,763.55 | 34,208.05 | 3.68 | 0.00 | 0.00 |
| DPIPC | 2.82 | 0.31 | 9.21 | 0.00 | 0.00 |
| UMICS | 354.74 | 214.89 | 1.65 | 0.10 | 0.05 |
| UR | −10,663.56 | 1,361.70 | −7.83 | 0.00 | 0.00 |
| PR | −4,705.72 | 1,100.07 | −4.28 | 0.00 | 0.00 |
| Q2 | 6,299.04 | 3,266.46 | 1.93 | 0.06 | 0.03 |
| Q3 | 14,896.56 | 3,322.56 | 4.48 | 0.00 | 0.00 |
| Q4 | 3,944.55 | 3,324.83 | 1.19 | 0.24 | 0.12 |
| Recession | −23,253.91 | 4,661.63 | −4.99 | 0.00 | 0.00 |

| Accuracy Measures | Value | Forecast Statistics | |
|---|---|---|---|
| AIC | 1,253.58 | Durbin- Watson (4) | |
| BIC | 1,255.67 | 1.00 | |
| MAPE | 4.21% | Durbin- Watson (1) | |
| Adjusted R-Square | 89.35% | 1.69 | |

demonstrate another application of a dummy variable. We will create a variable equal to one for all of 2008 and 2009 but zero otherwise. The statistical results are in Table 5.8, and the graphic result is shown in Figure 5.9.

We have already discussed **logic (step 1)** for DPIPC, UMICS, UR, PR, Q2, Q3, and Q4, and see that nothing has changed for this model. All have logical coefficients. For the recession variable, we would expect that other things being equal, NCS would go down during a recession, and thus, we would expect a negative coefficient. Remember that this variable is coded 1 during the recession and zero otherwise. The negative coefficient of -23,253.91 indicates that NCS decreased on average by 23,253.91 million dollars per quarter during the recession.

With regard to **statistical significance (step 2),** there is some question about what one would keep in the model. All the independent variables have low P/2 values (<,0.05) with the exception of UMICS and Q4. Earlier, we discussed a rationale for keeping Q4 in such a model. Regarding the UMICS, the precise P/2 value is 0.052. Some analysts would keep it; others would not. We will keep it.

In terms of **explanatory power (step 3),** we see that the adjusted $R^2$ indicates that 89.35 percent of the variation in car sales is accounted for by this model. This

**FIGURE 5.9**
**Actual New Car
Sales (NCS) and
Regression Model
Predictions**   The
predictions are
based on the model
shown in the figure
title.   (c5t8&f9)

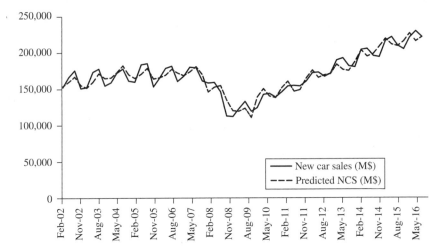

is higher than the model without the recession variable (without the regression variable, you have seen in Table 5.6 that the adjusted $R^2$ was 84.46 percent).

For **serial correlation (step 4),** we see that the DW(4) is 1.00, indicating positive serial correlation. The DW(1) is 1.69, which would indicate an indeterminate conclusion regarding serial correlation. This is a good example of why the seasonal DW is preferable. Given that we have a positive serial correlation, we should consider the consequence. We know that serial correlation causes a downward bias in standard errors, and thus, the $t$-statistics are biased upward. Most of the $t$-statistics are quite high, so this may not be too great a problem. How one thinks about this can be different depending on whether the model is to be used to make strategic decisions regarding the variables or whether one plans to use the model only as a forecasting tool. As long as the model performs well in forecasting, we might be less concerned about some serial correlation. In this case, the model appears to work well. We have a known value for NCS in the first quarter of 2017. It is 212,994 (M$). The percentage error for the first quarter of 2017 is -1.12 percent, which is quite small.

Finally, we will see if there is a **multicollinearity** problem **(step 5)** with adding the recession variable. The correlations between the other independent variables have been shown above, and those are not affected by adding the recession variable. All we need to look at are the correlations of the recession variable with the other variables.

|  | New Car Sales (M$) | DPIPC | UMICS | UR | PR | Q2 | Q3 | Q4 | Recession |
|---|---|---|---|---|---|---|---|---|---|
| Recession | −0.53 | −0.01 | −0.62 | 0.25 | −0.07 | −0.01 | 0.00 | 0.00 | 1.00 |

**FIGURE 5.10** The ForecastX™ Multiple Regression Forecast of New Car Sales (M$) for the
**Four Quarters of 2017** (c5t7&f9)

Source: John Galt Solutions

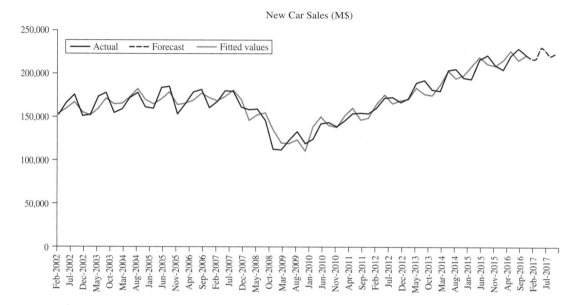

We see that the recession variable has low correlations with the other independent variables. Thus, we know that we do not have a multicollinearity problem with this model.

The forecast values for 2017 are:

| Feb-2017 | May-2017 | Aug-2017 | Nov-2017 |
|----------|----------|----------|----------|
| 215,385.63 | 231,209.34 | 221,192.76 | 224,371.99 |

The actual, fitted, and forecast values for 2017 are shown in Figure 5.10.

# EXTENSIONS OF THE MULTIPLE-REGRESSION MODEL

In some situations, nonlinear terms may be called for as independent variables in a regression analysis. Why? Business or economic logic may suggest that some nonlinearity is expected. A graphic display of the data may be helpful in determining whether the nonlinearity occurs over time. One common cause for nonlinearity is diminishing returns. For example, the effect of advertising on sales may diminish on a dollar-spent basis as increased advertising is used. Another common cause is referred to an Engel's law: As an individual's income doubles, the amount spent on food usually less than doubles (i.e., the proportion spent on food decreases). Both these situations are properly modeled as nonlinearities. In this

| Date | Sales |
|------|-------|
| Feb-13 | 2,010 |
| May-13 | 1,625 |
| Aug-13 | 1,612 |
| Nov-13 | 1,705 |
| Feb-14 | 1,646 |
| May-14 | 1,699 |
| Aug-14 | 1,705 |
| Nov-14 | 1,795 |
| Feb-15 | 2,099 |
| May-15 | 2,294 |
| Aug-15 | 2,301 |
| Nov-15 | 2,598 |
| Feb-16 | 2,689 |
| May-16 | 2,908 |

section, we will look at some sales data that are increasing at an increasing rate and compare linear and nonlinear trends. Both of these can be accomplished using ordinary least squares regression. We will use a time index and add the square of a time index as an independent variable to the regression model.

The basic models are:

$$Y = b_0 + b_1(X)$$

*and*

$$Y = b_0 + b_1(X) + b_2(X^2)$$

where a time index will be the $X$ variable and sales will be the $Y$ variable. So we will have:

$$Sales = b_0 + b_1(Time)$$

*and*

$$Sales = b_0 + b_1(Time) + b_2(Time^2)$$

The sales data we will use are in Table 5.9 and are graphed in Figure 5.11. As you look at the data in tabular form, it is hard to see whether the relationship over time is linear or nonlinear. However, in the graph, it becomes easy to see that over time, sales are increasing at an increasing rate. A clear nonlinear shape emerges that is not so obvious in the table. This is yet another example of the value of data visualization in a graphic form.

We first estimate the linear trend and second the nonlinear (quadratic) trend. The results of both are shown in Table 5.10 and Figure 5.12.

Look carefully at the statistical results for the two models in Table 5.10. Compare the bold-faced items for the linear regression trend with the corresponding bold-faced items for the nonlinear trend. These comparisons will help you understand the significance of adding a squared term to improve the model. Let's look at all of these comparisons.

**FIGURE 5.11**

**Fourteen Quarters of Sales Data**   A visual inspection suggests a nonlinear shape over time.   (c5t9&f11)

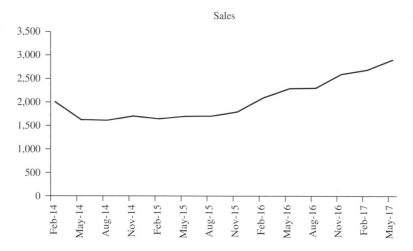

- First, look at the *t*-tests. You see that in the linear model that the slope for "Time" is very significant with a *t*-value of 5.66 and a P/2 of 0.00. For the nonlinear model, both *t*-tests show high significance with *t*-values for Time and Time$^2$ of −3.87 and 7.00, respectively.

- Second, look at the coefficients of determination. For the bivariate linear model, we see that *R*-squared is 72.76 percent. For the multiple regression (the quadratic model), the adjusted *R*-squared is 94.09 percent. This represents a big improvement in explanatory power for the nonlinear model.

- Third, look at the MAPEs. For the linear model, the MAPE is 8.64 percent, while for the nonlinear model, the MAPE drops to 4.06 percent. Again we see considerable improvement favoring the nonlinear model.

- Fourth, look at the Durbin-Watson results. For the linear model, the critical values for DW are $d_l = 1.08$ and $D_u = 1.36$. For the linear model, we see that DW = 0.57, which is less than $d_l = 1.08$, indicating **positive serial correlation**. You might have guessed this would be the result by looking at the graph at the top of Figure 5.12. Now, look at the Durbin-Watson statistic for the quadratic model. It is 1.67. The critical values for DW are $d_l = 0.95$ and $D_u = 1.54$. Using the DW test, we have 1.54 < 1.67 < 2.00, indicating **no serial correlation**. This shows again that the nonlinear (quadratic) model is superior to the linear model.

- Finally, compare the AIC and BIC values. The AIC and BIC statistics for the linear model are 193.01 and 193.66, respectively. For the nonlinear model, the AIC and BIC statistics are 169.27 and 169.91, respectively. For both AIC and BIC, the difference between the linear and nonlinear models is larger than 10, indicating model improvement favoring the nonlinear model.

Clearly, the nonlinear model is superior to the linear model based on all five of the above comparisons. The graphs in Figure 5.12 also support this conclusion. In this example, the graphs make it quite clear which model is superior. However,

**TABLE 5.10**  Linear and Nonlinear Regression Trends. The linear trend model is: Sales = f(Time). The nonlinear trend model is: Sales = f(Time, Time$^2$), which is a quadratic equation  (c5t10f12).

### Results for the Model with Time as the Only Independent Variable

#### Audit Trail—ANOVA Table (Multiple Regression Selected)

| Source of variation | SS | df | MS | SEE | Overall F-test |
|---|---|---|---|---|---|
| Regression | 1,843,110.02 | 1 | 1,843,110.02 | | 32.05 |
| Error | 690,163.98 | 12 | 57,513.67 | 239.82 | |
| Total | 2,533,274.00 | 13 | | | |

#### Audit Trail — Coefficient Table (Multiple Regression Selected)

| Series Description | Coefficient | Standard error | T-test | P-value | P/2 |
|---|---|---|---|---|---|
| Intercept | 1,373.93 | 135.38 | 10.15 | 0.00 | 0.00 |
| **Time** | 90.01 | 15.90 | **5.66** | 0.00 | **0.00** |

#### Audit Trail—Statistics

| Accuracy Measures | Value | Forecast Statistics | Value |
|---|---|---|---|
| **AIC** | **193.01** | Durbin Watson (1) | **0.57** |
| **BIC** | **193.65** | | |
| **MAPE** | 8.64% | | |
| **R-Square** | 72.76% | | |

### Results for the Model with Time and Time Squared as Independent Variables

#### Audit Trail—ANOVA Table (Multiple Regression Selected)

| Source of variation | SS | df | MS | SEE | Overall F-test |
|---|---|---|---|---|---|
| Regression | 2,406,605.23 | 2 | 1,203,302.62 | | 104.50 |
| Error | 126,668.77 | 11 | 11,515.34 | 107.31 | |
| Total | 2,533,274.00 | 13 | | | |

#### Audit Trail—Coefficient Table (Multiple Regression Selected)

| Series Description | Coefficient | Standard error | T-test | P-value | P/2 |
|---|---|---|---|---|---|
| Intercept | 1,930.36 | 99.98 | 19.31 | 0.00 | 0.00 |
| **Time** | −118.65 | 30.67 | **−3.87** | 0.00 | **0.00** |
| **Time$^2$** | 13.91 | 1.99 | **7.00** | 0.00 | **0.00** |

#### Audit Trail — Statistics

| Accuracy Measures | Value | Forecast Statistics | Value |
|---|---|---|---|
| **AIC** | **169.27** | Durbin Watson (1) | **1.67** |
| **BIC** | **169.91** | | |
| **MAPE** | 4.06% | | |
| **Adjusted R-Square** | 94.09% | | |

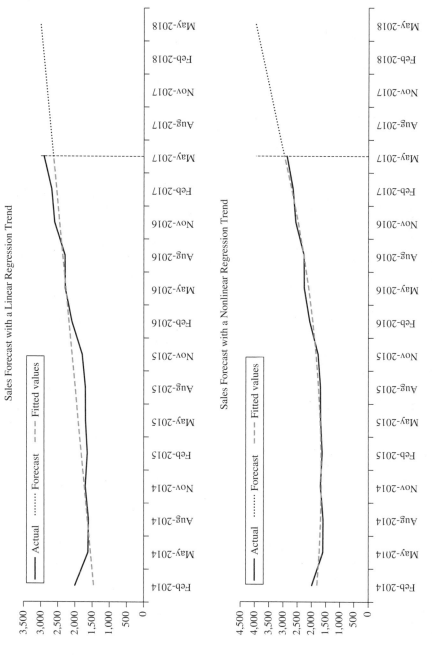

**FIGURE 5.12    The Linear And Nonlinear (Quadratic) Forecasts of Sales**    The linear trend model is: Sales = f(Time). The nonlinear trend model is: Sales = f(Time, Time$^2$). (c5t10f12).

It appears clear that the nonlinear model is likely to provide the better forecast of sales.

in many cases, the graphs may not make it quite so clear, so it is always good to evaluate the statistical properties of different models.

Using ForecastX™ to generate a forecast using each of the models, we get the forecasts pictured in Figure 5.12. In the top graph, we see that the forecast (dotted line) appears as though it would be too low for all of the four quarters being forecast. On the other hand, in the lower graph, we see that the nonlinear model is likely to give a more reasonable forecast. Of course, we never know for sure until the actual results for the forecast period are known.

# ADVICE ON USING MULTIPLE REGRESSION IN FORECASTING

Multiple-regression models are a very important part of the set of tools available to anyone interested in forecasting. Apart from their use in generating forecasts, they have considerable value in helping us to uncover structural relationships between the dependent variable and some set of independent variables. Knowing such relationships helps the forecaster understand the sensitivity of the variable to be forecast to other factors. This enhancement of our understanding of the business environment can only serve to improve our ability to make judgments about the future course of events. It is important not to downplay the role of judgments in forecasting. No one should ever rely solely on some quantitative procedure in developing a forecast. Expert judgments are crucial, and multiple-regression analyses can be helpful in improving your level of expertise.

In developing forecasts with regression models, perhaps the best advice is to follow the "KIS" principle: keep it simple.[9] The more complex the model becomes, the more difficult it is to use. As more causal variables are used, the cost of maintaining the needed database increases in terms of both time and money. Further, complex models are more difficult to communicate to others who may be the actual users of the forecast. They are less likely to trust a model that they do not understand than a simpler model that they do understand.

In evaluating alternative multiple-regression models, is it better to compare adjusted $R$-squared values or mean absolute percentage errors? Remember that $R$-squared relates to the in-sample period, that is, to the past. A model may work well for the in-sample period but not work nearly so well in forecasting. Thus, it is usually best to focus on the MAPE for actual forecasts (note that we say "focus on" and not "use exclusively"). You might track the MAPE for several alternative models for some period to see whether any one model consistently outperforms others in the forecast horizon. Use the AIC and BIC measures to help select appropriate independent variables. It is also desirable periodically to update the regression models to reflect possible changes in the parameter estimates.

---

[9] This is also called the *principle of parsimony* by Box and Jenkins. G. E. P. Box and G. M. Jenkins, *Time Series Analysis: Forecasting and Control*, 2nd ed. (San Francisco: Holden Day, 1976).

# INDEPENDENT VARIABLE SELECTION

Every forecaster who attempts to use demand planning models such as multiple causal regression has difficulty in predicting the turning points in their data with enough accuracy and timeliness to prove useful, and that is the source of most of the errors incurred. While every forecaster subscribes to monitoring certain economic time series, they rarely do it with confidence in the outcome. Finding relevant independent variables with the right periodicity and covering the historic period matching our data is difficult.

The results of the forecast errors we incur are poorly timed promotions, millions lost in safety stocks that are larger than necessary, and loss in market share. How large are the errors forecasters make in the real world? According to the Institute of Business Forecasting (IBF) study[10] by Chaman L. Jain, they are quite large. Jain estimated in 2015 that forecast errors of demand planners at the SKU (stock keeping unit) level average between 27 and 37 percent. For forecasts made at the "category" level, the error averaged between 15 and 26 percent. Not surprisingly, for higher level aggregate forecasts, the errors averaged between 10 and 15 percent. As the level of granularity increased, the average error level also increased. Jain was surprised at the large magnitude of the average errors. Could these errors be reduced?

Many of those errors made by practicing demand planners came from models that had very good fit statistics (recall that fit refers to "in-sample" measurements made with historic data); their MAPEs were low, and their coefficients of multiple determination ($R$-squared) were high. Some of those forecasters may have assumed that a model's fit to the historic data indicated how accurately the model would forecast the future values. So, if the error of the historic fit was 20 percent, then the error of the future forecasts would also be predicted to be about 20 percent. You know that is a very grave error. Remember that the dirty trick of software vendors is to only show potential clients how well the software can fit models to historic data but never show clients how well the software actually forecasts (i.e., predicts in a future period). For that reason, we have suggested using holdouts to form out-of-sample tests. Forecast accuracy will almost always be worse and often much worse than the fit of a model to historic data. That is exactly what the IBF study demonstrates. But what is the reason for the low errors in the historic period and much higher errors in the forecast period?

The primary reason why multiple regression demand planning models fit our historical data so well is that we have complete information available for the historic period on our independent variables; we know for certain the values of the independent right-hand side variables for the entire historic period! However, when we turn the model to forecasting the next 12 to 18 months into the future, the results deteriorate, as demonstrated by the large out-of-sample errors reported in the IBF study.

---

[10] Chaman L. Jain. *Benchmarking Forecast Errors: Research Report 13* (New York: Institute of Business Forecasting and Planning, 2015).

That means that the indicators we *should* use in our demand planning models had best be leading indicators, those that help us predict in advance what the value we are forecasting might be in a future period. We do not want to choose the forecasting model based solely on the model's "fit to history." It is common practice to choose the model that most closely matches the recent history; we then employ it for creating forecasts of the future. But our objective is not to just get the best fit: Our objective should be to find an appropriate model for forecasting future values. Having perfect fit to historic data is no guarantee that the model will generate good forecasts or is even acceptable for forecasting.

So where do we look for leading indicators, those indicators whose current values help predict future values of the dependent variable? We are helped out these days by firms that provide the service of collecting millions of time series and making them available to data scientists; they provide the raw data we need to estimate models that have a reasonable chance of predicting the future. We call these firms "data consolidators." It's estimated that about 85 percent of a company's performance comes about as a result of factors outside the firm. Internal factors such as price changes, product improvements, and advertising all have an effect on sales and the bottom line, but external factors play the much larger role. Unfortunately, most firms pay a great deal of attention to internal factors when building demand planning models because the data is readily at hand. The external factors that affect the firm are much more difficult to come by; they do not exist in internal databases and documents. By their very nature, they lie outside the firm, and a forecaster is going to have to track down this data; for this reason, they are sometimes ignored.

This is where the role of the data consolidator comes in. What types of external information provided by a data consolidator might be useful?

Think of the firm's inside information as the small slice of the circle in Figure 5.13 (say, 15 percent of the relevant information); that is the information

**FIGURE 5.13**
**Only About 15 Percent of the Relevant Information to use in Constructing a Forecast is Data Internal to the Company**

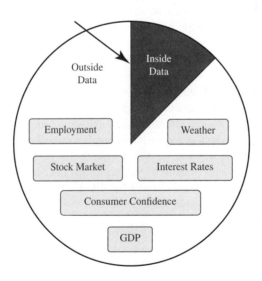

**FIGURE 5.14**
**There are Many**
**Sources and Types of**
**Outside Data**

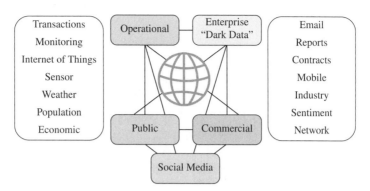

we have internally that we know will help us build the forecast. But the remainder of the circle includes the 85 percent of the information that would be useful to us but to which we do not have convenient access.

Where is this outside data? As Figure 5.14 shows, it comes from many sources: government statistics that are public, weather data, economic statistics from both public and private sources, data from industry organizations, and, increasingly today, data from sensors, the Internet of Things, and social media posts. We not only need information on outside data, we also need information on outside data that are specifically leading indicators for the particular item we are forecasting. The example in the next section might make this clear.

## THE GAP EXAMPLE (WITH LEADING INDICATORS)

Firms have always had access to some outside data. The U.S. Bureau of Economic Analysis and the U.S. Census Bureau provide many useful time series, albeit not in easily searchable and ready-to-use formats. By using a firm such as Prevedere (http://www.prevedere.com/), we can open a window to over 3.5 million time series worldwide. Some of these time series are provided by governments, some are proprietary and have been purchased by Prevedere, and others are available from industry groups. The first feature of the service provided by firms such as Prevedere is to collect and, more importantly, organize these time series so that they become searchable and useful for selection as independent variables (i.e., leading indicators).

But how could we possibly select from 3.5 million series? Even scrolling through the names of the different series would be time-consuming and haphazard. We need a tool that will aid us in selecting only those indicator series that will be helpful in our particular situation; we need indicators that "lead" our target series and indicators that are highly predictive (i.e., highly related to the target series). The advantage in using a tool such as Prevedere is that in addition to the data, Prevedere has built into it a search mechanism that helps build the model. The indicators (all 3.5 million) are arranged in tags (Figure 5.15).

**FIGURE 5.15**

**A Portion of the Tags that Allow Users to Narrow the Selection of Useful Indicator Variables**

Source: Prevedere Software, Inc.

## Available

Some of the tags relate to geographic areas of the world that might focus your search, while others represent industries or product types that could be appropriate. If we were to drill down on "consumer goods" as a category of interest, that would narrow down the search to 21,936 indicator time series (Figure 5.16).

But even searching over 21,936 indicators would be a problem. The second feature of the Prevedere type service is that the program contains a search mechanism that will search over the range of "areas" (such as consumer goods) and pull out indicators that match the pattern exhibited by your data. Even more importantly, the package matches the pattern in your data (the example used here is the Gap data) with calculated best lead times. Recall that to actually "forecast," you will need to have a current indicator value that predicts a future target value; if the variables have lead times, they can be used at least for the value of the lead time into the future (say, three quarters). The optimal lead times for the different indicators are calculated and displayed in the Prevedere engine (Figure 5.17).

**FIGURE 5.16**
**A Few of the
"Consumer Goods"
Indicators from
the List of 21,936
Indicators in this
Single Tag**

Source: Prevedere Software,
Inc.

G  **Goods, Value Of Imports For Euro Area**
International Monetary Fund

E  **Euro Area (18 Countries): Production In Industry: Volume Index Of Production;
MIG - Consumer Goods (Except Food, Beverages And Tobacco)**
Eurostat

E  **European Union (15 Countries): Production In Industry: Volume Index Of Production;
MIG - Consumer Goods**
Eurostat

E  **European Union (15 Countries): Production In Industry: Volume Index Of Production;
MIG - Consumer Goods (Except Food, Beverages And Tobacco)**
Eurostat

**FIGURE 5.17  Some of the Indicators, with Lead Times Shown in Quarters, for the Gap Data**

Source: Prevedere Software, Inc.

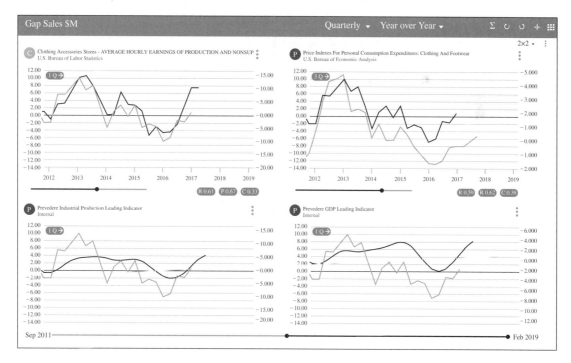

One of the selected indicators is "Price Indexes for Personal Consumption Expenditures," which is obtained from the U.S. Bureau of Economic Analysis. That series was chosen by the Prevedere software because it has a pattern that, with a lead time of three quarters, closely matches our target variable: Gap sales. This variable with an offset of three quarters is then used in the forecast model reported. Notice that all the indicators chosen (although we only display four here) do not have the same offset as the price indexes series; it is not unusual that different time series will have a distinctly different relationship to Gap sales. The regression model that we would build for Gap sales should then be "segmented." In other words, we would use all the indicators with at least a one-quarter lead to forecast for the first future quarter; we would then use all the indicators with at least a two-quarter lead to forecast out for the second future quarter; and so on. Each "segment" is actually a separate multiple regression just like those described earlier in this chapter. As we move from the first segment to the second segment, we would "lose" the indicators that have only a one-quarter lead; we cannot use those indicators to forecast for the second quarter in the future. The segments are constructed using a rolling holdout procedure throughout the historic period to ensure that the model was accurate (as opposed to simply "fitting" well).

Figures 5.18 and 5.19 display the first two segments of a Gap model. The first segment used five indicators; the second segment, however, used only four

**FIGURE 5.18**  Segment 1 of the Gap Forecasting Model Produced in Prevedere

Source: Prevedere Software, Inc.

## Statistics

SEGMENT 1  SEGMENT 2  SEGMENT 3

Segment For 04/2017 to 04/2017

P-Value 0.000   F Statistic 34.579   R-Squared 0.836   Adjusted R-Squared 0.812   Predictive R-Squared 0.773   Est. Of Standard Error 2.189

| Value | Standard Error | T Value | 90% Conf. Interval | 95% Conf. Interval |
|---|---|---|---|---|
| Intercept | | | | |
| −1.380 | 0.840 | −1.644 | [−2.7619, .0010] | [−3.0266, .2657] |
| Clothing accessories stores - AVERAGE HOURLY EARNINGS OF PRODUCTION AND NONSUPERVISORY EMPLOYEES | | | | |
| 0.249 | 0.079 | 3.147 | [.1190, .3796] | [.0940, .4046] |
| Architectural Billings Index - New Projects Inquiries | | | | |
| 0.077 | 0.044 | 1.775 | [.0057, .1491] | [−.0080, .1629] |
| Price Indexes for Personal Consumption Expenditures: Clothing and footwear | | | | |
| 1.104 | 0.299 | 3.692 | [.6121, 1.5955] | [.5179, 1.6897] |
| Corporate profits with inventory valuation adjustments: Domestic industries: Nonfinancial: Retail trade | | | | |
| 0.056 | 0.026 | 2.139 | [.0129, .0987] | [.0047, .1069] |
| Industrial Capacity - Apparel | | | | |
| −0.035 | 0.072 | −0.484 | [−.1524, .0832] | [−.1750, .1057] |

**FIGURE 5.19**  **Segment 2 of the Gap Forecasting Model Produced in Prevedere**   Note that this is a different regression from the one used in segment 1.

Source: Prevedere Software, Inc.

| Statistics | | | | | |
|---|---|---|---|---|---|

SEGMENT 1  SEGMENT 2  SEGMENT 3

Segment For 07/2017 to 10/2017

P-Value 0.000    F Statistic 32.488    R-Squared 0.788    Adjusted R-Squared 0.764    Predictive R-Squared 0.734    Est. Of Standard Error 2.452

| Value | Standard Error | T Value | 90% Conf. Interval | 95% Conf. Interval |
|---|---|---|---|---|
| Intercept | | | | |
| 0.237 | 0.744 | 0.319 | [−.9860, 1.4608] | [− 1.2203, 1.6951] |
| Architectural Billings Index - New Projects Inquiries | | | | |
| 0.091 | 0.049 | 1.870 | [.0110, .1708] | [−.0044, .1861] |
| Price Indexes for Personal Consumption Expenditures: Clothing and footwear | | | | |
| 1.629 | 0.278 | 5.868 | [1.1727, 2.0861] | [1.0852, 2.1736] |
| Corporate profits with inventory valuation adjustments: Domestic industries: Nonfinancial: Retail trade | | | | |
| 0.046 | 0.029 | 1.570 | [−.0022, .0932] | [−.0113, .1023] |
| Industrial Capacity - Apparel | | | | |
| 0.118 | 0.059 | 1.997 | [.0208, .2150] | [.0022, .2336] |

indicators. "Clothing Accessories Stores" was the indicator that was dropped when segment two was estimated; this indicator had only a one-quarter lead on the target variable (i.e., Gap sales). Using just a very simple model like the one described here, how well does the model perform?

The MAPE values shown in Figure 5.20 for the model are quite low, in the 1 percent to 2 percent range. The small number of indicators used is able to accurately match the actual Gap sales pattern. RaceTrac Petroleum used the same technique, identifying outside indicators that matched the pattern of their sales with some lead time, to significantly improve their forecasting effort. According to Brad Galland, RaceTrac director of financial planning, "We felt we were at the mercy of the market and specifically looked for a way to get our hands on external data—the right external data, though. We had internal sales data from the vendors, but this did not help us accurately project sales going forward. As a result, we were operating the business with hindsight as the guide. Ultimately, we wanted a simple model so we could know which product categories in different regions would be affected by different economic and other factors." That model for RaceTrac, using the method shown here, included economic data, weather patterns, customer demographics, competitor moves, and even social and cultural trend indicators.

The forecast for our particular example, as well as the actual Gap sales for 2016, are shown in Figure 5.21.

**FIGURE 5.20  Gap Model Performance**  MAPE values are shown in this plot.

Source: Prevedere Software, Inc.

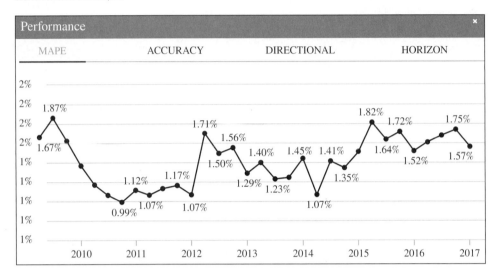

**FIGURE 5.21  The Forecast: Gap Actual Sales (solid line) and Forecasted Sales (Dotted Line)**

Source: Prevedere Software, Inc.

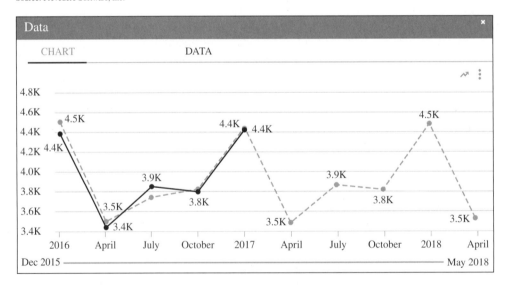

The key point to remember in constructing demand planning models with multiple regression is to realize that a great deal of the explanatory power of a good regression forecasting model will come from indicators that lie outside the firm's own data. The failure to recognize the reality that a firm exists in a particular economy in a particular location and at a particular moment in time will probably result in producing models much less capable than they could be. Finding those outside indicators has been difficult in the past, but with companies such as Prevedere[11] providing the data and a selection tool, the job is much less difficult today.

---

**Integrative Case**

# The Gap

## FORECASTING THE GAP SALES DATA WITH A MULTIPLE-REGRESSION MODEL

The sales of The Gap stores in millions of dollars for the 44 quarters covering their Q1 of 2006 (noted in the data file as April 2017) through their Q4 or 2016 (noted

in the data file as January 2017) are shown in the graph below. The Gap fiscal year ends in January, and the new fiscal year begins in February. Recall that The Gap sales data are quite seasonal.

(c5Gap)

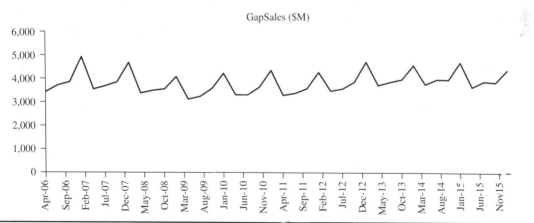

GapSales ($M)

[11] There are other companies that provide services somewhat like Prevedere. To see a list, search "Prevedere competitors."

# Case Questions

1. Have The Gap sales generally followed a linear path over time? Does the graph suggest to you that some accommodation for seasonality should be used in any forecast?
2. Based on the data provided, develop a multiple regression of model for nonseasonally adjusted Gap sales as the basis to forecast sales for 2017.
3. Discuss the MAPE for the historical period (2006 through 2015 fiscal years).
4. Does the model have a serial correlation problem?

# Solutions to Case Questions

1. The Gap sales appear to have followed a highly seasonal pattern over time. The peak season appears to be consistent during their fourth quarter (November, December, and January). This would be due to holiday buying by consumers. The data show that Gap sales have been relatively flat during this time frame, but with seasonality.
2. The raw (or nonseasonally adjusted) The Gap sales were used as a dependent variable in a multiple regression that includes the following explanatory (or independent) variables:

$$DPIPC = \text{Disposable personal income per capita}$$
$$DPIPC^2 = \text{Disposable personal income per capita squared}$$
$$\text{(to help with serial correlation)}$$
$$Q2 = \text{A seasonal dummy variable for quarter 2}$$
$$Q3 = \text{A seasonal dummy variable for quarter 3}$$
$$Q4 = \text{A seasonal dummy variable for quarter 4}$$
$$UMICS = \text{University of Michigan Index of Consumer Sentiment}$$

The regression results follow:

Audit Trail—ANOVA Table (Multiple Regression Selected)

| Source of variation | SS | df | MS | SEE | Overall F-test |
|---|---|---|---|---|---|
| Regression | 7,192,813.39 | 6 | 1,198,802.23 | | 50.49 |
| Error | 783,459.99 | 33 | 23,741.21 | 154.08 | |
| Total | 7,976,273.38 | 39 | | | |

Audit Trail—Coefficient Table (Multiple Regression Selected)

| Series Description | Coefficient | Standard error | T-test | P-value | P/2 |
|---|---|---|---|---|---|
| Intercept | −11,604.05 | 8,036.28 | −1.44 | 0.16 | 0.08 |
| DPIPC | 0.72 | 0.42 | 1.72 | 0.10 | 0.0475 |
| UMICS | 18.83 | 3.80 | 4.95 | 0.00 | 0.00 |
| Q2 | 170.27 | 69.52 | 2.45 | 0.02 | 0.01 |
| Q3 | 315.34 | 69.50 | 4.54 | 0.00 | 0.00 |
| Q4 | 1,002.77 | 69.53 | 14.42 | 0.00 | 0.00 |
| DPIPC2 | −0.000009 | 0.000006 | −1.69 | 0.10 | 0.0498 |

Audit Trail—Statistics

| Accuracy Measures | Value | Forecast Statistics | Value |
|---|---|---|---|
| AIC | 510.82 | Durbin Watson (4) | 1.57 |
| BIC | 512.51 | | |
| MAPE | 2.95% | | |
| Adjusted R-Square | 88.39% | | |

All of the independent variables are logical and statistically significant at our usual 95 percent confidence level. Note that the squared term for DPIPC has a negative coefficient. This suggests diminishing returns to income. The adjusted $R$-squared tells us that this model explains about 88.49 percent of the variation in Gap sales over this time period. The DW(4) value of 1.51 falls between $D_l = 1.29$ and $D_u = 1.78$, so the result is indeterminate with respect to serial correlation. However, since all the P/2 values are very small, it is unlikely that there is a meaningful upward bias to the $t$-test values. The following correlation matrix shows that there is not a multicollinearity problem:

| | GapSales ($M) | DPIPC | UMICS | Q2 | Q3 | Q4 | DPIPC^2 |
|---|---|---|---|---|---|---|---|
| GapSales ($M) | 1.00 | | | | | | |
| DPIPC | 0.26 | 1.00 | | | | | |
| UMICS | 0.41 | 0.36 | 1.00 | | | | |
| Q2 | −0.29 | −0.01 | −0.08 | 1.00 | | | |
| Q3 | −0.08 | 0.02 | −0.02 | −0.33 | 1.00 | | |
| Q4 | 0.85 | 0.08 | 0.08 | −0.33 | −0.33 | 1.00 | |
| DPIPC$^2$ | 0.27 | 1.00 | 0.38 | −0.01 | 0.02 | 0.08 | 1.00 |

The high correlation between DPIPC and DPIPC$^2$ is to be expected. These two variables are not measuring different constructs but rather measure income in a quadratic form. A graph of the Gap sales with multiple regression results follows:

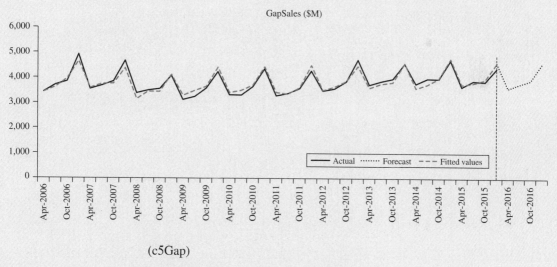

(c5Gap)

3. The MAPE is shown in the ForecastX$^{TM}$ results above. The exact calculations are shown below:

| Dates | Actual Sales Data | Fitted Data | Error = (A-F) | Absolute Error | Absolute % Error |
|---|---|---|---|---|---|
| Apr-2006 | 3,441.00 | 3,432.73 | 8.27 | 8.273 | 0.240 |
| Jul-2006 | 3,714.00 | 3,627.45 | 86.55 | 86.552 | 2.330 |
| Oct-2006 | 3,851.00 | 3,951.77 | −100.77 | 100.769 | 2.617 |
| Jan-2007 | 4,919.00 | 4,659.00 | 260.00 | 259.998 | 5.286 |
| Apr-2007 | 3,549.00 | 3,590.33 | −41.33 | 41.334 | 1.165 |
| Jul-2007 | 3,685.00 | 3,755.33 | −70.33 | 70.327 | 1.908 |
| Oct-2007 | 3,854.00 | 3,758.19 | 95.81 | 95.811 | 2.486 |
| Jan-2008 | 4,675.00 | 4,375.56 | 299.44 | 299.442 | 6.405 |
| Apr-2008 | 3,384.00 | 3,146.14 | 237.86 | 237.859 | 7.029 |
| Jul-2008 | 3,499.00 | 3,451.37 | 47.63 | 47.633 | 1.361 |
| Oct-2008 | 3,561.00 | 3,443.55 | 117.45 | 117.446 | 3.298 |
| Jan-2009 | 4,082.00 | 4,127.53 | −45.53 | 45.527 | 1.115 |
| Apr-2009 | 3,127.00 | 3,297.24 | −170.24 | 170.241 | 5.444 |
| Jul-2009 | 3,245.00 | 3,486.94 | −241.94 | 241.944 | 7.456 |
| Oct-2009 | 3,589.00 | 3,652.59 | −63.59 | 63.587 | 1.772 |
| Jan-2010 | 4,236.00 | 4,414.91 | −178.91 | 178.910 | 4.224 |
| Apr-2010 | 3,329.00 | 3,417.88 | −88.88 | 88.880 | 2.670 |
| Jul-2010 | 3,317.00 | 3,500.23 | −183.23 | 183.227 | 5.524 |
| Oct-2010 | 3,654.00 | 3,707.12 | −53.12 | 53.124 | 1.454 |
| Jan-2011 | 4,364.00 | 4,438.96 | −74.96 | 74.958 | 1.718 |
| Apr-2011 | 3,295.00 | 3,425.84 | −130.84 | 130.845 | 3.971 |
| Jul-2011 | 3,386.00 | 3,368.89 | 17.11 | 17.109 | 0.505 |
| Oct-2011 | 3,585.00 | 3,613.24 | −28.24 | 28.242 | 0.788 |
| Jan-2012 | 4,283.00 | 4,502.16 | −219.16 | 219.160 | 5.117 |
| Apr-2012 | 3,487.00 | 3,508.38 | −21.38 | 21.381 | 0.613 |
| Jul-2012 | 3,575.00 | 3,645.75 | −70.75 | 70.747 | 1.979 |
| Oct-2012 | 3,864.00 | 3,874.84 | −10.84 | 10.841 | 0.281 |
| Jan-2013 | 4,725.00 | 4,470.39 | 254.61 | 254.610 | 5.389 |
| Apr-2013 | 3,729.00 | 3,608.93 | 120.07 | 120.067 | 3.220 |
| Jul-2013 | 3,868.00 | 3,774.43 | 93.57 | 93.572 | 2.419 |
| Oct-2013 | 3,976.00 | 3,826.86 | 149.14 | 149.141 | 3.751 |
| Jan-2014 | 4,575.00 | 4,585.25 | −10.25 | 10.251 | 0.224 |
| Apr-2014 | 3,774.00 | 3,600.17 | 173.83 | 173.833 | 4.606 |
| Jul-2014 | 3,981.00 | 3,744.44 | 236.56 | 236.556 | 5.942 |
| Oct-2014 | 3,972.00 | 3,994.29 | −22.29 | 22.294 | 0.561 |
| Jan-2015 | 4,708.00 | 4,769.62 | −61.62 | 61.618 | 1.309 |
| Apr-2015 | 3,657.00 | 3,744.35 | −87.35 | 87.352 | 2.389 |
| Jul-2015 | 3,898.00 | 3,813.18 | 84.82 | 84.823 | 2.176 |
| Oct-2015 | 3,857.00 | 3,940.54 | −83.54 | 83.542 | 2.166 |
| Jan-2016 | 4,385.00 | 4,608.63 | −223.63 | 223.625 | 5.100 |
| | | | | MAPE = | 2.950 |

The MAPE is 2.95 percent. This is relatively low and a good metric to track over time.

4. The DW(4) is 1.57, which falls in the indeterminate range. Without the squared term for DPIPC (DPIPC$^{2)}$, the DW(4) would be 1.39, indicating positive serial correlation.

# USING FORECASTX™ TO MAKE MULTIPLE-REGRESSION FORECASTS

As usual, begin by opening your data file in Excel and start ForecastX™. Place your cursor in a cell with the data to be forecast (cell B6 in this example).

| | A | B | C | D | E | F | G | H |
|---|------|----------------|-----------|-------|----|----|----|---------------|
| 1 | Date | GapSales ($M) | DPIPC | UMICS | Q2 | Q3 | Q4 | DPIPC^2 |
| 2 | Apr-06 | 3441 | 33,217.00 | 83.8 | 0 | 0 | 0 | 1,103,369,089 |
| 3 | Jul-06 | 3,714 | 33,448.00 | 84 | 1 | 0 | 0 | 1,118,768,704 |
| 4 | Oct-06 | 3,851 | 33,696.00 | 92.4 | 0 | 1 | 0 | 1,135,420,416 |
| 5 | Jan-07 | 4,919 | 33,991.00 | 92.2 | 0 | 0 | 1 | 1,155,388,081 |
| 6 | Apr-07 | 3,549 | 34,457.00 | 86.9 | 0 | 0 | 0 | 1,187,284,849 |
| 7 | Jul-07 | 3,685 | 34,720.00 | 85.7 | 1 | 0 | 0 | 1,205,478,400 |
| 8 | Oct-07 | 3,854 | 34,918.00 | 77.5 | 0 | 1 | 0 | 1,219,266,724 |
| 9 | Jan-08 | 4,675 | 35,209.00 | 72.9 | 0 | 0 | 1 | 1,239,673,681 |
| 10 | Apr-08 | 3,384 | 35,688.00 | 59.6 | 0 | 0 | 0 | 1,273,633,344 |
| 11 | Jul-08 | 3,499 | 36,742.00 | 64.8 | 1 | 0 | 0 | 1,349,974,564 |

In the **Data Capture** dialog box, verify the data you want to use, as shown below. Check that the periodicity and other features are what you want. Then click the **Forecast Method** tab.

Source: John Galt Solutions

In the **Forecast Method** dialog box, click the down arrow in the **Forecasting Technique** box and select **Multiple Regression.** Make sure the desired variable is selected as the **Dependent Series**, which is **GapSales($M)** in this example. Then click the **Statistics** tab.

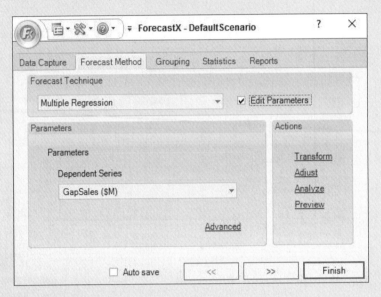

Source: John Galt Solutions

In this dialog box, select the statistics that you desire. Do not forget that there are more choices if you click the **More Statistics** button near the bottom right corner.

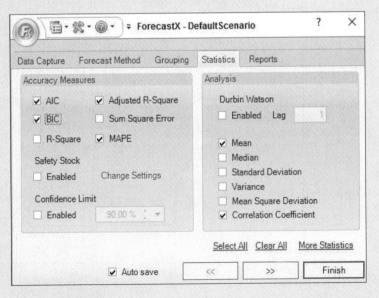

Source: John Galt Solutions

In the More Statistics dialog box, select **Regression** and check the boxes for **ANOVA**, **Coefficients**, and **P-values**. Then click on Ok.

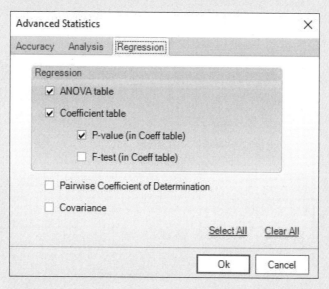

Source: John Galt Solutions

After selecting the statistics you want to see, click the **Reports** tab.

In the **Reports** dialog box, select those you want. Typical selections might be those shown here. If you click the Standard tab, you will want to be sure to select the **Chart in Table** box. In the **Audit Trail** tab, click the **Fitted Values Table**.

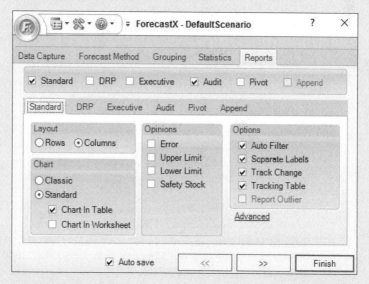

Source: John Galt Solutions

Source: John Galt Solutions

Then click the **Finish** button.

ForecastX™ will automatically apply a time-series method to forecast the independent variables. The methods used to forecast the independent variables are shown in the Standard Report. When you have seasonal dummy variables, ForecastX™ will use a Holt-Winters model since the data have a seasonal pattern.

Sometimes you will want to specify the forecast values for some (or all) of the independent variables. This will be illustrated in the appendix to this chapter.

## Suggested Readings

Akaike, Hirotugu. "A New Look at Statistical Model Identification." *IEEE Transactions on Automatic Control*, AC-19, 6 (1974).

Aykac, Ahmed; and Antonio Borges. "Econometric Methods for Managerial Applications." In *The Handbook of Forecasting: A Managers Guide*. Eds. Spyros Makridakis and Steven C. Wheelwright. New York: John Wiley & Sons, 1982, pp. 185–203.

Chase, Charles W. Jr. *Demand-Driven Forecasting: A Structured Approach to Forecasting, Second Edition*. Hoboken, New Jersey: John Wiley & Sons, 2013.

Doran, Howard; and Jan Kmenta. "Multiple Minima in the Estimation of Models with Autoregressive Disturbances." *Review of Economics and Statistics* 24 (May 1992), pp. 354–57.

Ellis, Joseph H. *Ahead of the Curve: A Commonsense Guide to Forecasting Business and Market Cycles*. Boston: Harvard Business Review Press, 2005.

Franses, Philip Hans. *Expert Adjustments of Model Forecasts: Theory, Practice and Strategies for Improvement*. Cambridge, U.K.: Cambridge University Press, 2014.

Griffiths, William E.; R. Carter Hill; and George G. Judge. *Learning and Practicing Econometrics*. New York: John Wiley & Sons, 1992.

Gujarati, Damodar N. *Essentials of Econometrics*. New York: McGraw-Hill, 2006.

Jarrell, Stephen B. *Basic Business Statistics*. Boston: Allyn & Bacon, 1988. Especially Chapter 23, "Regression," and Chapter 24, "Evaluating and Forecasting: Two Variable Regression Models."

Johnson, Aaron C., Jr.; Marvin B. Johnson; and Reuben C. Buse. *Econometrics: Basic and Applied*. New York: Macmillan, 1987.

Lewis-Beck, Michael S. *Applied Regression: An Introduction*. Beverly Hills, CA: Sage Publications, 1980.

Mendenhall, William; Robert J. Beaver; and Barbara M. Beaver. *Introduction to Probability and Statistics*. 13th ed. Belmont, CA: Brooks/Cole Cenage Learning, 2009.

Neter, John; William Wasserman; and Michael H. Kutner. *Applied Linear Regression Models*. New York: McGraw-Hill, 1996.

Tetlock, Philip E. and Dan Gardner. *Superforecasting: The Art and Science of Prediction*. New York: Crown Publishers, 2015.

Wallis, K. F. "Testing for Fourth Order Correlation in Quarterly Regression Equations." *Econometrica* 40 (1972), pp. 617–36.

## Exercises

1. Explain the difference between bivariate (simple) regression and multiple regression.
2. Explain the five-step process for evaluating a multiple regression model.
3. Describe how a regression plane differs from a regression line.
4. Explain what is meant by a "dummy variable."
5. Describe some ways dummy variables can be used in regression models.
6. Explain things that should be considered when selecting independent variables for a multiple regression model that will be used to make a forecast.
7. Explain why the adjusted $R$-squared should be used in evaluating multiple-regression models rather than the unadjusted value.
8. The following regression results relate to a study of fuel efficiency of cars as measured by miles per gallon of gas (adjusted $R$-squared = 0.569; $n = 120$).

| Variable* | Coefficient | Standard Error | t-Ratio |
|---|---|---|---|
| Intercept | 6.51 | 1.28 | |
| CID | −0.031 | 0.012 | |
| D | 9.46 | 2.67 | |
| M4 | 14.64 | 2.09 | |
| M5 | 14.86 | 2.42 | |
| US | −4.64 | 2.48 | |

CID = Cubic-inch displacement (engine size)
D = 1 for diesel cars and 0 otherwise
M4 = 1 for cars with a four-speed manual transmission and 0 otherwise
M5 = 1 for cars with a five-speed manual transmission and 0 otherwise
US = 1 for cars made in the United States and 0 otherwise

   *a.* Calculate the *t*-ratios for each explanatory variable.

   *b.* Use the first three quick-check regression-evaluation procedures to evaluate this model.

9. Develop a multiple-regression model for auto sales as a function of population and household income from the following data for 10 metropolitan areas:

(c5p9)

| Area | Auto Sales (AS) ($000) | Household Income (INC) ($000) | Population (POP) (000) |
|---|---|---|---|
| 1 | $ 185,792 | $ 23,409 | 133.17 |
| 2 | 85,643 | 19,215 | 110.86 |
| 3 | 97,101 | 20,374 | 68.04 |
| 4 | 100,249 | 16,107 | 99.59 |
| 5 | 527,817 | 23,432 | 289.52 |
| 6 | 403,916 | 19,426 | 339.98 |
| 7 | 78,283 | 18,742 | 89.53 |
| 8 | 188,756 | 18,553 | 155.78 |
| 9 | 329,531 | 21,953 | 248.95 |
| 10 | 91,944 | 16,358 | 102.13 |

a. Estimate values for $b_0$, $b_1$, and $b_2$ for the following model:

$$AS = b_0 + b_1(INC) + b_2(POP)$$

b. Are the signs you find for the coefficients consistent with your expectations? Explain.

c. Are the coefficients for the two explanatory variables significantly different from zero? Explain.

d. What percentage of the variation in AS is explained by this model?

e. What point estimate of AS would you make for a city where INC = $23,175 and POP = 128.07?

10. In Chapter 4, you worked with data on sales for a line of skiwear that is produced by HeathCo Industries. Barbara Lynch, the product manager for the skiwear, has the responsibility of providing forecasts to top management of sales by quarter one year ahead. One of Ms. Lynch's colleagues, Dick Staples, suggested that unemployment and income in the regions in which the clothes are marketed might be causally connected to sales. If you worked the exercises in Chapter 4, you have developed three bivariate regression models of sales as a function of time (TIME), unemployment (NRUR), and income (INC). Data for these variables and for sales are as follows: (c5p10)

a. Now you can expand your analysis to see whether a multiple-regression model would work well. Estimate the following model:

$$SALES\ b_0 + b_1(INC) + b_2(NRUR)$$

$$SALES = \underline{\quad} + / - \underline{\quad}(INC) + / \underline{\quad}(NRUR)$$

(Circle + or − as appropriate for each variable)

Do the signs on the coefficients make sense? Explain why.

b. Test to see whether the coefficients you have estimated are statistically different from zero, using a 95 percent confidence level and a one-tailed test.

c. What percentage of the variation in sales is explained by this model?

d. Use this model to make a sales forecast (SF1) for 2017Q1 through 2017Q4, given the previously forecast values for unemployment (NRURF) and income (INCF) as follows:

| Period | Sales | Inc | NRUR | Time |
|--------|-------|-----|------|------|
| Mar-07 | 72962 | 218 | 8.4 | 1 |
| Jun-07 | 81921 | 237 | 8.2 | 2 |
| Sep-07 | 97729 | 263 | 8.4 | 3 |
| Dec-07 | 142161 | 293 | 8.4 | 4 |
| Mar-08 | 145592 | 318 | 8.1 | 5 |
| Jun-08 | 117129 | 359 | 7.7 | 6 |
| Sep-08 | 114159 | 404 | 7.5 | 7 |
| Dec-08 | 151402 | 436 | 7.2 | 8 |
| Mar-09 | 153907 | 475 | 6.9 | 9 |
| Jun-09 | 100144 | 534 | 6.5 | 10 |
| Sep-09 | 123242 | 574 | 6.5 | 11 |
| Dec-09 | 128497 | 622 | 6.4 | 12 |
| Mar-10 | 176076 | 667 | 6.3 | 13 |
| Jun-10 | 180440 | 702 | 6.2 | 14 |
| Sep-10 | 162665 | 753 | 6.3 | 15 |
| Dec-10 | 220818 | 796 | 6.5 | 16 |
| Mar-11 | 202415 | 858 | 6.8 | 17 |
| Jun-11 | 211780 | 870 | 7.9 | 18 |
| Sep-11 | 163710 | 934 | 8.3 | 19 |
| Dec-11 | 200135 | 1010 | 8 | 20 |
| Mar-12 | 174200 | 1066 | 8 | 21 |
| Jun-12 | 182556 | 1096 | 8 | 22 |
| Sep-12 | 198990 | 1162 | 8 | 23 |
| Dec-12 | 243700 | 1187 | 8.9 | 24 |
| Mar-13 | 253142 | 1207 | 9.6 | 25 |
| Jun-13 | 218755 | 1242 | 10.2 | 26 |
| Sep-13 | 225422 | 1279 | 10.7 | 27 |
| Dec-13 | 253653 | 1318 | 11.5 | 28 |
| Mar-14 | 257156 | 1346 | 11.2 | 29 |
| Jun-14 | 202568 | 1395 | 11 | 30 |
| Sep-14 | 224482 | 1443 | 10.1 | 31 |
| Dec-14 | 229879 | 1528 | 9.2 | 32 |
| Mar-15 | 289321 | 1613 | 8.5 | 33 |
| Jun-15 | 266095 | 1646 | 8 | 34 |
| Sep-15 | 262938 | 1694 | 8 | 35 |
| Dec-15 | 322052 | 1730 | 7.9 | 36 |
| Mar-16 | 313769 | 1755 | 7.9 | 37 |
| Jun-16 | 315011 | 1842 | 7.9 | 38 |
| Sep-16 | 264939 | 1832 | 7.8 | 39 |
| Dec-16 | 301479 | 1882 | 7.6 | 40 |

| Period | NRURF (%) | INC ($ Billions) | SF1 |
|--------|-----------|------------------|-----|
| Mar-17 | 7.6 | 1,928 | _____ |
| Jun-17 | 7.7 | 1,972 | _____ |
| Sep-17 | 7.5 | 2,017 | _____ |
| Dec-17 | 7.4 | 2,062 | _____ |

*e.* Actual sales for 2017 were: Q1 = 334,271; Q2 = 328,982; Q3 = 317,921; Q4 = 350,118. On the basis of this information, how well would you say the model worked? What is the mean absolute percentage error (MAPE)?

*f.* Plot the actual data for 2017Q1 through 2017Q4 along with the values predicted for each quarter based on this model.

11. *a.* Construct a time-series graph of the sales data for HeathCo's line of skiwear (see data in c5p11). Does there appear to be a seasonal pattern in the sales data? Explain why you think the results are as you have found. (c5p11)

*b.* It seems logical that skiwear would sell better from October through March than from April through September. To test this hypothesis, begin by adding two dummy variables to the data: a dummy variable Q1 = 1 for each first quarter (January, February, March) and Q1 = 0 otherwise; and a dummy variable Q4 = 1 for each fourth quarter (October, November, December) and Q4 = 0 otherwise. Once the dummy variables have been entered into your data set, estimate the following trend model:

$$\text{SALES } b_0 + b_1(\text{TIME}) + b_2 Q1 + b_3 Q4$$

Evaluate these results by answering the following:

- Do the signs make sense? Why or why not?
- Are the coefficients statistically different from zero at a 95 percent confidence level (one-tailed test)?
- What percentage of the variation in SALES is explained by this model?

*c.* Use this model to make a forecast of SALES (SF2) for the four quarters of 2017 and calculate the MAPE for the forecast period.

| Period | SALES ($000) | SF2 |
|--------|--------------|-----|
| 2017Q1 | 334,271 | _____ |
| 2017Q2 | 328,982 | _____ |
| 2017Q3 | 317,921 | _____ |
| 2017Q4 | 350,118 | _____ |

*d.* Prepare a time-series plot of SALES (for 2007Q1 through 2016Q4) along with SF2 (for 2007Q1 through 2017Q4) to illustrate how SALES and SF2 compare.

12. AmeriPlas, Inc., produces 20-ounce plastic drinking cups that are embossed with the names of prominent beers and soft drinks. The sales data are:

| Date | Sales | Date | Sales |
|------|-------|------|-------|
| Jan-13 | 40,358 | Jan-14 | 37,255 |
| Feb-13 | 45,002 | Feb-14 | 38,521 |
| Mar-13 | 63,165 | Mar-14 | 55,110 |
| Apr-13 | 57,479 | Apr-14 | 51,389 |
| May-13 | 52,308 | May-14 | 58,068 |
| Jun-13 | 60,062 | Jun-14 | 64,028 |
| Jul-13 | 51,694 | Jul-14 | 52,873 |
| Aug-13 | 54,469 | Aug-14 | 62,584 |
| Sep-13 | 48,284 | Sep-14 | 53,373 |
| Oct-13 | 45,239 | Oct-14 | 52,060 |
| Nov-13 | 40,665 | Nov-14 | 51,727 |
| Dec-13 | 47,968 | Dec-14 | 51,455 |

(continued on next page)

(continued)

| Date | Sales | Date | Sales |
|------|-------|------|-------|
| Jan-15 | 47,906 | Jan-16 | 65,711 |
| Feb-15 | 53,570 | Feb-16 | 68,005 |
| Mar-15 | 69,189 | Mar-16 | 78,029 |
| Apr-15 | 64,346 | Apr-16 | 92,764 |
| May-15 | 77,267 | May-16 | 97,175 |
| Jun-15 | 75,787 | Jun-16 | 86,255 |
| Jul-15 | 74,052 | Jul-16 | 90,496 |
| Aug-15 | 79,756 | Aug-16 | 87,602 |
| Sep-15 | 73,292 | Sep-16 | 83,577 |
| Oct-15 | 77,207 | Oct-16 | 92,610 |
| Nov-15 | 68,423 | Nov-16 | 73,949 |
| Dec-15 | 67,274 | Dec-16 | 77,711 |

(c5p12)

*a.* Prepare a time-series plot of the sales data. Does there appear to be a regular pattern of movement in the data that may be seasonal? Ronnie Mills, the product manager for this product line, believes that her brief review of sales data for the four-year period indicates that sales are slowest in November, December, January, and February than in other months. Do you agree?

*b.* Since production is closely related to orders for current shipment, Ronnie would like to have a monthly sales forecast that incorporates monthly fluctuations. She has asked you to develop a trend model that includes a time index and dummy variables for all but the above mentioned four months. Do these results support Ronnie's observations? Explain.

*c.* Ronnie believes that there has been some increase in the rate of sales growth. To test this and to include such a possibility in the forecasting effort, she has asked that you add the square of the time index $(T)$ to your model (call this new term $T2$). Is there any evidence of increase of sales growth? Compare the results of this model with those found in part (b).

*d.* Use the model in part (c) to forecast sales for 2017. Calculate the mean absolute percentage error (MAPE) for the first six months of 2017. Actual sales for those six months were:

| | |
|------|------|
| Jan-2017 | 87327 |
| Feb-2017 | 84772 |
| Mar-2017 | 112499 |
| Apr-2017 | 102633 |
| May-2017 | 112996 |
| Jun-2017 | 119807 |

# Chapter **Five Appendix**

# Combining Forecasts (Ensemble Models)

## LEARNING OBJECTIVES

After studying this appendix, you should be able to:

1. Explain why a combination of two forecasts (called ensembles) may be better than either one alone.
2. Explain the process for checking to see if a combination of forecasts would create a bias.
3. Explain how to use regression analysis to select the weights for the forecasts that are being combined.
4. Set up the data table that should be used when combining forecasts.
5. Use ForecastX™ to combine forecasts.

## INTRODUCTION

The use of combinations of forecasts has been the subject of a great deal of research in forecasting. An indication of the importance of this concept is the fact that the prestigious *International Journal of Forecasting* had a special section, composed of seven articles, entitled "Combining Forecasts" in the year-end issue of the volume for 1989. In December 1992, an article in the same journal provided strong evidence on the importance of combining forecasts to improve accuracy. It was found that 83 percent of expert forecasters believe that combining forecasts will produce more accurate forecasts than could be obtained from the individual methods!

The idea of combining business forecasting models was originally proposed by Bates and Granger. Since the publication of their article, this strategy has received immense support in almost every empirical test of combined forecasts versus individual uncombined forecasts.

Throughout this book, we have emphasized the use of the mean absolute percentage error (MAPE) as a measure of the effectiveness of **one** particular forecasting model. In this appendix, instead of choosing the best model from among two or more alternatives, we are going to combine the forecasts from these different models to obtain *forecast improvement*. It may actually be unwise to simply determine which of a number of forecasting methods yields the most accurate predictions. A more reasoned approach, according to the empirical evidence, is to combine the forecasts already made in order to obtain a combined forecast that is more accurate than any of the separate predictions.

Any time a particular forecast is ignored because it is not the "best" forecast produced, it is likely that valuable independent information contained in the discarded forecast has been lost. The information lost is likely to be due to of one or both of the following:

1. Some variables included in the discarded forecast may not be included in the "best" forecast.
2. The discarded forecast may make use of a type of relationship ignored by the "best" forecast.

In the first of these cases, it is quite likely that various forecasts are based on different information. Thus, ignoring any one of these forecasts would necessarily exclude the explanatory power unique to the information included in the discarded model.

In the second situation, it is often the case that different assumptions are made in different models about the form of the relationship between the variables. Each of the different forms of relationship, however, may have some explanatory value. Choosing only the "best" of the relationships could exclude functional information. An example would be **accounting for seasonality** in a **multiplicative** manner with **Winters'** exponential smoothing and in an **additive** manner using seasonal dummy variables in **regression**.

# BIAS

To be useful, forecasts we wish to combine must be unbiased. ***To be unbiased, each of the forecasts cannot consistently overestimate or underestimate the actual value.*** If we combined an unbiased forecast with one that consistently overestimated the true value, we would always wind up with a biased estimate. Combining forecasts will not a eliminate systematic bias in a forecast.

The idea of bias related to a forecast can be explained in graphical manner. Consider the graphs in Figure 5A.1. In each of the three graphs, actual values of the variable to be forecast are on the vertical axis and the forecast values are on the horizontal axis. In the top graph, the 45-degree line represents a situation in which there is a perfect forecast. While a perfect forecast is very unlikely, the purpose of this line is to show that such a forecast would not have a bias. Note two important observations about the line in the upper graph: 1) The slope of such a 45-degree line is equal to one; and 2) the 45-degree line has an intercept equal to zero. The importance of these observations will become clear as we discuss bias in the context of combining forecasts,

**FIGURE 5A.1**

**One way to look at the concept of forecast bias.**

In these graphs, the solid line represents a forecast with no bias. The two dotted lines show forecasts that have a bias. The top graph shows a forecast with no bias. The middle graph illustrates a situation in which a forecast has an upward bias. In the lower graph, a downward bias is shown.

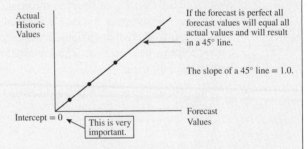

# A Two Dimensional View

Consider a plot with the actual values on the vertical axis and the forecast values on the horizontal axis. This example assumes that the forecast is perfect... an unlikely result.

Actual Historic Values

If the forecast is perfect all forecast values will equal all actual values and will result in a 45° line.

The slope of a 45° line = 1.0.

Forecast Values

Intercept = 0      This is very important.

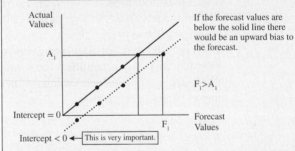

# Upward Bias in Forecasts

Now consider a plot with the actual values on the vertical axis and the forecast values on the horizontal axis with forecast values that are bias upward.

Actual Values

$A_1$

If the forecast values are below the solid line there would be an upward bias to the forecast.

$F_1 > A_1$

Intercept = 0

$F_1$      Forecast Values

Intercept < 0  ←  This is very important.

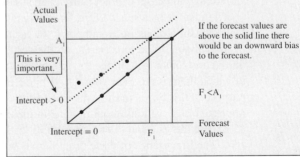

# Downward Bias in Forecasts

Now consider a plot with the actual values on the vertical axis and the forecast values on the horizontal axis with forecast values that are bias downward.

Actual Values

$A_1$

This is very important.

If the forecast values are above the solid line there would be an downward bias to the forecast.

$F_1 < A_1$

Intercept > 0

Intercept = 0      $F_1$      Forecast Values

Bias can arise from a number of sources, but perhaps the most common source is the forecaster's preconceived notions. Predictions of forecasters not only reflect what they believe to be the truth but also what they would *like* the truth to be. This statement is best demonstrated by the results obtained by Hayes in a survey of voters two weeks before the Roosevelt-Hoover election. Hayes found that of the people who intended to vote for Hoover, 84 percent thought that he would win the election. Of the people who intended to vote for Roosevelt, however, only 6 percent thought that Hoover would win. Apparently, those who intended to vote for a particular candidate are biased in the sense that they also believe that their favorite will actually win the election.[1]

Professional forecasters may suffer from the same bias as voters—they may look for forecasting models that confirm their own preconceived ideas. To eliminate bias, a forecaster will have to examine models that may contradict his or her current beliefs. What this means is that you must do something that runs counter to your intuition in order to examine models you may feel are incorrect; you must examine forecasting models that you may believe to be inferior to your "favorite" model. This prescription is more difficult to implement than it sounds. Much of a forecaster's time is spent in confirming existing beliefs of how the world works. However, we are suggesting that a forecaster should spend some time examining multiple forecasting models in the hope of combining some or all of these models into a combined forecast that is superior to any of the individual forecasts.

> A forecaster should spend some time examining multiple forecasting models in the hope of combining some or all of these models into a combined forecast that is superior to any of the individual forecasts.

## WHAT KINDS OF FORECASTS CAN BE COMBINED?

The example of combining forecasts we used in the previous section is one of the simpler combinations a researcher could try. In actual practice, it would be more common to find a forecaster using very different types of models in order to construct a combination forecast.

Recall that the premise in constructing combined forecasts is:

1. That the different forecasting models *extract different predictive factors* from essentially the same data, or
2. That the different models offer different predictions because they *use different variables*.

> We should expect that combinations of forecasts that use very different models are likely to be effective in reducing forecast error.

We should expect that combinations of forecasts that use very different models are likely to be effective in reducing forecast error.

Consider Figure 5A.2, which conceptually presents a 10-year forecast of air travel in the United States. The judgmental method represents a mail survey of experts outside the airline industry. The extrapolation method could be a form of exponential smoothing. The segmentation method surveys airline travelers in different segments of the market and then combines the results to obtain a total picture of the industry. The econometric method refers to a causal regression model.

---

[1] S. P. Hayes, Jr., "The Predictive Ability of Voters," *Journal of Social Psychology* 7 (1936), pp. 183–91.

**FIGURE 5A.2**
**Combining forecasts from different methods**

Note: The $w$'s, the relative weights on various forecasts, should sum to 1.0.

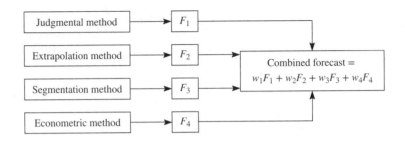

All four methods could be employed and their predictions weighted by the values $w_1$ to $w_4$ in order to calculate the combined forecast. Such a diverse combined forecast would benefit from both the use of the different techniques *and* the use of different sources of data. If each of the methods employed were also constructed and estimated by a different forecaster, another source of possible bias may also have been minimized; this provides a safeguard by making it difficult to cheat.

# CONSIDERATIONS IN CHOOSING THE WEIGHTS FOR COMBINED FORECASTS

Combined forecasts are used in place of individual forecasts in order to reduce forecast error, and the results of the combined methods are quite often impressive. Armstrong has reported results from reanalyzing eight separate studies that provided sufficient information to test the combined forecasting method against individual forecast models.[2] In each case, Armstrong used equal weights for the individual forecasts, following his belief that weight should be chosen *ex ante*. The combinations of two forecasts reduced error (measured as mean absolute percentage error) by a significant 6.6 percent. In no single case did the accuracy ever suffer.

Even though the use of equal weights for each of the individual forecasts offers the advantage of simplicity and precludes the forecaster's own bias in the selection of weighting factors, there may be a good reason for weighting one individual forecast more than another. Equal weights do not take into account the relative accuracy of the individual forecasting models that are combined. Bates and Granger were the first to indicate that, by weighting the more accurate of the methods more heavily, the overall forecast could be improved.[3]

It is the diversity of information included in the individual models that allows a combined forecast model to assemble the pieces to form a more powerful forecasting model than any one of the parts.

In general, a combined forecast will have a smaller error, as measured by MAPE, *unless individual forecasting models are almost equally good and their forecast errors are highly correlated.* If, however, the forecast model with the lower MAPE is more heavily weighted, the combined forecast should improve even further.

[2] See J. Scott Armstrong, *Long-Range Forecasting from Crystal Ball to Computer*. 2nd ed. (New York: John Wiley & Sons, 1985).

[3] See J. M. Bates and C. W. J. Granger. "The Combination of Forecasts." *Operational Research Quarterly* 20, no. 4 (1969), p. 452.

It is the diversity of information included in the individual models that allows a combined forecast model to assemble the pieces to form a more powerful forecasting model than any one of the parts.

# ONE TECHNIQUE FOR SELECTING WEIGHTS WHEN COMBINING FORECASTS

One technique that is used to combine forecasts in order to improve accuracy uses regression concepts you have now learned. This technique involves the use of a regression analysis in determining the weights. Charles Nelson suggests that if we are trying to weight a portfolio of forecasts in order to minimize the forecast error, an optimal linear composite forecast would be:[4]

$$F^* = b_1 F(1) + b_2 F(2)$$

where:

$F^* =$ Optimal combined forecast

$F(1) =$ First individual forecast

$F(2) =$ Second individual forecast

$b_1 =$ Weight allocated to the first forecast

$b_2 =$ Weight allocated to the second forecast

The actual values of $b_1$ and $b_2$ would be calculated by running a regression with the past actual values as the dependent variable and the forecasted values for each individual model as the independent variables. Note that this is not exactly the type of regression we have run before in the text; this regression has no intercept term, and so the equation must be calculated in a manner different from that we have used earlier.

Using this method, if the two (or more) individual forecasts are free of systematic bias, the values of $b_1$ and $b_2$ will sum roughly to 1. The $t$-ratios for the regression will essentially answer the question whether individual forecast 1 adds any explanatory power to what is already present in forecast 2 and similarly for forecast 2. If the $b_1$ value passes the $t$-test at some reasonable confidence level, we can be assured that the first individual model, $F(1)$, did add explanatory power when combined with the second model, $F(2)$, using the weights calculated by the regression.

To apply this method and to determine the best values for $b_1$ and $b_2$, a two-step regression process is used. First, you perform a standard multiple regression of the actual values (dependent variable) on the values predicted from the individual forecasting methods (independent variables in this regression). We can express this as:

$$A = a + b_1 F(1) + b_2 F(2)$$

---

[4] Charles R. Nelson, "A Benchmark for the Accuracy of Econometric Forecasts of GNP," *Business Economics* 19, no. 3 (April 1984), pp. 52–58.

The value of the intercept ($a$) should be (not statistically different from) zero if there is no bias in the combined forecast. A standard $t$-test can be used to test whether the intercept is significantly different from zero.[5] Note that a two-tailed test would be appropriate here because you want to know if the intercept is different from zero in either a positive or negative direction.

Assuming that you conclude that $a = 0$, you then redo the regression, forcing the regression through the origin. Most regression programs provide an option that allows this to be done quite easily. The result of regressing the actual values on the two forecast series, without an intercept, yields the desired result to determine the best weights to be used in combining the forecasts. We have:

$$F^* = b_1 F(1) + b_2 F(2)$$

Using these values of $b_1$ and $b_2$, along with the $F(1)$ and $F(2)$ forecast series, the optimal combined forecast, $F^*$, is easily determined.

As indicated, the values of $b_1$ and $b_2$ should sum roughly to 1. On occasion, one of these weights may be negative, in which case interpretation is tenuous. Some forecasters use such a model even if $b_1$ or $b_2$ is negative, as long as the MAPE for $F^*$ is lower than for $F(1)$ or $F(2)$ alone. However, we advise using this method only when both weights are positive. It should be noted that this method can be extended to include more than two forecast series in the combination process. Remember, however, that each method should have unique information content.

## An Application of the Regression Method for Combining Forecasts

To illustrate the widely used regression method of combining forecasts, we will apply it to the problem of forecasting the sales of women's clothing by a retail chain. Figure 5A.3 shows the data in graphic form.

You have learned in Chapter 3 how to develop a Winters' model for seasonal series such as this. In Chapter 5, you learned to build a regression model to make a forecast. Therefore, here we will only present the results of those two forecasts. Winters' is an obvious choice since it accounts for both trend and seasonality in the data. In the causal regression model, dummy variables were used to account for the seasonality. Thus, in this case, we have one extrapolation model (Winters') that deals with seasonality in a multiplicative way and a causal model that accounts for seasonality in an additive manner. The two methods bring different perspectives to the table in terms of forecasting.

Based on 2010 through 2015 quarterly data, the MAPEs for the Winters' and regression models alone are:

| | Winter's | Regression |
|---|---|---|
| Historical Period MAPEs | 2.04% | 4.04% |

---

[5] This is one of the few cases in which we are interested in testing to see whether the intercept is different from zero. Normally, we do this test only for the slope terms.

**FIGURE 5A.3**

**Six years of quarterly sales of women's clothing by a retailer.** In these sales data, there is clear seasonality and a very slight upward trend. (c5A3)

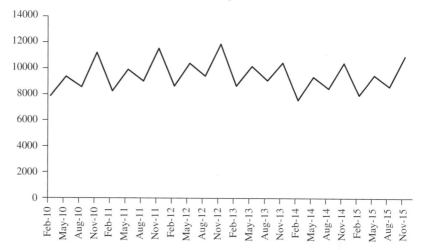

ABC Inc. Women's Clothing Sales: Thousands of dollars

Based on these historical period MAPEs, the Winters' model clearly appears to be a better forecasting model than the regression model. Both MAPEs are relatively low.

If we want to combine these two models, the first thing we must do is to check to see if this combination would create a bias. We first regress the actual sales as a function of the regression and Winters' predictions. Doing so yields the following result:

**Dependent Variable Is Sales of Women's Clothing by a Retailer**

| | Coefficients | Std Error | *t* Stat | P-value |
|---|---|---|---|---|
| **Intercept** | 145.425 | 501.486 | 0.290 | **0.775** |
| Regression Predictions | 0.241 | 0.140 | 1.724 | 0.099 |
| Winters' Predictions | 0.745 | 0.127 | 5.858 | 0.000 |

Go back and look at Figure 5A.1. You see that if there is no bias, the fit between actual and predicted values results in a line with a zero intercept and a slope of 1. Here we have a three-dimensional situation (actual sales, Winters' predictions, and regression predictions), but the concepts presented in Figure 5A.1 still hold.

The only thing we are interested in at this point is whether the intercept is significantly different from zero. To evaluate bias, we look at a *t*-test for the intercept. This is a test we have not previously done because in most regression applications, we do not care about whether the intercept is positive, negative, or zero. In the current application, we look for statistical evidence that combining the Winters' and regression forecasts will not create a bias. The hypothesis test is:

$$H_o: \beta = 0$$
$$H_1: \beta \neq 0$$

We can evaluate this by looking at either how the *t*-statistic compares with the table value at $[n - (k+1)]$ degrees of freedom. For the current example, this is $[(24-(1+1)] = 22$. Using a 95 percent confidence level, the table value of *t* is 2.074. We see above that the calculated *t* is only 0.290, which is less than 2.074. We could also compare the P-value with the desired significance level or 0.05 (remember, the significance level is 1 minus the confidence level). We see that the P-value is greater than 0.05. Either way one looks at this the statistical decision is to fail to reject the null hypothesis (fail to reject $H_0$: $\beta = 0$). Thus, we believe that the true intercept is essentially zero.

The next step is to do the regression forcing the intercept to be zero. This can be done in most statistical software. At the end of this appendix, you will see how to do it in ForecastX™. In Excel when doing regression, the dialog box looks as follows:

**In the red oval, you see that "Constant is Zero" is checked.**

Source: John Galt Solutions

Regressing sales on the Regression predictions and Winters' predictions with a zero constant gives us the following result:

|  | Coefficients | Std Error | t Stat | P-value |
|---|---|---|---|---|
| Intercept | 0 | #N/A | #N/A | #N/A |
| **Regression Predictions** | **0.258** | 0.124 | 2.076 | 0.0498 |
| **Winters' Predictions** | **0.743** | 0.124 | 5.976 | 0.000 |
| Sum of Weights | 1.001 | | | |

Now we have the optimal weights to assign to the regression and Winters' models. Recall that the MAPE for the regression model is 4.04 percent and the MAPE for the Winters' model is 2.04 percent. Thus, you would expect the Winters' model to get a higher weight in the combined model. The results above tell us exactly that. The Winters' model gets a weight of 74.3 percent, and the regression model gets a weight of 25.8 percent. The sum of these weights is about 1.001, which is essentially the 1.0 we would have expected.

## Summarizing the Steps for Combining Forecasts

First, consider how the data should be set up in Excel. The Excel file, in general, should be set up as shown to the left in Figure 5A.4. The number of rows of historical data will almost always greatly exceed the number of data rows for the forecast values. On the right side of Figure 5A.4, you see the data sheet for our current example.

Second, regress the actual values of the variable to be forecast on the two (or more) forecast results for the historic period. In our example, that result is:

**Dependent Variable Is Sales of Women's Clothing by a Retailer**

|  | Coefficients | Std Error | *t* Stat | P-value |
|---|---|---|---|---|
| Intercept | 145.425 | 501.486 | 0.290 | 0.775 |
| Regression Predictions | 0.241 | 0.140 | 1.724 | 0.099 |
| Winters' Predictions | 0.745 | 0.127 | 5.858 | 0.000 |

Since the P-value is greater than 0.05, we conclude that the intercept is essentially zero and thus combining the methods will not create a bias. If the P-value is less than 0.05, a bias would be created, so those forecasts should not be combined. In which case, stop here.

Assuming no bias, proceed to do the same regression but this time force the constant to be zero. In the current example, the result is:

|  | Coefficients | Std Error | *t* Stat | P-value |
|---|---|---|---|---|
| Intercept | 0 | #N/A | #N/A | #N/A |
| **Regression Predictions** | **0.258** | 0.124 | 2.076 | 0.0498 |
| **Winters' Predictions** | **0.743** | 0.124 | 5.976 | 0.000 |
| Sum of Weights | 1.002 |  |  |  |

This provides the weights to be applied to each of the two (or more) forecast methods. You will see that this process is easily done within ForecastX™.

288

**FIGURE 5A.4** The format for data file to combine forecasts. The actual and fitted values are at the top of the data file. In the forecast horizon, there are only values for the two forecasts. The left side is the general format, while the right side is the actual file for the current example. (c5A3)

This portion of the table shows the historical period and the fitted values from two different forecast methods.

These are forecast values.

| Date | ABC Inc. Women's Clothing Sales: Thousands of dollars | Regression Predictions | Winters' Predictions |
|---|---|---|---|
| Feb-10 | 7872 | 8,108.64 | 7,872.00 |
| May-10 | 9360 | 9,737.64 | 9,172.26 |
| Aug-10 | 8559 | 8,817.21 | 8,375.77 |
| Nov-10 | 11209 | 11,039.54 | 10,895.52 |
| Feb-11 | 8244 | 8,131.92 | 8,283.54 |
| May-11 | 9911 | 9,762.44 | 9,672.25 |
| Aug-11 | 9022 | 8,840.12 | 8,862.20 |
| Nov-11 | 11539 | 11,062.05 | 11,517.82 |
| Feb-12 | 8640 | 8,151.10 | 8,511.76 |
| May-12 | 10398 | 9,779.13 | 10,163.01 |
| Aug-12 | 9413 | 8,855.86 | 9,285.01 |
| Nov-12 | 11886 | 11,079.36 | 11,977.78 |
| Feb-13 | 8658 | 8,173.08 | 8,822.79 |
| May-13 | 10172 | 9,811.03 | 10,302.45 |
| Aug-13 | 9071 | 8,877.87 | 9,149.97 |
| Nov-13 | 10450 | 11,087.59 | 11,545.74 |
| Feb-14 | 7552 | 8,164.40 | 7,940.43 |
| May-14 | 9353 | 9,790.58 | 9,082.21 |
| Aug-14 | 8452 | 8,860.38 | 8,325.65 |
| Nov-14 | 10423 | 11,079.38 | 10,410.71 |
| Feb-15 | 7933 | 8,169.86 | 7,806.03 |
| May-15 | 9487 | 9,800.19 | 9,574.93 |
| Aug-15 | 8611 | 8,876.56 | 8,501.86 |
| Nov-15 | 10938 | 11,097.07 | 10,572.75 |
| Feb-16 | | 8,183.66 | 8,152.07 |
| May-16 | | 9,810.96 | 9,814.13 |
| Aug-16 | | 8,887.33 | 8,826.02 |
| Nov-16 | | 11,108.00 | 10,378.00 |

This is the general format for setting up the data file to combine forecasts.

| Date | Actual Data | Model 1 Forecast | Model 2 Forecast |
|---|---|---|---|
| | Historic Values | Fitted Values for Model 1 | Fitted Values for Model 2 |
| ? | | Forecast Values for Model 1 | Forecast Values for Model 2 |

**Integrative Case**

# The Gap

## FORECASTING THE GAP SALES DATA WITH A COMBINATION MODEL

The sales of The Gap stores for the 44 quarters covering 2006Q1 through 2017Q4 are again shown in the graph below. Recall that The Gap sales data are quite seasonal and are increasing over time. Use the full 2006Q1 through 2017Q4 data to construct your forecast models. (c5Gap)

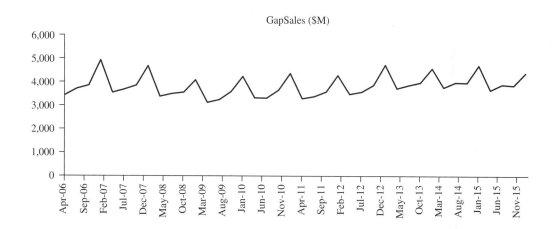

GapSales ($M)

| | |
| Case Questions | 1. Assume you would like to combine a Winters' model and a multiple-regression model. For Gap sales, a Winters' forecast result and a regression forecast result are provided in the c5Gap Excel file. You do not have to do those forecasts. Use regression analyses to check for bias and to determine the best weights for each individual model. |
| | 2. Combine the two methods (i.e., the Winters' and the multiple-regression models) using the weights found in question 1. |
| | 3. The MAPE for the Winters' model in the historical period is 2.60 percent. The comparable MAPE for the regression model is 2.87 percent. Calculate the mean absolute percentage error for the combined model in the historical period, and comment on any improvement. |
| Solutions to Case Questions | 1. To see if both models may reasonably be used in a combined forecast, run the regression that uses The Gap sales as the dependent variable and the two forecasts (one from the Winters' model and the other from the multiple-regression model) as the explanatory variables. The regression with a constant term indicates that the constant term is not significantly different from zero (at a 95 percent confidence level) because its |

*t*-statistic of 0.682 is smaller than 1.96. Also, you see that the P-value of 0.499 is greater than the desired significance level of 0.05. Thus, we may combine the models without creating a bias.

**Regression with a Constant Term** (c5Gap)

|  | Coefficients | Standard Error | *t* Stat | P-value |
|---|---|---|---|---|
| **Intercept** | 103.086 | 151.177 | 0.682 | **0.499** |
| Multiple Regression | 0.418 | 0.110 | 3.808 | 0.000 |
| Winters' | 0.554 | 0.098 | 5.657 | 0.000 |

Note that the constant term is not statistically different from zero.

**Regression without a Constant Term** (c5Gap)

|  | Coefficients | Standard Error | *t* Stat | P-value |
|---|---|---|---|---|
| Intercept | 0 | #N/A | #N/A | #N/A |
| **Multiple Regression** | **0.453** | 0.097 | 4.677 | 0.000 |
| **Winters'** | **0.546** | 0.097 | 5.652 | 0.000 |
| Sum = | 0.999 | | | |

2. The two models are combined by running the same regression through the origin, as shown in the lower part of the regression results in question 1. Here the dependent variable is again Gap sales. Note that the weight on the Winters' forecast (i.e., 0.546) is larger than the weight on the multiple-regression forecast (i.e., 0.453). This is to be expected since the Winters' forecast alone has a MAPE of 2.57 percent compared with the multiple-regression forecast MAPE of 2.87 percent. In this situation, the MAPEs are not dramatically different, and we see that the weights assigned to each method in the combination are also fairly close.

Note the very close association of the forecast with the original data, as shown in the graph below:

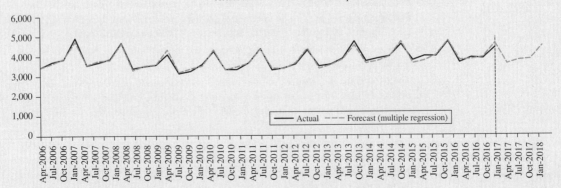

Actual and Combined Forecast Gap Sales

3. The combined forecast and the two candidate models can be compared by using the MAPE each model calculated on known historic data. The MAPEs are:

|  | RMSE |
| --- | --- |
| Winters' model | 2.57% |
| Regression model | 2.87% |
| Combination model | 2.14% |

Since the lowest MAPE calculated belongs to the combination model, it appears that there may be some support for forecast improvement from the combined model.

## USING FORECASTX™ TO COMBINE FORECASTS

The first thing you need to do is to set up a data file with dates in column A, the historical sales (or other variable you want to forecast) in column B, one of the forecasts to be combined in column C, and the other forecast to be combined in column D. This was illustrated in Figure 5A.4.

As another example, an abbreviated portion of the Gap sales data and two forecasts are shown below in the format you need in order to combine the Winters' and regression forecasts:

| Dates | Actual Gap Sales Data (M$) | Winters' | Regression |
| --- | --- | --- | --- |
| Apr-2006 | 3,441.00 | 3,441.00 | 3,432.73 |
| Jul-2006 | 3,714.00 | 3,646.70 | 3,627.45 |
| Oct-2006 | 3,851.00 | 3,824.94 | 3,951.77 |
| Jan-2007 | 4,919.00 | 4,793.62 | 4,659.00 |
| . | . | . | . |
| . | . | . | . |
| . | . | . | . |
| Apr-2014 | 3,774.00 | 3,650.75 | 3,600.17 |
| Jul-2014 | 3,981.00 | 3,775.77 | 3,744.44 |
| Oct-2014 | 3,972.00 | 4,054.75 | 3,994.29 |
| Jan-2015 | 4,708.00 | 4,751.40 | 4,769.62 |
| Apr-2015 | 3,657.00 | 3,825.59 | 3,744.35 |
| Jul-2015 | 3,898.00 | 3,816.05 | 3,813.18 |
| Oct-2015 | 3,857.00 | 3,899.29 | 3,940.54 |
| Jan-2016 | 4,385.00 | 4,617.29 | 4,608.63 |
| Apr-2016 |  | 3,573.47 | 3,606.92 |
| Jul-2016 |  | 3,762.95 | 3,773.15 |
| Oct-2016 |  | 3,746.51 | 3,914.18 |
| Jan-2017 |  | 4,385.00 | 4,597.56 |

As usual, begin by opening your data file in Excel. Place your cursor in one of the sales data cells such as B5. Then start ForecastX™. In the **Data Capture** dialog box, identify the data you want to use, as shown here. Note that in this example, we have a sheet that has the date, the actual values for the Gap sales, and then the two forecasts we want to combine. It is important that in the **Data Capture** box for the process of combining forecast you have the **Forecast Periods** set to the same number of periods as the number of empty cells for the dependent variable.

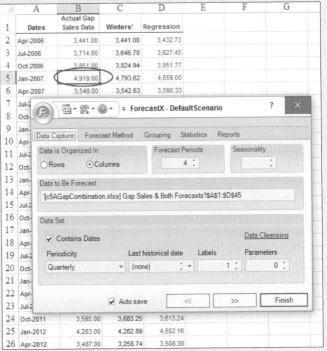

Source: John Galt Solutions

Then click the **Forecast Method** tab. In the **Method Selection** dialog box, click the down arrow in the **Forecasting Technique** box and select **Multiple Regression.** Make sure the desired variable is selected as the **Dependent Series,** which is the actual value of **Gap sales** in this example.

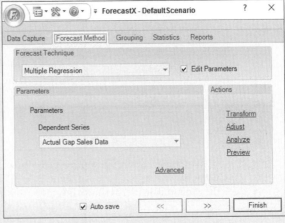

Source: John Galt Solutions

Click on **Advanced**. The following dialog box will appear.

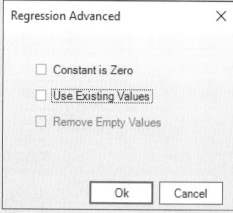

Make sure none of the boxes is checked. Click on **Ok** to return to the **Forecast Method** tab.

Then click the **Statistics** tab. In this dialog box, select the statistics that you desire. Here you are not particularly interested in the summary statistics. What you are looking for in this regression is whether the intercept is significantly different than zero, so you will want to get the coefficient table with P-values. That will be the next step.

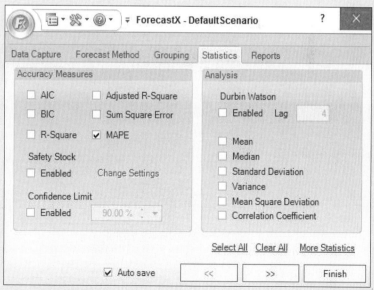

Remember that there are additional choices if you click the **More Statistics** button near the bottom right corner. In this dialog box, select **Regression** and check **Coefficient table** and **P-value**. Click **Ok,** and you will return to the **Statistics** tab.

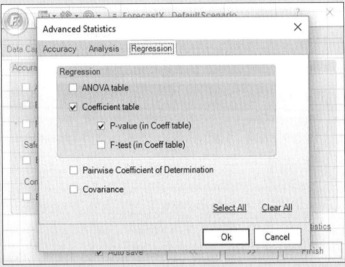

Source: John Galt Solutions

Now you are ready to click the **Reports** tab. In the **Reports** dialog box, for this application select the **Audit** tab. Then click **Finish**. The results will allow you to evaluate whether or not the constant term is significantly different than zero.

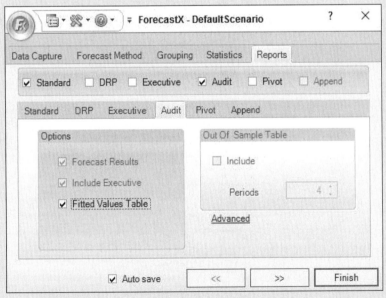

Source: John Galt Solutions

If the P-value for the intercept (or constant term or, in ForecastX™, the name of the dependent variable) is greater than 0.05, you know that the intercept is essentially zero. In this example, you see the P-value is 0.47.

| Audit Trail -- Coefficient Table (Multiple Regression Selected) | | | | | |
| --- | --- | --- | --- | --- | --- |
| Series Description | Included in model | Coefficient | Standard error | T-test | P-value |
| Actual Gap Sales Data | Dependent | 1,156.65 | 1,584.70 | 0.73 | 0.47 |
| Winters' | Yes | 2.01 | 1.04 | 1.94 | 0.06 |
| Regression | Yes | -1.40 | 1.15 | -1.22 | 0.23 |

Source: John Galt Solutions

If the P-value is less than 0.05, you would not want to do the combination because it would create a biased forecast. If the P-value is greater than 0.05, you may continue with the combining process.

To continue with a combination, redo the regression forcing the equation through the origin. To do this, in the **Method Selection** screen, click the **Advanced** button at the bottom. This time in the Regression Advanced box, check all three boxes. The regression coefficients in the resulting model are the optimum weights for the combined forecast, and the results provided by ForecastX™ are the combined forecast values.

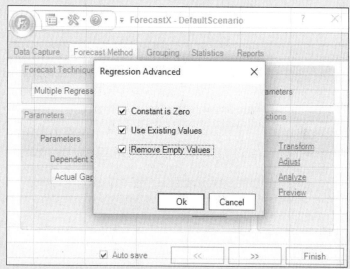

Source: John Galt Solutions

What happens when each of the above three boxes is checked? **First**, when the "Constant is Zero" box is checked, it tells ForecastX™ to do the regression model but to force the intercept (constant) to be zero. **Second**, when "Use Existing Values" is checked, it tells ForecastX™ to use the values of the independent variables that are already in the Excel sheet, rather than estimating those values with some extrapolation forecast method. Near the start of this discussion about using ForecastX™ to combine forecasts, you saw an abbreviated data sheet. Look at the last four rows, and you will see that values are already there for both the Winters' and regression forecasts. **Third**, "Remove Empty Values" tells ForecastX™ not to consider any empty cells, such as the last four cells in column A of this example.

It is a good idea when doing multiple regression forecasts to request both the Audit and the Standard Report, as shown below:.

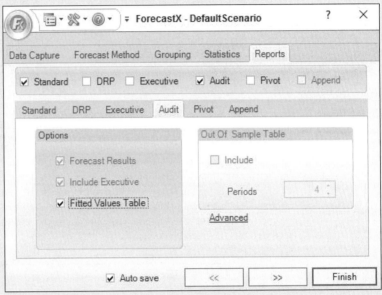

Source: John Galt Solutions

Let us now look at some results. Below is the graph and equation from the **Audit Report**. You see that the actual values are shown to fall to zero during the four-quarter forecast horizon. This is because when developing the graph, ForecastX™ **does** treat the empty cells as having zeros. That can be fixed in this graph, but it is cumbersome to do.

Actual Gap Sales Data

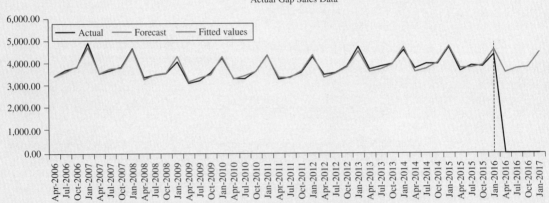

Now let us look at the result from the **Standard Report.** First is the graph and output as you will get them from ForecastX™.

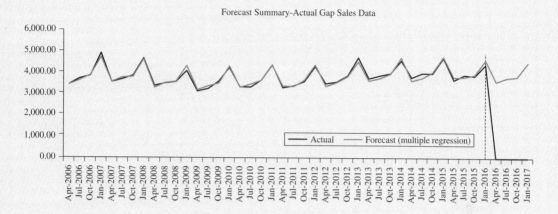

Forecast Summary-Actual Gap Sales Data

Source: John Galt Solutions

| Title0 Type | Actual Gap Sales Data Adjust | Actual Gap Sales Data Forecast (Multiple Regression) | Winters' Adjust | Winters' Forecast | Regression Adjust | Regression Forecast |
|---|---|---|---|---|---|---|
| **Apr-2016** | 0.00 | *3,584.69* | 3,573.47 | *3,573.47* | 3,606.92 | *3,606.92* |
| **Jul-2016** | 0.00 | *3,763.40* | 3,762.95 | *3,762.95* | 3,773.15 | *3,773.15* |
| **Oct-2016** | 0.00 | *3,818.51* | 3,746.51 | *3,746.51* | 3,914.18 | *3,914.18* |
| **Jan-2017** | 0.00 | *4,476.68* | 4,385.00 | *4,385.00* | 4,597.56 | *4,597.56* |
| **MAPE** | 2.17% | 2.17% | 100.00% | 100.00% | 100.00% | 100.00% |
| | 1.59 | 1.59 | 0.00 | 0.00 | 0.00 | 0.00 |

Actual Gap Sales Data = 0 + ( (Winters') * 0.544645 ) + ( (Regression) * 0.454242 )

You see again that the actual values are shown to fall to zero, when in fact, we know they are missing (not zero). We will fix that problem soon. Before we "fix" the graph, look at the values for the Winters' and regression forecasts during the four-quarter forecast horizon. They are exactly as shown in the abbreviated data table at the start of this section. We see that ForecastX™ did use the values provided because the **Use Existing Values** box was checked.

Now, how can we "fix" the graph? It is easy to get rid of the actual line that falls to zero. In the above output, simply delete the zeros for the forecast variable (Gap sales) during the forecast horizon. The result will look as follows:

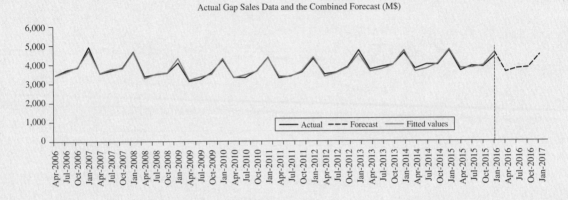

Actual Gap Sales Data and the Combined Forecast (M$)

Actual Gap Sales Data = 0 + ( (Winters') * 0.544645 ) + ( (Regression) * 0.454242 )

| Title0<br>Type | Actual Gap Sales Data<br>Adjust | Actual Gap Sales Data<br>Forecast (Multiple Regression) | Winters'<br>Adjust | Winters'<br>Forecast | Regression<br>Adjust | Regression<br>Forecast |
|---|---|---|---|---|---|---|
| Apr-2016 | 0.00 | 3,584.69 | 3,573.47 | 3,573.47 | 3,606.92 | 3,606.92 |
| Jul-2016 | 0.00 | 3,763.40 | 3,762.95 | 3,762.95 | 3,773.15 | 3,773.15 |
| Oct-2016 | 0.00 | 3,818.51 | 3,746.51 | 3,746.51 | 3,914.18 | 3,914.18 |
| Jan-2017 | 0.00 | 4,476.68 | 4,385.00 | 4,385.00 | 4,597.56 | 4,597.56 |
| MAPE | 2.17%<br>1.59 | 2.17%<br>1.59 | 100.00%<br>0.00 | 100.00%<br>0.00 | 100.00%<br>0.00 | 100.00%<br>0.00 |

Source: John Galt Solutions

Here you see that the lines have been reformatted also. This can often help make the lines more clearly different. The graph title was also edited to better reflect what the graph shows. Since all the ForecastX™ output is in Excel sheets, doing this kind of editing is not difficult.

# Suggested Readings

Armstrong, J. Scott. "Combining Forecasts: The End of the Beginning or the Beginning of the End?" *International Journal of Forecasting* 5, no. 4 (1989), pp. 585–88.

———. *Long-Range Forecasting from Crystal Ball to Computer.* 2nd ed. New York: John Wiley & Sons, 1985.

Bates, J. M.; and C. W. J. Granger. "The Combination of Forecasts." *Operational Research Quarterly* 20, no. 4 (1969), pp. 451–68.

Bessler, David A.; and Jon A. Brandt. "Composite Forecasting: An Application with U.S. Hog Prices." *American Journal of Agricultural Economics* 63 (1981), pp. 135–40.

Chase, Charles W., Jr. "Composite Forecasting: Combining Forecasts for Improved Accuracy." *Journal of Business Forecasting* 19, no. 2 (Summer 2000), pp. 2, 20–22.

Clemen, Robert T. "Combining Forecasts: A Review and Annotated Bibliography." *International Journal of Forecasting* 5, no. 4 (1989), pp. 559–83.

Collopy, Fred; and J. Scott Armstrong. "Expert Opinions about Extrapolation and the Mystery of the Overlooked Discontinuities." *International Journal of Forecasting* 8, no. 4 (December 1992), pp. 575–82.

Diebold, Francis X. "Forecast Combination and Encompassing: Reconciling Two Divergent Literatures." *International Journal of Forecasting* 5, no. 4 (1989), pp. 589–92.

Fair, Roy C. *Predicting Presidential Elections and Other Things.* Stanford, CA: Stanford University Press, 2002.

Flores, Benito E.; David L. Olson; and Christopher Wolfe. "Judgmental Adjustment of Forecasts: A Comparison of Methods." *International Journal of Forecasting* 7, no. 4 (1992), pp. 421–33.

Fullerton, Thomas M., Jr. "A Composite Approach to Forecasting State Government Revenues: Case Study of the Idaho Sales Tax." *International Journal of Forecasting* 5, no. 3 (1989), pp. 373–80.

Goodwin, Paul. "Connect or Combine? Mechanically Integrating Judgmental Forecasts with Statistical Methods." *International Journal of Forecasting* 16, no. 2 (April–June 2000), pp. 261–75.

Hayes, Samuel P., Jr. "The Predictive Ability of Voters." *Journal of Social Psychology* 7 (1936), pp. 183–91.

Hendry, David F.; and Michael P. Clements. "Pooling of Forecasts." *Econometrics Journal* 5 (2002), pp. 1–26.

Hogarth, Robin M. "On Combining Diagnostic 'Forecasts': Thoughts and Some Evidence." *International Journal of Forecasting* 5, no. 4 (1989), pp. 593–97.

Li, Fuchun; and Greg Tkacz. "Combining Forecasts with Nonparametric Kernel Regressions." *Studies in Nonlinear Dynamics & Econometrics* 8, no. 4 (2004), article 2, http://www.bepress.com/snde/vol8/iss4/art2.

Lobo, Gerald I. "Analysis and Comparison of Financial Analysts' Time Series, and Combined Forecasts of Annual Earnings." *Journal of Business Research* 24 (1992), pp. 269–80.

Mahmoud, Essam. "Combining Forecasts: Some Managerial Issues." *International Journal of Forecasting* 5, no. 4 (1989), pp. 599–600.

Makridakis, Spyros. "Why Combining Works." *International Journal of Forecasting* 5 (1989), pp. 601–603.

Nash, John C. and Mary M. Nash. *Practical Forecasting for Managers.* London: Oxford University Press, 2001.

Nelson, Charles R. "A Benchmark for the Accuracy of Econometric Forecasts of GNP." *Business Economics* 19, no. 3 (April 1984), pp. 52–58.

Swanson, N. R.; and T. Zeng. "Choosing among Competing Econometric Forecasts: Regression-Based Forecast Combining Model Selection." *Journal of Forecasting* 20 (2001), pp. 425–40.

Wilson, J. Holton; and Deborah Allison-Koerber. "Combining Subjective and Objective Forecasts Improve Results." *Journal of Business Forecasting* 11, no. 3 (1992), pp. 3–8.

Winkler, Robert L.; and Robert T. Clemen. "Multiple Experts vs. Multiple Methods: Combining Correlation Assessments." *Decision Analysis* 1, no. 3 (September 2004), pp. 167–76.

**Exercises**

1. Explain why a combined model might be better than any of the original contributing models. Could there be cases in which a combined model would show no gain in forecast accuracy over the original models? Give an example where this situation might be likely to occur.

2. Outline the process for combining forecast models explained in this appendix.

3. Develop an example to show how to set up a data file to apply regression analysis to combine forecasts.

4. Your company produces a favorite summertime food product, and you have been placed in charge of forecasting shipments of this product. The historical shipments data below represent your company's past experience with the product.

| Date | Shipments | Date | Shipments |
|------|-----------|------|-----------|
| Apr-2014 | 13,838 | Jun-2015 | 21,056 |
| May-2014 | 15,137 | Jul-2015 | 13,509 |
| Jun-2014 | 23,713 | Aug-2015 | 9,729 |
| Jul-2014 | 17,141 | Sep-2015 | 13,454 |
| Aug-2014 | 7,107 | Oct-2015 | 13,426 |
| Sep-2014 | 9,225 | Nov-2015 | 17,792 |
| Oct-2014 | 10,950 | Dec-2015 | 19,026 |
| Nov-2014 | 14,752 | Jan-2016 | 9,432 |
| Dec-2014 | 18,871 | Feb-2016 | 6,356 |
| Jan-2015 | 11,329 | Mar-2016 | 12,893 |
| Feb-2015 | 6,555 | Apr-2016 | 19,379 |
| Mar-2015 | 9,335 | May-2016 | 14,542 |
| Apr-2015 | 10,845 | Jun-2016 | 18,043 |
| May-2015 | 15,185 | Jul-2016 | 10,803 |

a. Since the data appear to have strong seasonality, estimate a Winters' model using ForecastX. Request the mean absolute percentage error.

b. You also have access to a survey of purchasers' intentions for your product. This information has been collected for some time, and it has proved to be quite accurate for predicting shipments in the past.

| Date | Purchasers' Intention Survey | Date | Purchasers' Intention Survey |
|------|------------------------------|------|------------------------------|
| Apr-2014 | 139 | Jun-2015 | 246 |
| May-2014 | 150 | Jul-2015 | 142 |
| Jun-2014 | 262 | Aug-2015 | 91 |
| Jul-2014 | 172 | Sep-2015 | 121 |
| Aug-2014 | 76 | Oct-2015 | 119 |
| Sep-2014 | 97 | Nov-2015 | 176 |
| Oct-2014 | 78 | Dec-2015 | 155 |
| Nov-2014 | 146 | Jan-2016 | 99 |
| Dec-2014 | 176 | Feb-2016 | 73 |
| Jan-2015 | 104 | Mar-2016 | 112 |
| Feb-2015 | 63 | Apr-2016 | 189 |
| Mar-2015 | 93 | May-2016 | 140 |
| Apr-2015 | 117 | Jun-2016 | 206 |
| May-2015 | 149 | Jul-2016 | 128 |

Use a regression model with shipments as a function of purchasers' intentions to make a second forecast using ForecastX. Again request the mean absolute percentage error for this model.

c. After checking for bias, combine the forecasts in parts (*a*) and (*b*), and determine if a combined model may forecast better than either single model based on its MAPE.

# Chapter **Six**

# Explanatory Models 2. Time-Series Decomposition

©VLADGRIN/Getty Images

The information provided by time-series decomposition is consistent with the way managers tend to look at data and often helps them to get a better handle on data movements by providing concrete measurements for factors that are otherwise not quantified.

Many business and economic time series contain underlying components that, when examined individually, can help the forecaster better understand data movements and therefore make better forecasts. As discussed in Chapter 2, these components include the long-term trend, seasonal fluctuations, cyclical movements, and irregular (or random) fluctuations. Time-series decomposition models can be used to identify such underlying components by breaking the series into its component parts and then reassembling the parts to construct a forecast.

These models are among the oldest forecasting techniques available and yet remain popular today. Their popularity is due primarily to three factors. First, in many situations, time-series decomposition models provide excellent forecasts. Second, these models are relatively easy to understand and to explain to forecast users. This enhances the likelihood that the forecasts will be correctly interpreted and properly used. Third, the information provided by time-series decomposition is consistent with the way managers tend to look at data and often helps them to get a better handle on data movements by providing concrete measurements for factors that are otherwise not quantified.

There are a number of different methods for decomposing a time series. The one we will use is usually referred to as *classical time-series decomposition* and involves the ratio-to-moving-average technique. The classical time-series decomposition model uses the concepts of moving averages presented in Chapter 3 and trend projections discussed in Chapter 4. It also accounts for seasonality in a multiplicative way that is similar to what you have seen in Winters' exponential smoothing and the way we used seasonal indices in earlier chapters.[1]

---

[1] Remember that you have also accounted for seasonality using dummy variables in regression models. That method uses additive factors rather than multiplicative ones to account for seasonal patterns.

# LEARNING OBJECTIVES

After studying this chapter, you should be able to:

1. Explain the similarity between how time series decomposition and Winters' exponential smoothing deal with seasonality.
2. Explain the four components of a time series. Discuss the trend, the seasonal, and the cyclical components.
3. Explain the difference between seasonal factors (SF) and seasonal indices (SI).
4. Explain how one determines the long-term trend for time-series decomposition.
5. Describe how "cycles" in a business environment differ from true cycles.

# THE BASIC TIME-SERIES DECOMPOSITION MODEL

Look at the data on single-family private housing starts (PHS) that are shown in Table 6.1 and Figure 6.1 While the series appears quite volatile, there is also some pattern to the movement in the data. The sharp increases and decreases in housing starts appear to follow one another in a reasonably regular manner, which may reflect a seasonal component. There also appears to be some long-term wavelike movement to the data as well as a slight negative trend. Patterns such as these are relatively common and can best be understood if they can each be isolated and examined individually. The classical time-series decomposition forecasting technique is a well-established procedure for accomplishing this end.

**TABLE 6.1** Single-Family Private Housing Starts (PHS) in Thousands of Units (c6t1&f1)

Source: Data from Economagic.com

| Date | PHS (000) | Date | PHS (000) | Date | PHS (000) |
|---|---|---|---|---|---|
| Feb-67 | 147.1 | Feb-84 | 236.5 | Feb-01 | 273.8 |
| May-67 | 254.7 | May-84 | 332.6 | May-01 | 373.8 |
| Aug-67 | 244.2 | Aug-84 | 280.3 | Aug-01 | 341.1 |
| Nov-67 | 197.8 | Nov-84 | 234.7 | Nov-01 | 284.5 |
| Feb-68 | 179.9 | Feb-85 | 215.3 | Feb-02 | 293.3 |
| May-68 | 266.2 | May-85 | 317.9 | May-02 | 386 |
| Aug-68 | 249 | Aug-85 | 295 | Aug-02 | 360.6 |
| Nov-68 | 204.2 | Nov-85 | 244.1 | Nov-02 | 318.6 |
| Feb-69 | 171.1 | Feb-86 | 234.1 | Feb-03 | 304.1 |
| May-69 | 259 | May-86 | 369.4 | May-03 | 406.3 |
| Aug-69 | 214.5 | Aug-86 | 325.4 | Aug-03 | 412 |
| Nov-69 | 165.9 | Nov-86 | 250.6 | Nov-03 | 376.7 |
| Feb-70 | 136.7 | Feb-87 | 241.4 | Feb-04 | 345.1 |
| May-70 | 231.6 | May-87 | 346.5 | May-04 | 455.7 |

(continued on next page)

**TABLE 6.1**
(continued)

| Date | PHS (000) | Date | PHS (000) | Date | PHS (000) |
|------|-----------|------|-----------|------|-----------|
| Aug-70 | 228.8 | Aug-87 | 321.3 | Aug-04 | 439.9 |
| Nov-70 | 215.8 | Nov-87 | 237.1 | Nov-04 | 369.8 |
| Feb-71 | 204.8 | Feb-88 | 219.7 | Feb-05 | 368.8 |
| May-71 | 348.5 | May-88 | 323.7 | May-05 | 484.7 |
| Aug-71 | 321.5 | Aug-88 | 293.4 | Aug-05 | 470.6 |
| Nov-71 | 276.2 | Nov-88 | 244.6 | Nov-05 | 391.7 |
| Feb-72 | 263.9 | Feb-89 | 212.7 | Feb-06 | 382.3 |
| May-72 | 386.9 | May-89 | 302.1 | May-06 | 432.7 |
| Aug-72 | 370.9 | Aug-89 | 272.1 | Aug-06 | 372.3 |
| Nov-72 | 287.6 | Nov-89 | 216.5 | Nov-06 | 278 |
| Feb-73 | 255.8 | Feb-90 | 217 | Feb-07 | 259.6 |
| May-73 | 366.9 | May-90 | 271.3 | May-07 | 332.9 |
| Aug-73 | 306 | Aug-90 | 233 | Aug-07 | 265.3 |
| Nov-73 | 203.3 | Nov-90 | 173.6 | Nov-07 | 188.3 |
| Feb-74 | 177.8 | Feb-91 | 146.7 | Feb-08 | 161.9 |
| May-74 | 297.8 | May-91 | 254.1 | May-08 | 193.9 |
| Aug-74 | 243.9 | Aug-91 | 239.8 | Aug-08 | 163 |
| Nov-74 | 168.4 | Nov-91 | 199.8 | Nov-08 | 103.2 |
| Feb-75 | 142.3 | Feb-92 | 218.5 | Feb-09 | 78.3 |
| May-75 | 260.9 | May-92 | 296.4 | May-09 | 123.7 |
| Aug-75 | 268 | Aug-92 | 276.4 | Aug-09 | 138.3 |
| Nov-75 | 221 | Nov-92 | 238.8 | Nov-09 | 104.7 |
| Feb-76 | 219 | Feb-93 | 213.2 | Feb-10 | 114.3 |
| May-76 | 339.6 | May-93 | 323.7 | May-10 | 142.2 |
| Aug-76 | 333.6 | Aug-93 | 309.3 | Aug-10 | 119 |
| Nov-76 | 270.1 | Nov-93 | 279.4 | Nov-10 | 95.6 |
| Feb-77 | 268.7 | Feb-94 | 252.6 | Feb-11 | 89.5 |
| May-77 | 440.1 | May-94 | 354.2 | May-11 | 123.4 |
| Aug-77 | 410.3 | Aug-94 | 325.7 | Aug-11 | 117.7 |
| Nov-77 | 331.8 | Nov-94 | 265.9 | Nov-11 | 99.9 |
| Feb-78 | 257.5 | Feb-95 | 214.2 | Feb-12 | 105.5 |
| May-78 | 449.1 | May-95 | 296.7 | May-12 | 151.1 |
| Aug-78 | 403.9 | Aug-95 | 308.2 | Aug-12 | 150.1 |
| Nov-78 | 322.9 | Nov-95 | 257.2 | Nov-12 | 128.6 |
| Feb-79 | 226.6 | Feb-96 | 240 | Feb-13 | 136.1 |
| May-79 | 386.9 | May-96 | 344.5 | May-13 | 174.1 |

**TABLE 6.1**
(continued)

| Date | PHS (000) | Date | PHS (000) | Date | PHS (000) |
|---|---|---|---|---|---|
| Aug-79 | 342.9 | Aug-96 | 324 | Aug-13 | 164.9 |
| Nov-79 | 237.7 | Nov-96 | 252.5 | Nov-13 | 142.6 |
| Feb-80 | 150.9 | Feb-97 | 237.8 | Feb-14 | 133.8 |
| May-80 | 203.3 | May-97 | 324.5 | May-14 | 182.6 |
| Aug-80 | 272.6 | Aug-97 | 314.5 | Aug-14 | 177.6 |
| Nov-80 | 225.3 | Nov-97 | 256.8 | Nov-14 | 153.8 |
| Feb-81 | 166.5 | Feb-98 | 258.4 | Feb-15 | 139.9 |
| May-81 | 229.9 | May-98 | 360.4 | May-15 | 205.4 |
| Aug-81 | 184.8 | Aug-98 | 348 | Aug-15 | 203.2 |
| Nov-81 | 124.1 | Nov-98 | 304.6 | Nov-15 | 166.1 |
| Feb-82 | 113.6 | Feb-99 | 287.2 | Feb-16 | 170.4 |
| May-82 | 178.2 | May-99 | 366.8 | May-16 | 217.7 |
| Aug-82 | 186.7 | Aug-99 | 347.2 | Aug-16 | 206.5 |
| Nov-82 | 184.1 | Nov-99 | 301.3 | Nov-16 | 186.9 |
| Feb-83 | 202.9 | Feb-00 | 278.2 | | |
| May-83 | 322.3 | May-00 | 357 | | |
| Aug-83 | 307.5 | Aug-00 | 320.5 | | |
| Nov-83 | 234.8 | Nov-00 | 275.2 | | |

**FIGURE 6.1**   **Single-Family Private Housing Starts in Thousands of Units by Quarter.**   (c6t1&f1)
This plot of private housing starts shows the volatility in the data. There are repeated sharp upward and downward movements that appear regular and may be of a seasonal nature. There also appears to be some wavelike cyclical pattern and perhaps a very slight negative trend.

Source: economagic.com.

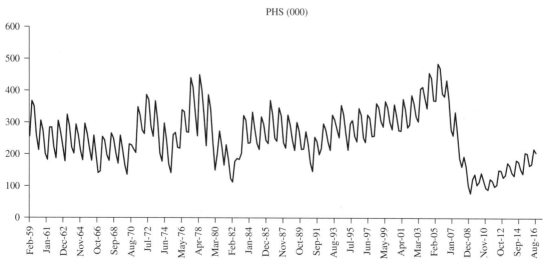

PHS (000)

The model can be represented by a simple algebraic statement, as follows:

$$Y = T \times S \times C \times I$$

where $Y$ is the variable that is to be forecast, $T$ is the long-term (or secular) trend in the data, $S$ is a seasonal adjustment factor, $C$ is the cyclical adjustment factor, and $I$ represents irregular or random variations in the series. Our objective will be to find a way to decompose this series into the individual components.

# DESEASONALIZING THE DATA AND FINDING SEASONAL INDICES

The first step in working with this model is to remove the short-term fluctuations from the data so that the longer-term trend and cycle components can be more clearly identified.

The first step in working with this model is to remove the short-term fluctuations from the data so that the longer-term trend and cycle components can be more clearly identified. These short-term fluctuations include both seasonal patterns and irregular variations. They can be removed by calculating an appropriate moving average (MA) for the series. The moving average should contain the same number of periods as there are in the seasonality that you want to identify. Thus, if you have quarterly data and suspect seasonality on a quarterly basis, a four-period moving average is appropriate. If you have monthly data and want to identify the monthly pattern in the data, a 12-period moving average should be used. The moving average for time period $t$ ($MA_t$) is calculated as follows:

*For quarterly data:*

$$MA_t = (Y_{t-2} + Y_{t-1} + Y_t + Y_{t+1})/4$$

*For monthly data:*

$$MA_t = (Y_{t-6} + Y_{t-5} + \cdots + Y_t + Y_{t+1} + \cdots + Y_{t+5})/12$$

The moving average represents a "typical" level of $Y$ for the year that is centered on that moving average.

The moving average for each time period contains one element from each of the seasons. For example, in the case of quarterly data, each moving average would contain a first-quarter observation, a second-quarter observation, a third-quarter observation, and a fourth-quarter observation (not necessarily in that order). The average of these four quarters should therefore not have any seasonality. Thus, the moving average represents a "typical" level of $Y$ for the year that is centered on that moving average. When an even number of periods is used in calculating a moving average, however, it is really not centered in the year. The following simple example will make that clear and also help you verify your understanding of how the moving averages are calculated.

Let $Y$ be the sales of a line of swimwear for which we have quarterly data (we will look at only six quarters of the data stream). $MA_3$ is the average of quarters 1 through 4. To be centered in the first year, it should be halfway between the second and third quarters, but the convention is to place it at the third quarter ($t = 3$). Note that each of the moving averages shown in the following example contains a first-, second-, third-, and fourth-quarter observation. Thus, seasonality in the data is removed. Irregular fluctuations are also largely removed, since such variations are random events that are likely to offset one another over time.

| | Time Index | Y | Moving Average | Centered Moving Average |
|---|---|---|---|---|
| **Year 1:** | | | | |
| First quarter | 1 | 10 | MISSING | MISSING |
| Second quarter | 2 | 18 | MISSING | MISSING |
| Third quarter | 3 | 20 | 15.0(MA$_3$) | 15.25(CMA$_3$) |
| Fourth quarter | 4 | 12 | 15.5(MA$_4$) | 15.75(CMA$_4$) |
| **Year 2:** | | | | |
| First quarter | 5 | 12 | 16.0(MA$_5$) | MISSING |
| Second quarter | 6 | 20 | MISSING | MISSING |

$$MA_3 = (10 + 18 + 20 + 12)/4 = 15.0$$
$$MA_4 = (18 + 20 + 12 + 12)/4 = 15.5$$
$$MA_5 = (20 + 12 + 12 + 20)/4 = 16.0$$

As noted, when an even number of periods is used, the moving averages are not really centered in the middle of the year. To center the moving averages, a two-period moving average of the moving averages is calculated.[2] This is called a *centered moving average.* The centered moving average for time period $t$ (CMA$_t$) is found as follows:

$$CMA_t = (MA_t + MA_{t+1})/2$$

For the swimwear data used in our example, we have:

$$CMA_3 = (15.0 + 15.5)/2 = 15.25$$
$$CMA_4 = (15.5 + 16.0)/2 = 15.75$$

This second moving average further helps to smooth out irregular or random fluctuations in the data.

Note the "MISSING" that appears under the moving average and centered moving average columns in the data table. With just six data points, we could not calculate four-period moving averages for the first, second, or sixth time period. We then lose one more time period at the end of the data stream when calculating the centered moving average. Thus, the smoothing process has a cost in terms of the loss of some data points. If an $n$-period moving average is used, $n/2$ points will be lost at each end of the data series by the time the centered moving averages have been calculated. This cost is not without benefit, however, since the process will eventually provide clarification of the patterns in the data.

The centered moving averages represent the deseasonalized data (i.e., seasonal variations have been removed through an averaging process). By comparing the actual value of the series in any time period ($Y_t$) with the deseasonalized value (CMA$_t$), you can get a measure of the degree of seasonality. In classical

By comparing the actual value of the series in any time period ($Y_t$) with the deseasonalized value (CMA$_t$), you can get a measure of the degree of seasonality.

[2] If the number of periods used is odd, the moving averages will automatically be centered, and no further adjustment is usually made.

time-series decomposition, this is done by finding the ratio of the actual value to the deseasonalized value. The result is called a *seasonal factor* ($SF_t$). That is:

$$SF_t = Y_t/CMA_t$$

A seasonal factor greater than 1 indicates a period in which $Y$ is greater than the quarterly average for the year, while the reverse is true if SF is less than 1. For our brief swimwear sales example, we can calculate seasonal factors for the third and fourth time periods as follows:

$$SF_3 = Y_3/CMA_3 = 20/15.25 = 1.31$$
$$SF_4 = Y_4/CMA_4 = 12/15.75 = 0.76$$

We see that the third period (third quarter of year 1) is a high-sales quarter, while the fourth period is a low-sales quarter. This makes sense, since swimwear would be expected to sell well in July, August, and September but not in October, November, and December.

When we look at all of the seasonal factors for an extended time period, we generally see reasonable consistency in the values for each season. We would not expect all first-quarter seasonal factors to be exactly the same, but they are likely to be similar. To establish a seasonal index (SI), we average the seasonal factors for each season. This will now be illustrated for the private housing starts data shown initially in Table 6.1 and Figure 6.1.

The data for private housing starts are reproduced in part in Table 6.2. Only the beginning and near the end of the series are shown, but that is sufficient to illustrate all of the necessary calculations. The four-period moving average for private housing starts is denoted as PHSMA4 (private housing starts four-period moving average) and is shown in the fourth column of Table 6.2. The elements included in two values of PHSMA are shown by the brackets in the table and are calculated by adding the corresponding four quarters and then dividing by four.

**TABLE 6.2** Time-Series Decomposition of Private Housing Starts   (c6t2&f2)

| Date | Time Index | PHS (000) | PHSMA4 | PHSCMA | PHSCMAT | CF | SF | SI |
|---|---|---|---|---|---|---|---|---|
| Feb-59 | 1 | 256.7 | | | 266.20 | | | **0.82** |
| May-59 | 2 | 367.3 | | | 266.11 | | | 1.19 |
| Aug-59 | 3 | 350.8 | 308.50 | 303.09 | 266.01 | 1.14 | 1.16 | 1.11 |
| Nov-59 | 4 | 259.2 | 297.68 | 289.96 | 265.92 | 1.09 | 0.89 | 0.89 |
| Feb-60 | 5 | 213.4 | 282.25 | 272.70 | 265.83 | 1.03 | 0.78 | **0.82** |
| May-60 | 6 | 305.6 | 263.15 | 255.90 | 265.73 | 0.96 | 1.19 | 1.19 |
| Aug-60 | 7 | 274.4 | 248.65 | 244.86 | 265.64 | 0.92 | 1.12 | 1.11 |
| Nov-60 | 8 | 201.2 | 241.08 | 238.45 | 265.55 | 0.90 | 0.84 | 0.89 |
| Feb-61 | 9 | 183.1 | 235.83 | 237.05 | 265.45 | 0.89 | 0.77 | **0.82** |
| May-61 | 10 | 284.6 | 238.28 | 240.93 | 265.36 | 0.91 | 1.18 | 1.19 |

**TABLE 6.2** (continued)

| Date | Time Index | PHS (000) | PHSMA4 | PHSCMA | PHSCMAT | CF | SF | SI |
|------|-----------|-----------|--------|--------|---------|-----|-----|-----|
| Aug-61 | 11 | 284.2 | 243.58 | 244.13 | 265.27 | 0.92 | 1.16 | 1.11 |
| Nov-61 | 12 | 222.4 | 244.68 | 247.24 | 265.17 | 0.93 | 0.90 | 0.89 |
| Feb-62 | 13 | 187.5 | 249.80 | 248.31 | 265.08 | 0.94 | 0.76 | **0.82** |
| May-62 | 14 | 305.1 | 246.83 | 247.33 | 264.99 | 0.93 | 1.23 | 1.19 |
| Aug-62 | 15 | 272.3 | 247.83 | 246.66 | 264.90 | 0.93 | 1.10 | 1.11 |
| Nov-62 | 16 | 226.4 | 245.50 | 247.90 | 264.80 | 0.94 | 0.91 | 0.89 |
| • | • | • | • | • | • | • | • | • |
| • | • | • | • | • | • | • | • | • |
| • | • | • | • | • | • | • | • | • |
| Feb-13 | 217 | 136.1 | 147.23 | 149.08 | 246.07 | 0.61 | 0.91 | **0.82** |
| May-13 | 218 | 174.1 | 150.93 | 152.68 | 245.97 | 0.62 | 1.14 | 1.19 |
| Aug-13 | 219 | 164.9 | 154.43 | 154.14 | 245.88 | 0.63 | 1.07 | 1.11 |
| Nov-13 | 220 | 142.6 | 153.85 | 154.91 | 245.79 | 0.63 | 0.92 | 0.89 |
| Feb-14 | 221 | 133.8 | 155.98 | 157.56 | 245.69 | 0.64 | 0.85 | **0.82** |
| May-14 | 222 | 182.6 | 159.15 | 160.55 | 245.60 | 0.65 | 1.14 | 1.19 |
| Aug-14 | 223 | 177.6 | 161.95 | 162.71 | 245.51 | 0.66 | 1.09 | 1.11 |
| Nov-14 | 224 | 153.8 | 163.48 | 166.33 | 245.41 | 0.68 | 0.92 | 0.89 |
| Feb-15 | 225 | 139.9 | 169.18 | 172.38 | 245.32 | 0.70 | 0.81 | **0.82** |
| May-15 | 226 | 205.4 | 175.58 | 177.11 | 245.23 | 0.72 | 1.16 | 1.19 |
| Aug-15 | 227 | 203.2 | 178.65 | 182.46 | 245.13 | 0.74 | 1.11 | 1.11 |
| Nov-15 | 228 | 166.1 | 186.28 | 187.81 | 245.04 | 0.77 | 0.88 | 0.89 |
| Feb-16 | 229 | 170.4 | 189.35 | 189.76 | 244.95 | 0.77 | 0.90 | **0.82** |
| May-16 | 230 | 217.7 | 190.18 | 192.78 | 244.85 | 0.79 | 1.13 | 1.19 |
| Aug-16 | 231 | 206.5 | 195.38 | | 244.76 | | | 1.11 |
| Nov-16 | 232 | 186.9 | | | 244.67 | | | 0.89 |

PHS = Private housing starts (in thousands)
PHSMA4 = Private housing starts four-period moving average
PHSCMA = Private housing starts centered moving average
PHSCMAT = Private housing starts centered moving-average trend (trend component)
CF = Cycle factor (PHSCMA4/PHSCMAT)
SF = Seasonal factor (PHS/PHSCMA4)
SI = Seasonal indices (normalized mean of seasonal factors)

The centered moving average (PHSCMA) is shown in the fifth column. The calculation of PHSCMA for Aug-59 is:

$$PHSCMA = (308.50 + 297.689)/2 = 303.09$$

Notice that for PHSCMA, there is no value for each of the first two and last two quarters. This loss of four quarters of data over 232 observations is not too

---

**FIGURE 6.2** **Private Housing Starts (PHS) with the Centered Moving Average of Private Housing Starts (PHSCMA) in Thousands of Units.** (c6t2&f2)

The centered moving-average series, shown by the darker line, is much smoother than the original series of private housing starts data (lighter line) because the seasonal pattern and the irregular or random fluctuations in the data are removed by the process of calculating the centered moving averages.

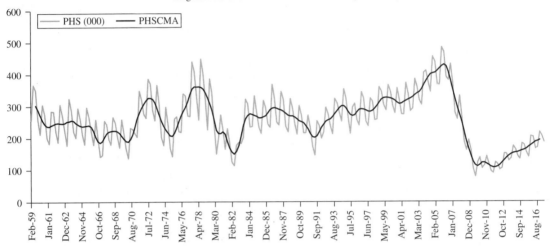

Original PHS and the Deseasonalized Values (PHSCMA)

severe. The two lost quarters that are most critical are the last two, since they are the closest to the period to be forecast.

Figure 6.2 shows a plot of the original private housing starts (PHS) data (lighter line) along with the deseasonalized data (darker line) represented by the centered moving averages (PHSCMAs). Notice how much smoother the data appear once seasonal variations and random fluctuations have been removed.

The process of deseasonalizing the data has two useful results:

*The deseasonalized data allow us to see better the underlying pattern in the data.*

1. The deseasonalized data allow us to see better the underlying pattern in the data, as illustrated in Figure 6.2.
2. It provides us with measures of the extent of seasonality in the form of seasonal indices.

The seasonal factors (SF) for each quarter are shown in the eighth column of Table 6.2. Recall that the seasonal factors measure the extent to which the observed value for each quarter is above or below the deseasonalized value (SF > 1 and SF < 1, respectively). For this example:

$$SF_t = PHS_t/PHSCMA_t$$

For the first two and the last two quarters, seasonal factors cannot be calculated, since there are no centered moving averages for those quarters. The calculations of the seasonal factor for Feb-13 is:

$$SF = 136.1/149.08 = 0.91$$

It makes sense that winter would have a low SF (less than 1), since this is often not a good period in which to start building. The reverse is true in the spring and summer.

Since the seasonal factors for each period are bound to have some variability, we calculate a seasonal index (SI) for each period, which is a standardized average of all of that period's seasonal factors. As shown below, the seasonal indices for the second and third quarter are above 1 and indicate that these quarters are generally high for private housing starts.

| SI |
|---|
| 0.82 |
| 1.19 |
| 1.11 |
| 0.89 |

These add to 4.00, as expected. The warmer spring and summer months are the strongest seasons for housing starts, whereas the fall and winter months are low.

As shown above, the private housing starts' seasonal index for the first quarter is 0.82. This means that the typical first-quarter PHS is only 82 percent of the average quarterly value for the year. Thus, if the housing starts for a year totaled 400, we would expect 82 to occur in the first quarter. The 82 is found by dividing the yearly total (400) by 4 and then multiplying the result by the seasonal index [$(400/4) \times 0.82 = 82$].

# FINDING THE LONG-TERM TREND

The long-term trend is estimated from the deseasonalized data for the variable to be forecast. Remember that the centered moving average (CMA) is the series that remains after the seasonality and irregular components have been smoothed out by using moving averages. Thus, to find the long-term trend, we estimate a simple linear equation as:[3]

$$CMA = f(TIME)$$
$$= a + b(TIME)$$

where TIME = 1 for the first period in the data set and increases by 1 each quarter thereafter. The values of $a$ and $b$ are normally estimated by using a computer regression program, but they can also be found quickly on most hand-held business calculators.

Once the trend equation has been determined, it is used to generate an estimate of the trend value of the centered moving average for the historical and forecast periods. This new series is the centered moving-average trend (CMAT).

For our example involving private housing starts, the linear trend of the deseasonalized data (PHSCMA) has been found to be slightly negative. The centered

---

[3] A linear trend is most often used, but a nonlinear trend may also be used. Looking at a graph such as the one shown in Figure 6.2 is helpful in determining which form would be most appropriate for the trend line.

**FIGURE 6.3**  **Private Housing Starts (PHS) with Centered Moving Average (PHSCMA) and Centered Moving-Average Trend (PHSCMAT) in Thousands of Units.**  (c6t2&f2)

The long-term trend in private housing starts is shown by the straight dotted line (PHSCMAT). The lighter line is the raw data (PHS), while the wavelike dark line is the deseasonalized data (PHSCMA). The long-term trend is seen to be slightly negative. The equation for the trend line is: PHSCMAT = 266.293 -0.093(TIME).

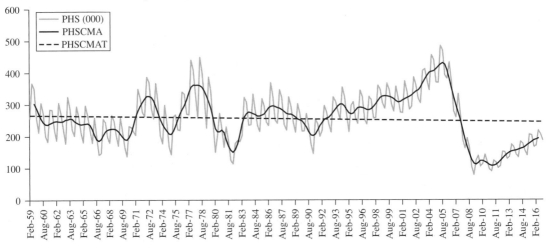

Original PHS, Deseasonalized Values (PHSCMA) and the Trend (PHSCMAT)

moving-average trend for this example is denoted PHSCMAT, for "private housing starts centered moving-average trend." The equation is:

$$PHSCMAT = 266.293 - 0.093(TIME)$$

where TIME = 1 for for the first quarter of 1959. Because there are no data for the first two quarters or the last two quarters for PHSCMA, the linear trend is estimated using quarters 3 through 230. This line is shown in Figure 6.3, along with the graph of private housing starts (PHS) and the deseasonalized data (PHSCMA).

## MEASURING THE CYCLICAL COMPONENT

The cyclical component of a time series is the extended wavelike movement about the long-term trend. It is measured by a cycle factor (CF), which is the ratio of the centered moving average (CMA) to the centered moving-average trend (CMAT). That is:

$$CF = CMA/CMAT$$

*Looking at the length and amplitude of previous cycles may enable us to anticipate the next turning point in the current cycle.*

A cycle factor greater than 1 indicates that the deseasonalized value for that period is above the long-term trend of the data. If CF is less than 1, the reverse is true.

The cycle factor is the most difficult component of a time series to analyze and to project into the forecast period. If analyzed carefully, however, it may also be the component that has the most to offer in terms of understanding where the industry may be headed. Looking at the length and amplitude of previous cycles may enable us to anticipate the next turning point in the current cycle. This is a major advantage of the time-series decomposition technique. An individual familiar with an industry can often explain cyclic movements around the trend line in terms of variables or events that, in retrospect, can be seen to have had some importance. By looking at those variables or events in the present, we can sometimes get some hint of the likely future direction of the cycle component.

## Overview of Business Cycles

Business cycles are long-term wavelike fluctuations in the general level of economic activity. They are often described by a diagram such as the one shown in Figure 6.4. The period of time between the beginning trough (*A*) and the peak (*B*) is called the *expansion phase,* while the period from peak (*B*) to the ending trough (*C*) is termed the *recession,* or *contraction, phase.*

The vertical distance between *A* and *B'* provides a measure of the degree of the expansion. The start of the expansion beginning at point *A* is determined by three consecutive months of increase in economic activity. Thus, the preceding recession is only officially over three months after the economy has turned around. Similarly, the severity of a recession is measured by the vertical distance between *B″* and *C*, and the official beginning of the recession is dated as the first of three consecutive months of decline.

If business cycles were true cycles, they would have a constant amplitude. That is, the vertical distance from trough to peak and peak to trough would always be the same. In addition, a true cycle would also have a constant periodicity. That would mean that the length of time between successive peaks (or troughs) would always be the same. However, with economic and business activity, this degree of regularity is unlikely. As you will see when we look at the cyclical component for private housing starts, the vertical distances from trough to peak (or peak to trough) have considerable variability, as does the distance between successive peaks and successive troughs.

**FIGURE 6.4**

**The General Business Cycle.**

A business cycle goes through successive periods of expansion, contraction, expansion, contraction, and so on.

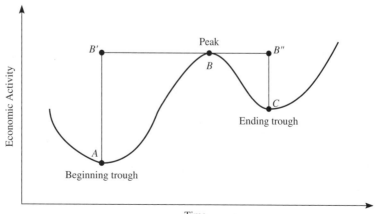

## Business Cycle Indicators

There are a number of possible business cycle indicators, but three are particularly noteworthy:

1. The index of leading economic indicators
2. The index of coincident economic indicators
3. The index of lagging economic indicators

The individual series that make up each index are shown in Table 6.4.

**TABLE 6.4   U.S. Business Cycle Indicators**

### Components of the Composite Indices

**Leading Index**

1 Average weekly hours, manufacturing
2 Average weekly initial claims for unemployment insurance
3 Manufacturers' new orders, consumer goods, and materials
4 ISM® new orders index
5 Manufacturers' new orders, nondefense capital goods excl. aircraft
6 Building permits, new private housing units
7 Stock prices, 500 common stocks
8 *Leading Credit Index*™
9 Interest rate spread, 10-year Treasury bonds less federal funds
10 Avg. consumer expectations for business conditions

**Coincident Index**

1 Employees on nonagricultural payrolls
2 Personal income less transfer payments
3 Industrial production
4 Manufacturing and trade sales

**Lagging Index**

1 Inventories to sales ratio, manufacturing and trade
2 Average duration of unemployment
3 Consumer installment credit outstanding to personal income ratio
4 Commercial and industrial loans
5 Average prime rate
6 Labor cost per unit of output, manufacturing
7 Consumer price index for services

The Conference Board, https://www.conference-board.org/pdf_free/press/US%20LEI%20-%20Tech%20Notes%20Jun%202017.pdf. Content reproduced with permission.

It is possible that one of these indices, or one of the series that makes up an index, may be useful in predicting the cycle factor in a time-series decomposition. This could be done in a regression analysis with the cycle factor (CF) as the dependent variable. These indices, or their components, may also be quite useful as independent variables in other regression models, such as those discussed in Chapters 4 and 5.

Figure 6.5 shows what are considered the official business cycles for the U.S. economy in recent years. The shaded vertical bars identify the officially designated periods of recession.

## The Cycle Factor for Private Housing Starts

Let us return to our example involving private housing starts to examine how to calculate the cycle factor and how it might be projected into the forecast period. In Table 6.2, the cycle factors (CF) are shown in column seven. As indicated previously, each cycle factor is the ratio of the deseasonalized data (CMA) to the trend value (CMAT). For the private housing starts data, we have:

$$CF = PHSCMA/PHSCMAT$$

The actual calculation for Feb-05 is:

$$CF = 419.64/249.05 = 1.68$$

You can see in Figure 6.3 that in Jun-06, the centered moving average was above the trend line.

The cycle factor is plotted in Figure 6.6. You can see that the cycle factor (CF) moves above and below the line at 1.00 in Figure 6.6 exactly as the centered moving average moves above and below the trend line in Figure 6.3. By isolating the cycle factor in Figure 6.6, we can better analyze its movements over time.

You see that the cyclical component for private housing starts does not have a constant amplitude or periodicity. The dates for peaks and troughs are shown in Figure 6.6b, along with the values of the cycle factor at those points. Identification of these dates and values is often helpful in considering when the cycle factor may next turn around (i.e., when the cycle factor turns from having a positive slope to a negative slope or vice versa).

For example, for the CF, the average height of the four peaks shown in Figure 6.6b is 1.38. That might be a good value to use for what you might expect for the height of the next peak. It would be reasonable to argue that the August 2005 peak (CF=1.73) was unusually high, so you might use the average of the other three peaks. That average is **1.27**. This would give you an expectation that the next peak would have a CF of 1.27. There is no perfect way to make this judgment. Others might suggest dropping both the highest and lowest values. But you need to have a reasonable logic for whatever decision you make. Once you have a decision about the expected height of the next peak, you need to decide when that next peak is likely to occur.

One way to approach this is to look at the historical peaks and see how many quarters there were between peaks. From the August 1972 to February 1978, the distance was 22 quarters. The next peak-to-peak distance was 34 quarters, and the

## FIGURE 6.5

**Official Business Cycles in the United States.**

For each graph, the periods identified as official recessions are indicated by the grey vertical bands.

The Conference Board, https: //www.conference-board.org /pdf_free/press/US%20LEI%20 -%20Tech%20Notes%20Jun%20 2017.pdf. Content reproduced with permission.

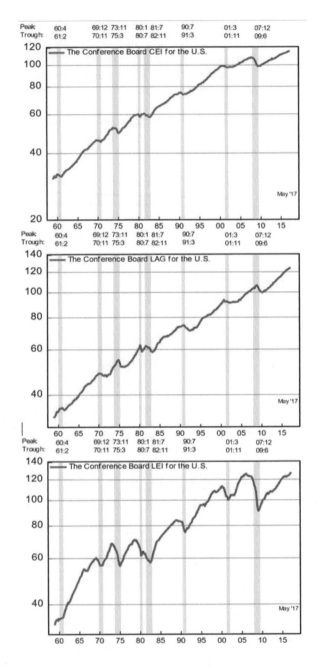

last peak-to-peak was 76 quarters. The latter covered an unusually long period from Feb-91 through Oct-05.[4] The average of these three is 44 quarters. Again one might suggest that because the last expansion was unusually long, only the

---

[4] As of the date of this edition of the text, a new peak had not yet been identified.

**FIGURES 6.6A AND 6.6B.** **Cycle Factor (Cf) for Private Housing Starts.** (c6f6a and c6f6b)
The cycle factor is the ratio of the centered moving average to the long-term trend in the data. As the upper graph (6.6a)
shows, the deseasonalized values move slowly around the trend line with little regularity. In the lower graph (6.6b), you
see that the actual cycle factor moves above and below the line at one in the same manner as PHSCMA moves around
the trend. Dates and values of cycle factors at peaks and troughs are shown in the boxes in 6.6b.

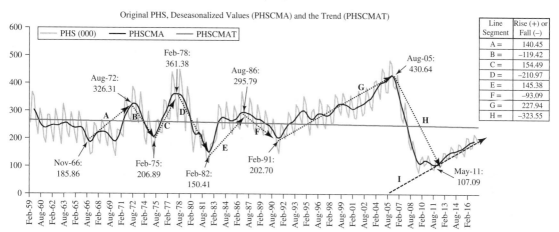

Original PHS, Deseasonalized Values (PHSCMA) and the Trend (PHSCMAT)

| Line Segment | Rise (+) or Fall (−) |
| --- | --- |
| A = | 140.45 |
| B = | −119.42 |
| C = | 154.49 |
| D = | −210.97 |
| E = | 145.38 |
| F = | −93.09 |
| G = | 227.94 |
| H = | −323.55 |

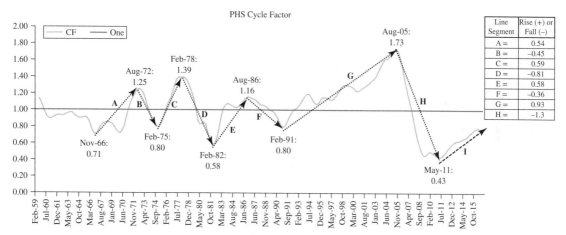

PHS Cycle Factor

| Line Segment | Rise (+) or Fall (−) |
| --- | --- |
| A = | 0.54 |
| B = | −0.45 |
| C = | 0.59 |
| D = | −0.81 |
| E = | 0.58 |
| F = | −0.36 |
| G = | 0.93 |
| H = | −1.3 |

average of the first two should be used. This would be 28 quarters. Again you see
that there is considerable room for judgment involved.

Another thing to consider is the slope of the dotted lines representing the
rate of expansion or contraction in the cycles. Look at the line segments labeled
G and compare the slopes with the line segments I. They have slopes that are
almost exactly the same based on a visual inspection of the two lines. Since we
do not know the next peak we can only base this on what has already been observed. Based on Figure 6.6b, for the 76 quarters between Feb-91 and Aug-05,
the change in the cycle factor was 0.93. Thus, over that period, the slope was
0.012 (0.93/76 = 0.012).

Now consider the slope of segment I in Figure 6.6b. We might expect the slope of I to remain at something close to 0.012. We see **1.27** is the height of the next peak, and we see the most recent trough is 0.43. The difference is 0.840 (1.27 - 0.43). At an increase of 0.012 per quarter, it will take an estimated 70 quarters to the next peak. Thus, our prediction would be that the next peak will be at a CF of 1.27 in the third quarter of 2028.

The seasonal index for the first quarter (designated by Feb here) is 0.82. Multiplying the predicted deseasonalised value (the centered moving average) by 0.82, we have: 327.83*0.82=268.82 as the prediction for private housing starts in the first quarter of 2025.

Here we made the judgment that the rate of recovery will be similar to the rate of the last recovery based on what we have observed thus far for the slope of line segment I. You can see that there is room for much debate about this prediction. Other analysts may focus more on the distances between peaks and troughs. We only know what is the best prediction in retrospect. The important thing is for you to have a logical and well-documented process to support your prediction.

Perhaps most frequently the cycle factor forecast is made on a largely judgmental basis by looking carefully at the historical values, especially historical turning points and the rates of descent or rise in the historical series. You might look at the peak-to-peak, trough-to-trough, peak-to-trough, and trough-to-peak distances by dating each turning point, such as we show in Figure 6.6. Then, you could calculate the average distance between troughs (or peaks) to get a feeling for when another such point is likely. You can also analyze the rates of increase and/or decrease in the cycle factor as a basis on which to judge the expected slope of the forecast of the cycle factor.

> It is important to recognize that there is no way to know exactly where the cycle factor will be in the forecast horizon, and there is no a priori way to determine the best technique for projecting the cycle factor. A thorough review of the past behavior of the cycle factor, along with alternative forecasts, should be evaluated for consistency and congruity before selecting values of the cycle factor for the forecast horizon.

It is important to recognize that there is no way to know exactly where the cycle factor will be in the forecast horizon, and there is no a priori way to determine the best technique for projecting the cycle factor. A thorough review of the past behavior of the cycle factor, along with alternative forecasts, should be evaluated for consistency and congruity before selecting values of the cycle factor for the forecast horizon.

## THE TIME-SERIES DECOMPOSITION FORECAST

You have seen that a time series of data can be decomposed into the product of four components:

$$Y = T \cdot S \cdot C \cdot I$$

where $Y$ is the series to be forecast. The four components are:

$T =$ The long-term trend based on the deseasonalized data. It is often called the *centered moving-average trend* (CMAT), since the deseasonalized data are centered moving averages (CMA) of the original $Y$ values.

$S =$ Seasonal indices (SI). These are normalized averages of seasonal factors that are determined as the ratio of each period's actual value ($Y$) to the deseasonalized value (CMA) for that period.

$C$ = The cycle component. The cycle factor (CF) is the ratio of CMA to CMAT and represents the gradual wavelike movements in the series around the trend line.

$I$ = The irregular component. This is assumed equal to 1 unless the forecaster has reason to believe a shock may take place, in which case $I$ could be different from 1 for all or part of the forecast period.

Previous sections of this chapter have illustrated how these components can be isolated and measured.

To prepare a forecast based on the time-series decomposition model, we simply reassemble the components. In general terms, the forecast for $Y$ (FY) is:

$$FY = (CMAT)(SI)(CF)(I)$$

For our private housing starts example, we will denote the forecast value based on the model as PHSFTSD. Thus,

$$PHSFTSD = (PHSCMAT)(SI)(CF)(I)$$

where PHSCMAT is the private housing starts centered moving-average trend, SI is the seasonal indices, and Cf is the cycle factor. The irregular factor ($I$) is assumed equal to 1, since we have no reason to expect it to be greater or less than 1 because of its random nature. The actual and forecast values for private housing starts are shown Figure 6.7. The actual values (PHS) are shown by the lighter solid line; fitted values are shown by the dashed line; and forecast values are shown by the dotted line. The forecast calculations are shown in Table 6.5 for

**FIGURE 6.7**  **Private Housing Starts (PHS) and A Time-Series Decomposition Forecast.**  (c6t4&f7)
The actual values for private housing starts are shown by the lighter blue line, the time-series decomposition fitted values are shown by the green dashed line, and a four-year forecast is shown by the dotted red line.

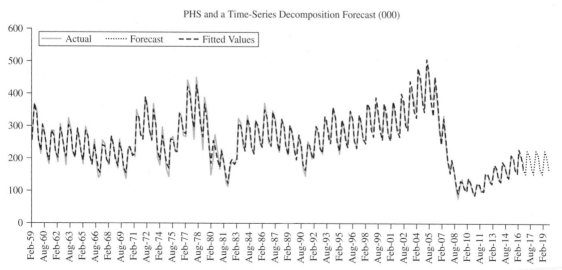

PHS and a Time-Series Decomposition Forecast (000)

**TABLE 6.5**   PHS
Time-Series
Decomposition
Forecast   (c6t4&f7)

| Date | Original Data | Forecasted Data | Centered Moving Average | CMA Trend | Seasonal Indices | Cycle Factors |
|------|------|------|------|------|------|------|
| Feb-1959 | 256.70 | | | | 0.82 | |
| May-1959 | 367.30 | | | | 1.19 | |
| Aug-1959 | 350.80 | 335.13 | 303.09 | 266.01 | 1.11 | 1.14 |
| Nov-1959 | 259.20 | 258.04 | 289.96 | 265.92 | 0.89 | 1.09 |
| Feb-1960 | 213.40 | 222.55 | 272.70 | 265.83 | 0.82 | 1.03 |
| May-1960 | 305.60 | 304.08 | 255.90 | 265.73 | 1.19 | 0.96 |
| Aug-1960 | 274.40 | 270.75 | 244.86 | 265.64 | 1.11 | 0.92 |
| Nov-1960 | 201.20 | 212.20 | 238.45 | 265.55 | 0.89 | 0.90 |
| . | . | . | . | . | . | . |
| . | . | . | . | . | . | . |
| . | . | . | . | . | . | . |
| Feb-2015 | 139.90 | 140.68 | 172.38 | 245.32 | 0.82 | 0.70 |
| May-2015 | 205.40 | 210.46 | 177.11 | 245.23 | 1.19 | 0.72 |
| Aug-2015 | 203.20 | 201.75 | 182.46 | 245.13 | 1.11 | 0.74 |
| Nov-2015 | 166.10 | 167.14 | 187.81 | 245.04 | 0.89 | 0.77 |
| Feb-2016 | 170.40 | 154.87 | 189.76 | 244.95 | 0.82 | 0.77 |
| May-2016 | 217.70 | 229.07 | 192.78 | 244.85 | 1.19 | 0.79 |
| Aug-2016 | 206.50 | 207.90 | | 244.76 | 1.11 | 0.77 |
| Nov-2016 | 186.90 | 168.56 | | 244.67 | 0.89 | 0.77 |
| Feb-2017 | | 154.91 | | 244.57 | 0.82 | 0.78 |
| May-2017 | | 225.57 | | 244.48 | 1.19 | 0.78 |
| Aug-2017 | | 209.08 | | 244.39 | 1.11 | 0.77 |
| Nov-2017 | | 168.51 | | 244.29 | 0.89 | 0.78 |
| Feb-2018 | | 154.52 | | 244.20 | 0.82 | 0.78 |
| May-2018 | | 224.85 | | 244.11 | 1.19 | 0.78 |
| Aug-2018 | | 209.06 | | 244.02 | 1.11 | 0.77 |
| Nov-2018 | | 168.25 | | 243.92 | 0.89 | 0.78 |
| Feb-2019 | | 154.24 | | 243.83 | 0.82 | 0.78 |
| May-2019 | | 224.47 | | 243.74 | 1.19 | 0.78 |
| Aug-2019 | | 208.79 | | 243.64 | 1.11 | 0.78 |
| Nov-2019 | | 167.99 | | 243.55 | 0.89 | 0.78 |
| Feb-2020 | | 153.99 | | 243.46 | 0.82 | 0.78 |
| May-2020 | | 224.13 | | 243.36 | 1.19 | 0.78 |
| Aug-2020 | | 208.48 | | 243.27 | 1.11 | 0.78 |
| Nov-2020 | | 167.73 | | 243.18 | 0.89 | 0.78 |

# Forecasting Winter Daily Natural Gas Demand at Vermont Gas Systems

1

**Mike Flock,** Distribution Engineer, Vermont Gas Systems, Inc.

Vermont Gas Systems is a natural gas utility with approximately 26,000 residential, business, and industrial customers in 13 towns and cities in northwestern Vermont. Vermont Gas Systems' Gas Control Department forecasts the gas demand and arranges the gas supply and transportation from suppliers in western Canada and storage facilities along the Trans-Canada Pipeline that deliver the gas to our pipeline. The quantities of gas must be specified to the suppliers at least 24 hours in advance. The Gas Control Department must request enough natural gas to meet the needs of the customers but must not over-request gas that will needlessly and expensively tax Trans-Canada Pipelines' facilities. Because Vermont Gas Systems has the storage capacity for only one hour's use of gas as a buffer between supply and demand, an accurate forecast of daily natural gas demand is critical.

**Source:** Flock, Mike, "Forecasting Winter Daily Natural Gas Demand at Vermont Gas Systems," *Journal of Business Forecasting* 13, no. 1 (Spring 1994), p. 23.

the first and last parts of the series. You will note that this method takes the trend (PHSCMAT) and makes two adjustments to it: the first adjusts it for seasonality (with SI), and the second adjusts it for cycle variations (with CF).

Because time-series decomposition models do not involve a lot of mathematics or statistics, they are relatively easy to explain to the end user. This is a major advantage, because if the end user has an appreciation of how the forecast was developed, he or she may have more confidence in its use for decision making.

## Integrative Case

# The Gap

## FORECASTING GAP SALES DATA WITH TIME-SERIES DECOMPOSITION

For time-series decomposition, we need a long data stream to be able to identify cycles. Therefore, in this Gap case, we have extended the data back to 1985. Previously, we have started with 2006. The sales of Gap for the 128 quarters covering fiscal 1985 through the end of Gap's 2016 fiscal year are shown below. (c6Gap)

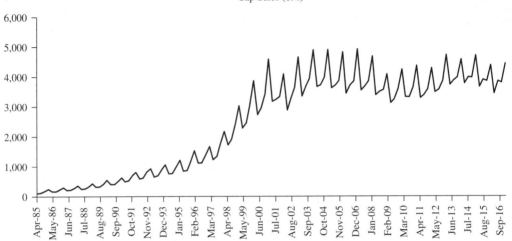

Gap Sales ($M)

**Case Questions**

1. Based on the graph of Gap sales, describe what you see in the 1985–2016 Gap sales using the terms used in time-series decomposition: *trend, seasonality,* and *cycle.*

2. For this question, use only Excel. Using Gap sales data for 1985Q1 through 2016Q4, calculate the four-period moving average (GapMA4), the centered moving average (GapCMA), and the CMAT using a time index that goes from 1 for 1985Q1 through 128 for 2016Q4. Extend the trend through the 2017 fiscal year.

3. Plot Gap sales, GapCMA, and GapCMAT on the same graph for the period from 1985Q1 through 2017Q4. There will be some quarters for which not all variables will have values.

4. Calculate the seasonal indices (SF). Are they consistent with your expectations? Explain.

5. Calculate the cycle factors (CF). Plot CF along with a horizontal line at one. Describe where you see peaks and/or troughs. Do you think you have enough data to clearly identify the cycle for Gap sales? Explain.

6. Now use ForecastX™ to prepare a forecast of Gap sales for the 12 quarters of the 2017 through 2019 fiscal years. Show the audit report plot of the actual, fitted, and forecast sales. Does the forecast look reasonable? Why or why not?

7. What are the four seasonal indices calculated by ForecastX™? Do these appear consistent with the seasonal factors that you calculated in Excel? Why or why not?

**Solutions to Case Questions**

1. The Gap sales exhibit an increasing positive trend over the time frame being evaluated and a very clear seasonal pattern that repeats itself year to year. It appears that the seasonality may be more pronounced in the more recent years than it was in the early years. From this graph, it is not clear that there are the long-term swings that are normally associated with a cyclical pattern.

(c6Gap)

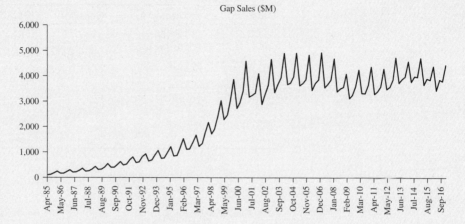

Gap Sales ($M)

2. Below is an abbreviated table of the requested series:

| Date | GapMA4 | GapCMA | GapCMAT |
|---|---|---|---|
| Apr-85 | | | |
| Jul-85 | | | |
| Oct-85 | 162.0 | 168.8 | 61.818 |
| Jan-86 | 175.5 | 181.1 | 101.15 |
| Apr-86 | 186.8 | 192.1 | 140.482 |
| Jul-86 | 197.5 | 204.8 | 179.814 |
| Oct-86 | 212.0 | 218.4 | 219.146 |
| Jan-87 | 224.8 | 231.4 | 258.478 |
| . | . | . | . |
| . | . | . | . |
| . | . | . | . |
| Apr-13 | 4,046.5 | 4,060.5 | 4388.338 |
| Jul-13 | 4,074.5 | 4,055.8 | 4427.67 |
| Oct-13 | 4,037.0 | 4,042.6 | 4467.002 |
| Jan-14 | 4,048.3 | 4,062.4 | 4506.334 |
| Apr-14 | 4,076.5 | 4,076.0 | 4545.666 |
| Jul-14 | 4,075.5 | 4,092.1 | 4584.998 |
| Oct-14 | 4,108.8 | 4,094.1 | 4624.33 |
| Jan-15 | 4,079.5 | 4,069.1 | 4663.662 |
| Apr-15 | 4,058.8 | 4,044.4 | 4702.994 |
| Jul-15 | 4,030.0 | 3,989.6 | 4742.326 |
| Oct-15 | 3,949.3 | 3,921.9 | 4781.658 |
| Jan-16 | 3,894.5 | 3,888.6 | 4820.99 |
| Apr-16 | 3,882.8 | 3,875.4 | 4860.322 |

(continued on next page)

(continued)

| Date | GapMA4 | GapCMA | GapCMAT |
|---|---|---|---|
| Jul-16 | 3,868.0 | 3,873.5 | 4899.654 |
| Oct-16 | 3,879.0 | | 4938.986 |
| Jan-17 | | | 4978.318 |
| Apr-17 | | | 5017.65 |
| Jul-17 | | | 5056.982 |
| Oct-17 | | | 5096.314 |
| Jan-18 | | | 5135.646 |

3. The requested graph is shown below.

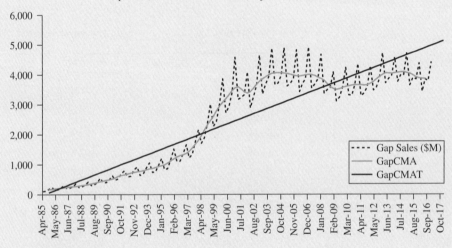

Gap Sales, Deseasonailzed Sales (GapCMA), and Trend (CMAT)

4. A sample of the calculation of seasonal factors is shown below:

| Date | GapSales ($M) | GapCMA | SF = GapSales/ GapCMA |
|---|---|---|---|
| Apr-85 | 106 | | |
| Jul-85 | 120 | | |
| Oct-85 | 182 | 168.75 | 1.08 |
| Jan-86 | 240 | 181.13 | 1.33 |
| Apr-86 | 160 | 192.13 | 0.83 |
| Jul-86 | 165 | 204.75 | 0.81 |
| Oct-86 | 225 | 218.38 | 1.03 |
| Jan-87 | 298 | 231.38 | 1.29 |

(continued on next page)

(continued)

| Date | GapSales ($M) | GapCMA | SF = GapSales/ GapCMA |
|------|---------------|--------|-----------------------|
| . | . | . | . |
| . | . | . | . |
| . | . | . | . |
| Apr-13 | 3729 | 4060.50 | 0.92 |
| Jul-13 | 3868 | 4055.75 | 0.95 |
| Oct-13 | 3976 | 4042.63 | 0.98 |
| Jan-14 | 4575 | 4062.38 | 1.13 |
| Apr-14 | 3774 | 4076.00 | 0.93 |
| Jul-14 | 3981 | 4092.13 | 0.97 |
| Oct-14 | 3972 | 4094.13 | 0.97 |
| Jan-15 | 4708 | 4069.13 | 1.16 |
| Apr-15 | 3657 | 4044.38 | 0.90 |
| Jul-15 | 3898 | 3989.63 | 0.98 |
| Oct-15 | 3857 | 3921.88 | 0.98 |
| Jan-16 | 4385 | 3888.63 | 1.13 |
| Apr-16 | 3438 | 3875.38 | 0.89 |
| Jul-16 | 3851 | 3873.50 | 0.99 |
| Oct-16 | 3798 | | |
| Jan-17 | 4429 | | |

5. The cycle factors are calculated as: CF = GapCMA/GapCMAT. The lighter line in the graph represents a horizontal line at one that is helpful when evaluating a cycle. The dark line is the cycle factor (CF) for each quarter.

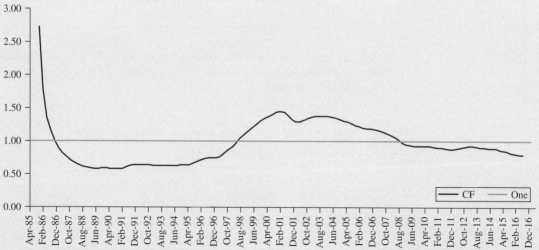

Gap Cycle Factor

Here we see only one trough at April 1989, where CF=0.58, and one peak at July 2001, where CF=1.39. In this case, even with the extended Gap sales data, there is not enough information to identify a cycle.

6. The ForecastX™ Audit Report graph of the time-series decomposition follows:

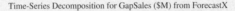

Time-Series Decomposition for GapSales ($M) from ForecastX

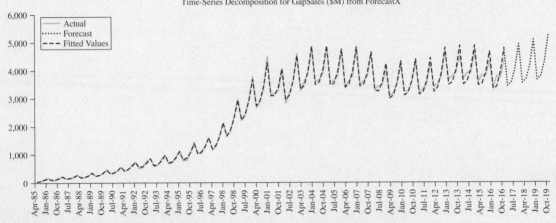

Everyone will not agree about whether the forecast looks reasonable. Many will think that the forecast looks high due to the declining cycle factors.

7. The seasonal indices from the ForecastX™ results are:

| Date | Seasonal Indices |
| --- | --- |
| First Quarter | 0.88 |
| Second Quarter | 0.90 |
| Third Quarter | 1.01 |
| Fourth Quarter | 1.22 |

These do appear consistent with the seasonal factors calculated in Excel. The third quarter is likely affected by back-to-school buying, while the fourth quarter sees the majority of holiday purchases.

# USING FORECASTX™ TO MAKE TIME-SERIES DECOMPOSITION FORECASTS

As usual, begin by opening your data file in Excel and select any cell in the data you want to forecast. In this example, we have selected cell B7.

| ◢ | A | B |
|---|---|---|
| 1 | **Date** | **Gap Sales ($M)** |
| 2 | Apr-85 | 106 |
| 3 | Jul-85 | 120 |
| 4 | Oct-85 | 182 |
| 5 | Jan-86 | 240 |
| 6 | Apr-86 | 160 |
| 7 | Jul-86 | 165 |
| 8 | Oct-86 | 225 |
| 9 | Jan-87 | 298 |
| 10 | Apr-87 | 211 |

Then start ForecastX$^{TM}$. In the **Data Capture** dialog box, check to be sure the data has been correctly identified. If the seasonality is not correctly identified, enter the number of seasons per year in the "Seasonality" box near the upper-right corner (four in this example using the Gap data). In **Forecast Periods,** make sure that you enter the number of periods that you want to forecast (eight in this example: a two-year forecast by quarters).

Source: John Galt Solutions

Then click the **Forecast Method** tab. In the **Forecast Method** dialog box, click the down arrow in the **Forecasting Technique** box and select **Decomposition** (note that in ForecastX$^{TM}$, this is simply called "Decomposition" rather than "Time-Series Decomposition"). Click **Multiplicative** and select **Trend (Linear) Regression** as the **Forecast Method for Decomposed Data.**

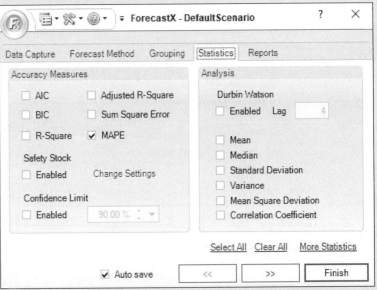

Source: John Galt Solutions

Then click the **Statistics tab.** In the Statistics dialog box, select the statistics that you desire. Remember that there are more choices if you click the **More Statistics** button near the bottom right. We have selected only the MAPE.

Source: John Galt Solutions

After selecting the statistics you want to see, click the **Reports** tab. In the **Reports** box, select those you want. The typical selection for decomposition would be the **Audit Report,** as shown here. The **Fitted Values Table** can be very long when you have an extended series for decomposition, so you may not want that long table when doing a time-series decomposition.

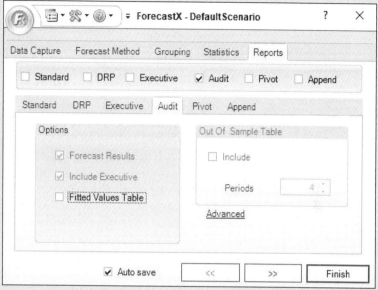

Source: John Galt Solutions

Then click the **Finish** button.

**Suggested Readings**

Aczel, Amir D.; and Jayavel Sounderpandian. "Time Series, Forecasting and Index Numbers." In *Complete Business Statistics*. 6th ed. Boston: McGraw-Hill/Irwin, 2006, pp. 582–602.

Austin, John S. "How to Use and Interpret Seasonal Factors." *Business Economics* 16, no. 4 (September 1981), pp. 40–42.

Campbell, Jeffrey R. "Entry, Exit, Embodied Technology, and Business Cycles." *Review of Economic Dynamics* 1 (1998), pp. 371–408.

Chatterjee, Satyajit. "From Cycles to Shocks: Progress in Business-Cycle Theory." *Business Review*, Federal Reserve Bank of Philadelphia (March/April 2000), pp. 27–37.

Chatterjee, Satyajit. "Productivity Growth and the American Business Cycle." *Business Review*, Federal Reserve Bank of Philadelphia, September/October 1995.

Espasa, Antoni; and Daniel Pena. "The Decomposition of Forecast in Seasonal ARIMA Models." *Journal of Forecasting* 14, no. 7 (December 1995), pp. 565–83.

Keating, Barry P. "Recession Forecasting: Using Leading Indicators and Decomposition." *The Journal of Business Forecasting*. Fall 2009, Volume 28, Number 3, pp. 23–30.

Layton, Allan P. "Dating and Predicting Phase Changes in the U.S. Business Cycle." *International Journal of Forecasting* 12, no. 3 (September 1996), pp. 417–28.

Majani, Bernard E. "Decomposition Methods for Medium-Term Planning and Budgeting." In *The Handbook of Forecasting*. Eds. Spyros Makridakis and Steven C. Wheelwright. New York: John Wiley & Sons, 1982, pp. 153–72.

Makridakis, Spyros; Steven C. Wheelwright; and Victor E. McGee. *Forecasting Methods and Applications.* 2nd ed. New York: John Wiley & Sons, 1983, pp. 130–78.

Sommers, Albert T. *The U.S. Economy Demystified.* Rev. ed. Lexington, MA: Lexington Books, 1988.

Temin, Peter. "The Causes of American Business Cycles: An Essay in Economic Historiography." In *Beyond Shocks: What Causes Business Cycles?* Eds. Jeffrey Fuhrer and Scott Schuh. Federal Reserve Bank of Boston, 1998.

Veloce, William. "An Evaluation of the Leading Indicators for the Canadian Economy Using Time Series Analysis." *International Journal of Forecasting* 12, no. 3 (September 1996), pp. 403–16.

Zellner, Arnold, ed. *Seasonal Analysis of Economic Time Series.* U.S. Department of Commerce, Bureau of the Census, 1978.

# Exercises

1. Explain the similarity between how time-series decomposition and Winters' exponential smoothing deal with seasonality.

2. Discuss the trend, the seasonal, and the cyclical components.

3. What is the difference between seasonal factors and seasonal indices?

4. How is the long-term trend determined for a time-series decomposition model?

5. How do true cycles and the cycles typically found in business data differ?

6. Using your own words, write a description of each of the four components of the classic time-series decomposition technique. Avoid using mathematical relationships and technical jargon as much as possible so that your explanations can be understood by almost anyone.

7. Suppose that sales of a household appliance are reported to be 13,000 units during the first quarter of the year. The seasonal index for the first quarter is 1.24. Use this information to make a forecast of sales for the entire year. Actual sales for the year were 42,000 units. Calculate your percentage error for the year. What percentage error would result if you forecast sales for the year by simply multiplying the 13,000 units for the first quarter by 4?

8. In a time-series decomposition of sales (in millions of units), the following trend has been estimated:

$$CMAT = 12.315 + 0.196(T)$$

The seasonal indices have been found to be:

| Quarter | Seasonal Index |
|---------|----------------|
| 1 | 1.27 |
| 2 | 1.02 |
| 3 | 0.73 |
| 4 | 0.98 |

For the coming year, the time index and cycle factors are:

| Quarter | T | CF |
|---------|-----|------|
| 1 | 21 | 1.01 |
| 2 | 22 | 1.04 |
| 3 | 23 | 1.06 |
| 4 | 24 | 1.04 |

*a.* From this information, prepare a forecast for each quarter of the coming year.

*b.* Actual sales for the year you forecast in part (*a*) were 17.2, 13.2, 10.8, and 14.2 for quarters 1, 2, 3, and 4, respectively. Use these actual sales figures along with your forecasts to calculate the mean absolute percentage error for the forecast period.

9. A tanning parlor located in a major shopping center near a large New England city has the following history of customers over the last four years (data are in hundreds of customers):

(c6p9)

| Year | Feb | May | Aug | Nov | Yearly Totals |
|------|-----|-----|-----|-----|---------------|
| | | **Mid-Month of Quarter** | | | |
| 2012 | 3.5 | 2.9 | 2.0 | 3.2 | 11.6 |
| 2013 | 4.1 | 3.4 | 2.9 | 3.6 | 14.0 |
| 2014 | 5.2 | 4.5 | 3.1 | 4.5 | 17.3 |
| 2015 | 6.1 | 5.0 | 4.4 | 6.0 | 21.5 |

*a.* Construct a table in which you show the actual data (given in the table), the centered moving average, the centered moving-average trend, the seasonal factors, and the cycle factors for every quarter for which they can be calculated in years 2012 through 2015.

*b.* Look at the seasonal index for each quarter as calculated in ForecastX™. Do they make sense to you? Explain why or why not.

*c.* Make a forecast of the number of customers for each quarter of 2016.

*d.* The actual numbers of customers served per quarter in 2016 were 6.8, 5.1, 4.7, and 6.5 for quarters 1 through 4, respectively (numbers are in hundreds). Calculate the MAPE for 2016.

*e.* Using the results provided in the tables produced by ForecastX™, prepare a time-series plot of the actual data, the centered moving averages, the long-term trend, and the values predicted by your model for 2012 through 2016 (where data are available).

10. Carl Lipke is the marketing VP for a propane gas distributor. He would like to have a forecast of sales on a quarterly basis, and he has asked you to prepare a time-series decomposition model. The data for 2005 through 2016 follow:(c6p10)

**Propane Gas Sales in Millions of Pounds**
**(Total at End-Month of Each Quarter)**

| Year | March | June | September | December |
|------|-------|------|-----------|----------|
| 2005 | 6.44 | 4.85 | 4.67 | 5.77 |
| 2006 | 6.22 | 4.25 | 4.14 | 5.34 |
| 2007 | 6.07 | 4.36 | 4.07 | 5.84 |

(continued on next page)

(continued)

| Year | March | June | September | December |
|------|-------|------|-----------|----------|
| 2008 | 6.06 | 4.24 | 4.20 | 5.43 |
| 2009 | 6.56 | 4.25 | 3.92 | 5.26 |
| 2010 | 6.65 | 4.42 | 4.09 | 5.51 |
| 2011 | 6.61 | 4.25 | 3.98 | 5.55 |
| 2012 | 6.24 | 4.34 | 4.00 | 5.36 |
| 2013 | 6.40 | 3.84 | 3.53 | 4.74 |
| 2014 | 5.37 | 3.57 | 3.32 | 5.09 |
| 2015 | 6.03 | 3.98 | 3.57 | 4.92 |
| 2016 | 6.16 | 3.79 | 3.39 | 4.51 |

a. To help Carl Lipke see how propane gas sales have varied over the 12-year period, prepare a time-series plot of the raw data and the deseasonalized data (i.e., the centered moving averages).

b. Use ForecastX$^{TM}$ to find seasonal indices for quarters 1 through 4. Write a short paragraph in which you explain to Carl Lipke exactly what these indices mean.

c. Plot the values of actual sales, the centered moving averages, and the trend. All of these can be found in your ForecastX$^{TM}$ results.

d. From ForecastX$^{TM}$, get a forecast for 2017Q1 through 2017Q4 based on the time-series decomposition model. Enter your forecast values into an Excel sheet that you set up like in the table shown below. Given the actual values shown in the table, calculate the mean absolute percentage error (MAPE) for 2017.

| Date | Actual Sales | Forecast Sales | Error | Absolute Error | Absolute % Error |
|------|-------------|----------------|-------|----------------|------------------|
| Mar-17 | 5.39 | | | | |
| Jun-17 | 3.56 | | | | |
| Sep-17 | 3.03 | | | | |
| Dec-17 | 4.03 | | | | |
| | | | | MAPE = | |

11. The Bechtal Tire Company (BTC) is a supplier of automotive tires for U.S. car companies. BTC has hired you to analyze its sales. For this problem, do all the work in ForecastX$^{TM}$ and be sure to request the MAPE in the statistics tab. Data from 1995Q1 through 2016Q4 are given in the following table (in thousands of units):

(c6p11)    **BTC Sales of Tires**

| Year | Q1 | Q2 | Q3 | Q4 |
|------|------|------|------|------|
| 1995 | 2,029 | 2,347 | 1,926 | 2,162 |
| 1996 | 1,783 | 2,190 | 1,656 | 1,491 |
| 1997 | 1,974 | 2,276 | 1,987 | 2,425 |
| 1998 | 2,064 | 2,517 | 2,147 | 2,524 |

(continued on next page)

(continued)

| Year | Q1 | Q2 | Q3 | Q4 |
|------|------|------|------|------|
| 1999 | 2,451 | 2,718 | 2,229 | 2,190 |
| 2000 | 1,752 | 2,138 | 1,927 | 1,546 |
| 2001 | 1,506 | 1,709 | 1,734 | 2,002 |
| 2002 | 2,025 | 2,376 | 1,970 | 2,122 |
| 2003 | 2,128 | 2,538 | 2,081 | 2,223 |
| 2004 | 2,027 | 2,727 | 2,140 | 2,270 |
| 2005 | 2,155 | 2,231 | 1,971 | 1,875 |
| 2006 | 1,850 | 1,551 | 1,515 | 1,666 |
| 2007 | 1,733 | 1,576 | 1,618 | 1,282 |
| 2008 | 1,401 | 1,535 | 1,327 | 1,494 |
| 2009 | 1,456 | 1,876 | 1,646 | 1,813 |
| 2010 | 1,994 | 2,251 | 1,855 | 1,852 |
| 2011 | 2,042 | 2,273 | 2,218 | 1,672 |
| 2012 | 1,898 | 2,242 | 2,247 | 1,827 |
| 2013 | 1,669 | 1,973 | 1,878 | 1,561 |
| 2014 | 1,914 | 2,076 | 1,787 | 1,763 |
| 2015 | 1,707 | 2,019 | 1,898 | 1,454 |
| 2016 | 1,706 | 1,878 | 1,752 | 1,560 |

a. Write a report to Bechtal Tire Company in which you explain what a time-series decomposition analysis shows about its tire sales. Include in your discussion seasonal, cyclical, and trend components.

b. Show a time-series graph with the actual data and the values that the time-series decomposition model would predict for each quarter from 1995Q1 through 2017Q4 (some data will be missing for certain historical quarters, and, of course for 2017, you will have only the forecast values).

c. If actual sales for 2017 were Q1 = 1,445.1, Q2 = 1,683.8, Q3 = 1,586.6, and Q4 = 1,421.3, what MAPE would result from your 2017 forecast? How does this MAPE compare to the MAPE ForecatsX$^{TM}$ calculated for the historic period?

12. A regional supplier of jet fuel is interested in forecasting its sales. These sales data are shown for the period from 2002Q1 to 2017Q4 (data in billions of gallons):

(c6p12)

**Jet Fuel Sales (Billions of Gallons)**

| Year | Q1 | Q2 | Q3 | Q4 |
|------|-------|-------|-------|-------|
| 2002 | 23.86 | 23.97 | 29.23 | 24.32 |
| 2003 | 23.89 | 26.84 | 29.36 | 26.30 |
| 2004 | 27.09 | 29.42 | 32.43 | 29.17 |
| 2005 | 28.86 | 32.10 | 34.82 | 30.48 |
| 2006 | 30.87 | 33.75 | 35.11 | 30.00 |

(continued on next page)

(continued)

| Year | Q1 | Q2 | Q3 | Q4 |
|------|------|------|------|------|
| 2007 | 29.95 | 32.63 | 36.78 | 32.34 |
| 2008 | 33.63 | 36.97 | 39.71 | 34.96 |
| 2009 | 35.78 | 38.59 | 42.96 | 39.27 |
| 2010 | 40.77 | 45.31 | 51.45 | 45.13 |
| 2011 | 48.13 | 50.35 | 56.73 | 48.83 |
| 2012 | 49.02 | 50.73 | 53.74 | 46.38 |
| 2013 | 46.32 | 51.65 | 52.73 | 47.45 |
| 2014 | 49.01 | 53.99 | 55.63 | 50.04 |
| 2015 | 54.77 | 56.89 | 57.82 | 53.30 |
| 2016 | 54.69 | 60.88 | 63.59 | 59.46 |
| 2017 | 61.59 | 68.75 | 71.33 | 64.88 |

*a.* Prepare a time series graph of these data. What, if any, seasonal pattern do you see in the plot? Explain.

*b.* Use ForecastX™ to make a time series decomposition forecast for 2018. Write a brief report explaining your forecast. Include a graph of the fitted values, the forecast values, and the actual sales.

*c.* Develop two other forecasts of jet fuel sales using the following methods:

1. A Winters' exponential smoothing model; and

2. A regression model using just time and quarterly dummy variables.

Compare the MAPEs for the three models you have developed, and comment on what you like or dislike about each of the three models for this application.

13. The following table contains quarterly data on Upper Midwest car sales (CS) in thousands for 1996Q1 through 2016Q4:

(c6p13)

**Upper Midwest Car Sales (CS)**

| Year | Q1 | Q2 | Q3 | Q4 |
|------|------|------|------|------|
| 1996 | 407.6 | 431.5 | 441.6 | 306.2 |
| 1997 | 328.7 | 381.3 | 422.6 | 369.4 |
| 1998 | 456.3 | 624.3 | 557.5 | 436.7 |
| 1999 | 485.0 | 564.3 | 538.3 | 412.5 |
| 2000 | 555.0 | 682.7 | 581.3 | 509.7 |
| 2001 | 662.7 | 591.1 | 616.9 | 529.7 |
| 2002 | 641.2 | 632.7 | 576.6 | 475.0 |
| 2003 | 542.8 | 558.9 | 581.7 | 537.8 |
| 2004 | 588.1 | 626.5 | 590.9 | 580.1 |
| 2005 | 589.2 | 643.2 | 593.9 | 612.2 |

(continued on next page)

(continued)

| Year | Q1 | Q2 | Q3 | Q4 |
|------|------|------|------|------|
| 2006 | 586.1 | 699.4 | 734.4 | 753.8 |
| 2007 | 691.6 | 793.4 | 864.9 | 840.8 |
| 2008 | 653.9 | 754.8 | 883.6 | 797.7 |
| 2009 | 722.2 | 788.6 | 769.9 | 725.5 |
| 2010 | 629.3 | 738.6 | 732.0 | 598.8 |
| 2011 | 603.9 | 653.6 | 606.1 | 539.7 |
| 2012 | 461.3 | 548.0 | 548.4 | 480.4 |
| 2013 | 476.6 | 528.2 | 480.4 | 452.6 |
| 2014 | 407.2 | 498.5 | 474.3 | 403.7 |
| 2015 | 418.6 | 470.2 | 470.7 | 375.7 |
| 2016 | 371.1 | 425.5 | 397.3 | 313.5 |

*a.* Prepare a time-series plot of Upper Midwest car sales from 1996Q1 through 2016Q4.

*b.* Use ForecastX$^{TM}$ to do a time-series decomposition forecast for 2017 (be sure to request the MAPE). In the results, you see the seasonal indices. Do they make sense? Why or why not?

*c.* ForecastX$^{TM}$ calculated the historic MAPE as a measure of fit. Write a short explanation of what this MAPE means to a manager.

*d.* Now calculate the MAPE for the 2017Q1–2017Q4 forecast horizon as a measure of accuracy, given that the actual values of CS for 2017 were:

| | |
|---|---|
| 2017Q1 | 301.1 |
| 2017Q2 | 336.7 |
| 2017Q3 | 341.8 |
| 2017Q4 | 293.5 |

*e.* Prepare a Winters' exponential smoothing forecast of CS using data from 1996Q1 through 2016Q4 as the basis for a forecast of 2017Q1–2017Q4. Compare these results in terms of fit and accuracy with the results from the time-series decomposition forecast.

# Chapter Seven

# Explanatory Models 3. ARIMA (Box-Jenkins) Forecasting Models

## INTRODUCTION

A time series of data is a sequence of numerical observations naturally ordered in time. The order of the data is an important part of the data. Some examples would be:

- Hourly temperatures at the entrance to Grand Central Station
- Daily closing price of IBM stock
- Weekly automobile production by the Chevrolet Division of General Motors
- Data from an individual firm: sales, profits, inventory, back orders
- An electrocardiogram

When a forecaster examines time-series data, two questions are of paramount importance:

1. Do the data exhibit a discernible pattern?
2. Can this pattern be exploited to make meaningful forecasts?

We have already examined some time-series data by using regression analysis to relate sequences of data to explanatory variables. Sales (as the dependent variable), for instance, might be forecast by using the explanatory (or independent) variables of product price, personal income of potential purchasers, and advertising expenditures by the firm. Such a model is a structural or causal forecasting model that requires the forecaster to know in advance at least some of the determinants or predictors of sales. But in many real-world situations, we do not know the determinants of the variable to be forecast, or data on these predictor variables are not readily available. It is in just these situations that the ARIMA technique has a decided advantage over standard regression models. ARIMA may also be used as a benchmark for other forecasting models; we could use an ARIMA model, for example, as a benchmark for comparison with our best structural regression model. The acronym ARIMA stands for autoregressive integrated moving average. Exponential smoothing, which we examined in Chapter 3, is actually just a special case of an ARIMA model.

The Box-Jenkins methodology of using ARIMA models is a technically sophisticated way of forecasting a variable by looking *only* at the past pattern of the time series. ARIMA thus ignores information that might be contained in a structural regression model; instead, it uses the most recent observation as a starting value and proceeds to analyze recent forecasting errors to select the most appropriate adjustment for future time periods. Since the adjustment usually compensates for only part of the forecast error, the Box-Jenkins process is best suited to longer-range rather than shorter-range forecasting (although it is used for short-, medium-, and long-range forecasts in actual practice).

> The Box-Jenkins methodology of using ARIMA models is a technically sophisticated way of forecasting a variable by looking *only* at the past pattern of the time series.

The Box-Jenkins methodology of using ARIMA models has some advantages over other time-series methods, such as exponential smoothing, time-series decomposition, and simple trend analysis. Box-Jenkins methodology extracts a great deal of information from the time series (more so than any other time-series technique), and it does so while using a minimum number of parameters. The Box-Jenkins method allows for greater flexibility in the choice of the "correct" model (this, we will see, is called "identification" in Box-Jenkins terminology). Instead of a priori choosing a simple time trend or a specific exponential smoothing method, for example, as the correct model, Box-Jenkins methodology includes a process that allows us to examine a large variety of models in our search for an acceptable one. This "open-ended" characteristic alone accounts for its appeal to many forecasters.

# LEARNING OBJECTIVES

After studying this chapter, you should be able to:

- Define ARIMA: (Autoregressive Integrated Moving Average).
- Explain the philosophy of ARIMA modelling.
- Relate an intuitive explanation of the ARIMA process to enhance understanding.
- Explain in detail the two contributing models: the autoregressive model and the moving average model.
- Discuss the importance of stationarity and demonstrate how to handle nonstationarity.
- Estimate an ARIMA model with ForecastX and use the appropriate diagnostic statistics to judge its fit and/or accuracy.
- Employ an ARIMA model for forecasting time-series data.

# THE PHILOSOPHY OF BOX-JENKINS

Pretend for a moment that a certain time series is generated by a "black box":

Black box → Observed time series

In standard regression analysis, we attempt to find the causal variables that explain the observed time series; what we take as a given for regression analysis is that the black box process is actually approximated by a linear regression technique:

$$\text{Explanatory} \atop \text{variables} \quad \rightarrow \quad {\text{Black box} \atop {\text{(approximated} \atop {\text{by linear} \atop \text{regression)}}}} \quad \rightarrow \quad {\text{Observed} \atop {\text{time} \atop \text{series}}}$$

In the Box-Jenkins methodology, on the other hand, we do not start with any explanatory variables but rather with the observed time series itself; what we attempt to discern is the "correct" black box that could have produced such a series from white noise:

$$\text{White noise} \rightarrow \text{Black box} \rightarrow \text{Observed time series}$$

The term *white noise* deserves some explanation. Since we are to use no explanatory variables in the ARIMA process, we assume instead that the series we are observing started as white noise and was transformed by the black box process into the series we are trying to forecast.

White noise is
essentially a purely
random series of
numbers.

White noise is essentially a purely random series of numbers. The numbers are normally and independently distributed. Some examples of white noise may serve to make its meaning clearer:

1. The winning numbers in the Illinois lottery's "Pick Four" game (where the four winning digits are drawn daily from four separate urns, each with 10 marked balls inside). Would knowledge of the numbers drawn for the past year help you pick a winner? (No, but there are those who actually believe some numbers are "better" than others.)

2. The last digit in the daily closing Dow Jones Industrial Average (or the last digit in the day-to-day change in the average). Would knowing the digit for the last two weeks help you to pick today's final digit?

White noise, then, has two characteristics:

1. There is no relationship between consecutively observed values.

2. Previous values do not help in predicting future values.

White noise is important in explaining the difference between the standard regression process and the Box-Jenkins methodology. The steps required in each method are shown in Table 7.1. In standard regression analysis, we move from the explanatory or indicator variables (which we choose as a result of some knowledge of the real world) to applying the linear regression technique in order to estimate the constant and slope coefficients of the model. We then use the regression equation to actually construct forecasts about future values of the time series. If our regression model does not have good summary statistics (e.g., $t$-statistics, $R$-squared, etc.), we may change some or all of the explanatory variables and try again until we are satisfied with the summary statistics (including the MAPE).

**TABLE 7.1**
Comparison of
Standard Regression
Analysis Box-Jenkins
Methodology

**For standard regression analysis:**

1. Specify the causal variables.
2. Use a linear (or other) regression model.
3. Estimate the constant and slope coefficients.
4. Examine the summary statistics and try other model specifications.
5. Choose the most desirable model specification (perhaps on the basis of RMSE).

**Start here:**

| Explanatory variables | → | Black box | → | Observed time series |

**For Box-Jenkins methodology:**

1. Start with the observed time series.
2. Pass the observed time series through a black box.
3. Examine the time series that results from passage through the black box.
4. If the black box is correctly specified, only white noise should remain.
5. If the remaining series is not white noise, try another black box.

**Start here:**

| Observed time series | → | Black box | → | White noise |

In Box-Jenkins methodology, however, we start instead with the observed time series itself (with no explanatory variables) and examine its characteristics in order to get an idea of what black box we might use to transform the series into white noise. We begin by trying the most likely of many black boxes, and if we get white noise, we assume that this is the "correct" model to use in generating forecasts of the series. If we try a particular black box and do not wind up with white noise, we try other likely black boxes until we finally wind up with white noise. The test to see whether we have succeeded in winding up with only white noise serves the same purpose as the set of summary statistics we generate with standard regression models; it lets us know when we have an acceptable model.

When choosing the correct black box, there are only three basic types of models for us to examine; there are, however, many permutations using these three types. The three types of models are: (1) moving-average (MA) models, (2) autoregressive (AR) models, and (3) mixed autoregressive–moving-average models (called ARMA models). We will examine each of these three models in turn in the following sections.

# MOVING-AVERAGE MODELS

A moving-average (MA) model is simply one that predicts $Y_t$ as a function of the past forecast errors in predicting $Y_t$. Consider $e_t$ to be a white noise series; a moving-average model would then take the following form:

$$Y_t = e_t + W_1 e_{t-1} + W_2 e_{t-2} + \cdots + W_q e_{t-q}$$

where:

$$e_t = \text{The value at time } t \text{ of the white noise series}$$
$$Y_t = \text{The generated moving-average time series}$$
$$W_{1, 2, \ldots, q} = \text{The coefficients (or "weights")}$$
$$e_{t-1}, t_{-2}, \ldots, t_{-q} = \text{Previous values of the white noise series}$$

The name *moving average* used by Box and Jenkins is actually not very descriptive of this type of model; we would do better to call it a weighted-average model since it is similar to exponential smoothing. An example of a moving-average model is constructed in Table 7.2, which is an abbreviated listing of the entire 200-observation data set.

**TABLE 7.2**
**Box-Jenkins Example Data Series**  (c7t2)

| | | White Noise | MA(1) | AR(1) | AR(2) | ARIMA111 |
|---|---|---|---|---|---|---|
| 1 | . | 0.256454 | 0.399867 | 0.240000 | 0.160000 | 0.160000 |
| 2 | . | 0.230240 | 0.409758 | 0.350240 | 0.040000 | 0.569758 |
| 3 | . | 0.675186 | 0.836354 | 0.850306 | 0.735186 | 1.40611 |
| 4 | . | 0.0475159 | 0.520146 | 0.472669 | 0.570146 | 1.92626 |
| 5 | . | 0.716827 | 0.750089 | 0.953162 | 1.26297 | 2.67635 |
| 6 | . | 0.854614 | 1.35639 | 1.33120 | 1.85272 | 4.03274 |
| 7 | . | 0.557983 | 1.15621 | 1.22358 | 2.10748 | 5.18895 |
| 8 | . | 0.0390320 | 0.429620 | 0.650822 | 1.88481 | 5.61857 |
| 9 | . | 0.184616 | 0.211938 | 0.510027 | 1.92548 | 5.83051 |
| 10 | . | 0.0167999 | 0.146031 | 0.271814 | 1.74160 | 5.97654 |
| 11 | . | 0.596069 | 0.607829 | 0.731976 | 2.20029 | 6.58437 |
| 12 | . | 0.235672 | 0.652921 | 0.601660 | 2.12419 | 7.23729 |
| 13 | . | 0.0724487 | 0.237419 | 0.373279 | 1.99944 | 7.47471 |
| 14 | . | 0.858917 | 0.909631 | 1.04556 | 2.68336 | 8.38434 |
| 15 | . | 0.830856 | 1.43210 | 1.35363 | 3.10910 | 9.81644 |
| 16 | . | 0.215927 | 0.797527 | 0.892744 | 2.92897 | 10.6140 |
| 17 | . | 0.223007 | 0.374156 | 0.669379 | 2.89511 | 10.9881 |
| 18 | . | 0.254166 | 0.410271 | 0.588855 | 2.86653 | 11.3984 |
| 19 | . | 0.764038 | 0.941954 | 1.05847 | 3.34963 | 12.3403 |
| 20 | . | 0.286438 | 0.821265 | 0.815671 | 3.20449 | 13.1616 |
| 191 | . | 0.323975 | 0.782538 | 0.820131 | 4.36400 | 150.720 |
| 192 | . | 0.162109 | 0.388892 | 0.572175 | 4.12794 | 151.109 |
| 193 | . | 0.702011 | 0.815488 | 0.988099 | 4.46437 | 151.924 |
| 194 | . | 0.854660 | 1.34607 | 1.34871 | 4.80531 | 153.270 |
| 195 | . | 0.480850 | 1.07911 | 1.15520 | 4.73744 | 154.349 |
| 196 | . | 0.843475 | 1.18007 | 1.42108 | 5.12074 | 155.530 |
| 197 | . | 0.408600 | 0.999033 | 1.11914 | 4.94061 | 156.529 |
| 198 | . | 0.581711 | 0.867731 | 1.14128 | 5.06429 | 157.396 |
| 199 | . | 0.975937 | 1.38313 | 1.54658 | 5.50906 | 158.779 |
| 200 | . | 0.683960 | 1.36712 | 1.45725 | 5.55316 | 160.147 |

In the first column of Table 7.2, we show a white noise series generated by randomly selecting numbers between 0 and 1. The moving-average series was constructed from the white noise series by using the following equation:

$$Y_t = e_t + W_1 e_{t-1}$$

where:

$Y_t$ = The series generated, which appears in column 2

$e_t$ = The white noise series appearing in column 1

$W_1$ = A constant (equal here to 0.7)

$e_{t-1}$ = The white noise value lagged one period

The process of identifying the correct model is a bit like identifying an animal from the tracks it makes in the soil.

This series—called an MA(1) series because it contains one lag of the white noise term—was constructed with known characteristics. Imagine how we might decide that a time series of unknown origin that we want to forecast could be similar to this known series. How could we go about examining this time series to determine whether it is an MA(1) series like that in column 2 of Table 7.2? We can get an insight into the answer by examining two characteristics of the time series we have purposely constructed to be an MA(1) series in Table 7.2. These characteristics are the autocorrelations and the partial autocorrelations of the series. These characteristics may be viewed graphically, and the process of identifying the correct model is a bit like identifying an animal from the tracks it makes in the soil.

First, we examine the autocorrelation (or "serial correlation") among successive values of the time series; this will be the first of two key tools in determining which model (or black box) is an appropriate representation of any given time series. As described in Chapter 2, autocorrelation is the concept that the association between values of the same variable at different time periods is nonrandom—that is, that if autocorrelation does exist in a time series, there is correlation or mutual dependence between the values of the time series at different time periods.

As a simple example of autocorrelation, consider the data in Table 7.3. The first column could represent sales of an item during successive periods; the second column is the first column lagged one period; the third column is the first column lagged two periods. We can now calculate the simple correlation coefficient between the numbers in the first column and the numbers in the second column, treating each column as if it were a separate variable. Remember that the correlation coefficient will always vary between +1 and −1. If it is +1, it indicates that there is a perfect positive correlation between the two columns; that is, as one increases, so does the other. If the correlation coefficient is −1, it indicates a perfect negative correlation; that is, as one goes up, the other goes down. The closer the number is to +1, the more positively correlated the columns; the closer the number is to −1, the more negatively correlated the columns.

**TABLE 7.3** A
Simple Example
of Autocorrelation
(c7t3)

| Original Variable | One Time Lag | Two Time Lags |
|---|---|---|
| 121 | — | — |
| 123 | 121 | — |
| 134 | 123 | 121 |
| 133 | 134 | 123 |
| 151 | 133 | 134 |
| 141 | 151 | 133 |
| 176 | 141 | 151 |
| 187 | 176 | 141 |
| 183 | 187 | 176 |
| 214 | 183 | 187 |

Correlation between original variable and one time lag = +0.867. Correlation between original variable and two time lags = +0.898.

Here, the correlation between the first and second columns is +0.867; the correlation between the first and third columns is +0.898. These values indicate the extent to which the original series values are correlated with themselves, lagged one and two periods (called *auto*correlation since the second and third columns of our table are not variables separate from column 1 but are actually the same variable viewed at different points in time).

Apparently, autocorrelation exists in this variable for both one and two lags, and the autocorrelation coefficients are approximately equal. These autocorrelations provide us with the first important tool for identifying the correct model; if the original data in Table 7.3 had been completely random white noise (ours were not!), the correlation among lagged values (one, two, or more lags) would have been approximately equal to zero, given a large enough data set. We will find that the pattern of the autocorrelations will help us identify a series that behaves as if it were created by a moving-average model.

The partial
autocorrelation
coefficient is the second
tool we will use to help
identify the relationship
between the current
values and past values
of the original time
series.

The partial autocorrelation coefficient is the second tool we will use to help identify the relationship between the current and past values of the original time series. Just as the autocorrelation function measures the association of a variable with successive values of the same variable in a time series, partial autocorrelations measure the degree of association between the variable and that same variable in another time period after partialing out (i.e., controlling for) the effects of the other lags. Partial autocorrelation coefficients measure the degree of association between $Y_t$ and $Y_{t-k}$ *when all the other time lags on Y are held constant.* The calculation of the partial autocorrelation terms is beyond the scope of this text, but they are calculated by ForecastX$^{TM}$ and most other statistical packages that deal with time-series analysis. It is possible, however, to explain how these coefficients are calculated without presenting the actual lengthy derivation.

The partial autocorrelation coefficient is defined in terms of the last autoregressive (AR) term of an AR-type model with *m* lags. Partial autocorrelations are calculated when we are unsure of the correct order of the autoregressive process to fit the time series. Consider the AR($m$) model (which will be explained in more detail in the section "Autoregressive Models") represented in the following equations:

$$Y_t = A_1 Y_{t-1} + e_t$$

$$Y_t = A_1 Y_{t-1} + A_2 Y_{t-2} + e_t$$

$$\vdots$$

$$Y_t = A_1 Y_{t-1} + A_2 Y_{t-2} + \cdots + A_m Y_{t-m} + e_t$$

By solving this system of equations for the $A_1$, $A_2$, ... , $A_{t-m}$ terms (which are the partial autocorrelation coefficients), we could determine their actual values.

It is most common to view both the autocorrelation coefficients and the partial autocorrelation coefficients in graphic form by constructing a correlogram (also called an autocorrelation plot) of the autocorrelation coefficients and a partial correlogram for the partial autocorrelation coefficients; both graphics look very much like the residuals output in the ForecastX$^{\text{TM}}$ program.

Consider the typical MA(1) correlogram and partial correlogram in Figure 7.1. Two distinctive patterns in the autocorrelation and partial autocorrelation functions are characteristically present and suggest an MA(1) model. The *a* frame of Figure 7.1 displays the first of these patterns. Note the gradual falling to zero of the partial autocorrelation function and the single spike in the autocorrelation function. In general, if the autocorrelation function abruptly stops at some point, we know the model is of the MA type; the number of spikes (commonly referred to as *q*) before the abrupt stop tells us the "order" of the MA model. In frame *a,* there is only one spike, and so we know the model is likely to be of the MA(1) variety. This identification process was first done by forecasters exactly as described by using a manual pattern recognition process. ForecastX$^{\text{TM}}$ has automated the procedure and will suggest an appropriate (though perhaps not the best) model.

Frame *b* represents a second variation of this distinctive pattern; here, the single spike (now negative) still appears in the autocorrelation function, but the partial autocorrelation function shows alternating positive and negative values, gradually falling to zero. This also would indicate to us an MA(1)-type model.

In any given data, there may be more than one significant moving-average term; if there were two significant moving-average terms, for instance, we could find either of the patterns in frames *c* and *d*. Both of these situations are characteristic of an MA(2) model; both frames show two distinct spikes in the autocorrelation function while the partial autocorrelation function gradually slides to zero, either monotonically decreasing or alternating between positive and negative values.

We are now ready to examine the autocorrelation and partial autocorrelation functions for the MA(1) series in column 2 of Table 7.2. The correlograms for each are shown for the first 24 lags in Figure 7.2. If we had not previously known that this was an MA(1) series, we should have been able to deduce this from the

**FIGURE 7.1**

**Examples of Theoretical Autocorrelation and Partial Autocorrelation Plots for MA(1) and MA(2) Models**

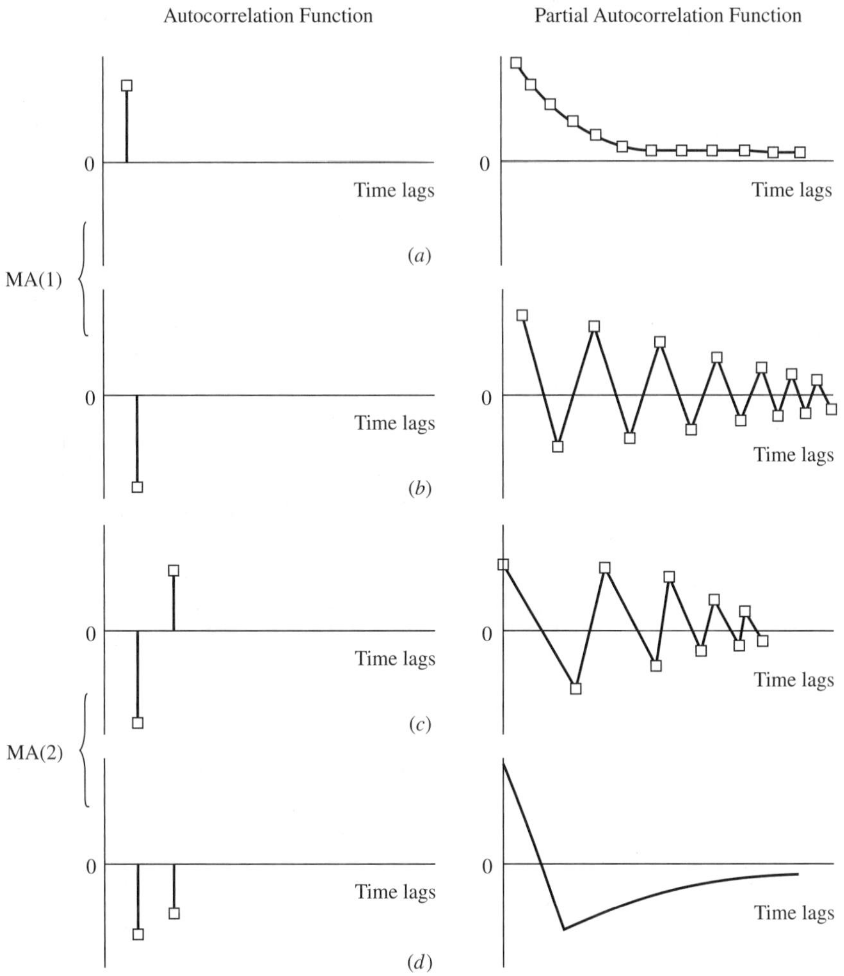

characteristic patterns shown in Figure 7.2: note that the autocorrelation function has only one spike that appears to be significantly different from zero. The approximate 95 percent confidence intervals are shown for both the autocorrelation and partial autocorrelation functions in Figure 7.2. A value between the confidence interval is seen to be not significantly different from zero. Also note that the partial autocorrelation function alternates from positive to negative *and* decreases in absolute value as it approaches zero. This pattern is similar to that shown in frame *b* of Figure 7.1 and identifies the time series for us as one of the MA(1) variety. This knowledge of what the autocorrelation and partial autocorrelation functions look like in an MA(1) model will allow us (and the ForecastX$^{TM}$ software) to use Box-Jenkins methodology to model and forecast any similar time series accurately.

**FIGURE 7.2**
**Autocorrelation**
**and Partial**
**Autocorrelation Plots**
**for the MA(1) Series**
**in Table 7.2** (c7t2)

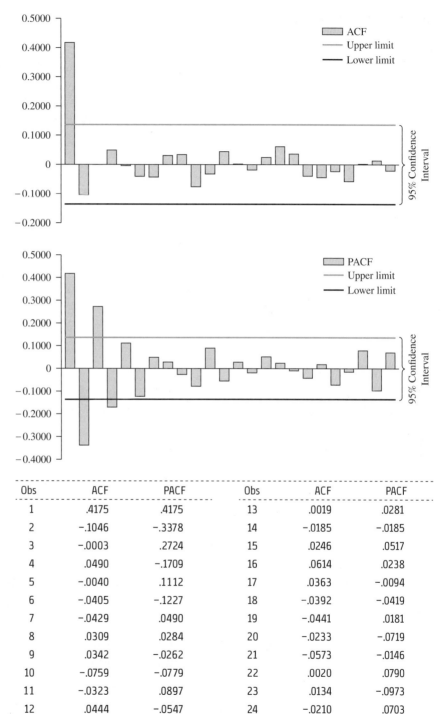

| Obs | ACF | PACF | Obs | ACF | PACF |
|-----|------|-------|-----|-------|-------|
| 1 | .4175 | .4175 | 13 | .0019 | .0281 |
| 2 | −.1046 | −.3378 | 14 | −.0185 | −.0185 |
| 3 | −.0003 | .2724 | 15 | .0246 | .0517 |
| 4 | .0490 | −.1709 | 16 | .0614 | .0238 |
| 5 | −.0040 | .1112 | 17 | .0363 | −.0094 |
| 6 | −.0405 | −.1227 | 18 | −.0392 | −.0419 |
| 7 | −.0429 | .0490 | 19 | −.0441 | .0181 |
| 8 | .0309 | .0284 | 20 | −.0233 | −.0719 |
| 9 | .0342 | −.0262 | 21 | −.0573 | −.0146 |
| 10 | −.0759 | −.0779 | 22 | .0020 | .0790 |
| 11 | −.0323 | .0897 | 23 | .0134 | −.0973 |
| 12 | .0444 | −.0547 | 24 | −.0210 | .0703 |

# AUTOREGRESSIVE MODELS

The second of the three classes of models we need to examine is the autoregressive (AR) model. The equation for the autoregressive model is similar to the moving-average model, except that the dependent variable $Y_t$ depends on its own previous values rather than the white noise series or residuals. The autoregressive model is produced from a white noise series by using an equation of the form:

$$Y_t = A_1 Y_{t-1} + A_2 Y_{t-2} + \cdots + A_p Y_{t-p} + e_t$$

where:

$$Y_t = \text{The moving-average time series generated}$$
$$A_1, A_2, \ldots, A_p = \text{Coefficients}$$
$$Y_{t-1}, Y_{t-2}, \ldots, Y_{t-p} = \text{Lagged values of the time series (hence the name } \textit{autoregressive}\text{)}$$
$$e_t = \text{White noise series}$$

If the model has only the $Y_{t-1}$ term on the right-hand side, it is referred to as an AR(1) model; if it has $Y_{t-1}$ and $Y_{t-2}$ terms, it is an AR(2); and so on. Column 3 of Table 7.2 is an AR(1) series produced by the following equation:

$$Y_t = A_1 Y_{t-1} + e_t$$

where

$$Y_t = \text{The series generated, which appears in column 2}$$
$$e_t = \text{The white noise series appearing in column 1}$$
$$A_1 = \text{A constant (equal here to 0.5)}$$
$$Y_{t-1} = \text{The series lagged one period}$$

(Note: The first number in the column [i.e., 0.24] is chosen arbitrarily.)

Once again, as with the MA(1) model presented in the "Moving-Average Models" section, the AR(1) series in column 3 is constructed from the white noise series with known characteristics; that is, it is an AR(1) series because we constructed it to be one. Again, ask the question: How might we decide that another time series, of unknown origin, that we were given to forecast could be similar to this AR(1) series? In other words, how would we go about examining a series to determine whether it is an AR(1)-type series?

We will answer the question by again examining the characteristics of the known series—the AR(1) series in column 3 of Table 7.2. Once again, we first examine the autocorrelation function of the series and then examine the partial autocorrelation function of the series. We are looking for distinctive patterns in each of these functions that will indicate that any time series under examination is an AR(1)-type series.

The typical correlograms and partial correlograms for an AR(1) series are shown in frames $a$ and $b$ of Figure 7.3. Either of two patterns is distinctive for an

**FIGURE 7.3**
**Examples of**
**Theoretical**
**Autocorrelation**
**and Partial**
**Autocorrelation Plots**
**of AR(1) and AR(2)**
**Models**

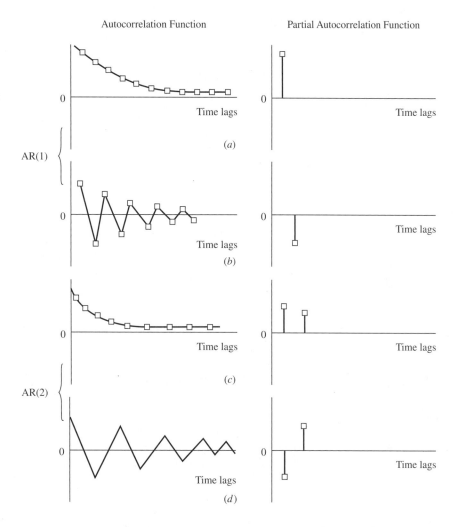

AR(1) model. In frame *a,* the autocorrelation function falls monotonically to zero while the partial autocorrelation function shows a single spike; note that this is the exact opposite of the pattern exhibited by an MA(1) time series. In general, if the partial autocorrelation function abruptly stops at some point, the model is of the AR type; the number of spikes (*p*) before the abrupt stop is equal to the "order" of the AR model. In frame *a,* there is just one spike in the partial autocorrelation function, and so the model is of the AR(1) type.

Frame *b* represents the second of two characteristic patterns for an AR(1) model; here, the single spike (now negative) still appears in the partial autocorrelation function, but the autocorrelation function tends to zero by alternating between positive and negative values.

As in MA-type models, there may be more than one significant autoregressive term; if this is the case, patterns like those shown in frames *c* and *d* of Figure 7.3 could result. Patterns like those in either frame *c* or *d* would indicate an AR(2)-type model because of the two significant spikes in the partial autocorrelation function. Note again that the autocorrelation function in both cases falls to zero, either monotonically (as in frame *c*) or alternating between positive and negative values (as in frame *d*).

We should now be able to evaluate the autocorrelation and partial autocorrelation functions for the AR(1) series in column 3 of Table 7.2. Recall that we know that this particular time series was produced from a white noise series by using the equation:

$$Y_t = A_1 Y_{t-1} + e_t$$

The correlograms for each are shown for the first 24 lags in Figure 7.4. If we had not known that this was an AR(1) series, we should have been able to deduce this from the characteristic patterns in Figure 7.4; note that the partial autocorrelation function has only one significant spike (i.e., it has only one spike that appears significantly different from zero, and so the order is $p = 1$). Also note that the autocorrelation function decreases in value, approaching zero. This pattern is similar to that shown in frame *a* of Figure 7.3, and this fact identifies the time series as one of the AR(1) variety.

## MIXED AUTOREGRESSIVE AND MOVING-AVERAGE MODELS

The third and final of the three classes of models that we need examine is really a combination of an AR and an MA model. This third class of general models is called *ARMA*, which stands for *autoregressive–moving-average model.* This model could be produced from a white noise series by introducing the elements we have already seen in both moving-average and autoregressive models:

$$Y_t = A_1 Y_{t-1} + A_2 Y_{t-2} + \cdots$$

$$+ A_p Y_{t-p} + e_t + W_1 e_{t-1}$$

$$+ W_2 e_{t-2} + \cdots + W_q e_{t-q}$$

This equation defines a mixed autoregressive–moving-average model of order *p, q,* and is usually written as ARMA($p, q$). To identify an ARMA model, we again look for characteristic patterns in the autocorrelation and partial autocorrelation functions.

Figure 7.5 shows the characteristic patterns for an ARMA(1, 1) model; note that *any* of the four frames in Figure 7.5 could be patterns that would identify an ARMA(1, 1) model. In Figure 7.5, in each of the frames, both the autocorrelations and partial autocorrelations gradually fall to zero *rather than abruptly stop.* This observation (both functions falling off gradually) is characteristic of any ARMA($p, q$) model.

**FIGURE 7.4**
**Autocorrelation
and Partial
Autocorrelation Plots
for the AR(1) Series
in Table 7.2**  (c7t2)

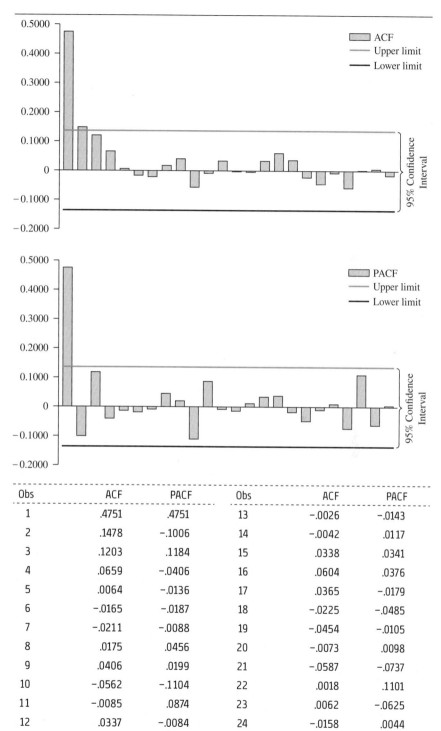

| Obs | ACF | PACF | Obs | ACF | PACF |
|-----|------|-------|-----|-------|-------|
| 1 | .4751 | .4751 | 13 | −.0026 | −.0143 |
| 2 | .1478 | −.1006 | 14 | −.0042 | .0117 |
| 3 | .1203 | .1184 | 15 | .0338 | .0341 |
| 4 | .0659 | −.0406 | 16 | .0604 | .0376 |
| 5 | .0064 | −.0136 | 17 | .0365 | −.0179 |
| 6 | −.0165 | −.0187 | 18 | −.0225 | −.0485 |
| 7 | −.0211 | −.0088 | 19 | −.0454 | −.0105 |
| 8 | .0175 | .0456 | 20 | −.0073 | .0098 |
| 9 | .0406 | .0199 | 21 | −.0587 | −.0737 |
| 10 | −.0562 | −.1104 | 22 | .0018 | .1101 |
| 11 | −.0085 | .0874 | 23 | .0062 | −.0625 |
| 12 | .0337 | −.0084 | 24 | −.0158 | .0044 |

**FIGURE 7.5**

**Examples of
Theoretical
Autocorrelation
and Partial
Autocorrelation Plots
of ARMA(1, 1) Models**

Autocorrelation Function

Partial Autocorrelation Function

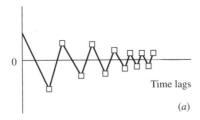

(a)

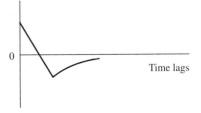

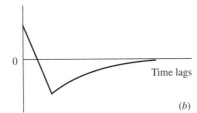

(b)

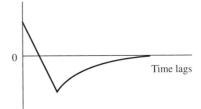

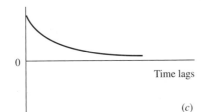

(c)

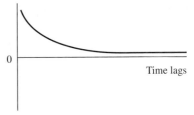

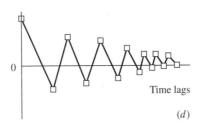

(d)

To identify the order of the AR and MA terms, we need to count the number of AR and MA terms significantly different from zero. In frame *b*, for instance, there is one spike in the partial autocorrelation function (AR process) and one spike in the autocorrelation function (MA process); this would imply an ARMA(1, 1) model. The other patterns exhibited in Figure 7.5 are less easily identified as ARMA(1, 1) processes.

In fact, the particular identification process we have outlined requires some experience to apply manually in the real world. We have, however, outlined the basic steps to be followed in applying the identification process; skill in the actual application requires the consideration of many examples and learning from past mistakes. But recall that the ForecastX™ software incorporates these identification skills and allows a user to identify an appropriate model quite easily. We have already seen that according to Box-Jenkins methodology, if we are able to identify the type and order of the model we are faced with when we are given a time series, then the repetitive pattern in that original time series offers us the method for forecasting it. When we are given a time series in the real world, however, we are not told the type of model that will fit it, and the first task is to figure out which of the infinite variations of the three models (autoregressive, moving average, or mixed) is the "correct" model for our data. This is where ForecastX™ excels.

Many real-world processes, once they have been adjusted for seasonality, can be adequately modeled with the low-order models.

Fortunately, for low-order processes like the ones we have examined so far, the correct specification of the $p$ and $q$ values is rather simple to make. Many real-world processes, once they have been adjusted for seasonality, can be adequately modeled with the low-order models, for example, MA(1), MA(2), AR(1), AR(2), ARMA(1, 1). If low-order models are not adequate (how to determine whether a model is adequate will be explained in the "The Box-Jenkins Identification Process" section), the selection of the proper $p$ and $q$ becomes more difficult. As a rule of thumb, however, spikes in the autocorrelation function indicate moving-average terms, and spikes in the partial autocorrelation function indicate autoregressive terms.

When the correct model is not of a low order, you may be forced to determine an adequate $p$ and $q$ by trial and error, but an acceptable model will usually be very close to the ForecastX™ suggestion; it will be possible, you will see, to check your guesses after the parameters of each model have been determined. However, manually searching for an adequate model is rarely done nowadays; ForecastX™ includes an automatic algorithm that forecasters have found useful.

## STATIONARITY

A *stationary* time series is one in which two consecutive values in the series depend *only* on the time interval between them and *not* on time itself.

In general, we have been approaching our data as if they were stationary. A *stationary* time series is one in which two consecutive values in the series depend *only* on the time interval between them and *not* on time itself. For all practical purposes, this would be consistent with a series whose mean value did *not* change over time. Real-world time series are most often nonstationary; that is, the mean value of the time series changes over time, usually because there is some trend in the series so that the mean value is either rising or falling over time. Nonstationarity can result in other ways (it could be that the variability of the time series changes over time; perhaps the variability becomes exaggerated through time), but the most common cause is simply a trend in the series.

If the series we examine are nonstationary, the autocorrelations are usually significantly different from zero at first and then gradually fall off to zero, or they show a spurious pattern as the lags are increased. Because autocorrelations dominate the pattern of a nonstationary series, it is necessary for us to modify a nonstationary series to make it stationary *before* we try to identify as the "correct" model one of the three models we have so far examined.

There is no single way to remove nonstationarity, but two methods help achieve stationarity most often in actual practice. First, if the nonstationarity is caused by a trend in the series, then differencing the time series may effectively remove the trend. Differencing refers to subtracting the previous observation from each observation in the data set:

$$Y_t' = Y_t - Y_{t-1}$$

where:

$Y_t'$ = The first difference of observation at time $t$

$Y_t$ = Time-series observation at time $t$

$Y_{t-1}$ = Time-series observation at time period $t - 1$

In some cases, the first difference will not remove the trend and it may be necessary to try a higher order of differencing. For example, second-order differences can be found as follows:

$$Y_t'' = Y_t' - Y_{t-1}'$$

where:

$Y_t''$ = The second difference

$Y_t'$ = The first difference of observation at time $t$

$Y_{t-1}'$ = The first difference of observation at time period $t - 1$

The second method for removing nonstationarity is used when there is a change in the variability of the series (i.e., when there is a trend in the variance). This method involves taking logs of the original time series, which usually transfers the trend in variance to a trend in the mean; this trend can then be handled by differencing. Other, more sophisticated methods of removing nonstationarity are sometimes used but will not be covered here.

Consider the series in column 5 of Table 7.2. Glancing at the numbers down the column, we can easily see that this series has some trend; the numbers are monotonically increasing throughout the time period. Figure 7.6 shows the autocorrelation function for this series. This autocorrelation function is entirely characteristic of series with a trend; that is, it shows dominant autocorrelations for the 24 lags shown, and these autocorrelations only gradually become smaller. Figure 7.7 shows the correlograms for the same series *after* first differences have been taken. Apparently, this series contains a trend and could probably easily be modeled with a simple time trend or a low-order ARMA model. Figure 7.7 (which shows the data after taking first differences) could perhaps be best modeled as an ARMA(3, 1), since there appears to be one dominant autocorrelation spike and three dominant partial autocorrelation spikes.

**FIGURE 7.6**
**Autocorrelation**
**and Partial**
**Autocorrelation Plots**
**for the ARIMA**
**(1, 1, 1) sSeries in**
**Table 7.2** (c7t2)

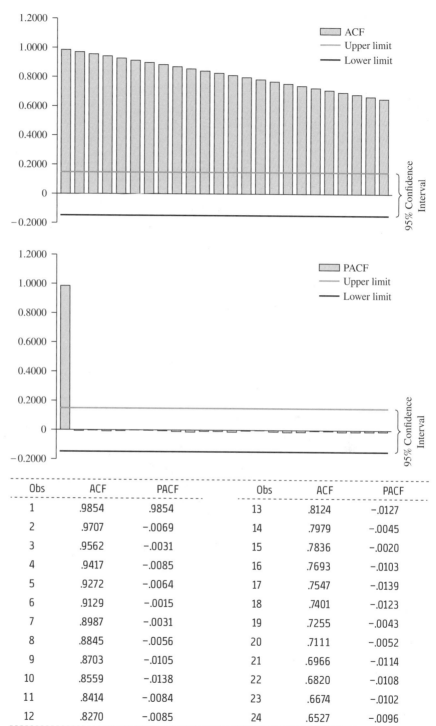

| Obs | ACF | PACF | Obs | ACF | PACF |
|-----|------|-------|-----|------|-------|
| 1 | .9854 | .9854 | 13 | .8124 | −.0127 |
| 2 | .9707 | −.0069 | 14 | .7979 | −.0045 |
| 3 | .9562 | −.0031 | 15 | .7836 | −.0020 |
| 4 | .9417 | −.0085 | 16 | .7693 | −.0103 |
| 5 | .9272 | −.0064 | 17 | .7547 | −.0139 |
| 6 | .9129 | −.0015 | 18 | .7401 | −.0123 |
| 7 | .8987 | −.0031 | 19 | .7255 | −.0043 |
| 8 | .8845 | −.0056 | 20 | .7111 | −.0052 |
| 9 | .8703 | −.0105 | 21 | .6966 | −.0114 |
| 10 | .8559 | −.0138 | 22 | .6820 | −.0108 |
| 11 | .8414 | −.0084 | 23 | .6674 | −.0102 |
| 12 | .8270 | −.0085 | 24 | .6527 | −.0096 |

**FIGURE 7.7**
**Autocorrelation and Partial Autocorrelation Plots for the ARIMA(1, 1, 1) Series in Table 7.2 After First Differences Have Been Taken** (c7t2)

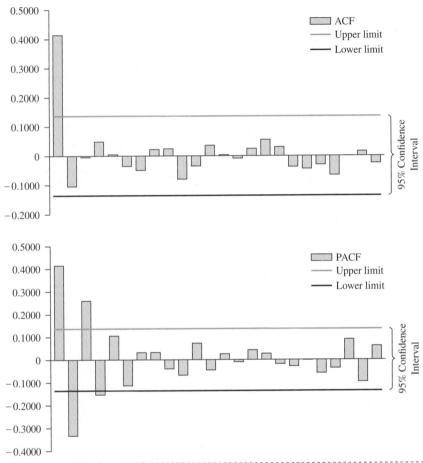

| Obs | ACF | PACF | Obs | ACF | PACF |
|-----|------|-------|-----|-------|-------|
| 1 | .4141 | .4141 | 13 | .0035 | .0255 |
| 2 | −.1046 | −.3333 | 14 | −.0087 | −.0102 |
| 3 | −.0047 | .2594 | 15 | .0246 | .0424 |
| 4 | .0486 | −.1538 | 16 | .0550 | .0269 |
| 5 | .0048 | .1049 | 17 | .0303 | −.0188 |
| 6 | −.0352 | −.1130 | 18 | −.0374 | −.0286 |
| 7 | −.0489 | .0320 | 19 | −.0442 | −.0013 |
| 8 | .0221 | .0324 | 20 | −.0301 | −.0585 |
| 9 | .0243 | −.0396 | 21 | −.0657 | −.0367 |
| 10 | −.0794 | −.0677 | 22 | .0003 | .0894 |
| 11 | −.0348 | .0724 | 23 | .0157 | −.0963 |
| 12 | .0357 | −.0452 | 24 | −.0248 | .0603 |

When differencing is used to make a time series stationary, it is common to refer to the resulting model as an ARIMA($p, d, q$)-type model. The "I" that has been added to the name of the model refers to the integrated or differencing term in the model; the $d$ inside the parentheses refers to the degree of differencing. An ARIMA($p, d, q$) model is then properly referred to as an *autoregressive integrated moving-average model.* For example, a model with one autoregressive term, one degree of differencing, and no moving-average term would be written as an ARIMA(1, 1, 0) model. An ARIMA model is thus classified as an "ARIMA($p, d, q$)" model, where:

- $p$ is the number (order) of autoregressive terms,
- $d$ is the number (order) of differences, and
- $q$ is the number (order) of moving-average terms.

ForecastX™ as part of its identification procedure will suggest and apply the differencing that it determines is necessary to suggest an adequate model. It is also possible, but not necessary, to manually apply differencing and see the graphic results like those described here.

# THE BOX-JENKINS IDENTIFICATION PROCESS

As a first step, the raw series is examined to *identify* one of the many available models that we will tentatively select as the best representation of this series.

We are finally in a position to set down the Box-Jenkins methodology in a patterned format. The approach is an iterative one, in which we may loop through the process many times before reaching a model with which we are comfortable. The four steps of the Box-Jenkins process are outlined in Figure 7.8.

As a first step, the raw series is examined to *identify* one of the many available models that we will tentatively select as the best representation of this series. If the raw series is not stationary, it will initially be necessary to modify the original series (perhaps using first differences) to produce a stationary series to model. The identification process is best done automatically with ForecastX™.

The first step in the process, if done manually, is usually accomplished by using an *identify* function, which is a part of every standard Box-Jenkins software package; the identify function simply calculates and displays the autocorrelation and partial autocorrelation functions as correlograms for the time series in question. Figure 7.2 shows these functions for the series in column 2 of Table 7.2, which you will recall is the MA(1) data we produced from white noise. By examining these correlograms, we can observe the distinctive pattern (like that in frame *b* of Figure 7.1) that we earlier identified as representing an MA(1)-type model. It is this pattern produced by the identify function that leads us to the tentative choice of an MA(1) model. The general rules to be followed in this identification stage of the process can be summed up as follows:

1. If the autocorrelation function abruptly stops at some point—say, after $q$ spikes—then the appropriate model is an MA($q$) type.
2. If the partial autocorrelation function abruptly stops at some point—say, after $p$ spikes—then the appropriate model is an AR($p$) type.

**FIGURE 7.8**

**The Box-Jenkins Methodology**

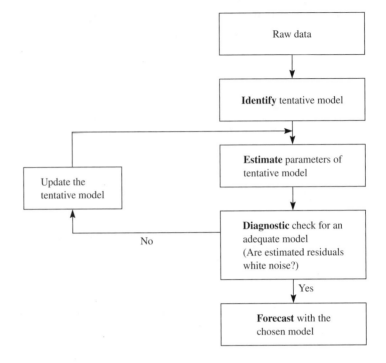

3. If neither function falls off abruptly, but both decline toward zero in some fashion, the appropriate model is an ARMA($p$, $q$) type.

The second step in the process begins after the tentative model has been identified; the actual *estimation* of the parameters of the model is similar to fitting a standard regression to a set of data. If an MA(1) model had been tentatively identified as the "correct" model, we would fit the equation

$$Y_t = e_t + W_1 e_{t-1}$$

The ForecastX™ software package would estimate the value for $W_1$, using a mean-squared error minimization routine in order to select the optimal value.

Consider again the series in column 2 of Table 7.2; we identified these data as being distinctive of an MA(1)-type model when we examined the autocorrelation and partial autocorrelation functions in Figure 7.2. If we now specify an MA(1)-type model—this could also be written as an ARIMA(0, 0, 1) model—in the software package, the output will be as shown in Figure 7.9

Keep in mind that the identification process and model estimation may be handled automatically in ForecastX™. While you may manually examine the autocorrelation and partial autocorrelation plots, most software packages do not require this as part of the ARIMA identification process.

The third step in the Box-Jenkins process is to *diagnose* in order to determine whether the "correct" model has been chosen. In order to do this, again for the example in column 2 of Table 7.2, we will examine the autocorrelation function

The second step in the process begins after the tentative model has been identified; the actual *estimation* of the parameters of the model is similar to fitting a standard regression to a set of data.

The third step in the Box-Jenkins process is to *diagnose* in order to determine whether the "correct" model has been chosen.

**FIGURE 7.9**   The MA(1) Model Estimate from ForecastX™ and Residual Autocorrelation Plot for the MA(1) Model Estimate   (c7t2)

## Audit Trail—Statistics

| Accuracy Measure | Value | Forecast Statistic | Value |
|---|---|---|---|
| AIC | 75.20 | Durbin-Watson | 2.08 |
| BIC | 81.80 | Mean | 0.80 |
| Mean Absolute Percentage Error (MAPE) | 43.45% | Max | 1.64 |
| Sum Squared Error (SSE) | 16.72 | Min | 0.14 |
| R-Square | 35.63% | Sum Squared Deviation | 25.97 |
| Adjusted R-Square | 35.30% | Range | 1.50 |
| Root Mean Square Error | 0.29 | Ljung-Box | 7.33 |

| Method Statistic | Value |
|---|---|
| Method selected | Box-Jenkins |
| Model selected | ARIMA(0,0,1) * (0,0,0) |
| T-test for constant | 39.07 |
| T-test for nonseasonal MA | −11.13 |

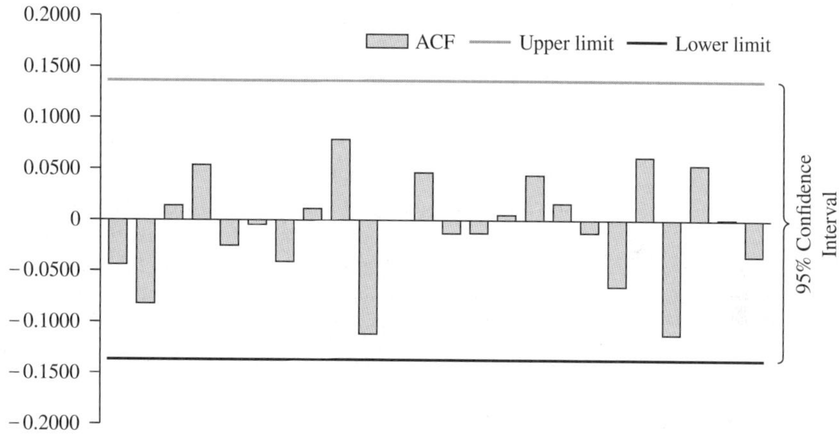

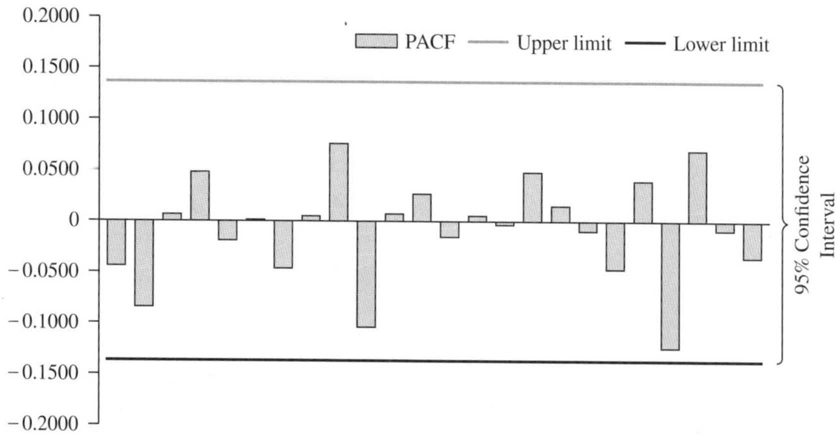

(continued on next page)

**FIGURE 7.9**
(continued)

| Obs | ACF | PACF | Obs | ACF | PACF |
|-----|------|------|-----|------|------|
| 1 | -.0440 | -.0440 | 13 | -.0128 | -.0152 |
| 2 | -.0820 | -.0841 | 14 | -.0125 | .0055 |
| 3 | .0140 | .0064 | 15 | .0053 | -.0033 |
| 4 | .0536 | .0481 | 16 | .0445 | .0481 |
| 5 | -.0254 | -.0191 | 17 | .0168 | .0152 |
| 6 | -.0048 | .0013 | 18 | -.0121 | -.0093 |
| 7 | -.0410 | -.0463 | 19 | -.0646 | -.0466 |
| 8 | .0113 | .0049 | 20 | .0620 | .0396 |
| 9 | .0789 | .0761 | 21 | -.1116 | -.1239 |
| 10 | -.1111 | -.1040 | 22 | .0542 | .0694 |
| 11 | .0000 | .0072 | 23 | .0010 | -.0087 |
| 12 | .0469 | .0268 | 24 | -.0350 | -.0352 |

of the residuals produced by the estimation program; this is also presented in Figure 7.9. Recall that we originally produced the "raw data" series from white noise by specifying a function we knew would behave as an MA(1) model. That is, we passed an MA(1) box over the white noise and turned it into an MA(1) data set. If we now reverse the process and pass an MA(1) box over the contrived data set, we should wind up with white noise. A look at the autocorrelation function will tell us whether we have been left with just white noise or whether we will have some unaccounted-for pattern in the series.

The autocorrelation function of the residual series in Figure 7.9 shows virtually no significant spikes. Apparently, the MA(1)-type model we estimated was an adequate representation of the data. It is most importantly the autocorrelation function that tells the forecaster when the tentative model is actually an adequate one. If you are left with only white noise in the residual series, the model chosen is likely the correct one.

A second test for the correctness of the model (but again, not a definitive test) is the Ljung-Box-Pierce $Q$ statistic. This is referred to simply as the *Ljung-Box* statistic in the ForecastX$^{TM}$ printout. The statistic is used to perform a chi-square test on the autocorrelations of the residuals (or error terms). The test statistic is

$$Q_m = n(n+2)\sum_{k=1}^{m} \frac{r_k^2}{n-k}$$

which is approximately distributed as a chi-square distribution with $m - p - q$ degrees of freedom, where:

$n$ = the number of observations in the time series

$k$ = the particular time lag to be checked

$m$ = the number of time lags to be tested

$r_k$ = sample autocorrelation function of the $k^{th}$ residual term

Values of $Q$ for different values of $k$ may be computed in a residual analysis. For an ARMA($p$, $q$) model, the statistic $Q$ is approximately chi-square distributed with $m - p - q$ degrees of freedom if the ARMA orders are correctly specified.

Thus, the Ljung-Box statistic tests whether the residual autocorrelations as a set are significantly different from zero. If the residual autocorrelations are significantly different from zero, the model specification should be reformulated. Note that the ForecastX$^{TM}$ software automatically checks for a lag length of 12 if a nonseasonal model has been selected; if a seasonal model has been selected, the lag is set equal to four times the seasonal length (e.g., the lag would be set to 16 if the data were quarterly).

The Ljung-Box statistic calculated for the Figure 7.9 model is 7.33 for the first 12 autocorrelations (which result in 11 degrees of freedom). A check with the chi-square table (see the appendix to this chapter) shows the critical value to be *about* 17 at the 0.10 significance level. Since the calculated value is less than the table value, the model is considered appropriate; that is, we believe the residuals to be uncorrelated. If this is a correct model, the residuals should be normally distributed and independent of one another (i.e., the residuals should resemble white noise).

If either the check of the residual series autocorrelations or the Ljung-Box statistic test had shown the model to be inappropriate, the tentative model would have been updated by trying another variation of the possible models. In Box-Jenkins methodology it is possible for two or more models to be very similar in their fit of the data; Occam's razor would suggest that the simpler of the similar models be chosen for actual forecasting. It is important to realize that the selection of an adequate ARIMA model is an art and not a science.

The ForecastX$^{TM}$ software will automatically select a model using Box-Jenkins methodology. The reported model may be examined in the two ways we have shown for checking the adequacy of the model: examine the residual autocorrelations visually and perform the Ljung-Box test. Any model, whether chosen by the forecaster manually or selected automatically by the ForecastX$^{TM}$ algorithm, is not necessarily the optimal model. While the Ljung-Box or $Q$ statistic is a reliable way to check for appropriateness of the ARIMA model chosen, it is not the only diagnostic that should be applied. Don't forget the other measures we have used up to this point to determine if our models would likely make good forecasts.

Simply getting the Ljung-Box to an acceptable value (i.e., lower than the critical value in the chi-square table) while ignoring other important measures such as the MAPE or RMSE begs the question of what is a good ARIMA model.

Just as in assessing other forecasting techniques we have examined earlier in this text, the researcher should pay close attention to whether the model fits the past data well: Does the plot of actual and forecast values show that the forecasts are a good fit? The use of adjusted $R^2$ (higher is better) is used with ARIMA in the same manner we have used it in the past. Likewise, measures of accuracy such as MAPE (lower is better) and RMSE (lower is also better) are also useful in estimating the degree of fit for an ARIMA model.

The principle of parsimony explained in Chapter 5 holds here as well. The best advice is to "KIS": Keep It Simple. The less complex the model, the more useful it is; simple models with few coefficients are best. With this in mind, the Akaike information criterion (and the Bayesian information criterion) can also be used with ARIMA techniques to sort out the best model. An AIC or BIC will be lower for better models, all other things being equal.

Using a holdout period to give the ARIMA model the acid test of forecasting outside the range of the data used for estimation is also a useful technique for choosing among competing models.

The final step in the Box-Jenkins process is to actually *forecast* using the chosen model.

The final step in the Box-Jenkins process is to actually *forecast* using the chosen model. ForecastX™ performs this function by substituting into the chosen model in much the same manner as a standard regression forecast would be made. It should be remembered that, as forecasts are made more than one period into the future, the size of the forecast error is likely to become larger.

When new observations of the time series become available, the model should be reestimated and checked again by the Box-Jenkins process; it is quite likely that the parameters of the model will have to be recalculated, or perhaps a different model altogether will be chosen as the best representation of the series. Consistent errors observed in estimation as more data become available are an indication that the entire model may require a change.

# ARIMA: A SET OF NUMERICAL EXAMPLES

### Example 1

Return to the first column of Table 7.2; this is the column containing white noise from which we constructed the other time series in the table. When we run an *identify* test on the white noise (that is, observe the autocorrelation and partial autocorrelation functions), we should be able to see that this column actually contains white noise. Figure 7.10 contains these correlograms; in each case, there is no distinctive pattern of spikes or significant but descending values as we observed with earlier time series.

In this case, the appropriate model would be an ARIMA(0, 0, 0); in other words, the best forecast would just be the mean value of the original time series (which is about 0.47).

### Example 2

The series in column 3 of Table 7.2 was constructed to be an AR(1) or ARIMA (1, 0, 0) model. When we examined the autocorrelation and partial autocorrelation functions in Figure 7.4, one of the characteristic patterns for an ARIMA(1, 0, 0) model appeared; in addition, no trend is apparent in the series, and so it is likely that no differencing is required. We should then be able to specify an ARIMA(1, 0, 0) model and correctly model the time series.

Figure 7.11 presents the results from estimating an AR(1) or ARIMA(1, 0, 0) model. Two tests will determine whether this model is an appropriate model: first, the examination of the autocorrelation coefficients of the residual series, and second, the Ljung-Box statistic.

The autocorrelation function for the residual series shows no distinctive pattern; it appears to be white noise. This would imply that we have chosen the correct model because when the original time series is modified by the model, only white noise remains.

**FIGURE 7.10**
**Autocorrelation
and Partial
Autocorrelation Plots
for the White Noise
Series in Table 7.2
(Example 1)** (c7t2)

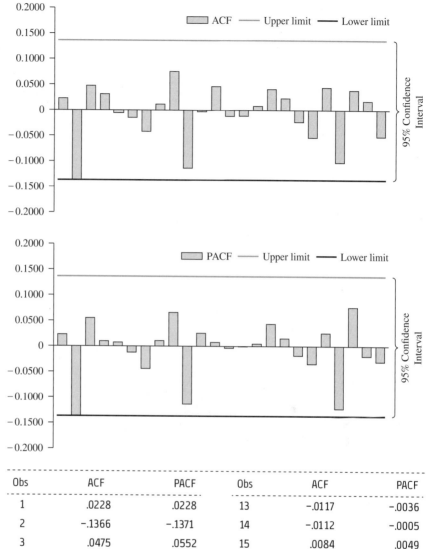

| Obs | ACF | PACF | Obs | ACF | PACF |
|-----|------|------|-----|-------|-------|
| 1 | .0228 | .0228 | 13 | −.0117 | −.0036 |
| 2 | −.1366 | −.1371 | 14 | −.0112 | −.0005 |
| 3 | .0475 | .0552 | 15 | .0084 | .0049 |
| 4 | .0313 | .0098 | 16 | .0414 | .0436 |
| 5 | −.0055 | .0074 | 17 | .0235 | .0153 |
| 6 | −.0149 | −.0122 | 18 | −.0230 | −.0183 |
| 7 | −.0420 | −.0440 | 19 | −.0534 | −.0344 |
| 8 | .0117 | .0107 | 20 | .0447 | .0257 |
| 9 | .0757 | .0661 | 21 | −.1022 | −.1223 |
| 10 | −.1134 | −.1132 | 22 | .0392 | .0763 |
| 11 | −.0031 | .0255 | 23 | .0181 | −.0193 |
| 12 | .0465 | .0078 | 24 | −.0516 | −.0302 |

**FIGURE 7.11** AR(1) Model Estimate (Example 2) and Residual Autocorrelation Plot for the AR(1) Model Estimate (c7t2)

| Audit Trail—Statistics | | | |
|---|---|---|---|
| Accuracy Measure | Value | Forecast Statistic | Value |
| AIC | 81.29 | Durbin-Watson | 1.92 |
| BIC | 87.88 | Mean | 0.94 |
| Mean Absolute Percentage Error (MAPE) | 33.12% | Max | 1.71 |
| Sum Squared Error (SSE) | 17.23 | Min | 0.24 |
| R-Square | 23.75% | Sum Squared Deviation | 22.60 |
| Adjusted R-Square | 23.37% | Range | 1.47 |
| Root Mean Square Error | 0.29 | Ljung-Box | 9.98 |

| Method Statistic | Value |
|---|---|
| Method selected | Box-Jenkins |
| Model selected | ARIMA(1,0,0) * (0,0,0) |
| T-test for nonseasonal AR | 8.00 |
| T-test for constant | 15.18 |

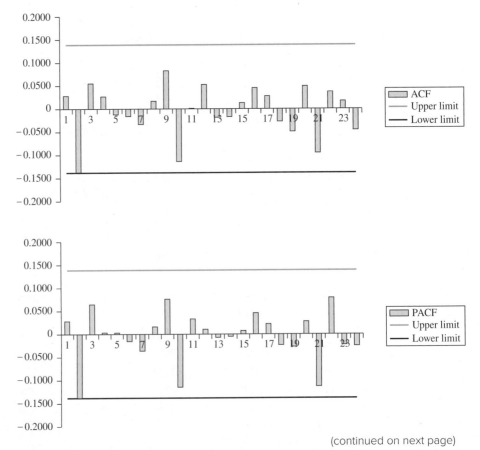

(continued on next page)

**FIGURE 7.11**
(continued)

| Obs | ACF | PACF |
|-----|------|------|
| 1 | .0283 | .0283 |
| 2 | −.1375 | −.1384 |
| 3 | .0547 | .0643 |
| 4 | .0266 | .0033 |
| 5 | −.0124 | .0030 |
| 6 | −.0163 | −.0156 |
| 7 | −.0336 | −.0365 |
| 8 | .0166 | .0160 |
| 9 | .0827 | .0755 |
| 10 | −.1140 | −.1148 |
| 11 | .0011 | .0330 |
| 12 | .0531 | .0104 |
| 13 | −.0185 | −.0071 |
| 14 | −.0175 | −.0055 |
| 15 | .0129 | .0074 |
| 16 | .0454 | .0456 |
| 17 | .0272 | .0217 |
| 18 | −.0278 | −.0240 |
| 19 | −.0493 | −.0274 |
| 20 | .0492 | .0272 |
| 21 | −.0952 | −.1135 |
| 22 | .0366 | .0787 |
| 23 | .0167 | −.0232 |
| 24 | −.0457 | −.0254 |

The Ljung-Box statistic offers further evidence that the correct model has been chosen. The calculated Ljung-Box $Q$ is 9.98 for 12 autocorrelations (which give us 11 degrees of freedom). Checking the chi-square table shows the critical value to be *about* 17.275 at the 0.10 significance level. (See the appendix to this chapter for the chi-square table.) Since the calculated Ljung-Box is less than the table value, the model is termed appropriate.

## Example 3

The AR(2) series in column 4 of Table 7.2 may be examined in like manner. Assume that we did not know the appropriate model for these data and examine the identification data presented in Figure 7.12. The autocorrelation function gradually falls over almost the entire 24 lags presented; the partial autocorrelation function shows one clear spike (and possibly a second). The pattern looks somewhat like that in frame *c* of Figure 7.3; this identifies the tentative model as an AR(2) or ARIMA(2, 0, 0). No differencing *appears* to be needed, because there does not appear to be any trend.

When the AR(2) model is run, however, the coefficients fail to damp to zero, indicating a possible problem. In many cases like this, the use of a differencing term eliminates the problem. Figure 7.13 presents the results of applying an ARIMA(2, 1, 0) model to this series.

**FIGURE 7.12**
**Autocorrelation and Partial Autocorrelation Plots for the AR(2) Series in Table 7.2 (Example 3)** (c7t2)

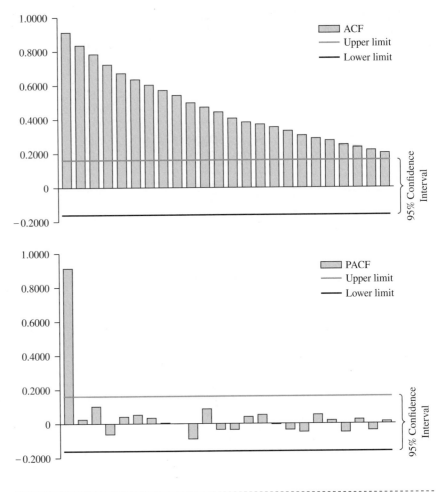

| Obs | ACF | PACF | Obs | ACF | PACF |
|-----|------|-------|-----|------|-------|
| 1 | .9120 | .9120 | 13 | .4063 | −.0358 |
| 2 | .8360 | .0252 | 14 | .3834 | .0399 |
| 3 | .7833 | .1012 | 15 | .3710 | .0511 |
| 4 | .7222 | −.0622 | 16 | .3540 | −.0045 |
| 5 | .6715 | .0406 | 17 | .3313 | −.0365 |
| 6 | .6349 | .0520 | 18 | .3047 | −.0493 |
| 7 | .6030 | .0335 | 19 | .2871 | .0514 |
| 8 | .5716 | .0042 | 20 | .2746 | .0182 |
| 9 | .5416 | −.0004 | 21 | .2506 | −.0508 |
| 10 | .4979 | −.0898 | 22 | .2345 | .0242 |
| 11 | .4720 | .0858 | 23 | .2182 | −.0394 |
| 12 | .4435 | −.0350 | 24 | .2014 | .0124 |

**FIGURE 7.13**   **ARIMA(2, 1, 0) Model Estimate (Example 3) and Residual Autocorrelation Plot for ARIMA(2, 1, 0) Model Estimate**   (c7t2)

Audit Trail—Statistics

| Accuracy Measure | Value | | Forecast Statistic | Value |
|---|---|---|---|---|
| AIC | 95.61 | | Durbin-Watson | 1.99 |
| BIC | 102.21 | | Mean | 4.40 |
| Mean Absolute Percentage Error (MAPE) | 8.06% | | Max | 6.36 |
| Sum Squared Error (SSE) | 18.51 | | Min | 0.04 |
| $R$-Square | 83.61% | | Sum Squared Deviation | 219.27 |
| Adjusted $R$-Square | 83.52% | | Range | 6.32 |
| Root Mean Square Error | 0.30 | | Ljung-Box | 4.41 |
| Theil | 0.96 | | | |

| Method Statistic | Value |
|---|---|
| Method selected | Box-Jenkins |
| Model selected | ARIMA(2,1,0) * (0,0,0) |
| T-test for nonseasonal AR | −2.51 |
| T-test for nonseasonal AR | −1.66 |

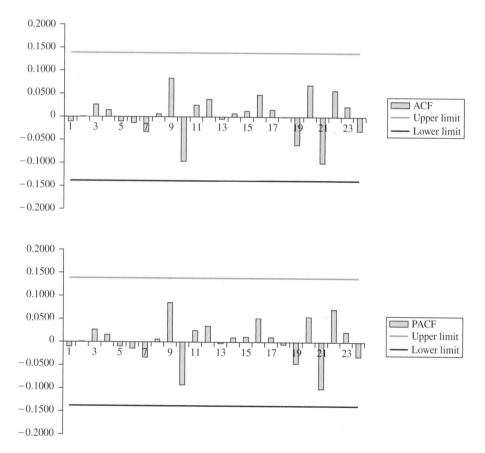

**FIGURE 7.13**
(continued)

| Obs | ACF | PACF |
|-----|-------|-------|
| 1 | −.0103 | −.0103 |
| 2 | .0003 | .0002 |
| 3 | .0269 | .0269 |
| 4 | .0149 | .0155 |
| 5 | −.0095 | −.0093 |
| 6 | −.0130 | −.0140 |
| 7 | .0320 | −.0332 |
| 8 | .0067 | .0063 |
| 9 | .0840 | .0854 |
| 10 | −.0958 | −.0926 |
| 11 | .0261 | .0251 |
| 12 | .0389 | .0346 |
| 13 | −.0043 | −.0027 |
| 14 | .0074 | .0099 |
| 15 | .0132 | .0117 |
| 16 | .0487 | .0518 |
| 17 | .0162 | .0107 |
| 18 | −.0001 | −.0047 |
| 19 | −.0601 | −.0462 |
| 20 | .0694 | .0549 |
| 21 | −.0994 | −.1010 |
| 22 | .0575 | .0715 |
| 23 | .0233 | .0217 |
| 24 | −.0298 | −.0311 |

The autocorrelation function for the residuals shows largely white noise in the 24 lags. The Ljung-Box statistic is 4.41 for the 12 autocorrelations (which give us 10 degrees of freedom). The table value from the chi-square table is about 15.987 at the 0.10 significance level; this would indicate that the ARIMA(2, 1, 0) model chosen is an accurate representation of the series.

The reader may wish to allow ForecastX$^{TM}$ to select a model for this series. Because ForecastX$^{TM}$ uses an exhaustive iterative process, the results are often more satisfactory than manual selection. In this case, ForecastX$^{TM}$ selects an ARIMA(0, 1, 1) model that is significantly better than the model presented above.

### Example 4

Consider finally the time-series data in Table 7.4 and assume we are given no clues to its origin. Applying the Box-Jenkins methodology, we would first use an identification function to examine the autocorrelation and partial autocorrelation functions; these are presented in Figure 7.14.

The autocorrelation function in Figure 7.14 is entirely characteristic of a series with a trend; that is, it shows dominant autocorrelations for the 24 lags shown. Look at the actual numbers in the original series in Table 7.4 and observe how

**TABLE 7.4**  **Example 4 Data Series**  (c7t4)

| ARIMA | | | | | | | | | | | |
|---|---|---|---|---|---|---|---|---|---|---|---|
| 1 | . | 0.160000 | 35 | . | 22.7092 | 69 | . | 45.2098 | 103 | . | 74.0750 |
| 2 | . | 0.544113 | 36 | . | 23.8470 | 70 | . | 46.0228 | 104 | . | 74.7422 |
| 3 | . | 1.35744 | 37 | . | 24.4950 | 71 | . | 46.5587 | 105 | . | 75.1037 |
| 4 | . | 1.81007 | 38 | . | 24.7342 | 72 | . | 47.2307 | 106 | . | 76.1463 |
| 5 | . | 2.55541 | 39 | . | 25.0825 | 73 | . | 47.9890 | 107 | . | 76.9680 |
| 6 | . | 3.84012 | 40 | . | 25.6879 | 74 | . | 49.2088 | 108 | . | 77.2119 |
| 7 | . | 4.91087 | 41 | . | 26.9086 | 75 | . | 50.5534 | 109 | . | 78.1276 |
| 8 | . | 5.28469 | 42 | . | 27.6985 | 76 | . | 51.9717 | 110 | . | 78.8356 |
| 9 | . | 5.49273 | 43 | . | 27.9592 | 77 | . | 52.5793 | 111 | . | 79.2148 |
| 10 | . | 5.62030 | 44 | . | 29.0047 | 78 | . | 52.7499 | 112 | . | 79.4252 |
| 11 | . | 6.22645 | 45 | . | 30.5438 | 79 | . | 53.1405 | 113 | . | 80.0609 |
| 12 | . | 6.81976 | 46 | . | 31.8912 | 80 | . | 53.3826 | 114 | . | 81.1088 |
| 13 | . | 7.03361 | 47 | . | 32.7602 | 81 | . | 54.3375 | 115 | . | 81.5818 |
| 14 | . | 7.93600 | 48 | . | 33.0873 | 82 | . | 55.8604 | 116 | . | 82.5728 |
| 15 | . | 9.28220 | 49 | . | 33.2974 | 83 | . | 57.3969 | 117 | . | 83.4074 |
| 16 | . | 9.99665 | 50 | . | 33.7224 | 84 | . | 58.2719 | 118 | . | 84.0063 |
| 17 | . | 10.3492 | 51 | . | 34.4206 | 85 | . | 59.1758 | 119 | . | 84.8875 |
| 18 | . | 10.7372 | 52 | . | 35.0356 | 86 | . | 60.4877 | 120 | . | 86.0977 |
| 19 | . | 11.6537 | 53 | . | 35.6169 | 87 | . | 61.6198 | 121 | . | 87.1734 |
| 20 | . | 12.3986 | 54 | . | 35.9999 | 88 | . | 62.2831 | 122 | . | 88.2206 |
| 21 | . | 12.7508 | 55 | . | 36.4831 | 89 | . | 62.6991 | 123 | . | 88.9342 |
| 22 | . | 13.0273 | 56 | . | 36.8279 | 90 | . | 63.5748 | 124 | . | 89.6704 |
| 23 | . | 13.7149 | 57 | . | 37.0943 | 91 | . | 64.3452 | 125 | . | 90.6897 |
| 24 | . | 14.6099 | 58 | . | 37.6164 | 92 | . | 65.0968 | 126 | . | 91.4675 |
| 25 | . | 15.1324 | 59 | . | 38.7882 | 93 | . | 65.4967 | 127 | . | 91.7072 |
| 26 | . | 15.6525 | 60 | . | 39.9187 | 94 | . | 66.4900 | 128 | . | 92.1157 |
| 27 | . | 16.3994 | 61 | . | 40.9344 | 95 | . | 67.6714 | 129 | . | 92.9512 |
| 28 | . | 17.3193 | 62 | . | 41.5441 | 96 | . | 68.1611 | 130 | . | 93.4450 |
| 29 | . | 18.1561 | 63 | . | 42.5229 | 97 | . | 68.2980 | 131 | . | 94.4363 |
| 30 | . | 19.0496 | 64 | . | 43.1073 | 98 | . | 68.9562 | 132 | . | 95.6413 |
| 31 | . | 19.8106 | 65 | . | 43.4389 | 99 | . | 70.3170 | 133 | . | 96.2160 |
| 32 | . | 20.7518 | 66 | . | 44.2401 | 100 | . | 71.5608 | 134 | . | 96.6762 |
| 33 | . | 21.2347 | 67 | . | 44.6401 | 101 | . | 72.3279 | 135 | . | 97.2641 |
| 34 | . | 21.5877 | 68 | . | 44.7896 | 102 | . | 73.2702 | 136 | . | 98.4736 |

(continued columns)

| 137 | . | 99.5781 | 171 | . | 126.771 |
|---|---|---|---|---|---|
| 138 | . | 100.248 | 172 | . | 128.169 |
| 139 | . | 101.396 | 173 | . | 129.070 |
| 140 | . | 102.778 | 174 | . | 130.199 |
| 141 | . | 103.951 | 175 | . | 131.363 |
| 142 | . | 105.195 | 176 | . | 132.159 |
| 143 | . | 106.493 | 177 | . | 132.600 |
| 144 | . | 107.602 | 178 | . | 132.974 |
| 145 | . | 108.921 | 179 | . | 133.496 |
| 146 | . | 109.953 | 180 | . | 134.223 |
| 147 | . | 110.384 | 181 | . | 134.735 |
| 148 | . | 111.074 | 182 | . | 135.831 |
| 149 | . | 112.112 | 183 | . | 136.911 |
| 150 | . | 113.163 | 184 | . | 137.315 |
| 151 | . | 113.903 | 185 | . | 137.517 |
| 152 | . | 114.280 | 186 | . | 137.859 |
| 153 | . | 115.156 | 187 | . | 138.897 |
| 154 | . | 116.267 | 188 | . | 139.979 |
| 155 | . | 116.826 | 189 | . | 140.426 |
| 156 | . | 117.822 | 190 | . | 141.150 |
| 157 | . | 118.461 | 191 | . | 141.867 |
| 158 | . | 118.806 | 192 | . | 142.224 |
| 159 | . | 119.679 | 193 | . | 143.023 |
| 160 | . | 120.198 | 194 | . | 144.299 |
| 161 | . | 120.534 | 195 | . | 145.293 |
| 162 | . | 121.418 | 196 | . | 146.425 |
| 163 | . | 121.895 | 197 | . | 147.339 |
| 164 | . | 122.030 | 198 | . | 148.166 |
| 165 | . | 122.893 | 199 | . | 149.491 |
| 166 | . | 123.409 | 200 | . | 150.761 |
| 167 | . | 123.898 | | | |
| 168 | . | 124.924 | | | |
| 169 | . | 125.618 | | | |
| 170 | . | 125.903 | | | |

they gradually creep upward in value. These data apparently have a trend and are therefore nonstationary. Before the Box-Jenkins process can be continued, the series must be transformed to a stationary series. The most common method of achieving stationarity is to take first differences of the original series. Taking these first differences and again applying the identification program to the resulting series gives the autocorrelation and partial autocorrelation functions in Figure 7.15.

**FIGURE 7.14**
**Autocorrelation and Partial Autocorrelation Plots for the Series in Table 7.4 (Example 4)**
(c7t2)

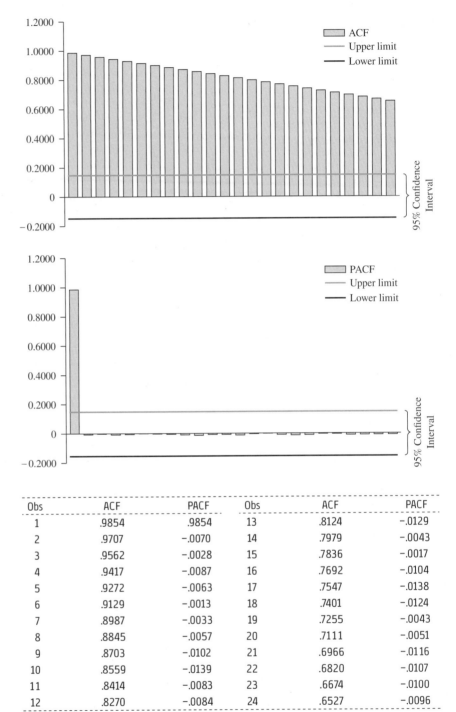

| Obs | ACF | PACF | Obs | ACF | PACF |
|-----|------|-------|-----|------|-------|
| 1 | .9854 | .9854 | 13 | .8124 | −.0129 |
| 2 | .9707 | −.0070 | 14 | .7979 | −.0043 |
| 3 | .9562 | −.0028 | 15 | .7836 | −.0017 |
| 4 | .9417 | −.0087 | 16 | .7692 | −.0104 |
| 5 | .9272 | −.0063 | 17 | .7547 | −.0138 |
| 6 | .9129 | −.0013 | 18 | .7401 | −.0124 |
| 7 | .8987 | −.0033 | 19 | .7255 | −.0043 |
| 8 | .8845 | −.0057 | 20 | .7111 | −.0051 |
| 9 | .8703 | −.0102 | 21 | .6966 | −.0116 |
| 10 | .8559 | −.0139 | 22 | .6820 | −.0107 |
| 11 | .8414 | −.0083 | 23 | .6674 | −.0100 |
| 12 | .8270 | −.0084 | 24 | .6527 | −.0096 |

**FIGURE 7.15**
**Autocorrelation**
**and Partial**
**Autocorrelation**
**Plots for the Series**
**in Table 7.4 After**
**First Differences**
**Have Been Taken**
**(Example 4)** (c7t4)

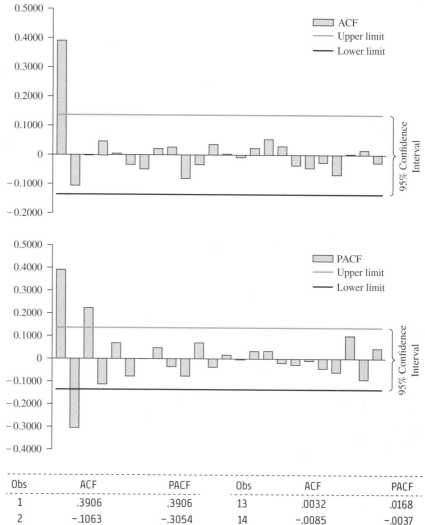

| Obs | ACF | PACF | Obs | ACF | PACF |
|-----|-------|--------|-----|--------|--------|
| 1 | .3906 | .3906 | 13 | .0032 | .0168 |
| 2 | −.1063 | −.3054 | 14 | −.0085 | −.0037 |
| 3 | −.0021 | .2231 | 15 | .0233 | .0333 |
| 4 | .0481 | −.1128 | 16 | .0537 | .0341 |
| 5 | .0046 | .0684 | 17 | .0296 | −.0186 |
| 6 | −.0336 | −.0772 | 18 | −.0358 | −.0266 |
| 7 | −.0488 | −.0006 | 19 | −.0451 | −.0084 |
| 8 | .0209 | .0480 | 20 | −.0260 | −.0424 |
| 9 | .0266 | −.0352 | 21 | −.0684 | −.0593 |
| 10 | −.0812 | −.0763 | 22 | .0027 | .1007 |
| 11 | −.0333 | .0702 | 23 | .0158 | −.0923 |
| 12 | .0359 | −.0366 | 24 | −.0269 | .0452 |

The pattern exhibited here (after differencing) is similar to frame *d* of Figure 7.5; perhaps the model is a mixed model, with both AR and MA terms in addition to the differencing required to make the series stationary. Figure 7.16 displays the results of estimating an ARIMA(3, 1, 2) model, that is, a model with three AR terms, one degree of differencing, and two MA terms.

**FIGURE 7.16**   **ARIMA(3, 1, 2) model estimate (Example 4) and residual autocorrelation plot for the ARIMA(3, 1, 2) model estimate.**   (Ic7t4)

Audit Trail—Statistics

| Accuracy Measure | Value | | Forecast Statistic | Value |
|---|---|---|---|---|
| AIC | 84.73 | | Durbin-Watson | 1.84 |
| BIC | 101.22 | | Mean | 72.55 |
| Mean Absolute Percentage Error (MAPE) | 1.12% | | Max | 150.76 |
| Sum Squared Error (SSE) | 17.01 | | Min | 0.16 |
| R-Square | 100.00% | | Sum Squared Deviation | 392,388.59 |
| Adjusted R-Square | 100.00% | | Range | 150.60 |
| Root Mean Square Error | 0.29 | | Ljung-Box | 5.14 |

| Method Statistic | Value |
|---|---|
| Method selected | Box-Jenkins |
| Model selected | ARIMA(3,1,2) * (0,0,0) |
| T-test for nonseasonal AR | 7.79 |
| T-test for nonseasonal AR | 0.02 |
| T-test for nonseasonal AR | 1.04 |
| T-test for nonseasonal MA | 2.43 |
| T-test for nonseasonal MA | 4.46 |

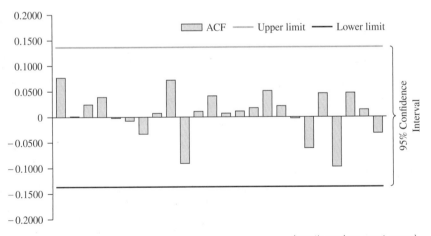

(continued on next page)

**FIGURE 7.16**
(continued)

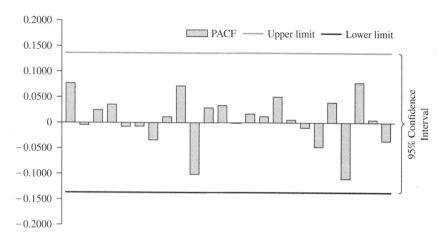

| Obs | ACF | PACF |
|-----|------|-------|
| 1 | .0769 | .0769 |
| 2 | .0013 | −.0046 |
| 3 | .0244 | .0248 |
| 4 | .0390 | .0355 |
| 5 | −.0019 | −.0076 |
| 6 | −.0075 | −.0072 |
| 7 | −.0334 | −.0343 |
| 8 | .0074 | .0114 |
| 9 | .0721 | .0718 |
| 10 | −.0910 | −.1013 |
| 11 | .0108 | .0291 |
| 12 | .0410 | .0340 |
| 13 | .0071 | −.0009 |
| 14 | .0112 | .0175 |
| 15 | .0175 | .0125 |
| 16 | .0510 | .0510 |
| 17 | .0214 | .0057 |
| 18 | −.0027 | −.0099 |
| 19 | −.0614 | −.0474 |
| 20 | .0460 | .0399 |
| 21 | −.0976 | −.1097 |
| 22 | .0469 | .0784 |
| 23 | .0142 | .0054 |
| 24 | −.0317 | −.0355 |

The results in the residual series autocorrelation function indicate that only white noise remains after applying the model. The Ljung-Box statistic is 5.14 for the 12 autocorrelations. The value from the chi-square table is about 12.017 for 7 degrees of freedom at the 0.10 significance level. We would then accept the ARIMA(3, 1, 1) model specification as a "correct" forecasting model for this series.

# FORECASTING SEASONAL TIME SERIES

In many actual business situations, the time series to be forecast are quite seasonal. Recall that seasonality refers to a consistent shape in the series that recurs with some periodic regularity (sales of lawn mowers during summer months, for instance, are always higher than in winter months). This seasonality can cause some problems in the ARIMA process since a model fitted to such a series would likely have a very high order. If monthly data were used and the seasonality occurred in every twelfth month, the order of the model might be 12 or more. There is a process for estimating "seasonal MA" and "seasonal AR" terms for the ARIMA process along with seasonal differencing, but the details of estimating such terms are quite complicated. We will use the ability of ForecastX$^{TM}$ to estimate these parameters with the total houses sold series.

# TOTAL HOUSES SOLD

The total houses sold figures show trend and appear to exhibit a high degree of seasonality. The mean of the series shifts significantly from period to period because of a strong seasonal variation. We will allow ForecastX$^{TM}$ to choose seasonal AR and MA terms and difference the data as appropriate.

The total houses sold data are seen to be very seasonal. Summer months are seen as high sales months ,while winter months have far fewer sales.

Examining the autocorrelation and partial autocorrelation plots in Figure 7.17, note the clear pattern of the autocorrelation function. This downward and to the right pattern of significant autocorrelations suggests that the series is nonstationary. The high degree of seasonality is clearly evident in the moguls of up-and-down movement that makes the plot look like a downhill mogul skiing slope. Using ForecastX$^{TM}$ to automatically choose an ARIMA model results in one degree of nonseasonal differencing but also includes seasonal one degree of nonseasonal differencing and seasonal AR and MA terms.

Figure 7.18 contains the diagnostic statistics for the estimation for an ARIMA (0, 1, 0) (2, 0, 2) model (the model estimation suggested by ForecastX$^{TM}$). The second set of $P$, $D$, $Q$ values (usually shown as uppercase letters) represents two seasonal AR and two seasonal MA terms. The Ljung-Box statistic for the first 48 lags is 45.43 and confirms the acceptability of the model.

Calculating the RMSE for the model gives 2.60.

This example introduces the use of *seasonal* AR, MA, and differencing terms. The ability of the ARIMA process to handle the complexity of periodic and recurring events (i.e., seasonality) greatly increases the usability of the ARIMA models. An ARIMA model incorporating seasonal terms, such as the total houses sold model represented in Figure 7.18, is usually designated as a model of type ARIMA $(p,d,q)$ $(P,D,Q)^s$. The upper case $P$, $D$, and $Q$ refer to the order of the seasonal terms, and the superscript $s$ refers to the length of the season used. Since our total houses sold model uses monthly data and the actual seasonality (i.e.,

**FIGURE 7.17**  **Autocorrelation and Partial Autocorrelation Plots for the Total Houses Sold Series**

Note that the series appears to be nonstationary.  (C7F17)

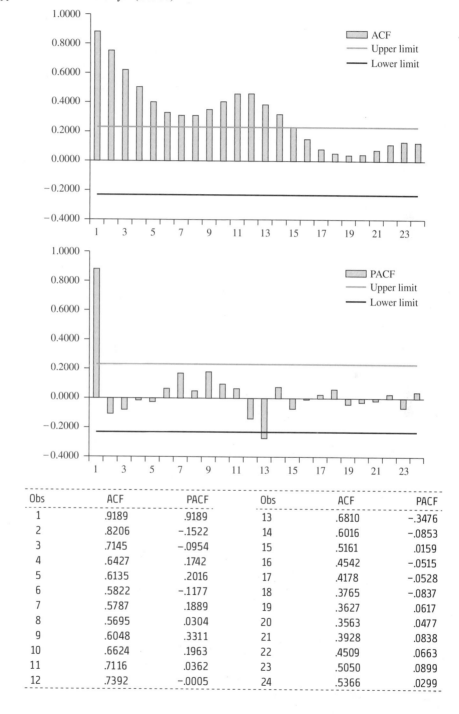

| Obs | ACF | PACF | Obs | ACF | PACF |
|---|---|---|---|---|---|
| 1 | .9189 | .9189 | 13 | .6810 | −.3476 |
| 2 | .8206 | −.1522 | 14 | .6016 | −.0853 |
| 3 | .7145 | −.0954 | 15 | .5161 | .0159 |
| 4 | .6427 | .1742 | 16 | .4542 | −.0515 |
| 5 | .6135 | .2016 | 17 | .4178 | −.0528 |
| 6 | .5822 | −.1177 | 18 | .3765 | −.0837 |
| 7 | .5787 | .1889 | 19 | .3627 | .0617 |
| 8 | .5695 | .0304 | 20 | .3563 | .0477 |
| 9 | .6048 | .3311 | 21 | .3928 | .0838 |
| 10 | .6624 | .1963 | 22 | .4509 | .0663 |
| 11 | .7116 | .0362 | 23 | .5050 | .0899 |
| 12 | .7392 | −.0005 | 24 | .5366 | .0299 |

**FIGURE 7.18** **Total Houses Sold Model Diagnostic Statistics**

| Audit Trail - Statistics | | | |
|---|---|---|---|
| **Accuracy Measures** | **Value** | **Forecast Statistics** | **Value** |
| AIC | 350.02 | Durbin Watson (12) | 1.74 |
| BIC | 359.12 | Mean | 36.17 |
| MAPE | 5.26% | Standard Deviation | 8.06 |
| R-Square | 89.43% | Root Mean Square | 8.00 |
| Adjusted R-Square | 88.97% | Ljung-Box | 45.43 |
| Root Mean Square Error | 2.60 | | |
| Theil | 0.75 | | |
| | | | |
| **Method Statistics** | **Value** | | |
| Method Selected | Box Jenkins | | |
| Model Selected | ARIMA(0,1,0) * (2,0,2) | | |
| T-Test For Seasonal AR | -4.66 | | |
| T-Test For Seasonal AR | -5.01 | | |
| T-Test For Seasonal MA | -4.25 | | |
| T-Test For Seasonal MA | -3.29 | | |

recurring pattern) appears to be 12 periods in length, the $s$ in our model is 12. The full model in Figure 7.18 would then be designated as an ARIMA $(0,1,0)$ $(2,0,2)^{12}$.

The complete designation for an ARIMA model would then be:

$$\text{ARIMA}(p, d, q)\,(P, D, Q)^s$$

where:

$p$ = Level of autoregressions

$d$ = Level of normal differencing

$q$ = Level of moving averages

$P$ = Seasonal level of autoregressions

$D$ = Level of seasonal differencing

$Q$ = Seasonal level of moving averages

$s$ = Period of seasonality (usually 4 for quarters, 12 for months, etc.)

When ForecastX$^{TM}$ calculates a seasonal model like this one, the corresponding Ljung-Box statistic requested should be one with a number of lags equaling 4 times the number of seasons; in this case, there would be 4 times 12 (or 48) lags used in the calculation of the reported Ljung-Box statistic. The appropriate degrees of freedom to use in evaluating this statistic would be $m - p - q - P - Q$. Thus, the degrees of freedom for this example would be $48 - 0 - 0 - 2 - 2 = 44$ degrees of freedom. The calculated Ljung-Box of 45.43 is smaller than the table value (imputed, because 42 degrees of freedom is outside the range of the chi-square table in the appendix to this chapter). This means that the model estimated is an acceptable model.

If you have ever driven on the ring road circling Atlanta or the M25 circling London, you know that congestion can be a problem. In both the United States and the United Kingdom, however, steps have been taken to reduce the costs of congestion not by changing the physical capacity of the existing roadways but by utilizing them more efficiently. Intelligent transportation systems (ITSs) focus on improving the operational efficiency of roadways by effectively using information about dynamic system conditions.

Much of the information about current system conditions is collected by sensors embedded in roads. The information is not only monitored but also collected and archived. Instrumentation on transportation networks became widespread throughout the world in the final years of the 20th century; the effort to collect data continues unabated.

The efficient use of the collected data requires accurate short-term forecasts of roadway conditions. If there are no such forecasts, traveler information and transportation management systems simply react only to currently sensed conditions. The result is that the transportation management systems are essentially using naive forecasts to manage the system; current conditions become the forecast of future conditions. According to professors Billy Williams of North Carolina State University and Lester Hoel of the University of Virginia, this is obviously a poor assumption, especially when traffic conditions are transitioning into or out of congestion.

Williams and Hoel have championed the use of ARIMA forecasting techniques to improve the use of information collected by ITS sensors. They see the need for accurate system forecasts to predict traffic conditions as the key factor in the deployment of smoothly functioning intelligent transportation systems. Their paper in the *Journal of Transportation Engineering* presents their case for a specific type of ARIMA model to predict traffic conditions using fixed in-road sensors. Unlike the data we have been using that tends to be collected quarterly or monthly, Williams and Hoel use data that is collected at intervals ranging from two seconds to two minutes. They selected a discrete time period to work with that they felt was appropriate to fitting traffic patterns; 15-minute intervals were created by averaging the higher periodicity data. They believed longer intervals would not create the necessary correlations to create stable models of traffic flow.

The problem they tackled was then one of producing short-term (i.e., 15-minute) forecasts of various measures of traffic flow based only on past observations. Measures of traffic flow included vehicle flow rate per hour, the average speed of vehicles, and lane occupancy (the percentage of time a vehicle is present in sensor range).

Not surprisingly, Williams and Hoel first examined the data for stationarity. Their inspection revealed little if any trend week to week but a high degree of seasonality from week to week. This suggested the use of a "season" of 672 periods. This seemingly strange period was arrived at by using 15-minute intervals and assuming that seasonal patterns would probably occur weekly (i.e., 4 intervals per hour × 24 hours per day × 7 days per week = 672 periods).

The data used to examine the accuracy of an ARIMA forecast was collected from the Georgia Department of Transportation 10048 sensor located on northbound I-75. The empirical results produced an ARIMA $(1,0,1)$ $(0,1,1)^{672}$ model. The model allowed recursive forecasts for a number of periods into the future. The acid test of this type of forecasting procedure is to examine whether it is superior to those methods now in use in Georgia.

Willams and Hoel used root-mean-squared error, mean absolute percentage error, and mean absolute deviation to compare their ARIMA forecasts with forecasts from models currently in use. With both measures, the ARIMA technique proved to be a superior forecast:

### I-75 Station 10048 Sensor

| Model | RMSE | MAPE | MAD |
|---|---|---|---|
| Seasonal ARIMA | 141.73 | 8.97 | 75.02 |
| Random walk | 180.02 | 10.10 | 95.05 |
| Historical average | 192.63 | 12.85 | 123.56 |

The conclusion was that "the seasonal ARIMA models provided the best forecasts based on all prediction performance statistics." The authors suggested that ITS units begin using ARIMA forecasting with updated parameter estimates as new data are collected. The more accurate forecasts provided by ARIMA would be useful in optimizing traffic flows in many transportation environments.

*Source:* Williams, Billy M., and Hoel, Lester A. "Modeling and Forecasting Vehicular Traffic Flow as a Seasonal ARIMA Process: Theoretical Basis and Empirical Results," *Journal of Transportation Forecasting* 129 (November–December 2003), 664–72.

## Integrative Case

# Forecasting Sales of the Gap

The sales of The Gap stores for the 44 quarters covering the second quarter of 2006 through the first quarter of 2017 are shown below. From this graph, it is clear that The Gap sales are quite seasonal over time. Thus, an optimal ARIMA model will likely require some seasonal terms.

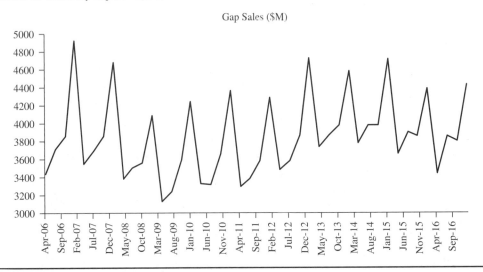

Gap Sales ($M)

**Case Questions**

1. From your previous experience plotting The Gap sales over time, what ARIMA parameters might you expect ForecastX™ to suggest when forecasting with this data?
2. Prepare a plot of the autocorrelation and partial autocorrelation coefficients of The Gap sales data. Does this correlogram suggest an ARIMA approach that could be used for forecasting The Gap sales?
3. Apply a model suggested by ForecastX™ and calculate the cumulative MAPE for your forecast using a holdout of four quarters (i.e., use a "holdout" or "out of sample" period of four quarters in the data as part of your estimation procedure). Recall that the "out of sample" request is made in ForecastX™ in the Reports/Audit tab.

**Solutions to Case Questions**

1. The seasonal pattern and trend should now be familiar. These data will not be stationary, and some adjustment will have to be made to obtain stationarity. The strong seasonal pattern could require some adjustment. It is also the case that the pattern of the data is quite regular and some ARIMA technique should do a reasonable job of fitting a model.
2. The correlogram for the unadjusted Gap sales shows the possibility of nonstationarity (see Figure 7.19). Since we already know that the data are seasonal, the nonstationarity and the seasonality might be accounted for by using seasonal differencing.

**FIGURE 7.19**
**Autocorrelation**
**and Partial**
**Autocorrelation**
**Plots for The Gap**
**Sales ($000, for the**
**Historical Period of**
**1985Q1 Through**
**2005Q4)** (c7Gap)

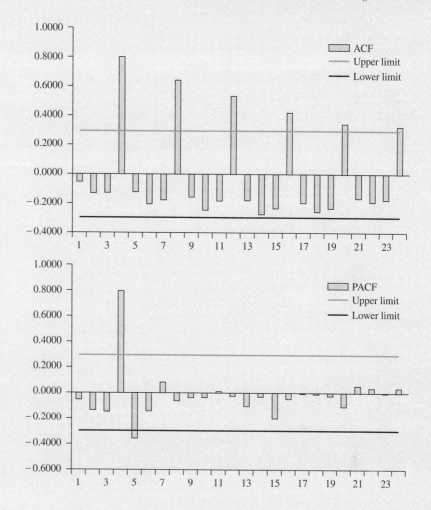

3. While a number of models may perform quite well, the ARIMA(1, 0, 1) (1, 1, 2) model suggested by ForecastX™ seems to provide a good fit. The model estimation in Figure 7.20 indicates that the Ljung-Box statistic is 11.22 for the 16 autocorrelations, which confirms the acceptability of the model.

   Note that the Durbin Watson (4) is just 1.86, showing little residual effects of seasonality in the historic period.

   The actual (original data) and predicted (fitted data) values for the second quarter of 2016 through the first quarter of 2017 (i.e., the out of sample data) are shown below. The average MAPE is only 2 percent.

**FIGURE 7.20** The Gap Sales Model Actual and Predicted Sales and the Diagnostic Statistics for the ARIMA(1, 0, 1) (1, 1, 2) Model Estimate (C7F20)

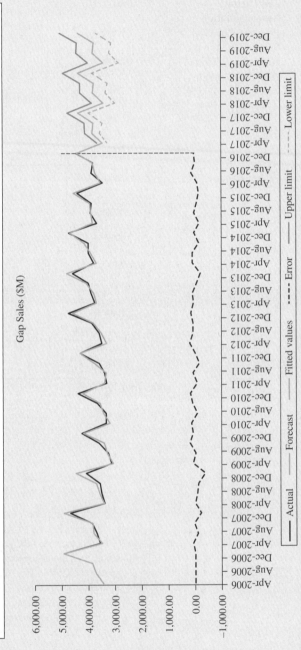

**Audit Trail - Statistics**

| Accuracy Measures | Value |
|---|---|
| AIC | 556.04 |
| BIC | 564.96 |
| MAPE | 2.46% |
| R-Square | 92.56% |
| Adjusted R-Square | 91.79% |
| Root Mean Square Error | 119.82 |
| Theil | 0.21 |

| Forecast Statistics | Value |
|---|---|
| Durbin Watson (4) | 1.86 |
| Mean | 3,844.80 |
| Standard Deviation | 444.23 |
| Root Mean Square | 439.16 |
| Ljung-Box | 11.22 |

| Method Statistics | Value |
|---|---|
| Method Selected | Box Jenkins |
| Model Selected | ARIMA(1,0,1) * (1,2) |
| T-Test For Non Seasonal AR | 4.01 |
| T-Test For Seasonal AR | -0.42 |
| T-Test For Non Seasonal MA | 0.03 |
| T-Test For Seasonal MA | -0.04 |
| T-Test For Seasonal MA | -0.46 |

Gap Sales ($M)

— Actual  — Forecast  — Fitted values  ---- Error  — Upper limit  ---- Lower limit

| Audit Trail -- Out of Sample Table (Box Jenkins Selected) | | | | | | | |
|---|---|---|---|---|---|---|---|
| Date | Original Data | Fitted Data | MAD | Cumulative MAD | MAPE | Cumulative MAPE | Cumulative SSE |
| Apr-2016 | 3,438.00 | 3,530.91 | 92.91 | 92.91 | 2.70% | 2.70% | 8,632.90 |
| Jul-2016 | 3,851.00 | 3,792.15 | 58.85 | 75.88 | 1.53% | 2.12% | 6,047.91 |
| Oct-2016 | 3,798.00 | 3,770.64 | 27.36 | 59.71 | 0.72% | 1.65% | 4,281.50 |
| Jan-2017 | 4,429.00 | 4,380.76 | 48.24 | 56.84 | 1.09% | 1.51% | 3,793.00 |

# OVERFITTING

There is one special problem in forecasting that occurs most often with the ARIMA procedure; that problem is called "overfitting." Sometimes forecasts are too good to be true. Forecasters build models that use historical data to predict future data values. The goal of the forecaster is to extend the predictions of a model into a time period we've not yet observed. To do this, we try to find the sweet spot between predicting the past and predicting the future, where data analysis is at its best. It can improve our predictions and give us more time to respond to the forecasted values.

Overfitting occurs when a model describes the historical data better and better but gets worse and worse on out-of-sample forecasts of the same data.

Overfitting occurs when a model describes the historical data better and better but gets worse and worse on out-of-sample forecasts of the same data. This can make the whole forecasting process worthless. A good way to observe overfitting is to use a holdout by setting aside some data (i.e., out-of-sample data) that the algorithm does not use in model estimation. Clearly, the more complex the model, the more information the model will contain about the known (or historical) data. But when we look at the error of the estimated model on the holdout data (i.e., out of sample data), for a model that has overfitting, we will usually see that after an initial phase of acceptable error, the error suddenly becomes catastrophically bad.

An algorithm, especially if it is very complex like an ARIMA model, may fit the noise in the historical data. When the algorithm uses the pattern of the noise to forecast the future, the model produces large errors. Remember that "noise" is random up-and-down movements in the data; noise is not able to be forecasted because it has no pattern! If a model matches the seeming pattern of the noise in the historic period and projects that into the forecast period, large errors will be the result.

That method for avoiding overfitting is called a stability test.

ARMA models are essential to forecasters and are often used to model time series. But they also suffer badly from overfitting. If we want to use ARIMA models with the best algorithmic properties for our forecasts, we need a method for avoiding overfitting. That method for avoiding overfitting is called a stability test. There is no one test statistic we can use, but the general procedure is easy to understand and implement.

Take the last column of Table 7.2 (labeled "ARIMA111"), which is close to an ARIMA 111 series. Let's assume it is a time series (the periodicity does not matter) and that we use ForecastX™ to suggest an appropriate model. The model automatically suggested by ForecastX™ is an ARIMA (0,1,1) (1,0,0). If we now hold out the last ten observations in this 200-observation data set and re-estimate the model, the suggested model remains an ARIMA (0,1,1) (1,0,0). The fact that the model did not change parameters suggests the ARIMA estimation procedure is not overfitting this particular data. If the suggested model had turned out to be very different from the original suggested model, that would have been an indication of possible overfitting.

Now consider the Gap data from the Integrative Case. We used ForecastX™ to suggest an ARIMA (1,0,1) (1,1,2) model for the full data set. Now hold out the last four quarters of data and estimate the model again. The result is an ARIMA (1,0,1) (0,1,0) model. The two model estimates are not alike, and there is a suggestion that the original model may not be stable; it may be overfitting by attempting to forecast the noise in the data as well as the actual reoccurring patterns.

Overfitting is not often a significant problem with any of the techniques we have used with the exception of ARIMA. Why is it the case that ARIMA, in particular, has the tendency to overfit data? The answer lies in the fact that the ARIMA algorithm has the ability to estimate very complex patterns (often using many AR and MA terms) and that ability includes the possibility of misinterpreting noise as a forecastable pattern. When we begin using analytics algorithms, we will find that some of those algorithms also have a problem with overfitting.

# USING FORECASTX™ TO MAKE ARIMA (BOX-JENKINS) FORECASTS

What follows is a brief discussion of how to use ForecastX™ for preparing an ARIMA (Box-Jenkins) forecast. As with other methods, start with your data in an Excel spreadsheet in column format, such as the sample of The Gap data shown in the table below. Once you have your data in this format, while in Excel highlight the data you want to use, then start ForecastX™. The dialog box to the right of the table appears.

**A Sample of The Gap Data in Column Format (C7Gap)**

| Date | The Gap Sales ($m) |
|------|--------------------|
| Apr-2006 | 3441 |
| Jul-2006 | 3714 |
| Oct-2006 | 3851 |
| Jan-2007 | 4919 |
| Apr-2007 | 3549 |
| Jul-2007 | 3685 |
| Oct-2007 | 3854 |
| Jan-2008 | 4675 |
| Apr-2008 | 3384 |
| Jul-2008 | 3499 |
| Oct-2008 | 3561 |
| Jan-2009 | 4082 |
| Apr-2009 | 3127 |
| Jul-2009 | 3245 |
| Oct-2009 | 3589 |
| Jan-2010 | 4236 |
| Apr-2010 | 3329 |
| Jul-2010 | 3317 |
| Oct-2010 | 3654 |
| Jan-2011 | 4364 |

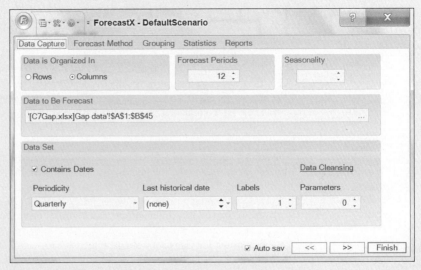

Source: John Galt Solutions

Set the **Dates** window to the periodicity of your data (**Quarterly** for this example); then click the **Forecast Method** tab at the top and the following appears.

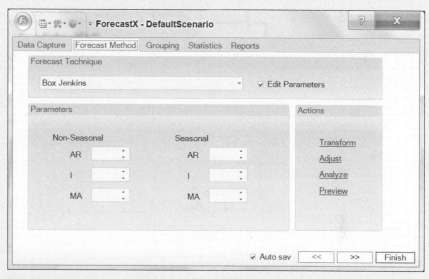

Source: John Galt Solutions

Click the down arrow in the **Forecasting Technique** window and select **Box Jenkins**. You can enter values for the **AR, I,** and **MA** terms, or you can leave those spaces blank and let ForecastX™ select a suggested set of values. We recommend the latter (i.e., don't fill in the values for AR, I and MA).

Next click the **Statistics** tab and the **Statistics** dialog box will appear.

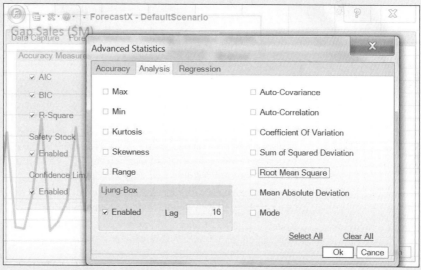

Source: John Galt Solutions

Here, you select the statistics you want to have reported. You will want to experiment with various selections. Use the **More** button to select the **Ljung-Box** statistic.We have enabled 16 lags in this example.

Next click the **Reports** tab and the **Report Options** dialog box will appear.

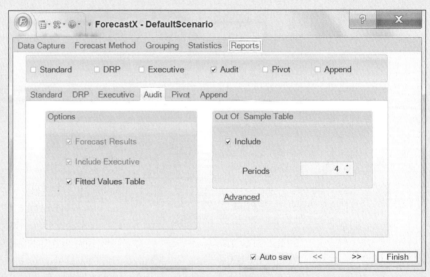

Source: John Galt Solutions

As you place a check next to each of the five boxes for various reports, the options available in that report will appear below. We suggest using the **Audit** report, which provides both graphic and text output that is quite complete. You may also wish to check the Out Of Sample Include box to check how well the estimated ARIMA does in the future or the Out Of Sample period.

Again, you will want to experiment with the various reports to get a feel for the ones that will give you the output you want for your specific application.

After you click **Finish!** in the lower right corner, ForecastX$^{TM}$ will complete the forecast and, as part of the output, will identify the exact model used. Reports will be put in new Excel workbooks—Book 2, Book 3, and so forth.

## Suggested Readings

Armstrong, Scott J.; and Edward J. Lusk. "Research on the Accuracy of Alternative Extrapolation Models: Analysis of a Forecasting Competition through Open Peer Review." *Journal of Forecasting* 2 (1983), pp. 259–62.

Box, G. E. P.; G. M. Jenkins; and G. C. Reinsel. *Time Series Analysis: Forecasting and Control.* 3rd ed. Englewood Cliffs, NJ: Prentice-Hall, 1994.

Brandon, Charles H.; Jeffrey E. Jarrett; and Saleha Khumawala. "Revising Forecasts of Accounting Earnings: A Comparison with the Box-Jenkins Method." *Management Science* 29 (1983), pp. 256–63.

Chase, Charles W. Jr. *Demand-Driven Forecasting: A Structured Approach to Forecasting, Second Edition*. Hoboken, NJ: Wiley, 2013. pp. 203–237.

Chatfield, C.; and D. L. Prothero. "Box-Jenkins Seasonal Forecasting Problems in a Case Study." *Journal of the Royal Statistical Society* Series A 136 (1973), pp. 295–352.

Libert, G. "The M-Competition with a Fully Automatic Box-Jenkins Procedure." *Journal of Forecasting* 3 (1984), pp. 325–28.

Ljung, G. M.; and G. E. P. Box. "On a Measure of Lack of Fit in Time Series Models." *Biometrika* 65 (1978), pp. 297–303.

Ludlow, Jorge; and Walter Enders. "Estimating Non-Linear ARMA Models Using Fourier Coefficients." *International Journal of Forecasting* 16, no. 3 (July–September 2000), pp. 333–47.

Lusk, Edward J.; and Joao S. Neves. "A Comparative ARIMA Analysis of the 111 Series of the Makridakis Competition." *Journal of Forecasting* 3 (1984), pp. 329–32.

Makridakis, S.; and M. Hibon. "The M3-Competitions: Results, Conclusions and Implications." *International Journal of Forecasting* 16, no. 4 (2000), pp. 451–476.

Nelson, Charles R. *Applied Time Series Analysis for Managerial Forecasting*. San Francisco: Holden-Day, 1973.

Peña, Daniel. "George Box: An Interview with the *International Journal of Forecasting*." *International Journal of Forecasting* 17, no. 1 (January–March 2001), pp. 1–9.

## Exercises

1. A student collects data on the use of the university library electronic portal on an hourly basis for eight consecutive Mondays. What type of seasonality would you expect to find in these data?

2. When would you use differencing, and when would you expect to employ seasonal differencing?

3. Evaluate the following statement: "If an ARIMA model is properly constructed, it has residual autocorrelations that are nearly equal to zero."

4. Of what use is the chi-square test as applied to residual autocorrelations?

5. *a.* Calculate and display the first 50 autocorrelations for the four data series in the accompanying table, labeled A, B, C, and D; consider each of the four data series to be a quarterly time series. How many of the autocorrelations fall outside the 95 percent confidence interval (positive or negative)?

   *b.* Is there a pattern to those autocorrelation coefficients falling outside the 95 percent confidence interval?

   *c.* Calculate and display the first 50 partial autocorrelations for the 100 time-series observations. How many of the partial autocorrelation coefficients fall outside the 95 percent confidence interval?

   *d.* Is there a pattern to those partial autocorrelation coefficients falling outside the 95 percent confidence interval?

   *e.* Estimate the appropriate model as determined from your inspections carried out in parts *a* through *d* and forecast for four quarters into the future. Calculate the RMSE for each model.

## EXERCISE 5 Four Data Series

| A | B | C | D | A | B | C | D |
|---|---|---|---|---|---|---|---|
| 1.62 | 0.38 | 0.68 | 1.11 | 0.40 | 0.80 | 3.97 | 40.68 |
| 1.55 | 1.02 | 0.71 | 2.27 | 1.13 | 0.41 | 4.29 | 41.19 |
| 1.59 | 0.70 | 1.22 | 3.71 | 1.06 | 0.93 | 4.22 | 41.58 |
| 1.55 | 1.16 | 1.29 | 4.52 | 0.31 | 0.66 | 4.34 | 42.23 |
| 1.10 | 1.11 | 1.53 | 5.04 | 0.67 | 1.29 | 4.85 | 43.33 |
| 0.82 | 0.93 | 1.52 | 6.10 | 0.68 | 1.11 | 4.39 | 44.27 |
| 1.06 | 1.32 | 1.53 | 7.61 | 0.72 | 1.16 | 4.74 | 44.89 |
| 0.69 | 0.78 | 2.08 | 8.89 | 0.58 | 1.52 | 5.09 | 45.41 |
| 0.74 | 0.50 | 2.57 | 9.73 | 0.74 | 1.28 | 4.83 | 45.69 |
| 0.73 | 0.72 | 3.15 | 10.85 | 1.14 | 0.76 | 5.21 | 46.39 |
| 0.44 | 0.69 | 3.71 | 11.99 | 1.42 | 0.74 | 4.74 | 46.96 |
| 0.98 | 0.41 | 3.76 | 12.87 | 0.94 | 0.53 | 4.90 | 47.34 |
| 0.62 | 1.16 | 3.73 | 13.44 | 0.59 | 0.44 | 5.06 | 47.61 |
| 0.44 | 1.35 | 3.49 | 14.26 | 0.32 | 0.92 | 5.29 | 48.21 |
| 0.66 | 0.98 | 3.94 | 14.91 | 0.68 | 0.57 | 4.90 | 48.77 |
| 0.83 | 1.21 | 4.01 | 15.37 | 1.40 | 0.33 | 4.90 | 49.17 |
| 1.25 | 0.69 | 3.97 | 15.90 | 1.52 | 0.99 | 4.80 | 49.85 |
| 0.89 | 0.35 | 4.35 | 17.10 | 1.20 | 1.24 | 4.88 | 50.55 |
| 1.02 | 0.70 | 3.84 | 18.39 | 1.33 | 0.77 | 4.46 | 51.55 |
| 0.72 | 0.74 | 3.60 | 18.98 | 0.69 | 0.48 | 5.09 | 52.20 |
| 0.79 | 0.52 | 3.43 | 19.50 | 0.30 | 1.16 | 4.56 | 53.06 |
| 0.77 | 0.26 | 3.43 | 20.21 | 0.49 | 0.62 | 4.37 | 54.46 |
| 1.18 | 0.21 | 3.69 | 20.85 | 0.43 | 0.83 | 4.20 | 55.70 |
| 1.26 | 1.06 | 3.85 | 21.69 | 0.95 | 0.62 | 4.65 | 56.51 |
| 0.81 | 1.27 | 4.20 | 22.69 | 1.50 | 1.11 | 4.37 | 57.41 |
| 1.05 | 1.63 | 4.05 | 23.56 | 1.58 | 0.73 | 4.67 | 58.81 |
| 0.63 | 0.98 | 4.33 | 24.65 | 0.92 | 0.61 | 5.00 | 60.10 |
| 0.71 | 0.98 | 4.76 | 25.92 | 0.40 | 0.90 | 5.03 | 61.00 |
| 1.02 | 1.13 | 4.79 | 26.87 | 0.47 | 1.01 | 4.78 | 61.69 |
| 0.79 | 1.30 | 4.69 | 28.07 | 1.03 | 1.01 | 5.21 | 62.63 |
| 1.22 | 1.61 | 4.65 | 29.63 | 1.33 | 0.61 | 5.31 | 63.12 |
| 1.01 | 1.31 | 4.49 | 30.41 | 1.11 | 1.13 | 5.14 | 63.28 |
| 0.43 | 1.20 | 4.91 | 31.42 | 0.60 | 1.05 | 5.18 | 63.52 |
| 0.27 | 1.26 | 5.01 | 32.66 | 0.30 | 0.89 | 4.92 | 64.08 |
| 0.41 | 1.32 | 4.59 | 33.49 | 0.93 | 1.21 | 5.24 | 64.45 |
| 0.94 | 0.85 | 4.62 | 34.23 | 0.92 | 1.48 | 4.80 | 64.62 |
| 1.42 | 1.13 | 4.83 | 35.00 | 0.85 | 1.62 | 5.37 | 64.78 |
| 1.22 | 1.24 | 4.86 | 36.27 | 0.52 | 1.15 | 5.19 | 65.52 |
| 1.31 | 1.08 | 4.53 | 37.07 | 0.07 | 1.43 | 4.71 | 66.18 |
| 0.67 | 0.85 | 4.44 | 37.25 | 0.41 | 1.33 | 4.62 | 67.16 |
| 0.22 | 1.32 | 4.74 | 38.10 | 1.21 | 1.26 | 4.42 | 68.63 |
| 0.50 | 1.53 | 4.54 | 39.51 | 0.96 | 1.16 | 5.00 | 69.67 |
| 0.64 | 1.75 | 4.13 | 40.20 | 0.31 | 1.04 | 4.53 | 70.17 |
| 0.41 | 1.11 | 4.22 | 40.27 | 0.33 | 1.19 | 4.44 | 70.53 |

(continued on next page)

**EXERCISE 5** (continued)

| A | B | C | D | A | B | C | D |
|---|---|---|---|---|---|---|---|
| 0.52 | 1.22 | 4.56 | 71.32 | 1.29 | 1.51 | 4.31 | 75.15 |
| 0.77 | 0.70 | 4.48 | 71.99 | 0.87 | 1.11 | 4.74 | 75.81 |
| 0.85 | 0.74 | 4.88 | 72.53 | 0.86 | 1.42 | 4.64 | 76.86 |
| 1.27 | 0.73 | 4.70 | 72.89 | 0.76 | 1.38 | 4.39 | 77.83 |
| 1.48 | 1.00 | 4.92 | 73.81 | 0.36 | 1.68 | 4.15 | 78.95 |
| 1.42 | 1.39 | 4.74 | 74.74 | 0.17 | 1.49 | 4.35 | 80.27 |

6. *a.* Calculate and display the first 50 autocorrelations for the four data series in the table for this exercise, labeled A, B, C, and D; consider each of the four data series to be a quarterly time series. How many of the autocorrelations fall outside the 95 percent confidence interval (positive or negative)?

   *b.* Is there a pattern to those autocorrelation coefficients falling outside the 95 percent confidence interval?

   *c.* Calculate and display the first 50 partial autocorrelations for the 100 time-series observations. How many of the partial autocorrelation coefficients fall outside the 95 percent confidence interval?

   *d.* Is there a pattern to those partial autocorrelation coefficients falling outside the 95 percent confidence interval?

   *e.* Which frame in Figures 7.1, 7.3, and 7.5 does this pattern of autocorrelation and partial autocorrelation coefficients most closely resemble?

   *f.* Estimate the appropriate model as determined from your inspections carried out in parts *a* through *e,* and forecast for four quarters into the future. Calculate the RMSE for each model.

**EXERCISE 6** **Four Data Series**

| A | B | C | D | A | B | C | D |
|---|---|---|---|---|---|---|---|
| 0.77 | 0.37 | 0.20 | 0.93 | 0.45 | 0.68 | 3.16 | 13.37 |
| 0.31 | 0.32 | 0.93 | 1.24 | 0.21 | 0.48 | 3.13 | 13.58 |
| 0.88 | 0.95 | 1.62 | 2.12 | 0.36 | 0.50 | 3.71 | 13.93 |
| 1.48 | 1.40 | 1.66 | 3.60 | 1.06 | 1.13 | 3.77 | 15.00 |
| 0.99 | 1.04 | 2.41 | 4.59 | 1.17 | 1.12 | 3.50 | 16.17 |
| 1.16 | 1.44 | 2.63 | 5.75 | 0.50 | 0.67 | 3.86 | 16.67 |
| 1.26 | 1.33 | 2.75 | 7.01 | 0.74 | 0.99 | 3.72 | 17.41 |
| 0.86 | 1.10 | 2.64 | 7.87 | 0.78 | 0.82 | 3.54 | 18.19 |
| 0.48 | 0.73 | 2.66 | 8.35 | 0.39 | 0.57 | 3.92 | 18.58 |
| 0.39 | 0.63 | 2.75 | 8.74 | 0.82 | 0.99 | 4.31 | 19.39 |
| 0.55 | 0.68 | 2.97 | 9.29 | 1.35 | 1.35 | 4.28 | 20.74 |
| 0.76 | 0.85 | 2.84 | 10.05 | 1.02 | 1.25 | 4.11 | 59.39 |
| 0.56 | 0.63 | 3.55 | 10.62 | 1.08 | 1.16 | 4.70 | 21.82 |
| 1.12 | 1.29 | 3.55 | 11.74 | 1.18 | 1.42 | 4.56 | 23.00 |
| 1.18 | 1.14 | 3.30 | 12.91 | 1.00 | 1.12 | 4.71 | 24.00 |

(continued on next page)

**EXERCISE 6** (continued)

| A | B | C | D | A | B | C | D |
|---|---|---|---|---|---|---|---|
| 1.07 | 0.97 | 4.68 | 43.00 | 0.82 | 1.04 | 5.36 | 32.13 |
| 1.00 | 1.11 | 4.64 | 44.01 | 0.59 | 0.93 | 5.15 | 32.72 |
| 0.90 | 1.05 | 4.56 | 65.15 | 0.60 | 0.78 | 5.05 | 33.32 |
| 1.11 | 1.30 | 4.57 | 46.02 | 0.59 | 0.75 | 5.56 | 33.91 |
| 0.71 | 0.81 | 4.46 | 46.73 | 0.35 | 0.46 | 4.05 | 62.04 |
| 0.38 | 0.68 | 4.46 | 47.12 | 1.06 | 1.07 | 4.12 | 63.09 |
| 0.61 | 0.76 | 4.71 | 47.73 | 1.16 | 1.10 | 4.19 | 64.25 |
| 0.99 | 1.07 | 4.69 | 48.72 | 0.90 | 1.02 | 4.97 | 44.91 |
| 0.99 | 1.04 | 4.61 | 49.71 | 1.15 | 1.33 | 4.23 | 66.30 |
| 0.74 | 0.86 | 4.87 | 76.58 | 0.76 | 0.86 | 4.18 | 67.06 |
| 0.28 | 0.46 | 4.11 | 50.73 | 0.45 | 0.74 | 4.59 | 67.51 |
| 0.27 | 0.49 | 3.95 | 50.99 | 1.03 | 1.18 | 5.02 | 68.54 |
| 0.42 | 0.49 | 3.72 | 51.42 | 1.65 | 1.75 | 5.44 | 71.73 |
| 0.30 | 0.38 | 3.49 | 51.72 | 1.25 | 1.37 | 5.22 | 35.16 |
| 0.19 | 0.29 | 3.33 | 51.91 | 1.02 | 1.01 | 5.65 | 36.18 |
| 0.21 | 0.28 | 4.01 | 52.12 | 1.11 | 1.39 | 5.85 | 37.29 |
| 1.08 | 1.13 | 3.91 | 53.21 | 1.47 | 1.55 | 5.53 | 38.76 |
| 1.12 | 0.99 | 4.09 | 54.33 | 0.90 | 1.08 | 5.23 | 39.66 |
| 0.85 | 1.05 | 3.94 | 55.18 | 0.40 | 0.73 | 5.14 | 40.06 |
| 0.68 | 0.82 | 4.50 | 55.86 | 0.50 | 0.73 | 4.68 | 40.56 |
| 1.13 | 1.33 | 4.30 | 56.99 | 0.29 | 0.40 | 4.47 | 40.86 |
| 1.00 | 1.03 | 4.03 | 57.99 | 0.19 | 0.37 | 4.07 | 41.05 |
| 0.38 | 0.64 | 4.61 | 58.37 | 0.12 | 0.19 | 4.50 | 41.17 |
| 1.54 | 1.56 | 5.40 | 70.08 | 0.76 | 0.85 | 4.51 | 41.93 |
| 0.73 | 0.71 | 4.11 | 60.12 | 1.33 | 1.53 | 4.91 | 73.07 |
| 0.36 | 0.66 | 4.20 | 60.48 | 0.48 | 0.79 | 5.33 | 73.55 |
| 0.71 | 0.83 | 3.81 | 61.19 | 0.82 | 1.20 | 5.62 | 74.37 |
| 0.40 | 0.47 | 3.56 | 61.59 | 1.48 | 1.51 | 5.11 | 75.84 |
| 0.09 | 0.29 | 3.57 | 61.69 | 0.74 | 0.91 | 4.18 | 50.45 |
| 0.87 | 1.14 | 5.19 | 24.87 | 0.25 | 0.60 | 4.81 | 76.83 |
| 1.38 | 1.55 | 5.26 | 26.25 | 0.50 | 0.68 | 5.25 | 77.33 |
| 1.37 | 1.46 | 5.24 | 27.62 | 1.18 | 1.25 | 5.45 | 78.51 |
| 1.01 | 1.26 | 5.63 | 28.62 | 1.45 | 1.44 | 5.37 | 79.95 |
| 1.28 | 1.54 | 5.77 | 29.90 | 1.08 | 1.23 | 5.35 | 81.03 |
| 1.42 | 1.55 | 5.43 | 31.32 | 0.86 | 1.11 | 5.02 | 81.89 |

7. *a.* An autoregressive model is given by:

$$Y_t = 20.58 + 0.046Y_{t-1} + 0.019Y_{t-2}$$

where $Y_t$ = sales of a product. Explain the meaning of the terms in this autoregressive model.

b. Write the expressions for the following models:

| | |
|---|---|
| AR(3) | MA(4) |
| AR(4) | ARMA(1, 2) |
| MA(3) | ARIMA(2, 1, 2) |

8. A twenty-foot equivalent unit (TEU) is a standard measurement of volume in container shipping. The majority of containers are either 20 or 40 feet in length. A 20-foot container is 1 TEU; a 40-foot container is 2 TEUs. Although the height of containers can also vary, this does not affect the TEU measurement. The following data are the total number of containers shipped from the port of Los Angeles for the years 1995 through 2007.

| Date | Total TEUs | Date | Total TEUs | Date | Total TEUs |
|---|---|---|---|---|---|
| Jan-95 | 1,23,723 | Dec-97 | 1,34,315 | Nov-00 | 2,10,209 |
| Feb-95 | 99,368 | Jan-98 | 1,25,930 | Dec-00 | 2,03,021 |
| Mar-95 | 1,18,549 | Feb-98 | 1,22,976 | Jan-01 | 2,12,323 |
| Apr-95 | 1,23,411 | Mar-98 | 1,54,947 | Feb-01 | 1,63,332 |
| May-95 | 1,14,514 | Apr-98 | 1,54,522 | Mar-01 | 2,17,284 |
| Jun-95 | 1,14,468 | May-98 | 1,67,204 | Apr-01 | 2,21,465 |
| Jul-95 | 1,25,412 | Jun-98 | 1,59,638 | May-01 | 2,13,860 |
| Aug-95 | 1,22,866 | Jul-98 | 1,58,948 | Jun-01 | 2,43,053 |
| Sep-95 | 1,15,473 | Aug-98 | 1,71,152 | Jul-01 | 2,50,344 |
| Oct-95 | 1,21,523 | Sep-98 | 1,57,267 | Aug-01 | 2,61,705 |
| Nov-95 | 1,04,880 | Oct-98 | 1,69,364 | Sep-01 | 2,75,559 |
| Dec-95 | 1,03,821 | Nov-98 | 1,58,255 | Oct-01 | 2,74,954 |
| Jan-96 | 1,11,494 | Dec-98 | 1,40,165 | Nov-01 | 2,41,730 |
| Feb-96 | 99,785 | Jan-99 | 1,42,116 | Dec-01 | 2,25,886 |
| Mar-96 | 96,906 | Feb-99 | 1,42,080 | Jan-02 | 2,20,810 |
| Apr-96 | 1,11,204 | Mar-99 | 1,41,926 | Feb-02 | 2,44,167 |
| May-96 | 1,15,513 | Apr-99 | 1,53,559 | Mar-02 | 2,29,954 |
| Jun-96 | 1,19,422 | May-99 | 1,82,975 | Apr-02 | 2,76,373 |
| Jul-96 | 1,29,984 | Jun-99 | 1,69,682 | May-02 | 2,84,385 |
| Aug-96 | 1,34,296 | Jul-99 | 1,85,017 | Jun-02 | 3,01,447 |
| Sep-96 | 1,34,657 | Aug-99 | 1,88,281 | Jul-02 | 2,71,933 |
| Oct-96 | 1,44,430 | Sep-99 | 1,87,081 | Aug-02 | 3,39,690 |
| Nov-96 | 1,28,521 | Oct-99 | 2,08,163 | Sep-02 | 3,30,967 |
| Dec-96 | 1,22,428 | Nov-99 | 1,84,662 | Oct-02 | 2,65,218 |
| Jan-97 | 1,27,065 | Dec-99 | 1,78,493 | Nov-02 | 3,01,333 |
| Feb-97 | 1,12,733 | Jan-00 | 1,94,180 | Dec-02 | 3,06,099 |
| Mar-97 | 1,13,063 | Feb-00 | 1,75,890 | Jan-03 | 2,76,482 |
| Apr-97 | 1,29,797 | Mar-00 | 1,88,438 | Feb-03 | 2,74,740 |
| May-97 | 1,36,712 | Apr-00 | 2,20,157 | Mar-03 | 2,98,495 |
| Jun-97 | 1,40,220 | May-00 | 2,17,749 | Apr-03 | 3,26,709 |
| Jul-97 | 1,43,756 | Jun-00 | 2,20,071 | May-03 | 3,48,276 |
| Aug-97 | 1,43,389 | Jul-00 | 2,43,695 | Jun-03 | 3,05,892 |
| Sep-97 | 1,43,700 | Aug-00 | 2,50,551 | Jul-03 | 3,31,741 |
| Oct-97 | 1,44,425 | Sep-00 | 2,27,848 | Aug-03 | 3,60,046 |
| Nov-97 | 1,31,877 | Oct-00 | 2,60,469 | Sep-03 | 3,50,476 |

(continued on next page)

(continued)

| Date | Total TEUs | Date | Total TEUs | Date | Total TEUs |
|------|-----------|------|-----------|------|-----------|
| Oct-03 | 3,72,112 | Mar-05 | 2,62,173 | Aug-06 | 4,14,004 |
| Nov-03 | 3,38,379 | Apr-05 | 3,36,087 | Sep-06 | 4,31,283 |
| Dec-03 | 3,06,984 | May-05 | 3,19,472 | Oct-06 | 4,21,694 |
| Jan-04 | 3,45,412 | Jun-05 | 3,40,582 | Nov-06 | 3,90,209 |
| Feb-04 | 2,47,710 | Jul-05 | 3,56,716 | Dec-06 | 3,65,591 |
| Mar-04 | 3,40,748 | Aug-05 | 3,49,655 | Jan-07 | 3,67,096 |
| Apr-04 | 3,45,339 | Sep-05 | 3,56,912 | Feb-07 | 3,58,601 |
| May-04 | 3,67,128 | Oct-05 | 3,75,051 | Mar-07 | 3,23,472 |
| Jun-04 | 3,47,056 | Nov-05 | 3,32,037 | Apr-07 | 3,75,512 |
| Jul-04 | 3,65,901 | Dec-05 | 3,28,244 | May-07 | 3,68,874 |
| Aug-04 | 3,44,109 | Jan-06 | 3,27,009 | Jun-07 | 3,93,187 |
| Sep-04 | 3,24,346 | Feb-06 | 2,51,812 | Jul-07 | 3,87,573 |
| Oct-04 | 3,52,718 | Mar-06 | 3,45,401 | Aug-07 | 3,79,027 |
| Nov-04 | 3,40,051 | Apr-06 | 3,70,171 | Sep-07 | 4,07,915 |
| Dec-04 | 2,83,268 | May-06 | 3,68,864 | Oct-07 | 3,93,948 |
| Jan-05 | 3,05,102 | Jun-06 | 3,87,957 | Nov-07 | 3,83,241 |
| Feb-05 | 2,94,022 | Jul-06 | 4,13,357 | Dec-07 | 3,46,140 |

*a.* Plot the series. What can you learn from examining this plot?

*b.* Calculate and display the first 24 autocorrelations for the series. What do the ACF and PACF suggest about the series?

*c.* Suggest and estimate an optimal set of differencing to use with the series.

*d.* Estimate the ARIMA model that you believe to be a good candidate for forecasting container shipments. It may help to specify the seasonality as "12." Test the Ljung-Box statistic and report your findings. Finally, plot the first 24 autocorrelations of the residuals to your best model.

9. The data below show the average hourly megawatts of electricity used in New York City for the years 1993 through 2004.

| Month | Mean Usage | Month | Mean Usage | Month | Mean Usage |
|-------|-----------|-------|-----------|-------|-----------|
| Jan-93 | 17,074.66 | Jan-94 | 18,404.18 | Jan-95 | 17,056.81 |
| Feb-93 | 17,822.51 | Feb-94 | 17,884.69 | Feb-95 | 17,695.12 |
| Mar-93 | 16,900.10 | Mar-94 | 16,754.90 | Mar-95 | 16,351.09 |
| Apr-93 | 15,417.28 | Apr-94 | 15,277.75 | Apr-95 | 15,495.87 |
| May-93 | 14,986.03 | May-94 | 15,040.02 | May-95 | 15,291.26 |
| Jun-93 | 16,929.04 | Jun-94 | 17,836.91 | Jun-95 | 17,252.93 |
| Jul-93 | 18,694.29 | Jul-94 | 19,349.14 | Jul-95 | 19,154.12 |
| Aug-93 | 18,332.28 | Aug-94 | 17,734.60 | Aug-95 | 19,166.08 |
| Sep-93 | 16,468.28 | Sep-94 | 16,015.75 | Sep-95 | 16,178.87 |
| Oct-93 | 15,474.31 | Oct-94 | 15,382.20 | Oct-95 | 15,619.46 |
| Nov-93 | 16,028.48 | Nov-94 | 15,941.85 | Nov-95 | 16,434.09 |
| Dec-93 | 17,155.07 | Dec-94 | 16,833.42 | Dec-95 | 17,627.00 |

(continued on next page)

(continued)

| Month | Mean Usage | Month | Mean Usage | Month | Mean Usage |
|---|---|---|---|---|---|
| Jan-96 | 17,932.43 | Jan-99 | 18,014.58 | Jan-02 | 17,808.09 |
| Feb-96 | 17,669.17 | Feb-99 | 17,472.08 | Feb-02 | 17,404.08 |
| Mar-96 | 16,816.22 | Mar-99 | 17,188.13 | Mar-02 | 16,809.13 |
| Apr-96 | 15,702.85 | Apr-99 | 15,811.44 | Apr-02 | 16,561.17 |
| May-96 | 15,478.36 | May-99 | 15,913.57 | May-02 | 16,168.09 |
| Jun-96 | 17,209.71 | Jun-99 | 19,271.75 | Jun-02 | 18,691.46 |
| Jul-96 | 17,770.67 | Jul-99 | 21,652.70 | Jul-02 | 21,372.06 |
| Aug-96 | 18,314.77 | Aug-99 | 19,652.57 | Aug-02 | 21,300.47 |
| Sep-96 | 16,906.53 | Sep-99 | 18,180.01 | Sep-02 | 18,505.90 |
| Oct-96 | 15,745.02 | Oct-99 | 16,478.46 | Oct-02 | 17,157.60 |
| Nov-96 | 16,486.24 | Nov-99 | 16,739.43 | Nov-02 | 17,201.31 |
| Dec-96 | 16,880.53 | Dec-99 | 17,742.58 | Dec-02 | 18,362.16 |
| Jan-97 | 17,860.97 | Jan-00 | 18,485.60 | Jan-03 | 19,065.90 |
| Feb-97 | 17,030.63 | Feb-00 | 17,955.94 | Feb-03 | 18,741.54 |
| Mar-97 | 16,586.05 | Mar-00 | 16,834.31 | Mar-03 | 17,400.20 |
| Apr-97 | 15,712.44 | Apr-00 | 16,218.50 | Apr-03 | 16,358.73 |
| May-97 | 15,236.65 | May-00 | 16,656.62 | May-03 | 15,929.05 |
| Jun-97 | 17,608.56 | Jun-00 | 18,980.76 | Jun-03 | 17,999.87 |
| Jul-97 | 18,964.37 | Jul-00 | 18,745.26 | Jul-03 | 20,717.03 |
| Aug-97 | 18,145.33 | Aug-00 | 19,480.04 | Aug-03 | 20,730.96 |
| Sep-97 | 16,788.25 | Sep-00 | 18,018.60 | Sep-03 | 18,038.57 |
| Oct-97 | 16,103.79 | Oct-00 | 16,607.91 | Oct-03 | 16,531.88 |
| Nov-97 | 16,499.30 | Nov-00 | 17,231.95 | Nov-03 | 16,758.73 |
| Dec-97 | 17,389.77 | Dec-00 | 18,737.37 | Dec-03 | 18,137.06 |
| Jan-98 | 17,056.34 | Jan-01 | 18,439.91 | Jan-04 | 19,333.36 |
| Feb-98 | 17,036.37 | Feb-01 | 18,069.88 | Feb-04 | 18,313.19 |
| Mar-98 | 16,833.40 | Mar-01 | 17,608.38 | Mar-04 | 17,351.52 |
| Apr-98 | 15,739.52 | Apr-01 | 16,140.74 | Apr-04 | 16,384.22 |
| May-98 | 16,059.23 | May-01 | 16,556.55 | May-04 | 17,001.84 |
| Jun-98 | 17,779.28 | Jun-01 | 19,185.78 | Jun-04 | 18,798.57 |
| Jul-98 | 19,460.53 | Jul-01 | 19,157.38 | Jul-04 | 20,040.84 |
| Aug-98 | 19,705.33 | Aug-01 | 21,327.08 | Aug-04 | 20,222.35 |
| Sep-98 | 17,751.83 | Sep-01 | 17,540.95 | Sep-04 | 18,643.92 |
| Oct-98 | 16,035.26 | Oct-01 | 16,663.81 | Oct-04 | 16,775.23 |
| Nov-98 | 16,490.67 | Nov-01 | 16,624.80 | Nov-04 | 17,308.72 |
| Dec-98 | 17,349.93 | Dec-01 | 17,267.98 | Dec-04 | 18,617.75 |

*a.* Plot the series and explain what can be learned from this plot.

*b.* Calculate the first 24 autocorrelations for the series, and explain what characteristics of the data are shown in the ACF and PACF.

*c.* Suggest and estimate an optimal ARIMA model.

*d.* Estimate the ARIMA model that you believe to be a good candidate for forecasting electricity usage. Test the Ljung-Box statistic and report your findings. Finally, plot the first 24 autocorrelations of the residuals to your best model.

10. The data below show retail sales at hardware stores in the United States monthly between January 1992 and December 2005. The data are in millions of dollars and are not seasonally adjusted.

| Date | Sales | Date | Sales | Date | Sales |
|------|-------|------|-------|------|-------|
| Jan-92 | 846 | May-95 | 1,343 | Sep-98 | 1,297 |
| Feb-92 | 822 | Jun-95 | 1,340 | Oct-98 | 1,302 |
| Mar-92 | 962 | Jul-95 | 1,230 | Nov-98 | 1,227 |
| Apr-92 | 1,077 | Aug-95 | 1,182 | Dec-98 | 1,363 |
| May-92 | 1,235 | Sep-95 | 1,153 | Jan-99 | 1,104 |
| Jun-92 | 1,170 | Oct-95 | 1,141 | Feb-99 | 1,007 |
| Jul-92 | 1,147 | Nov-95 | 1,193 | Mar-99 | 1,210 |
| Aug-92 | 1,086 | Dec-95 | 1,241 | Apr-99 | 1,416 |
| Sep-92 | 1,056 | Jan-96 | 977 | May-99 | 1,495 |
| Oct-92 | 1,110 | Feb-96 | 920 | Jun-99 | 1,447 |
| Nov-92 | 1,041 | Mar-96 | 1,028 | Jul-99 | 1,390 |
| Dec-92 | 1,168 | Apr-96 | 1,251 | Aug-99 | 1,301 |
| Jan-93 | 883 | May-96 | 1,369 | Sep-99 | 1,286 |
| Feb-93 | 808 | Jun-96 | 1,306 | Oct-99 | 1,296 |
| Mar-93 | 987 | Jul-96 | 1,242 | Nov-99 | 1,295 |
| Apr-93 | 1,097 | Aug-96 | 1,186 | Dec-99 | 1,384 |
| May-93 | 1,289 | Sep-96 | 1,083 | Jan-00 | 1,073 |
| Jun-93 | 1,210 | Oct-96 | 1,187 | Feb-00 | 1,035 |
| Jul-93 | 1,186 | Nov-96 | 1,177 | Mar-00 | 1,316 |
| Aug-93 | 1,101 | Dec-96 | 1,229 | Apr-00 | 1,429 |
| Sep-93 | 1,077 | Jan-97 | 1,003 | May-00 | 1,598 |
| Oct-93 | 1,111 | Feb-97 | 880 | Jun-00 | 1,551 |
| Nov-93 | 1,098 | Mar-97 | 1,027 | Jul-00 | 1,445 |
| Dec-93 | 1,204 | Apr-97 | 1,203 | Aug-00 | 1,433 |
| Jan-94 | 959 | May-97 | 1,339 | Sep-00 | 1,328 |
| Feb-94 | 866 | Jun-97 | 1,303 | Oct-00 | 1,326 |
| Mar-94 | 1,053 | Jul-97 | 1,277 | Nov-00 | 1,306 |
| Apr-94 | 1,232 | Aug-97 | 1,224 | Dec-00 | 1,384 |
| May-94 | 1,296 | Sep-97 | 1,172 | Jan-01 | 1,092 |
| Jun-94 | 1,271 | Oct-97 | 1,246 | Feb-01 | 1,063 |
| Jul-94 | 1,217 | Nov-97 | 1,140 | Mar-01 | 1,290 |
| Aug-94 | 1,193 | Dec-97 | 1,184 | Apr-01 | 1,441 |
| Sep-94 | 1,138 | Jan-98 | 971 | May-01 | 1,657 |
| Oct-94 | 1,198 | Feb-98 | 900 | Jun-01 | 1,574 |
| Nov-94 | 1,165 | Mar-98 | 1,105 | Jul-01 | 1,460 |
| Dec-94 | 1,243 | Apr-98 | 1,323 | Aug-01 | 1,437 |
| Jan-95 | 875 | May-98 | 1,425 | Sep-01 | 1,328 |
| Feb-95 | 848 | Jun-98 | 1,427 | Oct-01 | 1,386 |
| Mar-95 | 1,061 | Jul-98 | 1,357 | Nov-01 | 1,399 |
| Apr-95 | 1,157 | Aug-98 | 1,313 | Dec-01 | 1,457 |

(continued on next page)

(continued)

| Date | Sales | Date | Sales | Date | Sales |
|------|-------|------|-------|------|-------|
| Jan-02 | 1,158 | May-03 | 1,743 | Sep-04 | 1,520 |
| Feb-02 | 1,097 | Jun-03 | 1,665 | Oct-04 | 1,483 |
| Mar-02 | 1,297 | Jul-03 | 1,616 | Nov-04 | 1,478 |
| Apr-02 | 1,539 | Aug-03 | 1,537 | Dec-04 | 1,581 |
| May-02 | 1,691 | Sep-03 | 1,485 | Jan-05 | 1,241 |
| Jun-02 | 1,605 | Oct-03 | 1,498 | Feb-05 | 1,170 |
| Jul-02 | 1,560 | Nov-03 | 1,432 | Mar-05 | 1,442 |
| Aug-02 | 1,471 | Dec-03 | 1,511 | Apr-05 | 1,688 |
| Sep-02 | 1,325 | Jan-04 | 1,186 | May-05 | 1,803 |
| Oct-02 | 1,406 | Feb-04 | 1,126 | Jun-05 | 1,770 |
| Nov-02 | 1,400 | Mar-04 | 1,406 | Jul-05 | 1,607 |
| Dec-02 | 1,460 | Apr-04 | 1,619 | Aug-05 | 1,603 |
| Jan-03 | 1,186 | May-04 | 1,781 | Sep-05 | 1,562 |
| Feb-03 | 1,110 | Jun-04 | 1,717 | Oct-05 | 1,614 |
| Mar-03 | 1,337 | Jul-04 | 1,670 | Nov-05 | 1,582 |
| Apr-03 | 1,490 | Aug-04 | 1,555 | Dec-05 | 1,673 |

*a.* Plot the series. What can you learn from examining this plot?

*b.* Calculate and display the first 24 autocorrelations for the series. What do the ACF and PACF suggest about the series?

*c.* Suggest a possible set of differencing to use with the series.

*d.* Estimate an ARIMA model that you believe to be a good candidate for forecasting future retail sales at hardware stores. Test the Ljung-Box statistic and report your findings. Finally, plot the first 24 autocorrelations of the residuals to your best model.

# Appendix

## Critical Values of Chi-Square

This table provides values of chi-square that correspond to a given upper-tail area and a specified degrees of freedom. For example, for an upper-tail area of 0.10 and 4 degrees of freedom, the critical value of chi-square equals 7.779. When the number of degrees of freedom exceeds 30, the chi-square can be approximated by the normal distribution.

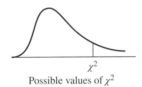

Possible values of $\chi^2$

| Degrees of Freedom (df) | RIGHT-TAIL AREA | | | |
|---|---|---|---|---|
| | 0.10 | 0.05 | 0.02 | 0.01 |
| 1 | 2.706 | 3.841 | 5.412 | 6.635 |
| 2 | 4.605 | 5.991 | 7.824 | 9.210 |
| 3 | 6.251 | 7.815 | 9.837 | 11.345 |
| 4 | 7.779 | 9.488 | 11.668 | 13.277 |
| 5 | 9.236 | 11.070 | 13.388 | 15.086 |
| 6 | 10.645 | 12.592 | 15.033 | 16.812 |
| 7 | 12.017 | 14.067 | 16.622 | 18.475 |
| 8 | 13.362 | 15.507 | 18.168 | 20.090 |
| 9 | 14.684 | 16.919 | 19.679 | 21.666 |
| 10 | 15.987 | 18.307 | 21.161 | 23.209 |
| 11 | 17.275 | 19.675 | 22.618 | 24.725 |
| 12 | 18.549 | 21.026 | 24.054 | 26.217 |
| 13 | 19.812 | 22.362 | 25.472 | 27.688 |
| 14 | 21.064 | 23.685 | 26.873 | 29.141 |
| 15 | 22.307 | 24.996 | 28.259 | 30.578 |
| 16 | 23.542 | 26.296 | 29.633 | 32.000 |
| 17 | 24.769 | 27.587 | 30.995 | 33.409 |
| 18 | 25.989 | 28.869 | 32.346 | 34.805 |
| 19 | 27.204 | 30.144 | 33.687 | 36.191 |
| 20 | 28.412 | 31.410 | 35.020 | 37.566 |
| 21 | 29.615 | 32.671 | 36.343 | 38.932 |

(continued on next page)

| Degrees of Freedom (df) | RIGHT-TAIL AREA | | | |
|---|---|---|---|---|
| | 0.10 | 0.05 | 0.02 | 0.01 |
| 22 | 30.813 | 33.924 | 37.659 | 40.289 |
| 23 | 32.007 | 35.172 | 38.968 | 41.638 |
| 24 | 33.196 | 36.415 | 40.270 | 42.980 |
| 25 | 34.382 | 37.652 | 41.566 | 44.314 |
| 26 | 35.563 | 38.885 | 42.856 | 45.642 |
| 27 | 36.741 | 40.113 | 44.140 | 46.963 |
| 28 | 37.916 | 41.337 | 45.419 | 48.278 |
| 29 | 39.087 | 42.557 | 46.693 | 49.588 |
| 30 | 40.256 | 43.773 | 47.962 | 50.892 |

**Source:** Hall, Jr., Owen P. and Adelman, Harvey M. *Computerized Business Statistics* (Homewood, IL: Richard D. Irwin, 1987), p. 91.

# Chapter **Eight**

# Predictive Analytics: Helping to Make Sense of Big Data

Richard Sherlund of Barclays says the challenge for CIOs in dealing with big data is what to do with all this information.[1]

One rule of thumb today is that almost anything that a typical person can do with less than one second of mental thought we can either now or in the very near future automate.[2]

©VLADGRIN/Getty Images

## LEARNING OBJECTIVES

After studying this chapter, you should be able to:

- Define data mining.
- Explain the categories of tools available in data mining.
- Relate common data mining terminology to standard statistical terminology.
- Explain the relationship between correlation and data mining.
- Examine the common diagnostic tests used in data mining.

[1] "Why CIOs Aren't Prepared for Big Data," *Wall Street Journal,* March 7, 2017, (https://www.wsj.com/articles/why-cios-arent-prepared-for-big-data-1488855666).

[2] "How Artificial Intelligence Will Change Everything," *Wall Street Journal,* March 7, 2017, (https://www.wsj.com/articles/how-artificial-intelligence-will-change-everything-1488856320).

# Applying Analytics in Financial Institutions' Fight Against Fraud

Using data along with other cutting-edge tools can help organizations make better decisions and step up efforts to monitor fraudulent transactions.

Forty years ago, banking fraud might have involved simply forging an account holder's signature on a withdrawal slip. Now the speed and intricacy of the schemes are mind-boggling: a student bank account (with details obtained by a crime gang) receives a payment of £10,000. Within minutes, the funds have been cycled through dozens of accounts before being forwarded to an international account, where the trail suddenly goes cold. No alarm bells go off. No inquiries are made to the bank. The fraud is only discovered much later, at which point the money and the fraudsters are long gone.

Around the world, fraud is an ever-increasing risk for businesses of all stripes. The *2015/16 Global Fraud Report* by Kroll and the Economist Intelligence Unit found that 75 percent of companies surveyed had been victims of fraud in the past year, an increase of 14 percentage points from three years earlier. And, perhaps unsurprisingly, fraud is a particularly serious issue for financial institutions. The Association for Financial Professionals' 2016 Payments Fraud and Control Survey found that 73 percent of finance professionals reported an attempted or actual payments fraud in 2015.

As prevalent as the fraud problem is for financial institutions, it can be difficult to address. Factors that contribute to the challenge include the sheer volume of transactions handled by most institutions versus the relatively small number of fraudulent transactions, the speed with which technology allows fraudsters to operate, poor or incomplete data, and the lack of information sharing among financial institutions. All too often, banks lack the technology and capabilities to implement the necessary safeguards, responding to a primarily digital problem in an analog way—for example, phone calls attempting to piece together the path of a rapid series of money transfers.

For financial institutions, data and analytics can speed the decision cycles used to observe, orient, decide, and act in fighting fraud. Since the best insights are often at the margins of where industries or data sets overlap, it's necessary to pose targeted questions and develop solutions from a variety of information sources. By combining proprietary data sets with industry benchmarks and government information, financial institutions can use artificial intelligence, machine learning, and analytics in the fight against financial fraud. Financial executives should move now to adopt appropriate processes, develop and acquire the necessary talent, and create the right culture to integrate analytics into their fraud-detection efforts.

## DEFINING THE ROLE OF ANALYTICS IN ADDRESSING THE CHALLENGES OF FINANCIAL FRAUD

A vast amount of data flows through financial-services organizations, so the ability to harness those data and analyze them effectively could transform the industry's fraud-detection efforts and provide a host of other benefits. Coupling these rich data sets with appropriate analytical models provides a way to harvest the information needed to identify and prevent fraud more effectively. In some cases, an institution's data can be combined with other fraud markers necessary to provide a data set for training the analytics models used to detect possible incidents of fraud.

For financial institutions and government agencies looking to fight fraud, then, the goal should be to aggregate the existing data needed to support more timely detection and to couple those data with the expertise needed to create and apply the most effective fraud-detection models. Doing so successfully can not only produce financial savings but also protect the company's reputation and maintain public confidence. A recent example demonstrates how applying analytics to fraud detection can provide immediate and significant benefits.

## A NEW MODEL DETECTS AN UNPRECEDENTED VOLUME OF INVOICE REDIRECTION

Imagine receiving an email from your CEO requesting an update to the payment details of a key supplier. Coming from a trusted source, you might carry out the task without question. But in doing so, you would become an unknowing accomplice to CEO fraud. In this crime, imposters gain access to business email accounts and use them to convince unsuspecting employees to send funds to bogus accounts. CEO fraud has jumped 270 percent from 2015 through Q3 2016 and has led to losses of more than $2.3 billion over the past few years.

Most banks have manual fraud-detection procedures or rules-based solutions, but their effectiveness is limited. The task is especially challenging for invoice redirection, where banks must spot bogus accounts that look very much like the real thing. It's truly like looking for fraud needles in the banking-transaction haystack. In such cases, banks have no way of knowing whether they are paying a legitimate account.

Assembling the data needed to train an analytics model that can accurately identify potential invoice redirection can be a potent weapon in the fight against fraud. QuantumBlack worked with a major bank looking to reduce invoice-redirection fraud—some tens of millions of dollars in value in such invoice redirections from 2010 to 2015—leveraging one of the largest data sets in its country of operation. The goal was to develop a tool that could provide daily reports of suspicious transactions and identify more than 80 percent of fraud cases in both value and incidence.

To score every one of the millions of daily transactions for fraud risk, QuantumBlack built a supervised machine learning model (Figure 8.1). But while the model needed a sufficiently large data set to learn to detect fraud, the number of potentially fraudulent transactions on any given day is so small that waiting for the natural operational work flow to generate the needed number would have taken too long. In response, the QuantumBlack team decoupled the training process from the day-to-day operation and created a partially synthetic data set to train the model.

**FIGURE 8.1**  **A Supervised Machine Learning Model Helped Monitor Transactions for Fraud.**

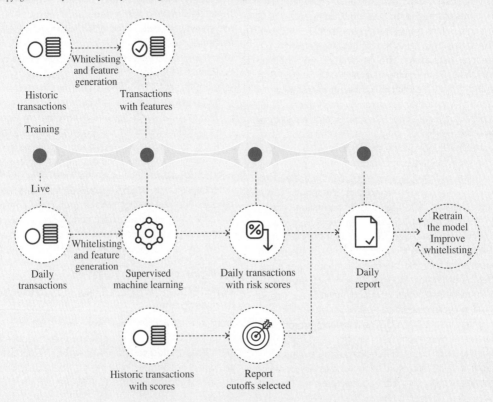

Our team worked closely with the client's data engineering team to ensure computational performance, database best practices, and legal compliance. The curated data sets successfully trained the model to determine which transactions are safe and which are potentially fraudulent.

In actual use, most daily transactions can be immediately categorized as nonfraudulent. The remaining few thousand transactions are run through the machine learning model, which provides a risk score indicating which transactions are most suspicious and which can be assumed safe. By using analytics to combine the value and risk probability of each transaction, the model can instantly rank transactions by risk score. The risk score is computed taking into consideration two different transaction patterns: one between the source and the destination account and one that covers relationships established at the destination account.

The result is that the bank now has a tool that significantly improves its capability to detect high-value fraudulent transactions (Figure 8.2). The live product notifies the bank of an average of 35 high-risk transactions a day out of the several million processed, allowing the bank's fraud team to focus on the transactions that truly demand closer investigation. The investigation results are then used to continue training the

**FIGURE 8.2** The Tool Helped a Bank Improve its Fraud-Detection Capability.

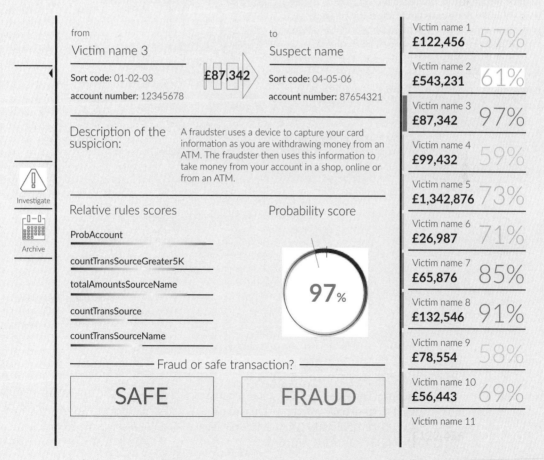

machine learning model on both new fraudulent cases as well as new relationships validated as safe.

The predictive model identifies more than 85 percent of fraud cases in value and incidents on the day the transaction is processed, allowing the bank to halt transactions before close of business and recover the funds. Within the first few weeks of live-scoring transactions, the model detected approximately $100,000 in fraudulent transactions. Other banks have expressed interest in the product, which is just the first step of applying analytics and modeling to the financial fraud-detection space.

## WORKING TOGETHER TO CRAFT PRACTICAL SOLUTIONS

These use cases reinforce the opportunities for financial institutions to wield analytics to implement real solutions to fraud. The projects often involve bringing multiple players to the table to assemble the data needed to train the models that will identify fraud; those combined efforts are handsomely rewarded through a significant reduction in fraud losses and increased public confidence in financial institutions.

To benefit from the opportunities that data analytics present to fight fraud, executives of financial institutions could implement a framework centered on four key areas:

- *Empower the organization with targeted tools and capabilities.* On top of advanced-analytics solutions, ensure that people can get results out of analytics by providing the training needed to help them understand the results and the markers of fraud. A key element will be creating a culture of vigilance and data-driven decisions. In some cases, it will be necessary to bring in new talent.
- *Redesign processes for speed and efficiency.* Determine how the organization will apply or alter its processes to improve fraud detection, possibly involving changes to the information that's reported or using new tools to obtain better information. An audit to identify data sources and measure data quality could be part of this phase.

- *Mobilize the entire enterprise through effective communications.* Craft a story around the fraud-detection effort and the new advanced-analytics capabilities, how they will be deployed, and their expected benefits. More important, make clear how each individual member of the organization has to change the way he or she operates to deploy those capabilities in day-to-day tasks. Use internal channels to share the story across the organization.
- *Activate the C-suite.* Drive change from the top down. Executives should be involved in analytics initiatives and be vocal advocates for integrating data-driven decision making into all facets of the organization.

Finally, institutions should determine whether to build their own internal data-science capability or work with an outside organization to close any gaps in analytics skills.

## USING ANALYTICS TO FIGHT FRAUD

Fraud is a significant problem for all types of financial institutions, but analytics offers the potential to identify fraud cases more quickly and frequently, sometimes even before the fraudulent act occurs. Fortunately, financial institutions already collect a tremendous amount of data that can be used to help fight fraud. The data sets don't have to be perfect to be useful, but a good first step for most organizations is to assess existing data and their quality and determine what other useful data might be collected.

To benefit from the fraud-fighting potential of data analytics, financial institutions must commit to developing the necessary skills and creating the appropriate culture. Given the potentially sizable rewards of reduced fraud losses and maintaining public trust, that commitment should be one all organizations are willing to make.

This article was first published on the QuantumBlack website.

McKinsey Analytics, McKinsey & Company, April 2017

## About the authors

Jacomo Corbo is the chief data scientist at QuantumBlack, Chris Wigley is the chief commercial officer at QuantumBlack and a partner in McKinsey's London office, and Carlo Giovine is a manager at QuantumBlack and a consultant in McKinsey's London office.

# INTRODUCTION³

It became popular to declare oneself dead in order to avoid paying taxes.

A first step in the origin of predictive analytics goes back to the City of London in the 17ᵗʰ century. In 1665 and 1666, the bubonic plague swept through England. The "Great Plague," as it was called, is said to have killed 100,000 individuals. That amounted to about a fifth of the entire population of London at the time. Probably because the plague affected so many inhabitants of London and over such a short period of time, records of deaths fell a bit behind. In fact, it became popular to declare oneself dead in order to avoid paying taxes (even though one was very much alive). The king, of course, would not be in favor of such a practice as the crown was cheated out of taxes due. To prevent this practice, the king instituted the requirement of a death certificate that would include some basic information. As part of this new bureaucratic death certificate process, the king received a report that summarized the recent mortality details. In the preparation of the report (titled the *Bills of Mortality*), patterns were discovered; this may be the first instance recorded in which data collected resulted in the recognition of patterns abstracted from data and not simply the result of using one's eyes to observe a physical pattern in nature (e.g., the stars in the night sky, leaf structure in plants, or the in and out action of sea tides). We have already touched on mortality in Chapter 3; Benjamin Gompertz studied fruit flies to create the model we know today as the Gompertz Curve. That same pattern was exhibited in the London plague data. Recall the pattern of exponential death that showed up as an S-curve in the Gompertz model for new product forecasting. The pattern Gompertz wrote about is a special case of the generalized logistic function we use in present-day data mining.

So, the *Bills of Mortality* may be the first recorded instance of what we now refer to as data mining or predictive analytics. The scribes in London who collected the information were not looking for patterns (other than tax evaders), but unexpected patterns became evident in the numbers as they were collected (think of the process as an early version of streaming data). Data mining today is quite different from what most of us know as standard statistical techniques (sometimes called "frequentist" statistics). In most forecasting situations up to this point in the text, a particular model has been imposed on the data to produce the forecasts; that particular model has been chosen by the forecaster. In most business situations, we assume that our data will, or could, exhibit the patterns we have found to be common in most business data: trend, seasonality, and cyclicality. We have then chosen a model that we believe will represent the data well, say a Holt-Winter's smoothing model; we may believe this model is appropriate because we had visually observed all previous data to include these patterns. In a word, we selected the model and that model was capable of only recognizing certain types of patterns. If we thought "events" were an important pattern in our data, we likely chose an event model with an appropriate underlying model meant to capture the remainder of the pattern. For most of the history of forecasting, including the use of both time series models and demand planning models, this has been

³ The author would like to thank Professor Eamonn Keogh of the Department of Computer Science & Engineering at the University of California, Riverside; Keogh has provided web readers with excellent examples and explanations of data mining tools and issues.

accepted practice. More recently, our access to large volumes of data and our access to many different types of data, along with some new algorithms, have changed the way data scientists approach prediction. While it is true that prediction is still the goal of data and text mining, the data itself and the tools used to manipulate it have changed in the last decade. The fact that the field of "analytics" is often referred to as "predictive analytics" is a good indicator that the goal of our efforts has not changed: analytics is, like forecasting proper, in the business of making accurate predictions.

If we fast-forward 200 years from the Great Plague, we could observe another early precursor to modern data mining. Florence Nightingale is thought of as the first modern nurse; she was a trailblazing nurse during the Crimean War in the mid-1850s. But Florence Nightingale was also a statistician and quite a skilled one. She was the first woman to be elected as a Fellow to the prestigious Royal Statistical Society in London (called the Statistical Society of London at the time).[4]

During the war, in addition to caring for wounded and infirm soldiers, Nightingale kept meticulous records and displayed them graphically to discern the patterns she thought so evident. She advocated for the uniform collection of medical statistics. Her "Nightingale Rose" (Figure 8.3) diagram, which depicted the collected Crimean War statistics, clearly showed that most soldiers did not die from wounds incurred in battle but rather from preventable diseases mitigated by conditions that could have been alleviated. While she is truly the mother of modern nursing, Nightingale is also one of the first data miners to extract useful information from abstract data. The roots of data mining go far back to the Great Plague and the Crimean War.

The data mining approach is today an altogether different way of viewing the world and the data in it compared to the methods we have employed in previous chapters. IBM is fond of using the term *Big Data* to represent this altogether distinct view of the data we are working with and the techniques used to produce knowledge from that data. But the term *Big Data* does not belong to just IBM; it is also a term commonly used in describe data mining in general.

## BIG DATA

Distilling actionable knowledge from the mass of data is a bit like trying to drink from a firehose.

The sheer volume of the data sets we work with in predictive analytics are often, but not always, much larger than what we have used with time series models and demand planning models in previous chapters. While the size of many of the demonstration data sets we will use in the next few chapters are not appreciably larger than we have used in previous chapters, the algorithms we employ are often designed specifically to work with large data sets with reasonable calculation times. The reason for the emphasis on volume in predictive analytics is clear; while we used to have little data to work with and some firms were lax about saving everything that could be considered data, today firms have so

[4] Helen Joyce, "Florence Nightingale: A Lady with More Than a Lamp," *Significance*, December 2008, pp. 181—182.

**FIGURE 8.3**   Nightingale Rose (*www.hugh-small.co.uk*).

Source: Nightingale, Florence, *Notes on Matters Affecting the Health, Efficiency, and Hospital Administration of the British Army. Founded Chiefly on the Experience of the Late War. Presented by Request to the Secretary of State for War*, London: John W. Parker, 1853.

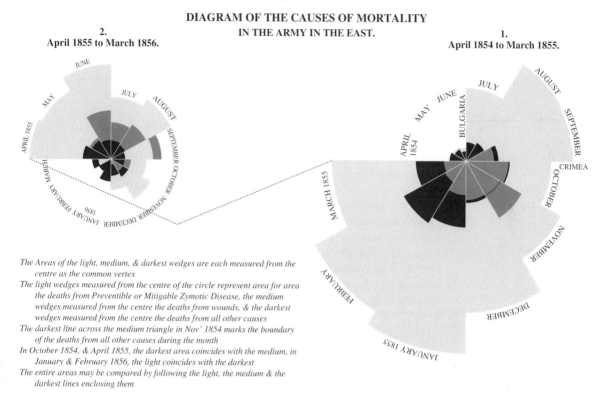

DIAGRAM OF THE CAUSES OF MORTALITY
IN THE ARMY IN THE EAST.

2.
April 1855 to March 1856.

1.
April 1854 to March 1855.

*The Areas of the light, medium, & darkest wedges are each measured from the centre as the common vertex*
*The light wedges measured from the centre of the circle represent area for area the deaths from Preventible or Mitigable Zymotic Disease, the medium wedges measured from the centre the deaths from wounds, & the darkest wedges measured from the centre the deaths from all other causes*
*The darkest line across the medium triangle in Nov' 1854 marks the boundary of the deaths from all other causes during the month*
*In October 1854, & April 1855, the darkest area coincides with the medium, in January & February 1856, the light coincides with the darkest*
*The entire areas may be compared by following the light, the medium & the darkest lines enclosing them*

much data that distilling actionable knowledge from the mass of data is a bit like trying to drink from a firehose. The data scientist's job is to isolate the important patterns in this mass of data so that a firm can take actions to their benefit.

## Analytics

The term *analytics* is used in a number of different ways; your authors use it to encompass all three areas of prediction: time series analysis, demand planning, and data/text mining. However, the term *analytics* is sometimes used to refer simply to the latest forms of prediction: data mining and text mining and their many variants. Data mining refers to the tools and techniques that are used in the large scale, or big data, arena. In the physical world, we have used tools such as the telescope or the microscope to see the characteristics of objects we were unable to examine with the naked eye. More recently, the radio telescope (a nonoptical instrument that is the combination of an antenna system and a radio receiver) and the electron microscope (which uses a beam of accelerated electrons for illumination) have allowed us to examine physical data in dimensions we could only previously hypothesize about. In much the same way, data mining tools allow us to examine big data in order to make sense of what was previously unable to be seen; we can even discover patterns that were previously unknowable. Hal Varian, a Google data scientist, has termed this new area of statistics "the sexy profession."[5] What Varian has seen in the past decade is a fruitful relationship between statisticians and computer scientists working in machine learning. Together, those two groups are finding new ways to add value to data; when actionable information can be distilled from data, businesses and their customers stand to benefit. According to Varian, data mining applied to huge amounts of largely Internet-acquired data sets presents a whole set of new powers to the data scientist.

With data mining, the models we have used in previous chapters are turned a bit on their head. In data mining, we don't know what pattern or family of patterns may fit a particular set of data. It is not as simple as suggesting that specific patterns are expected to exist in the data, such as trend, seasonality, and cyclicality. We don't even know sometimes what it is we are attempting to predict or explain. This seems strange to a traditional forecaster; it's not the method of attacking the data we have been pursuing throughout our examination of time series forecasting and demand planning. To begin data mining and using big data, we require a new mindset. We need to be open to finding relationships and patterns we never imagined existed in the data we are about to examine. To use data mining is to let the data tell us the story (rather than to impose a model on the data that we feel will replicate the actual patterns in the data).

## Big Data and Its Characteristics

Data mining traditionally uses very large data sets, oftentimes far larger than the data sets we are used to using in most business forecasting situations. But big data is not simply defined by the size of the data set. Think of big data as having four characteristics. Each of the characteristics begins with the letter V.

Volume

Velocity

Variety

Value

"Volume" of course refers to the size of the data set. And while some of the data sets used in analytics are quite large, not all of them need be so large in order to produce good usable results. What has changed in the last decade or so has been the "datafication"[6] of almost everything. Text has been turned into data, and we will examine how that takes place and how to analyze textual data in a later chapter. But voice (i.e., speech) has also been turned into data; "speech to text" tools are on

---

[5] "Hal Varian and the Sexy Profession," *Significance,* March 2011, pp. 32–34.

[6] "Datafication" is a term that has not yet made it into any dictionary we are aware of, but we first saw it used in Victor Mayer-Schonberger and Kenneth Cukier, *Big Data: A Revolution That Will Transform How We Live, Work and Think.* New York: Houghton Mifflin Harcourt, 2013, p. 77.

almost every computer, tablet, and phone. And once that speech is text, it is subject to datafication. You are probably familiar with the device called the Amazon Echo; it is a digital assistant that allows you to give it voice commands and it responds with information gleaned from the Internet. You "wake up" the Echo by calling on Alexa, the disjointed voice that answers your questions, provides directions, and responds to a very wide set of commands. Notice the announcement Amazon carries on its website that explains how to set up your Echo device (Figure 8.4):

**FIGURE 8.4**    **Amazon's Disclosure of Alexa Properties  http://alexa.amazon.com/spa/index.html#welcome**

Source: "Alexa Terms of Use," Amazon. June 23, 2017.

Amazon's Disclosure of Alexa Properties

Amazon processes and retains audio and other information in the cloud to provide and improve our services, and may exchange information with third party serivces to fulfill your requests. Learn more. Alexa also allows purchasing by voice using your default payment and shipping settings. You can require a speakable confirmation code, turn purchasing off, and see product and order details in your Alexa app. Learn more.

Alexa responds to her name; when it is voiced, Alexa begins processing the next question or comment and gives a response. That means that the Echo's microphone must be on all the time; it's always listening for the "Alexa" wake-up word. Notice that Amazon in their statement says they retain audio in the cloud. Does that mean that everything you say, whether preceded by the codeword "Alexa" or not, is recorded by Amazon? The answer is probably yes, and even more importantly, that information is shared with other firms (i.e., the "third party services" mentioned). In return for Amazon's datafication of everything you utter, you do get some value. Your questions are answered; you can check the latest baseball scores; unfamiliar words can be defined; music can be chosen and played; the latest news can be read to you from a chosen source (you can choose the "spin" you like).

How long does Amazon keep this data? What form do they keep the data in? How do they share it with "third party services?" We don't know the answer to those questions, but we can certainly see that if they collect and store this data for every Alexa user, it amounts to a large volume of data. But Amazon is not alone in collecting "datafied" information. "Google Now," "Siri," and "Cortana" all act as digital assistants, and presumably they all collect data and likely share that data like the Echo. That is a lot of data!

That brings us to our second big data characteristic; the velocity or the rate at which the data arrives is also big in one sense. Each of those digital assistants operates in real time; we expect the assistant to be instantly available and to perform its task quickly. If more than a few seconds' elapses before we get our information, we are disappointed. Some of the algorithms we use in analytics will have to operate very quickly indeed if we are to provide usable results in real time. When you swipe a credit card or use Apple Pay or Android Pay, a data mining algorithm is used to check whether the transaction initiated is legitimate; that algorithm must work quickly unless you expect to wait for more than the few seconds it usually takes to spit out your receipt indicating a completed (and likely legitimate) transaction. We did not mention the speed of any of the forecasting algorithms because it is rarely an issue, but the speed of a data mining algorithm may be relevant, especially with streaming data.

Unstructured data does not have a predefined data model.

The third characteristic of big data is variety. In the preceding chapters, we have dealt with numbers arranged in a database-like format, usually an Excel spreadsheet. But the data available now is more than just numbers. Social media posts, video, and audio are all data; they are unstructured data. Our databases and Excel spreadsheets were uniformly structured; the items were numbers, and they were arranged in a particular pattern within the database. Unstructured data does not have a predefined data model, nor is it organized in a particular manner. Social media posts are a good example of unstructured data. The posts are not exclusively numbers but also contain text. The posts are not arranged in a rigid format; posters may say anything they want in any order, often mixing words and phrases with numbers and punctuation. But the social media posts are data; they can be analyzed. In the chapter on text mining, we will learn exactly how that is done. For now, it is enough to know that data may vary in the characteristic of variety.

Finally, the fourth characteristic of what we call big data is value. Not everything that qualifies as data is of value to a given firm. But a great deal of what may not have been considered data in the past is of value to the firm today. It is the task of a data scientist to sort out the value that might be gleaned from what appears to be otherwise uninteresting "stuff." Consider the case of Luis von Ahn. You may have seen van Ahn on a *Nova* special on public television or read about him in *Wired* magazine. Shortly after graduating from college, he created something you have seen and used many times; he is the inventor of the CAPTCHA box (Figure 8.5). CAPTCHA stands for Completely Automated Public Turing Test to Tell Computers and Humans Apart. It is the little box that pops up sometimes when first entering a website and ostensibly is meant to ensure that the entrant is really a human and not a spambot or computer. This was just the first invention von Ahn became famous for creating. Have you ever used the free program called Duolingo on the Internet? It's a language learning device that doubles as a proficiency exam for various languages (more than 20 languages at last count). Millions of people have learned or brushed up on a foreign language with Duolingo. Von Ahn is quite clever in some of his creations; he is able to create value in a seemingly innocuous manner.

In a Ted Talk Luis von Ahn discusses the CAPTCHA boxes and the reCAPTCHA boxes as well as Duolingo. You might want to watch this Ted Talk at: https://www.ted

**FIGURE 8.5**
**An Example of
One of van Ahn's
ReCAPTCHA Boxes.**

Source: Google

.com/talks/luis_von_ahn_massive_scale_online_collaboration#t-314305. You would also find exploring https://www.duolingo.com interesting as an example of a useful application of these concepts. It may even help you in a foreign language class.

## "Datafication"

Take the case of the CAPTCHA box. The successor to the original version is marketed by von Ahn's successor as ReCAPTCHA. In the newer ReCAPTCHA, the user upon attempting to enter a website is faced with a box containing two random words that are taken from a computer-scanned document. The user is requested to type those words in the provided box. Doing so correctly allows the user to pass through to the website. The entire process takes only moments of your time. But how does von Ahn gain or create value from providing this free service to websites that wish to exclude spambots? Google explains the value creation this way:

> "reCAPTCHA improves our knowledge of the physical world by creating CAPT-CHAs out of text visible on Street View imagery. As people verify the text in these CAPTCHAs, this information is used to make Google Maps more precise and complete. So if you're a Google Maps user, your experience (and everyone else's) will be even better."[7]

By taking a few moments of your time, von Ahn is provided with the value of your expertise to help refine a character recognition algorithm. That algorithm will help to "datify" documents and decipher unclear words in digitized text, no matter where it exists. If you have ever filled in a ReCAPTCHA box, pat yourself on the back for helping with the effort to make clear what was previously unclear!

A great deal of what we have previously considered as "stuff" with little or no value to the firm has become data with some inherent value. Comments and reviews were once considered interesting and viewed one at a time provided some, but very little, value to a firm. Ingested by the hundreds of thousands, they become valuable data from which insights may be derived. Companies that excel in "datafication" such as Amazon and Google benefit in very tangible ways when they can predict more ably than their competitors. It could be reasonably argued that all data will become valuable at some point. Data storage costs have plummeted. and our ability to draw predictions from data increase with every new data mining algorithm. The data we have now may not be valuable, but if we keep it long enough, there are likely some valuable insights to be mined from it. Data has the curious characteristic that when it is used and creates value, the process does not diminish the value that is left. The same data may be used over and over:

Data has the property of "nonrivalry" so that one person's use of the good to create value does not diminish the value another can extract from the data. economists say a good such as data has the property of "nonrivalry" so that one person's use of the good to create value does not diminish the value another can extract from the data. Most material goods do not have that characteristic, and so it is worth noting that data is different. The first use of a particular set of data by a data scientist may be quite different from the purpose another researcher may employ, and yet both may find the data to add value to the firm. Data's full value is rarely extracted with its first use.

---

[7] "Creation of Value," Google. https://www.google.com/recaptcha/intro/#creation-of-value

Not only is the data itself somewhat different in analytics, the tools or algorithms we use are also somewhat different than standard business forecasting tools of time series and demand planning; some of the data mining tools will seem familiar, but they may be used in different ways than we have used them in previous chapters. The premise of data mining is that there is a great deal of information locked up in any database; it's up to us to use appropriate tools to unlock the information hidden within.

Business forecasting is explicit in the sense that we used specific models to estimate and forecast known patterns (e.g., seasonality, trend, cyclicality, the effects of advertising, etc.). Data mining, on the other hand, involves the extraction of implicit (often unknown) intelligence or valuable information from data. We need to be able to process very large quantities of data to find patterns and regularities that we did not know existed beforehand. Some of what we find will be quite useless and uninteresting (at the moment), perhaps only coincidences. But, from time to time, we will be able to find true gems in the mounds of data; the objective of this chapter is to introduce a variety of data mining methods for you to consider. Some of these methods are simple and meant only to introduce you to how the basic concept of data mining works. We will leave the more commercially used tools for the following chapters.

If you wish to work with your own data (or that provided with this text), we recommend the Analytic Solver© Data Mining software.[8] Everyone capable of using an Excel spreadsheet will find Analytic Solver© Data Mining an excellent introduction into actually using most of the algorithms used by data miners. Just as with time series models and demand planning models, the best method for mastering predictive analytics is to work through the examples and algorithms yourself with the aid of proficient software tools such as Analytic Solver©.

## DATA MINING

Not long ago one of the most pressing problems for a forecaster was the lack of data collected intelligently by businesses; forecasters were limited to few pieces of data and only limited observations on the data that existed. Computing power was also limited, but the real shortage was a lack of data. Today, however, we are overwhelmed with data. It is collected at grocery store checkout counters, while inventory moves through a warehouse, when users click a button on the World Wide Web, and every time a credit card is swiped. The rate of data collection is not abating; it seems to be increasing with no clear end in sight. The presence of

---

[8] Analytic Solver© Data Mining is an Excel add-in that is part of an integrated analytics solver from FrontlineSolvers (http://www.solver.com/). Both student and full versions of the software are available from FrontlineSolvers. It provides an excellent way to learn about data mining by applying the algorithms to medium-sized data sets within an Excel setting. A version of the tool is available for instructors who adopt this text to make available to their students. Instructors should contact FrontlineSolvers (http://www.solver.com/) for more information. The Analytic Solver© Data Mining software is provided with a complete manual (see the "help" menu) titled "Analytic Solver Data Mining User Guide." This user manual contains complete step-by-step examples of the procedures presented in this text.

large cheap storage devices means that it is easy to simply keep every piece of data produced. It may even be prudent to keep every piece of data produced; while not valuable for insights now, that could change in the future. The pressing problem now is not the generation of the data, but the attempt to understand it.

The job of a data scientist is to make sense of the mounds of data we now have available by probing the data for patterns. The single most important reason for the current fascination with data mining is due to the large volumes of data currently obtainable for analysis; there is a need for business professionals to convert data into useful information by "mining" it for the presence of patterns. You should not be at all startled by the emphasis on patterns; this entire text has been about patterns of one sort or another. Indeed, humans have looked for patterns in almost every endeavor undertaken by humankind. Early humans looked for patterns in the night sky, for patterns in the movement of the stars and planets, and to predict the best times of the year to plant crops. Modern humans still search for patterns in early election returns, in global temperature changes, and in sales data for new products. Over the last few decades, there has been an evolution from data processing to what we call data mining today. In the 1960s, businesses customarily collected data and processed it using database management techniques that allowed indexing, organization, and some query activity. Online transaction processing (OLTP) became routine, and the rapid retrieval of stored data was made easier by more efficient storage devices and quicker and more capable computing.

## Database Management

Man has looked for patterns in almost every endeavor undertaken by mankind.

Database management advanced rapidly to include very sophisticated query systems (SQL or Structured Query Language is one commonly used example); it became routine not only in business situations but also in scientific inquiry. Databases began to grow at previously unheard of rates and for even routine activities. The volume of data in all the world's databases has been estimated recently to double in less than every two years.[9] That torrent of data would seem to call for analysis in order to make sense of the patterns locked within. Firms now routinely have what are called data warehouses and data marts. "*Data warehouse*" is the term used to describe a firm's central repository of integrated historical data; it is the "memory" of the firm, collective information on every relevant aspect of what has happened in the past. A "*data mart*," on the other hand, is a subset of a data warehouse; it routinely holds information that is specialized and has been grouped or chosen specifically to help companies make better decision on future actions.

## Data Mining Versus Database Management

*Data mining* as a term for many years had an altogether different connotation than it enjoys today; instead of being an analysis that finds useful patterns in data, it carried the meaning that the researcher was imposing a model on data, whether

---

[9] "Extracting Value from Chaos," study sponsored by EMC (June 2011). The multimedia content may be viewed at https://www.emc.com/collateral/analyst-reports/idc-extracting-value-from-chaos-ar.pdf.

Data mining is the extraction of useful information from large, often unstructured databases.

it fit or not. It was a notably derogatory term. When someone was called a "data miner," it was meant to be an insulting term applied to a person who tortured data until it "told" the preconceived story the researcher wanted to tell. The term *data mining* today denotes the analysis of databases, data warehouses, and data marts that already exist for the purpose of discovering new patterns or to answer some pressing question. Data mining is the extraction of useful information from large, often unstructured databases; it is about extracting knowledge or information from large amounts of data.[10] Data mining has come to be referenced by a few similar terms; in most cases, they all refer to much the same set of techniques that we will refer to as data mining in this chapter:

- Machine (or supervised) learning
- Business intelligence/analytics/analysis
- Data-driven discovery
- Knowledge discovery in databases (KDD)

Data mining is, however, quite separate from database management. Keogh points out that in database management, queries are well defined; we even have a language to write these queries (Structured Query Language or SQL, pronounced as "sequel"). A query in database management might take the form of "find all the customers in South Bend" or "find all the customers that have missed a recent payment."

Data mining, however, uses very different queries; they tend to be less structured and are sometimes quite vague. For example: "Find all the customers that are likely to purchase recreational vehicle insurance in the next six months" or "group all the customers with similar buying habits." In one sense, data mining is like statistical forecasting in that we are forward-looking in an attempt to obtain information about future likely events and drive better decision-making.

Many companies are data rich, but some of those same companies are information poor; data mining is the set of algorithms and techniques that can aid firms in making sense of the mountains of data they likely already have available. These available databases may be about customer profiles and the choices those customers have made in the past. There are possible patterns of behavior displayed in the data, but the sheer amount of the data will mask the underlying patterns and even an expert researcher, testing for patterns she believes will be exhibited in the data, will miss a great deal of the information locked within. Some of those underlying patterns may be interesting but unusable to a firm for informing future decisions, but some patterns may be predictive in ways that are very worthwhile to firms. If, for example, you "know" which of your customers are likely to switch their supplier in the near future, you may be able to prevent the customers from jumping ship and going with your competitor; it's always less costly to keep existing customers than to enlist new ones.[11] The evidence shows

[10] D. Hand, H. Mannila, and P. Smyth, *Principles of Data Mining*. Cambridge, MA: MIT Press, 2001.

[11] Amy Gallo, "The Value of Keeping the Right Customers," *Harvard Business Review*, October 29, 2014 (https://hbr.org/2014/10/the-value-of-keeping-the-right-customers).

that it is from five to 25 times more expensive to obtain a new customer. If you were to "know" which customers were likely to default on their loans in the near future you might be able to take pre-emptive measures to forestall the defaults or you might be less likely to try and enlist such individuals in the future. If you "know" (i.e., are able to predict) the characteristics of potential customers that are quite likely to continually purchase your product or service, you would be better able to direct your advertising and promotional efforts than if you were to blanket the market with advertising and promotions; a well-targeted approach is usually better than an unknowing "shotgun" approach. Data mining can help to define the appropriate target.

### Patterns in Data Mining

What types of patterns can be mined? The answer is quite different from the patterns we expected to find in data with time series forecasting methods such as the Holt Winters' smoothing model. When a forecaster applies a Holt Winters' smoothing model to time series data, the expectation is that the data contain some level variation, some trend, and some seasonal variability. Experience with business data has taught us to expect those pattern types in virtually all business time series data.

Data mining, however, does not prespecify the patterns to be expected. In a sense, there is no preconception of what will be found in the data with most data mining techniques. We are simultaneously searching for several different kinds of patterns in parallel. At the same time, we are measuring the certainty or trustworthiness associated with the patterns we discover in somewhat the same vein as we do in standard business forecasting.

## THE TOOLS OF ANALYTICS

Shmueli, Patel, and Bruce use a taxonomy of analytics tools that is useful for seeing the big picture. There are basically four categories of analytics tools or techniques; they represent the four very general types of patterns we would like to search across:

1) Prediction;
2) Classification;
3) Clustering (sometimes called segmentation); and
4) Association.

Prediction tools are most like the methods we have covered in previous chapters that dealt with time series models and demand planning; these tools most often attempt to predict the value of a numeric variable (e.g., sales or shipments). We might, for example, be attempting to predict the value of a piece of residential property or the amount that an individual might contribute yearly to a particular charity. The variable we are attempting to predict in these instances could be a continuous variable. But the variable to be predicted could also be a categorical variable. For example, we might wish to predict whether an individual will contribute to a particular cause rather than how much they might contribute or whether an individual will make a certain purchase this year rather than how much they likely will spend on the purchase. Prediction then involves two types of variables: continuous and categorical.

**Classification** tools are the most commonly used methods in data mining. Classification tools distinguish between data classes or concepts; the purpose is to create a model that allows us to predict a class of objects whose label is unknown to us. For instance, when you present your credit card for a purchase in a retail store, the business must determine whether the impending transaction is a legitimate one (i.e., you are who you say you are, you have requisite purchasing power, etc.). Businesses do not find it profitable to hand over merchandise to everyone who presents a piece of plastic at the checkout counter. For this reason, there is a short delay between when your card is swiped and when the receipt begins to print. In those few seconds, a data mining algorithm's rules have been applied to your situation and a determination has been made; either the transaction is in the classification of "legitimate," or it is in the classification of "illegitimate."

Another example of classification involves banking. When you apply for a bank loan, your credit score is calculated based upon some personal characteristics, financial characteristics, and personal characteristics such as age and family status. That calculated credit score alerts the bank to the risk associated with making a loan to you; the bank is attempting to classify you as a creditworthy customer or an individual they would prefer sought a loan elsewhere.

Sometimes the classifications we are trying to make do not involve numbers at all; the U.S. Post Office must read the destination you place on a letter (including the street name, city, and the zip code). If you have handwritten the information on the envelope, it could be read by a human, but the Postal Service has automated the process by allowing a data mining algorithm to take the scan of the address and recognize (i.e., classify) the alphabetic characters and numbers, even though a human has handwritten them. Even if the algorithm has never seen your particular handwriting, it is able to recognize the characters; you receive mail every day that has been subjected to such a process.

**Clustering** (segmentation) analysis tools analyze data objects without consulting a known class label. The classes of the objects are not input by the user, it is the function of the clustering technique to define and attach the class labels. The clustering technique generates the labels. Clustering techniques group objects based upon maximizing the intraclass similarity and/or minimizing the interclass similarity. Whether the clusters unearthed by the techniques are useful to the business manager is subjective; some clusters will be interesting but not useful in a business setting, while others will be quite informative and will also be able to be exploited to advantage. Universities use cluster analysis to identify students with special needs; using the characteristics of a given student's background, the university is able to cluster the student with others who require some specialized attention or above-average support in order to be successful.

**Association** rules discovery is sometimes called "affinity analysis." It is the discovery of rule attribute characteristics that often occur together in a given data set. If you have been handed coupons at a grocery store checkout counter, your purchasing patterns have probably been subjected to association rules discovery; Netflix will recommend movies you might like based upon movies you have watched and rated in the past. In each instance, an association rules discovery has taken place. Amazon will offer items that you have not selected but that they believe you may wish to purchase as a result of their affinity analysis.

# STATISTICAL FORECASTING AND DATA MINING

Data mining allow the data itself to reveal the patterns within, rather than imposing the patterns on the data at the outset.

In time series forecasting and demand planning, we sought verification of previously held hypotheses; that is, we "knew" which patterns existed in the time series data we tried to forecast and we applied appropriate statistical models (e.g., Holt Winter's or regression) to accurately estimate those patterns. When an electric power company looks at their load demand, they expect that past patterns, such as trend, seasonality, and cyclicality, will replicate themselves in the future. Thus, the electric utility might reasonably use a regression with independent variables such as the previous day's temperature, the hour of the day, the day of the week, and the month of the year as a model to forecast future electric usage. Data mining, however, seeks the discovery of new knowledge from the data; it does not seek to merely verify the previously chosen hypotheses regarding the types of patterns in the data but seeks to discover new facts or rules from the data itself. Data mining allow the data itself to reveal the patterns within, rather than imposing the patterns on the data at the outset.

# TERMINOLOGY IN DATA MINING: SPEAK LIKE A DATA MINER

The terminology used in data mining is a bit different than that used in statistical forecasting models; while the terms are different, their meanings are quite similar.

| Data Mining Terminology | Statistical Terminology |
| --- | --- |
| Output variable = Target variable | Dependent variable |
| Algorithm | Forecasting Model |
| Attribute = Feature | Explanatory variable |
| Record | Observation |
| Score | Forecast |

Courtesy of Eamonn Keogh.

The subject of our interest in time series forecasting models and demand planning models was termed the dependent variable or the Y-variable. It referred to the value we were forecasting. In a data mining world, the corresponding term would be the "target." In some data mining algorithms, we specify the target variable, but in a few algorithms, there is no analog of the dependent variable and thus no target. Those variables that contributed toward forecasting the dependent variable were called explanatory variables in our previous models. Their analog in data mining would be "attributes." In forecasting proper, we spoke of using models (e.g., Holt Winters' model) but in data mining, the proper term is *algorithm*. Our data sets in forecasting were made up of numbers of observations, but in data mining, we refer to "records." Finally, our goal in using forecasting models was to make forecasts. In data mining, that process is called "scoring."

# CORRELATION

One term that means the same whether speaking either about data mining, time series forecasting, or demand planning is *correlation*. As explained in Chapter 2, correlation is the degree of association between two variables or two data sets, whether causal or not. The Pearson product-moment correlation coefficient usually designated by $\rho$ (rho) for a population and $r$ for a sample, measures not only the direction of association but also its magnitude.

Data mining thrives in an environment that is not data starved, but rather data rich.

With forecasting data, we worked hard to reduce error rates in our models and spent a great deal of effort in sampling, testing samples for bias, and ensuring that our data represented the true population we were ultimately representing. With the move toward using big data, we are going to worry much less about whether our data in the remainder of the text represents the true population; in some cases, it is the population (or close to it). Data mining thrives on an environment that is not data starved but rather data rich. The quantity of data is now so vastly abundant compared to just a few decades ago that the tools we use to gain information from it must recognize the change in the situation. Individual data points are such a small part of the big picture that we will spend much less time worrying about whether they will bias the final result. In some cases, even incorrect values and outright mistakes in individual observations may be relatively unimportant in determining the final results. Much like the "wisdom of crowds"[12] eliminates errors because of compensating mistakes, big data provides a vast mesh of data in which a few mistakes will not affect the outcomes predicted by the preponderance of the data.

There is nothing inherently messy or mistake prone in big data; it's just that the data scientist may be a bit less troubled by mistakes or messiness because of the

---

[12] James Surowiecki, *The Wisdom of Crowds: Why the Many Are Smarter Than the Few and How Collective Wisdom Shapes Business, Economies, Societies and Nations.* New York: Knopf Doubleday Publishing Group, 2004.

sheer volume of the data. Logic would say that spending great effort and expense to correct mistakes in the big data may make little economic sense unless the results would appreciably change. The mantra of the data scientist may be "more data is better than less." With more data and lots more than we have used in any analysis up to this point, we can put aside the interest in larger and more random samples and live with some mistakes and missing observations. Conventional forecasting based on frequentist statistics is increasingly at odds with reality. The age of big data has arrived and along with it data of varying types (numbers, text, video, audio, etc.) and varying quality. Not only will this big data not fit into neatly defined categories, but the answers we seek may not even be visible before we begin the analysis. The data we analyzed and predicted in previous chapters was often created with SQL; it was by definition "structured" to begin with and rigid. Our shift in this and the remaining chapters is to accept data of varying types, sizes, and messiness. The plummeting costs of data storage and processing power are pushing the industry toward computationally intensive predictions.

## Early Uses of Analytics

Everyone reading this has experienced suggestions from a website, in their morning email or from an in-store reminder app like those used by McDonald's, Burger King, and Walgreens. Sometimes these suggestions seem to be reading your mind, and at other times they just feel intrusive. They don't have to be on target all the time; they just have to be predictive some of the time (and they are). One of the early developers of the "recommendation engine," for want of a better term, is Greg Linden. He's written a blog about the early (1997) days he spent at Amazon.[13] In a rundown brick structure near Pike's Place Market in Seattle, he started working for the small Internet book seller (i.e., Amazon); in 1997, the concept of online book sales, or sales of anything online, was quite novel. Nobody knew if this would work. Did people really want to purchase anything online?

Linden started as a coder assigned to projects that placed him in contact with the early data collected by the small online company; he worked first on discounts. We would probably call it dynamic pricing these days. At some point, Linden began the early work on recommendations with BookMatcher, but he soon created an altogether different recommendation engine that operated in real time and was scalable. Based on what people bought, the engine started making recommendations of other things they might like to buy. What was originally done by humans at Amazon actually worked in real time; unfortunately, most of those humans lost their jobs when it became clear that the data driven recommendation engine could do a better job (and probably at lower cost). "According to Sucharita Mulpuru, a Forrester analyst, Amazon's conversion to sales of on-site recommendations could be as high as 60 percent in some cases based on the performance of other e-commerce sites."[14] So, if you are expecting fewer recommendations in

[13] http://glinden.blogspot.com/2006/05/early-amazon-end.html.

[14] Mangalindan, J. P. "Amazon's Recommendation Secret," *Fortune*, July 30, 2012 (http://fortune.com/2012/07/30/amazons-recommendation-secret/).

the future, you are probably out of luck; the recommendation systems work and increase the profits of the companies that use them. Some of us actually appreciate the service from time to time.

Correlation becomes a sledgehammer in the hands of a data scientist who has access to big data.

But how does any recommendation engine work? At the core of these algorithms is the concept of correlation, the same correlation we covered in Chapter 2. Correlation is certainly a useful tool when working with samples of data, but correlation becomes a sledgehammer in the hands of a data scientist who has access to big data. According to Linden, these engines are often based on a clustering algorithm that, in part, has its basis in correlation. Correlation is not causation. How can it be used for making suggestions?

The "mechanism of action" that would tell us exactly why someone might purchase something would be very valuable to know and allow us to build recommendations. But in the real world, we do not need to know the mechanism of action; we only need to know when two things are related. With big data and correlation, there is no certainty, just probability. As our calculated probabilities become better than guesses, our recommendations become more and more useful. With large amounts of data and correlation, we can find links that are useful; Amazon does it every day to great advantage. In 2004, Hurricane Frances was headed toward the Florida coast and Walmart was tracking the storm. A week before the hurricane hit, Walmart's CIO requested information on what had happened at Walmart stores when other hurricanes had occurred. She was looking for correlations. What correlated with a hurricane? The shopping history from Walmart stores indicated that Pop-Tart sales spiked up to seven times the normal rate when a hurricane was imminent. Walmart started predicting what to do based on correlations. The decisions they made to change inventories certainly benefited Walmart, but they also provided a welcome service to individuals in the affected area.[15] With 3,600 Walmart locations and over 100 million customers per week in those stores in 2004, Walmart had plenty of data with which to make correlation calculations.

Walmart probably didn't have a hypothesis that described why they were seeing spikes in Pop-Tart sales; they just needed the correlation to create a clear case for corporate action. When we examined regression models, we were building causal models; we assumed that changes in our independent variables were causing the changes we observed in the dependent variable. We had good reason to believe that these causal models were accurate; economists, for example, call the causal relationship between price and sales "the law of demand." The models we will describe in the coming chapters, however, do not imply causality and often do not rely on any hypothesis such as

---

[15] Constance L, Hays, "What Wal-Mart Knows About Customers' Habits," *The New York Times*, November 14, 2004 (http://www.nytimes.com/2004/11/14/business/yourmoney/what-walmart-knows-about-customers-habits.html?_r=0).

the law of demand. We have been very concerned with exactly what variables to include as independent variables in a regression; the AIC and BIC were described as tools that would help in the selection of appropriate independent variables. But with big data available, it may not be necessary to spend as much time on selecting which variables to examine. It is correlation that is going to be the basis of our predictions.

# THE "STEPS" IN A DATA MINING PROCESS

One of the important commercial analytics software companies, SAS, has an approach they teach users that are embedded in their software as a series of steps. The tabs in SAS Enterprise Miner are labeled *SEMMA*, which is an acronym for *Sample*, *Explore*, *Modify*, *Model*, and *Assess*.[16]

The *explore* activity involves all those activities we referred to as data cleansing in earlier chapters. Missing data must be handled intelligently. The collected data may contain mistakes such as values outside reasonable ranges. People represented in the data may be referenced in a number of ways; Joseph Smith might also be listed as Joe Smith and J. Smith. Are they the same person? We don't wish to count them three times as separate individuals if we can correctly combine the records and attribute all the characteristics to a single individual. Measurements in the data are important; some of the techniques are topographical, and consistency may be important. Time periods, if used, should be understood. The explore activity may involve examining the data graphically, creating summary statistics of the attributes, or running an "audit" of the values in the data. In some cases, the data may need modification, but that will first require a clear understanding of the data as it is.

*Modify* may involve creating, selecting, or transforming data. Part of the modification may be eliminating rare variables, eliminating records with missing variables, replacing missing values, or modifying the data set attributes in some manner.

The *model* phase of this methodology is what most probably think data mining is all about. In the model phase, your goal will be to determine the data mining task required (classification, prediction, clustering, etc.), select an appropriate algorithm, and set whatever parameters are necessary to execute the process. Understanding exactly what the algorithm does is an important part of making the correct selection; the following chapters will detail the processes used by the most important data mining (and text mining) algorithms. It is in the model phase that we fit the predictive analytics algorithm by training the model with a portion of the data.

The final step is to *assess* the results obtained. It may involve making a choice among a number of different algorithms chosen as candidates for the analysis.

---

[16] SAS Institute. *Applied Analytics Using SAS Enterprise Miner*. Carey, NC.: SAS Institute, Inc., 2011, pp. 1-7–1-9.

Testing the final model is performed by data scientists in a manner that mimics our use of a "holdout" or "holdback" in traditional forecasting. Because most of the data we use in data mining is not time series data, it is possible to make many partitions of the data; some we use for training the algorithm, and others we use for validating the results.

## THE DATA ITSELF

Beginning a project in analytics will always involve some preliminary steps before we can begin the more interesting portion of the analysis; these beginning steps are not optional and will be performed each time we begin to analyze new data. Data scientists always perform their data analysis on less than the total number of records that are available. This will allow the validation of whatever algorithm is chosen. Different algorithms will also have varying limitations on what types of variables they are able to handle and the numbers of records and attributes. The software used and the computing power may also be a consideration on the amount and type of data that can be handled.

The types of variables used differ from traditional forecasting because there are more types available in unstructured data. There are several ways of classifying variables. Variables can be numeric or text (character). The data can be continuous (taking on any real numeric value), integer values, or categorical (taking on one of a limited number of values such as "1," "2," or "3"). Categorical variables can also be either numeric or text (loan, mortgage, CD, or checking account). Continuous variables like those we have commonly used in forecasting can be handled by most data mining algorithms. The Naive Bayes algorithm will be unusual because it will exclusively accept categorical variables. Because much of what follows involves classification as a goal, some continuous variables will be transformed into categorical variables (data mining software includes routines to handle this process). Unordered categorical variables, however, cannot be used as is. They will commonly be decomposed into a series of dummy binary variables. To do this, you should remember the "iron law of dummy variables," which states that the maximum number of dummy variables must be one less than the states of nature. For example, a single variable that can have possible values of male or female would be split into two dummy variables of which only one would be used in analysis (either one could be used):

$$Male - 1/0$$
$$Female - 1/0$$

Only one of these variables would be used to represent an individual's gender (just as we only used three dummy variables to represent four quarters of the year). Creating dummy variables from categorical variables is usually done in the software; in text mining, it will become part of the dimension reduction process that is the hallmark of text mining.

## Overfitting

When we include more attributes in the process, there is always a risk of
overfitting the data. What is overfitting? If we put too many attributes (or try
to account for too many patterns) in a model, including some unrelated to the
target, we are *overfitting*. If we put too few attributes (or try to account for too
few patterns) in the algorithm, leaving out attributes (or patterns) that could
help explain the target, we are *underfitting*. Data scientists are always trying
to balance the possibility of overfitting against the possibility of underfitting.

Suppose we have some data that follow a cubic model:

$$Y = 10 - 8x + 4x^2 + 1x^3$$

The true model is shown in Figure 8.6 as the curved line that looks like a
sinoid. The circles represent data points in our data set that have random variations about the true model. The straight line running from upper-left to lower-right
is a trend line; note that it does a very poor job of describing the true model.

If we used a cubic function to estimate the true model, we would get a result like
that in the left pane of Figure 8.7; the true model and the estimate are quite alike.
Alternatively, we could connect up all the data points with a smooth but complicated
polynomial function, one that explains all these data points perfectly and leaves no
error (residuals). This can be seen in the right-hand pane in Figure 8.7. The model

**FIGURE 8.6**
**Fitting Example: The
Curved Line
Represents the True
Underlying Model.
The Straight Line
Represents a Trend
Model. The Circles
Represent the Actual
Sample Data Points.**

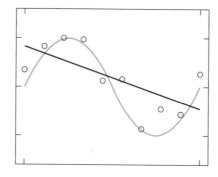

**FIGURE 8.7**
**The True Model
(Lighter Line) and a
Reasonable Estimate
(Darker Line) are
Shown on the Left.
The True Model and
an Overfit Estimate
(Dark Line) are
Shown on the Right.**

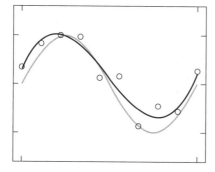
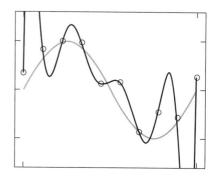

estimate goes through every data point, and the fit to the data is thus perfect. However, this estimate would do a very poor job indeed of predicting future iterations of the pattern; it has been overfit. It has fitted the noise as well as the actual pattern in the data and noise, because it is random, cannot be predicted well in a future period.

## Accuracy and Fit (Again)

The primary goal in model construction is to describe relationships among attributes so that this description will do a reasonable job of predicting future outcome (target) values on the basis of future predictor (attribute) values. We certainly want the model estimated to do a good job in representing the data we now have (our known data set). But what we want more importantly is for the model to have predictive power outside the known data set. We want "accuracy" and not just "fit" to be a characteristic of the chosen model. But if we model the noise in the data (as well as the true signal), we end up explaining incorrectly some variation in the data that was nothing more than chance variation. We will be guilty of mislabeling the noise in the data as if it were part of the true signal. This is the classic definition of overfitting the model. In such a case, the misclassification rate will be extremely low (maybe even zero) with the known data, and thus the model will appear to be predicting well.

However, this low misclassification rate on the known data is misleading because it includes a representation of what in the known data was actually just noise (random variation unable to be predicted in future data). Some of the data mining models we will examine are so good at classification that they have a natural tendency to overfit the known data (much like ARIMA models). We will have to recognize this and correct for the tendency.

## Some Other Data Considerations

Data mining differs from previous models we have used in that many more variables (i.e., attributes) may be used at one time. While we want the attributes to be correlated to the target, we should also be concerned when they are highly correlated with one another. The overfitting problem may be exacerbated by the inclusion of highly correlated variables. Some of the data mining algorithms are highly sensitive to attributes correlated one with another. It may also be costly to collect variables that simply "tell the same story" as variables we already have in the data. "Dimensionality" of a model is the number of attribute or predictor variables used by the model. A standard practice in data mining is finding ways to reduce dimensionality without sacrificing accuracy.

Data mining software often includes an "audit" routine to allow the data scientist to examine different aspects of the data that might otherwise be obscured in a tabular format. In XLMiner©, the user may examine any of the target or attribute variables in a number of dimensions. The Universal Bank data is a data set with approximately 5,000 customers of a bank with a broad range of attributes available for each customer. We might, for instance, be considering an analysis of what the characteristics are of an individual who holds a personal loan with the bank (Figure 8.8). An "audit" of the personal loan variable produces an answer.

**FIGURE 8.8**
**The Personal Loan Variable from the Universal Bank Data Set Produced Using the "Explore" Feature in XLMiner©.**
(C8F8)

Source: Frontline Systems Inc.

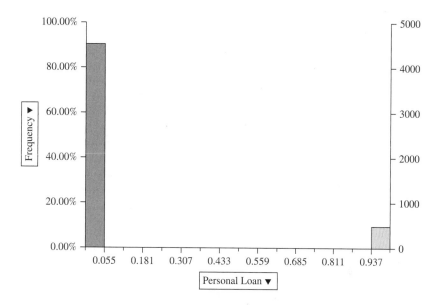

The number of individuals who hold a loan with the bank is quite small; it is only about 10 percent of the customer base (about 500 individuals). This fact may be useful when we begin modeling bank customer behavior; if we are interested in predicting customers who will take out a loan, we should realize that only a small portion of the customer base fits into that category. In this particular situation, no missing data or possible outliers were detected, and so no action was necessary, but if either of these two instances occurs, some action will be necessary. Again, the data preparation of your analytics software will contain options for these situations.

The "Transform" drop-down menu in XLMiner© (Figure 8.9) will allow both the handling of missing data as well as the transformation of data that may contain outliers; locating possible outliers may be accomplished with the "Explore" drop-down menu.

**FIGURE 8.9**
**The Data Handling Section of XLMiner©.**

Source: Frontline Systems Inc.

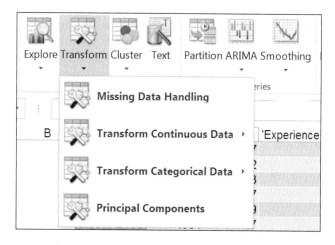

Partitioning and
testing for accuracy
are standard practice in
analytics.

## Sampling/Partitioning

In most cases, we will not use the entire data set to build a model; since our data is not time series, we have the ability to "partition" the data, using one partition to build the model and the other partition to test the model's accuracy. This partitioning and testing for accuracy are standard practice in analytics, and it has its roots in the "holdouts" or "holdbacks" we used when testing the accuracy (as opposed to fit) of standard forecasting models.

We can use our Universal Bank data to demonstrate this basic analytics procedure. The entire data set consists of 5,000 records; each record is an individual bank customer. If we build the model using the entire data set, we do not have any effective way of estimating how well the algorithm will work on classifying unseen data. Our goal here is to predict (classify in this case) whether an existing bank customer is likely to take out a personal loan; we will use all the attributes of bank customers to aid in the prediction.

Instead of using the entire data set of 5,000 records, we partition the data into two parts. The partition we use to build the model is traditionally called the "Training" data, while the remainder of the data forms the partition we call the "Validation" data. Since the data is not time series data and the order of the data is not important, we may randomly create the partition. The important point here is why we create the partitions in the first place. The two partitions are created in order to allow the data scientist to gauge the accuracy of the created model. We are interested in comparing the performance of this model with others so that we may choose the one we believe will perform the best when used in actual practice. Why not just choose the model that works best (in terms of fit) on the entire data set? Why partition at all? The answer is that when we use the same data to both build and test the model, we introduce bias. The model chosen in this manner would suffer the chance that some features of the data happen to match the chosen model better than any other model, and that is the main reason this model was chosen. If we are using an algorithm that is prone to overfitting (and some data mining algorithms are), using the entire data set to build the model will almost certainly result in overfitting; the overfitting will result in great "fit" but quite poor "accuracy." Since ultimately it is accuracy we desire in our models, we had best partition and build as a matter of practice.

In XLMiner©, there is a partitioning menu (Figure 8.10) that allows the construction of a standard data partition, including a training data partition and a validation partition; the defaults are set to choose 60 percent of the records for the training partition and 40 percent of the records for the validation partition. The records for each partition are randomly chosen with the random number generator either using a set "seed" number (so that the results may be reproduced exactly) or with a seed number generated by the software. The latter method is chosen in actual practice, but we will use the seed number 12345 so that the results may be exactly duplicated.

The validation portion of the data is not used to build the model and is only used after the model is built to test whether or not it works well on unseen data (i.e., the validation data partition). To test how well the model performs on the validation partition, data scientists use a number of measures (none of which we have used up to this point). The standard diagnostics we have used in past

**FIGURE 8.10**   **Data Partition Menu in XLMiner©.**   (C8F8)

Source: Frontline Systems Inc.

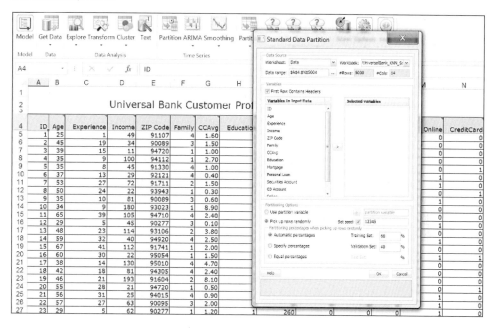

chapters, such as MAPE and $R^2$, are measures of fit and may not be appropriate to data mining algorithms. If we are classifying a categorical variable, a misclassification rate is one useful measure of model performance. A "lift chart" that reorders the predicted classifications may provide even more information on performance. A "confusion matrix" (also called a coincidence matrix) will provide additional information about model performance.

## Diagnostics (Evaluating Predictive Performance)

In the Universal Bank data, we are seeking to predict the state of a categorical variable titled "personal loan." The model will either predict an individual is likely to take out a personal loan given the individual's attributes (as detailed in the data) or the individual is unlikely to do so. The target (what we are predicting) consists of just two categories, and the model will decide which is more likely for every individual scored. In Chapter 9, we will detail the specifics of the model we might use, but for now, we will examine the results of the modeling process. We have obtained the data, cleaned it up to eliminate missing attribute values and adjust outliers, and partitioned the data into training and validation data partitions.

## The Confusion Matrix and Misclassification Rate

We normally request diagnostic statistics on both partitions of the data, although the results for the validation partition (the unseen data) are most relevant to evaluating the model.

**FIGURE 8.11** Universal Bank kNN Model Validation Partition Confusion Matrix and Error Report where n = 2,000 or 40 percent of the 5,000 Records. (C8F8)

Source: Frontline Systems Inc.

## Validation: Classification Summary

| Confusion Matrix | | |
|---|---|---|
| Actual\Predicted ▼ 0 | ▼ 1 | ▼ |
| 0 | 1809 | 3 |
| 1 | 80 | 108 |

| Error Report | | | | |
|---|---|---|---|---|
| Class ▼ | # Cases ▼ | # Errors ▼ | % Error ▼ | |
| 0 | 1812 | 3 | 0.165562914 | |
| 1 | 188 | 80 | 42.55319149 | |
| Overall | 2000 | 83 | 4.15 | |

Figure 8.11 shows the validation partition confusion matrix; recall that this indicates model performance in classification on data that was not used to build the model. A matrix like this one is a standard output in data mining when a classification is the goal. The matrix gives results for the correct (i.e., true) classifications and the incorrect results or misclassifications. These are estimates, but if the model has a sufficiently large data set to examine, the results are likely to be accurate. We would expect the confusion matrix for the training data to provide better results; in this case, it does (see Figure 8.12). Note the figure in the far lower-right

**FIGURE 8.12** Universal Bank kNN Model Training Partition Confusion Matrix and Error Report where n = 3,000 or 60 percent of the 5,000 Records. (C8F8)

Source: Frontline Systems Inc.

## Training: Classification Summary

| Confusion Matrix | | |
|---|---|---|
| Actual\Predicted ▼ 0 | ▼ 1 | ▼ |
| 0 | 2704 | 4 |
| 1 | 98 | 194 |

| Error Report | | | | |
|---|---|---|---|---|
| Class ▼ | # Cases ▼ | # Errors ▼ | % Error ▼ | |
| 0 | 2708 | 4 | 0.147710487 | |
| 1 | 292 | 98 | 33.56164384 | |
| Overall | 3000 | 102 | 3.4 | |

of the Error Report; this is the misclassification rate on the entire partition. The misclassification rate for the training data partition is a very low 3.4 percent. The same rate for the validation partition is a somewhat higher 4.15 percent. Both are quite low, but the algorithm performs a bit better on the partition that was used to build the model, the training partition, and a bit worse on the validation partition. The estimated misclassification rate is calculated by taking the total records scored incorrectly (80 + 3 in the validation partition) and dividing it by the total number of records classified (80 + 3 + 1809 + 108 in the validation partition).

$$\frac{(80 + 3)}{(80 + 3 + 1809 + 108)} = 0.0415 \; or \; 4.15\%$$

The same calculation could be made for the training partition.

$$\frac{(98 + 4)}{(98 + 4 + 2704 + 194)} = 0.0340 \; or \; 3.4\%$$

If the data set is reasonably large, the misclassification estimates are probably reasonably accurate.

## The Lift Chart

*The lift chart and its resulting lift calculation is the standard for accuracy in data mining.*

Another routinely used diagnostic device is to use a "lift chart." The lift chart and its resulting lift calculation is the standard for accuracy in data mining. A useful way to think of a lift chart is to examine the Universal Bank model that attempts to identify the likely individuals who will take out a personal loan by assigning each case a "probability of responding" score. The lift chart helps to determine how effectively the model can reorder the data set, placing those individuals who will take out a loan at the top of the list and those that are unlikely to do so at the bottom of the list, according to their scores. To construct a lift curve, we use the validation data set after it has been "scored" by appending to each case the estimated probability that it will belong to a given class. The data partition is then reordered from "most likely" to "least likely" to accept a loan.

It is convenient to look at the lift chart (sometimes called a cumulative gains chart when displayed in the default manner of XLMiner©), which summarizes the information into a graph. The graph is constructed with the cumulative number of cases (in descending order of probability) on the *x*-axis and the cumulative number of true positives on the *y*-axis, as shown in Figure 8.13. True positives are those observations from the important class (here "take out a personal loan") that are classified correctly. Figure 8.13 is the corresponding lift chart. The 45-degree line is a reference line. For any given number of cases (the *x*-axis value), the 45-degree line represents the expected number of "successes" we would predict if we did not have a model but simply selected the most common category. Remember that the most common category for this data set was "do not take out a personal loan." It provides a benchmark against which we can see the performance of the model. Because this reference line is drawn by assuming that we always choose the most prevalent category when scoring a new record, it is called the naive model, and we use it as a reference in the same manner we used a somewhat different naive model in previous chapters. The fact that the cumulative gains curve rises above the reference line indicates that the model estimated has "lift."

**FIGURE 8.13**
The Validation
Partition Lift Chart
(or Cumulative Gains
Chart as Shown in the
XLMiner© Default) for
the Universal
Bank Classification.
(C8F8)

Source: Frontline Systems Inc.

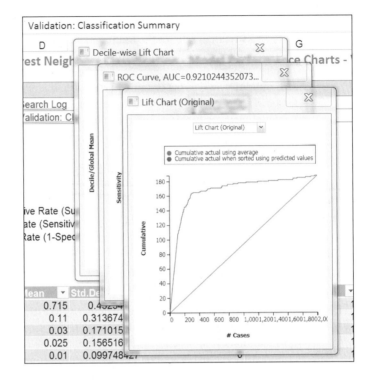

The same information may be displayed using one of the alternative lift charts in XLMiner© called the decile-wise lift chart, as in Figure 8.14. The x-axis displays the 10 deciles in the validation partition, while the y-axis shows the lift associated with each decile. Note carefully that the data used to construct the chart is again reordered so that the most likely individuals to take out a loan (i.e., successes) are at the top of the data partition and the records representing individuals not likely to take out a personal loan are at the bottom of the data partition. The bars show the factor by which our model outperforms a naive model. Reading the first bar on the left, we see that taking the first 10 percent of the records that are ranked by the model as the most probable individuals to take out a loan yields almost eight times as many correct classifications as would a random selection of 10 percent of the records (i.e., the naive model). That "eight times" as successful as a naive model is the lift associated with this model.

XLMiner© has one additional way of displaying the same information; it is perhaps the most standard manner in which to display lift. Figure 8.15 shows the "true" lift chart with deciles on the x-axis. Most data mining software uses this standard type of display for lift. Remember again that we have always reordered the records from most likely to least likely before drawing the chart; failure to recognize this makes the chart impossible to interpret. Looking at the first decile in Figure 8.15 (0.1 on the x-axis) and following up to see the height of the fitted classifier at that point gives a number on the y-axis of between 8 and 9; this is the measure of lift for the first 10 percent of the records, or we could say it is the lift of the first decile. Note that we have accounted for most of the successes in the first decile; the lift curve in Figure 8.15 falls off quickly after the

**FIGURE 8.14**
**Decile-wise Lift Chart for the Universal Bank Classification.** (C8F8)

Source: Frontline Systems Inc.

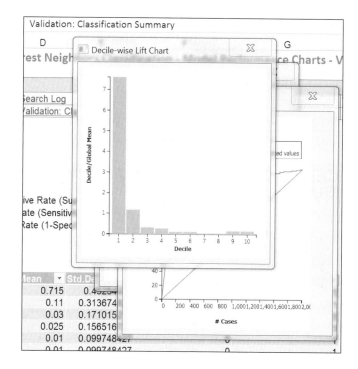

**FIGURE 8.15**
**The "alternative" Lift Chart from XLMiner© for the Universal Bank Classification. This is the Standard Display Format used by Most Data Mining Software Packages.** (C8F8)

Source: Frontline Systems Inc.

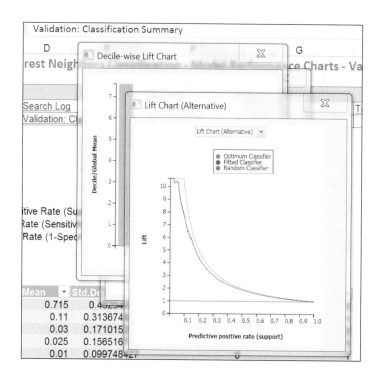

first decile. There were very few successes in the entire data set (we know that from our audit of the data), and most of those successes are accounted for in the first decile. This model appears to be highly predictive in categorizing bank customers in the first few deciles (the ones on the left of the chart). These first few deciles are of most interest to the data scientist. If we wanted to target customers for a personal loan campaign, we would only approach those near the top of our reordered list. The model has reordered the list by using the attributes considered in the analysis to categorize individuals as either successes or failures (i.e., "take out a loan" or "do not take out a loan").

## THE RECEIVER OPERATING CURVE (ROC) AND AREA UNDER THE CURVE (AUC)

There is one final way of displaying essentially the same information. It is another method of explaining lift. It was developed during WWII by radar engineers (not data scientists). The engineers were using signals to detect hostile aircraft in the battlefield, and they wanted to better visualize the trade-off between correctly and incorrectly identifying an aircraft as a foe. The method they devised is called a receiver operating curve (ROC); Figure 8.16 shows the ROC for the Universal Bank classification model. The ROC provides an especially handy way to compare competing algorithms with a single number. It uses the same variable on the y-axis as the lift curve but

**FIGURE 8.16**
**The Receiver Operating Curve for the Universal Bank Classification.**
(C8F8)

Source: Frontline Systems Inc.

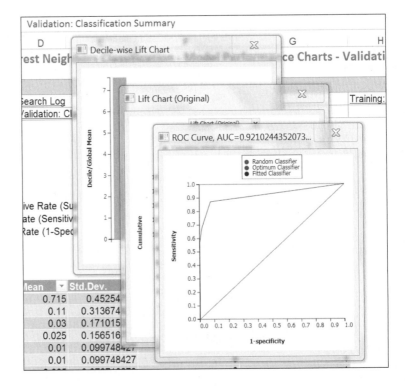

expressed as a percentage of the maximum. The *x*-axis displays the false positives, also expressed as a percentage of the maximum.

Thus, the receiver operating curve is a plot of the true positive rate against the false positive rate. Another way of saying this is to say that the curve shows the trade-off between sensitivity and specificity (any increase in sensitivity will be accompanied by a decrease in specificity). Higher sensitivity will eventually find all the likely loan applicants, but it will also misclassify a large number of individuals as likely to take out a loan. Higher specificity, on the other hand, will eventually preclude incorrectly selecting any individuals as loan candidates, except ones who are certain to accept an offer, but it will also miss many likely loan candidates. Once again, recall that the data has been reordered according to the algorithm from most successful to least successful.

The closer the curve follows the left-hand border and then the top border of the ROC space, the more accurate the algorithm. The curve allows you to quickly access the false positive rate that is associated with a true positive rate. The area under the ROC curve (designated as AUC or "Area Under the Curve" in XLMiner©) is a reflection of how good the test is at distinguishing (or "discriminating") between likely loan takers and those individuals not likely to take out a loan. The greater the area, the better the algorithm. Look at Figure 8.16, which shows a good test (that has a high sensitivity and specificity) and an AUC of 0.921. A worthless classification model would be described by the diagonal line in Figure 8.16.

## What Is to Follow

In the following chapters, we will learn about and employ a number of classification algorithms. Why explain more than one classification algorithm? Each algorithm has its strong points and weaknesses. Just as with physical tools, it is best to use the appropriate tool for the particular job. Driving in a screw with a hammer is possible but not recommended. We will also learn about and employ clustering techniques; these algorithms are a form of unsupervised learning (because there is no target). Finally, we will learn about text mining; this will be a foray into unstructured data.

| | |
|---|---|
| **Suggested Readings** | Davenport, Thomas H. *Big Data at Work: Dispelling the Myths, Uncovering the Opportunities*. Boston: Harvard Business Review Press, 2014. |
| | Foreman, John W. *Data Smart*. Indianapolis, IN: John Wiley & Sons, Inc., 2014. |
| | Hays, Constance L. "What Wal-Mart Knows About Customers' Habits." *The New York Times*, November 14, 2004. |
| | Keating, Barry. "Analytics Off the Shelf." *Applied Marketing Analytics*, 2, no. 1 (Winter 2015–16), pp. 12–24. |
| | Mangalindan, J. P. "Amazon's Recommendation Secret," *Fortune*, July 30, 2012. |
| | Mayer-Schonberger, Viktor, and Kenneth Cukier. *Big Data: A Revolution That Will Transform How We Live, Work, and Think*. New York: Houghton Mifflin Harcourt, 2013. |
| | Pierce, John R. *An Introduction to Information Theory: Symbols, Signals and Noise, Second Revised Edition*. New York: Dover Publications, 1980. |
| | SAS Institute. *Applied Analytics Using SAS Enterprise Miner*. Carey, NC.: SAS Institute, Inc., 2011. |

Shannon, Claude. "A Mathematical Theory of Communication," *Bell System Techincal Journal*, 27 (July, October 1948). pp. 379–423, 623–656.

Shmueli, Galit; Nitin R. Patel; and Peter C. Bruce. *Data Mining for Business Analytics.* Hoboken, NJ: John Wiley & Sons, Inc., 2016

Siegel, Eric. *Predictive Analytics: The Power to Predict Who Will Click, Buy, Lie, or Die.* Hoboken, NJ: John Wiley & Sons, Inc., 2013.

Silver, Nate. *The Signal and the Noise: Why So Many Predictions Fail - But Some Don't.* New York: Penguin Press, 2012.

Soni, Jimmy and Rob Goodman. *A Mind at Play: How Claude Shannon Invented the Information Age.* New York: Simon & Schuster, 2017.

Wendler, Tito; and Soren Grottrup. *Data Mining with SPSS Modeler.* Switzerland: Springer International Publishing, 2016.

# Exercises

1. A classification model's misclassification rate on the validation data is a better measure of the model's predictive ability on new (unseen) data than its misclassification rate on the training data. Explain whether this statement is accurate and why that is so.

2. The first step in data mining procedures according to SAS and IBM/SPSS is to "sample" the data. Sampling here refers to dividing the data available for analysis into at least two parts: a training data set and a validation data set. Why do both SAS and IBM/SPSS recommend this as a first step? What are the risks of ignoring this procedural requirement?

3. How do "structured" and "unstructured" data differ? Which is the more prevalent form of data? How would the following be classified: numbers in an Excel spreadsheet, a thousand text files, a thousand video images, and a thousand audio files?

4. In the Universal Bank classification model estimated with XLMiner©, the software produced the validation data set lift chart shown.

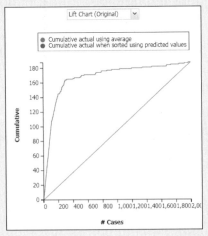

Source: Frontline Systems Inc.

How is the naive model displayed in this diagram? What does the other line in the model represent?

5. Some data mining algorithms work so "well" that they have a tendency to overfit the training data. What does the term *overfit* mean, and what difficulties does overlooking it cause for the data scientist?

6. The validation data set confusion matrix for the Universal Bank data classification model is shown.

## Validation: Classification Summary

| Confusion Matrix | | |
|---|---|---|
| Actual\Predicted ▾ 0 | ▾ 1 | ▾ |
| 0 | 1809 | 3 |
| 1 | 80 | 108 |

Source: Frontline Systems Inc.

How many records were in the validation data set? How many of these records were correctly classified by the algorithm? How many records were incorrectly classified? What is the "misclassification rate" for the entire validation data set? Would you predict that the misclassification rate for the training data set would be higher or lower on average than the rate you calculated for the entire validation data set?

7. Show the computation for the misclassification rate of this confusion matrix.

| Confusion Matrix | | |
|---|---|---|
| Actual\Predicted | 0 | 1 |
| 0 | 970 | 20 |
| 1 | 2 | 8 |

Source: Frontline Systems Inc.

8. In the Universal Bank data in this chapter, only 10 percent of the records represented customers who had taken out a personal loan (the target variable). If we were to score a new customer based upon the attributes we used in the algorithm, we would be accurate in the prediction about 90 percent of the time if we always scored the individual as "not accepting a personal loan" because that indeed is what most customers have done in the past. Why not accept being correct 90 percent of the time with this very simple decision rule?

9. Data has the characteristic of "nonrivalry." What is nonrivalry and why is it important to realize that data has this characteristic?

10. The lift chart and the confusion matrix are both standard diagnostic tools used to evaluate a data mining algorithm. Don't the two measures display the same information? Explain any differences between the two measures.

# Chapter **Nine**

# Classification Models: The Most Used Models in Analytics

"The key to big data is whether it's going to give you actionable insights that you can then grow your business on."

*Xavier Amatriain, Netflix's director of algorithms engineering*[1]

## LEARNING OBJECTIVES

After reading this chapter, you should be able to:

1. Explain the use of classification algorithms.
2. Construct and employ four different classification algorithms.
3. Interpret the standard diagnostic statistics for these algorithms.
4. Explain how better decisions can be made through the use of classification algorithms.
5. Relate the pros and cons of each of the classification algorithms.
6. Apply classification algorithms to make business predictions.

## INTRODUCTION

The statistical forecasting models we have introduced previously in this text, have been applied to continuous, numeric target variables. For instance, we used exponential smoothing and regression to predict sales at The Gap. This chapter introduces the situation in which we wish to assign a category to each instance of the target. These classification algorithms will be data driven in the sense that we will not use assumptions about the structure of the data as we have used prior

---

[1] James Willhite, "Getting Started in 'Big Data,'" *Wall Street Journal,* February 4, 2014, (https://blogs.wsj.com/cfo/2014/02/04/getting-started-in-big-data/).

to chapter eight. So these are not model driven algorithms; they are referred to as data driven algorithms.

Classification algorithms are the most used techniques in predictive analytics. That fact is probably due to the value to firms in making correct classification predictions. The use of classification algorithms is not limited to any single industry; consumer products, entertainment, health care, and the fast food industry all use classification effectively. These industries (and many others) mine mountains of data trying to smooth supply chains, improve product design, enhance customer service, and add to the company's bottom line. Classification models are not all there is to predictive analytics, but there is a reason why they are the most used of the techniques.

Douglas Laney of Gartner Inc. reported an astounding finding that should probably convince any firm that there is real value in using predictive analytics.[2] Laney and a colleague, Somendra Tripathi, compared firms that heavily used predictive analytics and those that did not. What they measured was the Tobin's q of each firm. Tobin's q is the market-to-book value of a firm; it represents the market's estimate of the value of the firm compared to the accounting or book value. If one firm's Tobin's q is higher than another's, it indicates that the market (comprised of thousands, perhaps hundreds of thousands, of investors) has identified the one firm as more valuable than the other firm regardless of accounting (i.e., historical) value. What Laney and Tripathi reported was that the Tobin's q of firms heavily using predictive analytics was 200 to 300 percent higher than the norm. The Tobin's q for information-centered firms (those in the business of selling data) using predictive analytics were higher yet: 400 to 500 percent above the average. Apparently, the market recognizes the value of firms using predictive analytics. The market value of these firms is substantially enhanced as a result of the leverage they gain by using predictive analytics. This information, with the knowledge that the most used of the data mining algorithms are in the classification category, should provide an incentive to discover how the classification algorithms presented in this chapter work and how they are employed by firms.

Classification is a form of supervised learning in which we wish to predict the class (classification) of each record in our data; our statistical forecasts were also a form of supervised learning, but in those forecasts, the prediction took the form of a continuous outcome variable.

When Vermont Country Store (a largely nostalgic catalog mail order company) sends a catalog to a prospective customer, they would like to know that they are mailing the costly catalog to a person or family likely to purchase from the catalog; they are classifying prospective customers as "likely to purchase" or "not likely to purchase" and contacting only the likely purchasers. John Wanamaker, a Philadelphia retailer who was also the U.S. Postmaster General, once is reputed

*Classification algorithms are the most used techniques in predictive analytics.*

*The Tobin's q of firms heavily using predictive analytics was 200 to 300 percent higher than the norm.*

[2] Douglas Laney, "The Hidden Shareholder Boost from Information Assets," *Forbes,* July 21, 2014, (https://www.forbes.com/sites/gartnergroup/2014/07/21/the-hidden-shareholder-boost-from-information-assets/#698bdd397628).

to have said, "Half the money I spend on advertising is wasted; the trouble is I don't know which half." If Wanamaker had been able to use the classification algorithms used by Vermont Country Store, he might have known which half of his advertising was wasted.

Amazon also uses classification algorithms; up to 60 percent of Amazon sales results from up-selling or cross-selling, according to *Fortune*.[3] Amazon is predicting which customers would likely be susceptible to an offer of a more expensive version of a product or a compatible product; apparently, they are correct more often than not.

eHarmony helps people meet each other; their mantra is "Beat the odds, bet on love." The implication is that the online dating site can suggest individuals to you who have a high probability of being compatible. They have attributes gleaned from a lengthy questionnaire that each of their users has filled out, and they are classifying which individuals in their database may likely be compatible with you. You are scored as being either compatible or not compatible with another individual by the eHarmony classification algorithm. eHarmony CEO Neil Clark Warren believes the site is a better way of meeting possible partners than the random process of letting luck determine your fate.

Whirlpool Corporation uses classification algorithms to predict which dishwashers coming down the assembly line are likely to fail in some manner within one year. Warranty repairs on these failing machines is very costly and erodes profit. By using a series of test results performed along the assembly line as attributes and classifying the dishwashers as either "likely to fail" or "unlikely to fail," the company is able to significantly reduce warranty claims and has probably increased customer satisfaction as well.

Each of these examples has a common feature: what is being predicted is a "class," or one of a few categories. The prediction does not involve the forecast of a continuous variable but it is still prediction. As such, the tools you learned in earlier chapters will be of little use here; classification models are, like those earlier models, a form of supervised learning, but they will require algorithms that are quite different than you learned in earlier chapters.

The types of things for which categories are predicted vary widely. Firms will often gain value by making predictions for individuals; they may make a decision who to send a mailing to; they may decide who to lend to; they may choose who to investigate for crime or fraud; and they may decide to treat one medical patient differently than another. In each case, however, the prediction that is being made is to place an individual into one category or another; it is not to predict a numeric value such as dollars of sales.

The value of being able to make such categorizations is quite important. If I send an advertising mailer to an individual likely to use my services or purchase my product, the outcome will probably be better than if I sent the same

---

[3] J. P. Mangalindan, "Amazon's Recommendation Secret," *Fortune,* July 30, 2012, http://fortune.com/2012/07/30/amazons-recommendation-secret/.

The types of things for which categories are predicted vary widely. Firms will often gain value by making predictions for individuals.

information to an individual who was unlikely to ever take advantage of the offer. I would rather lend to an individual who is likely to repay the loan than to an individual likely to default. If I am going to spend time and effort to investigate someone for crime or fraud, I would like to know that the individual is likely to be guilty and my efforts will have been worthwhile. If I choose to treat a patient with a drug known to be effective in curing a certain disease, I would like to know that the probability is high that the person I am considering treating actually has the disease. When correct category decisions are made, firms sell more product, banks suffer fewer defaults, crime fighting is toughened, and health care is made more robust.

Firms and their customers, suppliers, and financiers benefit when these correct categories are predicted. eHarmony tries to predict whether you will be compatible with another individual; if they get the category (i.e., compatible or not compatible) predicted correctly, you might benefit for the remainder of your life. Linkedin makes suggestions of people you may know in the hopes that a formal connection on their social media platform may prove useful to both of you. It is a category that Linkedin is predicting; either you know someone or you don't. Amazon will often display products you may wish to purchase; it is making a category prediction and placing you in the "might purchase" category. Remember that estimates indicate that a significant portion of Amazon sales result from such predicted categories.[4] Target predicted the pregnancy of some of its customers in 2011 and acted upon the information by sending coupons appropriate for a mother-to-be to individuals identified.[5] In 2017, the BBC announced that the biggest killer you may not know was sepsis; it kills more people each year than bowel, breast, and prostate cancer combined.[6] The Sisters of Mercy Health Systems uses patient vital signs to accurately categorize patients with sepsis and those without sepsis so that "likely sepsis" patients can be treated earlier than otherwise was available and to improve their chances of survival. Early detection would seem to be a priority since sepsis costs hospitals between $28 and $33 billion dollars per year, according to Booz Allen Hamilton.[7] The Chicago Police Department tried to determine which individuals would be shot in the near future.[8] An analytics algorithm assigned a category based on arrests, shootings, affiliations with gang members, and other attributes. It produced a list predicting who was most likely to

[4] Ibid.

[5] Charles Duhigg, "How Companies Learn Your Secrets," *New York Times,* February 16, 2012 (http://www.nytimes.com/2012/02/19/magazine/shopping-habits.html).

[6] James Gallagher, "The Biggest Killer You May Not Know," *BBC,* March 10, 2017 (http://www.bbc.com/news/health-39219765).

[7] Mark Adams, Reechlyk Chatterjee, and Sharma Yugal, "Improving Patient Outcomes Through Advanced Biomedical Analytics," Booz Allen Hamilton, March 2012 (https://www.boozallen.com/content/dam/boozallen/media/file/leveraging-advanced-data-collection-cs.PDF).

[8] "Monica Davey, "Chicago Police Try to Predict Who May Shoot or Be Shot," *New York Times,* May 23, 2016, (https://www.nytimes.com/2016/05/24/us/armed-with-data-chicago-police-try-to-predict-who-may-shoot-or-be-shot.html?_r=0).

be shot soon or to shoot someone. The algorithm proved all too predictive for one unfortunate man named Shaquon Thomas. His name appeared on the list as likely to be shot right after the department began to use the classification algorithm. The 19-year-old was fatally shot shortly afterward on May 29, 2015.

# A DATA MINING CLASSIFICATION EXAMPLE: k-NEAREST-NEIGHBOR (kNN)

Many data mining techniques are able to be shown in graphic form, and this makes them easier to understand.

Consider the following data mining example from Eamonn Keogh; while it is not business related, it is easy to see the technique unfold visually. Many data mining techniques are able to be shown in graphic form, and this makes them easier to understand. We will attempt to use a graphical approach for explanation when possible. Suppose you are a researcher attempting to classify insects you have found into one of two groups (i.e., you are attempting to predict the correct classification for new insects found). The insects you find may be either katydids or grasshoppers. These insects look quite a bit alike, but there are subtle differences. They are much like ducks and geese: many similarities but some important differences as well.

You have five examples of insects that you know are katydids and five examples that you know are grasshoppers. These 10 insects will comprise our known data set. The unknown is thought to be either a katydid or a grasshopper. Could we

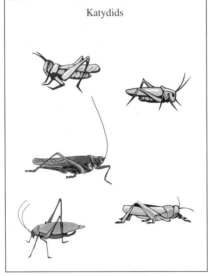
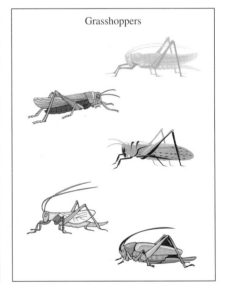

Courtesy of Eamonn Keogh.

use this known data set to come up with a set of rules that would allow us to classify any unknown insect as either a katydid or a grasshopper? By examining how this might be done by hand through trial and error, we can begin to understand one general process that classification data mining algorithms use.

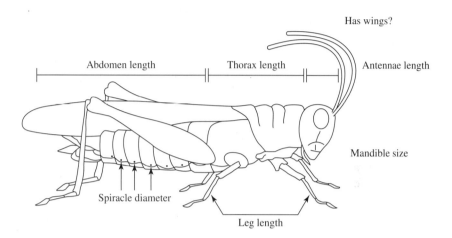

There are many characteristics we could use to aid in our classification. Some of them would include abdomen length, thorax length, leg length, antenna length, the presence of wings, and so on. The 10 insects we have in our known database have the following values for the attributes titled abdomen length and antenna length.

| Insect ID | Abdomen Length (mm) | Antenna Length (mm) | Insect Class |
|---|---|---|---|
| 1 | 2.7 | 5.5 | Grasshopper |
| 2 | 8.0 | 9.1 | Katydid |
| 3 | 0.9 | 4.7 | Grasshopper |
| 4 | 1.1 | 3.1 | Grasshopper |
| 5 | 5.4 | 8.5 | Katydid |
| 6 | 2.9 | 1.9 | Grasshopper |
| 7 | 6.1 | 6.6 | Katydid |
| 8 | 0.5 | 1.0 | Grasshopper |
| 9 | 8.3 | 6.6 | Katydid |
| 10 | 8.1 | 4.7 | Katydid |
| Unknown | 5.1 | 7.0 | ? |

The unknown insect is represented by the last row in the table. We have only included two insect attributes in our table for demonstration purposes because this makes the classification method easy to replicate graphically. As we have seen in discussing business forecasting techniques, it is usually a good idea to first graph the data in order to look for obvious relationships. We can do the same here by arbitrarily placing abdomen length on one axis and antenna length on the other, thus creating a scatterplot of the data.

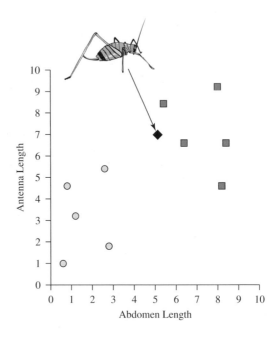

The resulting plot is quite informative; the katydids (shown as squares) cluster in the upper right-hand corner of our plot, while the grasshoppers (shown as circles) cluster in the lower left-hand corner of the plot. It is important to note that neither characteristic by itself would do well in making a perfect classification; the combination of the two attributes, however, might more accurately define unknown insects. This unknown insect appears to fall closest to the katydids. But can we come up with a mechanistic (i.e., a rules-based algorithm) way of classifying the unknown as a katydid rather than as a grasshopper? One method would be to look at the geographical neighbors of the unknown insect. Which neighbors are the closest to the unknown? We could describe this process by drawing distance lines between the unknown insect and its neighbors.

If the distance to the unknown insect is closest to the katydids (as measured by summing the distance to katydid neighbors and comparing this to the sum of the distances to grasshopper neighbors), then the unknown is likely a katydid. In essence, the k-Nearest-Neighbor model of data mining works in a similar manner. In actual practice, it is not necessary to calculate the distance to every neighbor; only a small subset of the neighbors is used. The "k" in k-Nearest-Neighbor refers to the number of nearest neighbors used in determining a category correctly.

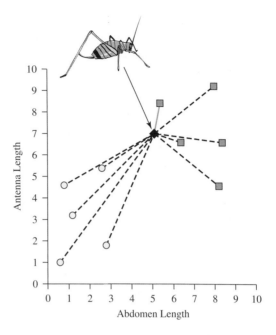

When using k-Nearest-Neighbor, we use a subset of the total data we have available (called the *training data* set) to attempt to identify observations in the training data set that are similar to the unknown. Scoring (or predicting) new unknowns is assigning the unknowns to the same class as their nearest neighbors. While Euclidian distance is shown in the diagrams here, there are other metrics possible that can be used to define neighbors, and they are at times used in the various commercial data mining packages.

What we are truly interested in is classifying future unknown insects, not the past classification performance on known data. We already know the classifications of the insects in the training data set; that's why we call it a training data set. It trains the model to correctly classify the unknowns by selecting closeness to the k-nearest-neighbors. So, the error rate on known data will not be very helpful in determining if we have a good classification model. An error rate on a training set is not the best indicator of future performance.

The real test of a business forecast was the "out-of-sample" test; the real test of a data mining algorithm will be the test statistics on the validation data.

To predict how well this model might do in the real world at classifying unknowns, we need to use it to classify some data that the model has not previously had access to (the unseen data); we need to use data that was not part of the training data set. This separate data set is called the *validation data* (sometimes called the testing data). In one sense, this separation of data into a training data set and a validation data set is much like the difference between "in-sample" test statistics and "out-of-sample" test statistics in standard forecasting. The real test of a business forecast was the "out-of-sample" test; the real test of a data mining algorithm will be the test statistics on the validation data, not the statistics calculated from the training data.

In order to produce reliable measures of the effectiveness of a data mining tool, researchers *partition* a data set before building a data mining model. It is standard practice to divide the data set into partitions using some random procedure. We could, for instance, assign each instance in our data set a number and then randomly partition the data set into two parts called the training data and the validation data. If there is a great deal of data (unlike the simple example of the katydids and grasshoppers), there is little trouble in using, for example, 60 percent of the records as a training set and the remaining 40 percent as a validation data set. This will ensure that no effectiveness statistics are drawn from the data used to create the model. Thus, an early step in any real data mining procedure is to partition the data.

# A BUSINESS DATA MINING CLASSIFICATION EXAMPLE: k-NEAREST-NEIGHBOR (kNN)

What would such a model look like in a business situation? We now turn again to examining a data set used by Shmueli, Patel, and Bruce.[9] The Universal Bank data is also included as an example data set with the Frontline Systems Inc. Solver software. This data set represents information on the customers a bank has in its data warehouse. These individuals have been customers of the bank at some time in the past; perhaps many remain current customers in one dimension or another. The type of information the bank has on each of these 5,000 customers is represented in Tables 9.1 and 9.2.

**TABLE 9.1**
**Universal Bank (Fictitious) Data**
The bank has data on a customer-by-customer basis for 5,000 customers in these categories.

| Variable Name | Explanation |
|---|---|
| Age | Customer's age in completed years |
| Experience | No. of years of professional experience |
| Income | Annual income of the customer ($000) |
| ZIP code | Home address, ZIP code |
| Family | Family size of the customer |
| CC Avg. | Average spending on credit cards per month ($000) |
| Education | Education level (1) Undergrad; (2) Graduate; (3) Advanced/Professional |
| Mortgage | Value of house mortgage if any ($000) |
| Personal loan | Did this customer accept the personal loan offered in the last campaign? |
| Securities account | Does the customer have a securities account with the bank? |
| CD account | Does the customer have a certificate of deposit (CD) account with the bank? |
| Online | Does the customer use Internet banking facilities? |
| Credit card | Does the customer use a credit card issued by Universal Bank? |

[9] Galit Shmueli, Nitin Patel, and Peter Bruce, *Data Mining for Business Intelligence*. New York: John Wiley & Sons, 2007.

## TABLE 9.2  Universal Bank Customer Profiles

The data includes both continuous variables such as income as well as dummy variables such as personal loan.   (C9T2)

| ID | Age | Experience | Income | ZIP Code | Family | CCAvg | Education | Mortgage | Personal Loan | Securities Account | CD Account | Online | CreditCard |
|----|-----|-----------|--------|----------|--------|-------|-----------|----------|---------------|--------------------|-----------|--------|-----------|
| 1 | 25 | 1 | 49 | 91107 | 4 | 1.60 | 1 | 0 | 0 | 1 | 0 | 0 | 0 |
| 2 | 45 | 19 | 34 | 90089 | 3 | 1.50 | 1 | 0 | 0 | 1 | 0 | 0 | 0 |
| 3 | 39 | 15 | 11 | 94720 | 1 | 1.00 | 1 | 0 | 0 | 0 | 0 | 0 | 0 |
| 4 | 35 | 9 | 100 | 94112 | 1 | 2.70 | 2 | 0 | 0 | 0 | 0 | 0 | 0 |
| 5 | 35 | 8 | 45 | 91330 | 4 | 1.00 | 2 | 0 | 0 | 0 | 0 | 0 | 1 |
| 6 | 37 | 13 | 29 | 92121 | 4 | 0.40 | 2 | 155 | 0 | 0 | 0 | 1 | 0 |
| 7 | 53 | 27 | 72 | 91711 | 2 | 1.50 | 2 | 0 | 0 | 0 | 0 | 1 | 0 |
| 8 | 50 | 24 | 22 | 93943 | 1 | 0.30 | 3 | 0 | 0 | 0 | 0 | 0 | 1 |
| 9 | 35 | 10 | 81 | 90089 | 3 | 0.60 | 2 | 104 | 0 | 0 | 0 | 1 | 0 |
| 10 | 34 | 9 | 180 | 93023 | 1 | 8.90 | 3 | 0 | 1 | 0 | 0 | 0 | 0 |
| 11 | 65 | 39 | 105 | 94710 | 4 | 2.40 | 3 | 0 | 0 | 0 | 0 | 0 | 0 |
| 12 | 29 | 5 | 45 | 90277 | 3 | 0.10 | 2 | 0 | 0 | 0 | 0 | 1 | 0 |
| 13 | 48 | 23 | 114 | 93106 | 2 | 3.80 | 3 | 0 | 0 | 1 | 0 | 0 | 0 |
| 14 | 59 | 32 | 40 | 94920 | 4 | 2.50 | 2 | 0 | 0 | 0 | 0 | 1 | 0 |
| 15 | 67 | 41 | 112 | 91741 | 1 | 2.00 | 1 | 0 | 0 | 1 | 0 | 0 | 0 |
| 16 | 60 | 30 | 22 | 95054 | 1 | 1.50 | 3 | 0 | 0 | 0 | 0 | 1 | 1 |
| 17 | 38 | 14 | 130 | 95010 | 4 | 4.70 | 3 | 134 | 1 | 0 | 0 | 0 | 0 |
| 18 | 42 | 18 | 81 | 94305 | 4 | 2.40 | 1 | 0 | 0 | 0 | 0 | 0 | 0 |

Universal Bank would like to know which customers are likely to accept a personal loan. The bank is considering a promotion to customers that will offer personal loans. What attributes would predict which specific customers would be likely to respond positively to such an offer? If the bank were to consider expending advertising efforts to contact customers who would be likely to consider a personal loan, which customers should the bank contact first? By answering this question correctly, the bank will be able to optimize its advertising effort by directing its attention to the highest-yield customers.

This is an iconic classification problem not unlike the situation of deciding in what class to place an unknown insect. The two classes in this example would be: (1) those with a high probability of accepting a personal loan (*acceptors*), and (2) those with a low probability of accepting a personal loan (*nonacceptors*). We will be unable to classify customers with certainty about whether they will accept a personal loan, but we may be able to classify the customers better than a naive model into one of these two mutually exclusive categories if we estimate a kNN model. Naive model here means to always assign new customers to the most prevalent category in the training data (in this case that would be nonacceptor).

Figure 9.1 shows that there were only 480 acceptors among the 5,000 records in the full data set. Less than 10 percent of the bank's customers had accepted a personal loan. The naive model would then be to classify every new customer as a nonacceptor, and the naive model would be correct more than 90 percent of the time. The goal of the data scientist here would be to make better classifications than the naive model.

The researcher would begin by first partitioning the Universal Bank data. Recall that partitioning the data set is the first step in any data mining technique. Since each row, or record, is a different customer, we could assign a number to each row and use a random selection process to choose 60 percent of the data as

**FIGURE 9.1**
**Universal Bank**
**Personal Loan**
**Variable Distribution**
**("0" Indicates**
**a Nonacceptor;**
**"1" Indicates an**
**Acceptor)** (C9T2)

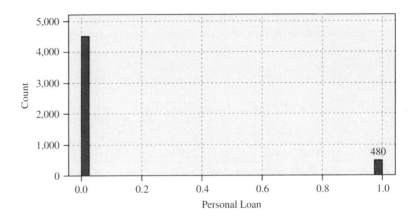

a training set. The remaining 40 percent of the data set would be the validation partition. All data mining software has such an option available. Once the data is selected into a training set, it would look that in Table 9.3. This partial rendition of the table is produced using the XLMiner© software.

Examining the Partition Summary at the top left of Table 9.3, you will note that there were 5,000 customers in the original data set that have now been divided into a training data set of 3,000 customers and a validation data set of 2,000 customers.

When we instruct the software to perform a k-Nearest-Neighbor analysis of the training data, the real data mining analysis takes place. Just as in the insect classification example, the software will compare each customer's personal loan experience with the selected attributes. This example is, of course, much more multidimensional since we have many attributes for each customer (as opposed to only the two attributes we used in the insect example). For this analysis, we have used all the attributes available in the data set except ID and zip code (zip code is left out arbitrarily in this example; it could be included). The program will compute the distance associated with each attribute. For attributes that are measured as continuous variables, the software will normalize the distance and then measure it

**TABLE 9.3** **Training Data (Only the First Few Records Shown)**
This is a subset of the complete data set. (C9T2)

**Partition Summary**

| Partition | # Records |
|---|---|
| Training | 3000 |
| Validation | 2000 |

**Partitioned Data**

| Record ID | ID | Age | Experience | Income | Family | CCAvg | Education | Mortgage | Personal Loan | Securities Account | CD Account | Online | CreditCard |
|---|---|---|---|---|---|---|---|---|---|---|---|---|---|
| Record 3 | 3 | 39 | 15 | 11 | 1 | 1 | 1 | 0 | 0 | 0 | 0 | 0 | 0 |
| Record 7 | 7 | 53 | 27 | 72 | 2 | 1.5 | 2 | 0 | 0 | 0 | 0 | 1 | 0 |
| Record 8 | 8 | 50 | 24 | 22 | 1 | 0.3 | 3 | 0 | 0 | 0 | 0 | 0 | 1 |
| Record 9 | 9 | 35 | 10 | 81 | 3 | 0.6 | 2 | 104 | 0 | 0 | 0 | 1 | 0 |
| Record 10 | 10 | 34 | 9 | 180 | 1 | 8.9 | 3 | 0 | 1 | 0 | 0 | 0 | 0 |
| Record 13 | 13 | 48 | 23 | 114 | 2 | 3.8 | 3 | 0 | 0 | 1 | 0 | 0 | 0 |
| Record 14 | 14 | 59 | 32 | 40 | 4 | 2.5 | 2 | 0 | 0 | 0 | 0 | 1 | 0 |
| Record 16 | 16 | 60 | 30 | 22 | 1 | 1.5 | 3 | 0 | 0 | 0 | 0 | 1 | 1 |

Source: Frontline Systems Inc.

TABLE 9.4   Validation Confusion (or Classification) Matrix for the Universal
Bank Data   The number of nearest neighbors chosen by the XLMiner© software is 4
(not shown in this table).   (C9T2)

## Validation: Classification Summary

| Confusion Matrix | | |
|---|---|---|
| Actual\Predicted ▼ 0 | ▼ 1 | ▼ |
| 0 | 1794 | 18 |
| 1 | 52 | 136 |

Source: Frontline Systems Inc.

(because different continuous attributes are measured in different scales). For the
dummy type or categorical attributes, most programs use a weighting mechanism
that is beyond the scope of this treatment. XLMiner© allows the user to normalize
distances by using the "rescale" procedure.

*The diagnostic statistics for the estimated model will tell if we have possibly found a useful classification scheme.*

The diagnostic statistics for the estimated model will tell if we have possibly
found a useful classification scheme. In this instance, we want to find a way to
classify customers as likely to accept a personal loan. How accurately can we do
that by considering the range of customer attributes in our data? Are there some
attributes that could lead us to classify some customers as much more likely to
accept a loan and other customers as quite unlikely? While the accuracy measures
are often produced by the software for both the training data set and the validation data set, our emphasis should clearly be on those measures pertaining to
the validation data. There are two standard accuracy measures we will examine:
the *classification matrix* (also called the *confusion matrix*) and the *lift chart*.
The validation classification matrix for the Universal Bank data training data is
shown in Table 9.4.

When our task is classification, accuracy is often measured in terms of error
rate, the percentage of records we have classified incorrectly (the converse, of
course, would be the percentage of records correctly classified). The error rate is
often displayed for both the training data set and the validation data set in separate
tables. Table 9.4 is the confusion matrix for the validation data set in the Universal
Bank case. The misclassification rate is the number misclassified (52 + 18 = 70)
divided by the total records (52 + 18 + 1794 + 136 = 2,000). This gives a misclassification in this instance of 3.5% (70/2,000 = 0.035).

The table is correctly called either a *confusion matrix* or a *classification matrix*. In Table 9.4, there were 136 records that were correctly classified as "class 1"
(i.e., probable personal loan candidates). They were correctly classified because
these records represented individuals that did indeed take out a personal loan.
However, 18 records were classified as class 1 incorrectly; these were individuals
that the model expected to take out a personal loan when, in fact, they did not historically do so. In addition, the table shows 1,794 records predicted to be class 0
(i.e., not probable loan candidates). These records were classified correctly since

**TABLE 9.5**

Validation Classification Matrix (Confusion Matrix) for the Universal Bank Data

The number of nearest neighbors selected was 4 (not shown in this table). (C9T2)

Source: Frontline Systems Inc.

**Validation: Classification Summary**

**Confusion Matrix**

| Actual\Predicted | 0 | 1 |
|---|---|---|
| 0 | 1794 | 18 |
| 1 | 52 | 136 |

**Error Report**

| Class | # Cases | # Errors | % Error |
|---|---|---|---|
| 0 | 1812 | 18 | 0.993377483 |
| 1 | 188 | 52 | 27.65957447 |
| Overall | 2000 | 70 | 3.5 |

historically these individuals did not take out personal loans. Finally, 52 records were incorrectly classified as class 0 when they actually were loan acceptors. The table can then be used to compute a *misclassification rate*. This calculation simply shows the percentage of the records that the model has placed in the incorrect category. In this case, we have 2,000 records in the validation data set, and we have correctly classified 1,930 of them (1,794 + 136). But we have incorrectly classified 18 records as class 1 when they were actually in class 0. We have also incorrectly classified 52 records as class 0 when they were actually in class 1. Thus, we have incorrectly classified 70 records (18 + 52). The misclassification rate is the total number of misclassifications divided by the total records classified (and is usually reported as a percentage). Most packages show the calculation and report it.

In Table 9.5, the misclassification rate is shown in the lower right-hand corner as 3.5 percent (calculated as 70/2,000 and expressed as a percentage). It should be noted that there are two ways in which the error occurred in our example, and although some errors may be worse than others, the misclassification rate groups these two types of errors together.

While this may not be an ideal reporting mechanism, it is commonly used and displayed in the same manner by all data mining software. Some software programs allow placing different costs on the various types of errors as a way of differentiating their impacts to the firm. While the overall error rate of 3.5 percent in the validation data is low in this example, the error of classifying an actual loan acceptor incorrectly as a nonacceptor (52 cases) is much greater than that of incorrectly classifying an actual nonacceptor as a loan acceptor (only 18 cases).

Notice that in both Tables 9.4 and 9.5, the summary report is for the k=4 case, meaning that we have used four neighbors (*not* four attributes) to classify the records. The number 4 for the k value is chosen by the algorithm. The algorithm has taken a "vote" of the four nearest neighbors in order to classify each record as either a loan acceptor or a nonacceptor. The algorithm actually varied the number of nearest neighbors used from a small number to a large number and selected and reported the best value of k to use. Usually the researcher may specify the range of k values over which the program searches, and the program will respond

**TABLE 9.6**
**Search Log for the Universal Bank Data**
The best number of nearest neighbors has been chosen to be 4 because this provides the lowest validation misclassification rate. (C9T2)

Source: Frontline Systems Inc.

# Search Log

| K | Training: % Incorrect | Validation: % Incorrect |
|---|---|---|
| 1 | 0 | 4.1 |
| 2 | 1.833333333 | 4.6 |
| 3 | 2.5 | 3.65 |
| Best: 4 | 2.166666667 | 3.5 |
| 5 | 3.166666667 | 4.3 |
| 6 | 2.8 | 3.85 |
| 7 | 3.266666667 | 4.15 |
| 8 | 2.933333333 | 4 |
| 9 | 3.8 | 4.2 |
| 10 | 3.466666667 | 4.15 |
| 11 | 4.1 | 4.6 |
| 12 | 3.666666667 | 4.55 |

**Note:** Scoring will be done using K=4

by choosing the number of neighbors that optimizes the results (in this situation, XLMiner© minimized the validation misclassification error rate).

In Table 9.6, the XLMiner© program provides an easy way to visualize how the number of nearest neighbors has been chosen. The validation misclassification error rate of 3.5 percent is lowest for four neighbors.

A second way of examining the predictive capability and usefulness of a data mining model can be demonstrated with our Universal Bank example. All data mining software will display a lift chart for any calculated solution; the one for the Universal Bank k-Nearest-Neighbor model is displayed two ways in Figure 9.2.

Lift charts are the most common way (and perhaps the most important way) to compare different classification models. *Lift* is actually a ratio. Lift measures the change in concentration of a particular class when the model is used to select a group from a portion of the general population. Recall from Chapter 8 that lift charts use only reordered data for display; that is, the original order of the data has been replaced by ordering the data from those individuals most likely to accept a personal loan to those least likely to accept a personal loan. Recall that understanding that lift charts are drawn with "reordered" data is key to interpreting correctly what they mean. The most likely acceptors then are represented on the left in each of the charts and the least likely acceptors are represented towards the right-hand side of the chart.

Consider why Universal Bank is attempting to classify the records in its database into *acceptors* and *nonacceptors*. Perhaps Universal Bank is considering a direct solicitation to individuals in the database in order to obtain new personal loan applications. Based on previous experience, the percentage of individuals who respond favorably and take out a personal loan is slightly less than 10 percent

**FIGURE 9.2** **Decile-Wise Lift Chart and Cumulative Gains Lift Chart for the Universal Bank Validation Data Set** (C9T2)

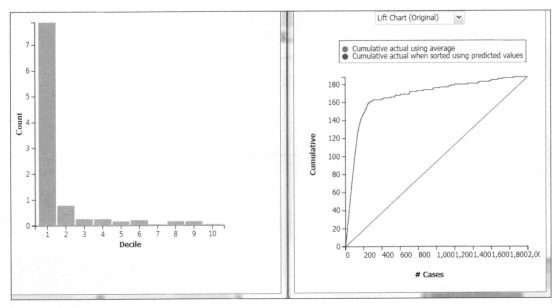

Source: Frontline Systems Inc.

(480 out of 5,000 persons in the data set took out a personal loan). But what if the bank could identify (i.e., predict), before sending a personal loan offer solicitation, the most likely *acceptors*? And what if the number of these likely *acceptors* was quite small relative to the size of the entire database? If the bank could successfully classify the database and identify these likely acceptors, then it might pay for the bank to restrict the solicitation to only those most "likely to respond" individuals. Preparation and delivery costs would be saved, and the bank would receive a *lift* in the percentage of recipients actually accepting a loan. What we may be able to help the bank do is to offer only to those customers with a high probability of loan acceptance, as opposed to offering to everyone in the database. Remember, over 90 percent of the people represented in the database are not likely loan acceptors. Only a relatively small number of the records in the database represent acceptors.

The lift curve is drawn from information about what the k-Nearest-Neighbor model predicted in each case and what actually took place. The lift chart shown on the right-hand side in Figure 9.2 is sometimes called a cumulative gains chart. It is constructed with the records arranged on the *x*-axis *left to right from the highest probability to the lowest probability of accepting a loan.* The *y*-axis reports the number of true positives at every point (i.e., the *y*-axis counts the number of records that represent loan acceptors).

Looking at the decile-wise lift chart on the left-hand side in Figure 9.2, we can see that if we were to choose the top 10 percent of the records classified by our model (i.e., the 10 percent that the algorithm predicts are most likely to accept a personal loan), our selection would include more than seven times as many correct classifications than if we were to select a random 10 percent of records from the database. That's a dramatic lift provided by the model when compared to a random selection.

The same information is displayed in a different manner in the lift chart on the right-hand side of Figure 9.2. This lift (or cumulative gains) chart represents the cumulative records correctly classified (on the *y*-axis), with *the records arranged in descending probability order* on the *x*-axis. Since the curve inclines steeply upward over the first few hundred cases displayed on the *x*-axis, the model appears to provide significant lift relative to a random or naïve selection of records (the naive model selection is depicted by the 45 degree line). Generally, a better model will display higher lift than other candidate models. Lift can be used to compare the performance of different kinds of algorithms (e.g., the k-Nearest-Neighbor algorithm compared with other classification algorithms) and is a good tool for relating the performance of two or more data mining algorithms using the same or comparable data. Notice carefully the straight line rising at a 45-degree angle in the lift chart in Figure 9.2: this could be called a reference line. The line represents how well you might do by classifying as a result of random selection (called a naive model in this context). If the calculated lift line is significantly above this reference line at any point, you may expect the model to outperform a random selection. In the Universal Bank case, the k-Nearest-Neighbor model outperforms a random selection by a very large margin.

# CLASSIFICATION TREES: A SECOND CLASSIFICATION TECHNIQUE

Our second data mining technique is variously called a classification tree, a decision tree, or a regression tree. As the name implies, it is, like k-Nearest Neighbor, a way of classifying or dividing up a large number of records into successively smaller sets in which the members become similar to one another. Data miners commonly use a tree metaphor to explain (and to display results from) this technique. Because the term *regression* is most often used to forecast a numeric quantity, when this classification technique is predicting numeric quantities, it is called a *regression tree*. When the technique is classifying by category, it is usually called either a *classification tree* or a *decision tree*. For this reason, the general technique is often called a CART model; CART stands for classification and regression tree.

The general technique is often called a CART model; CART stands for regression and classification tree.

As a child you may have played a game called "Animal, Mineral, or Vegetable." The origin of the game's name, some believe, arises from the 15th-century belief that all living organisms were either animal or vegetable, while all inanimate objects were mineral. Thus, the three categories could effectively separate all matter into three neat classes. In the game, as you may recall, one player picks any object and the other players must try to guess what it is by asking a limited number of yes or no questions. The object is to ask the least number of questions before correctly guessing the item. In a sense, classification trees are like the game: we begin by knowing virtually nothing about the items we are sorting, but we make up rules along the way that allow us to place the records into different bins, with each bin containing like objects. In "Animal, Mineral, or Vegetable," the set of questions you successfully used to determine the object's name would be the set of rules you could again use to correctly guess a class if the same object were to be chosen by another participant. In the same manner, we create a set of rules from our successful classification attempts, and these rules become the solution to the classification problem and allow the prediction of the class of any unknown.

We now return to our insect classification problem.

In Figure 9.3, we ask first if the abdomen length is greater than 7.1. The vertical line drawn at a value of 7.1 is the graphical representation of this question (or rule). Note that when we draw this line, all the known instances to the right of the line are katydids—we have a uniform classification on that side of the line. To the left of the line, however, we have a mix of katydids and grasshoppers in the known instances. Reasonable questions to ask are why did we choose to split on the attribute "abdomen length" and why did we choose a split value of exactly "7.1?" Would a different attribute to split on or a different value for the split have given better results?

A CART algorithm chooses the attribute to split on (and the particular value for the split) by using the concept of "information entropy." Entropy, or information entropy, is actually a mathematical concept hijacked (from Claude

**FIGURE 9.3**
**The Insect Classification Problem Viewed as a Classification Tree Exercise**

Courtesy of Eamonn Keogh.

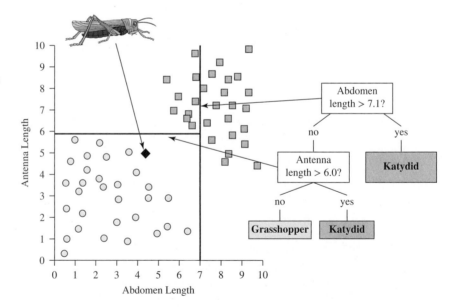

Shannon) by data scientists to aid in the tree-building process. Entropy is a measure of uncertainty associated with a random variable. It is a measure of disorder or, more precisely, unpredictability. The lower the entropy value, the less the uncertainty; the higher the entropy variable, the greater the uncertainty. We are attempting to lower uncertainty, and so the algorithm is directed to look for which particular attribute, and which particular value of that attribute, should be chosen to lower entropy by the greatest value; that attribute and that particular split value are then chosen as the first split. In Figure 9.3, we see the result of the entropy calculation as choosing to split on the attribute abdomen length at a value of 7.1. All records with values greater than 7.1 fall on the right side of the line drawn, and the remainder of records fall to the left. Note that the remaining two "sets" (i.e., all the records to the right or all the records to the left) have more homogeneity (less entropy) than the entire set of records we had at the beginning of the process.

A further question (or split) is necessary to continue the classification. But again we choose the next split attribute and split value by using an entropy calculation. Which attribute and which split value will now offer us the greatest reduction in entropy? The entropy reduction calculation suggests that next split on "antenna length" and at a value of 6 for this second split. This time, we ask whether the antenna length is greater than 6. The horizontal line drawn at a value of 6 in Figure 9.3 is the graphical representation of this split (or rule). An examination now of the entire set of known instances shows that there is homogeneity in each region (or minimum entropy in each region) defined by our two splits. The right-hand region contains *only* katydids, as does the topmost region in the upper left-hand corner. The bottommost region in the lower left-hand corner, however, contains *only* grasshoppers. Thus, we have divided the geometric attribute space into three regions, each containing only a single class of insect.

In performing two splits to create the three regions, we have also *created* the rules necessary to perform further classifications on unknown insects. Take the unknown insect shown in the diagram with an antenna length of 5 and an abdominal length of 4.5. By asking whether the unknown has an abdominal length of greater than 7.1 (answer no) and then asking whether the antenna length is greater than 6 (answer no), the insect is correctly classified as a grasshopper.

In our example, we have used only two attributes (abdomen length and antenna length) to construct the classification routine so that we could represent the results in Cartesian coordinate two-space. The rule we used to select split attributes and split values was to "reduce entropy." In a real-world situation, however, we need not confine ourselves to only two attributes. In fact, we can use many attributes. The geometric picture might be difficult (or impossible) to draw, but the decision tree (shown on the right-hand side of Figure 9.3) would look much the same as it does in our simple example. In data mining terminology, the two decision points in Figure 9.3 (shown as "abdomen length 7.1" and "antenna length 6") are called *decision nodes*. Nodes in XLMiner© are shown as circles with the decision value shown inside. They are called decision nodes because we classify unknowns by "dropping" them through the tree structure and letting the splitting rules sort them down different branches.

The bottom of our classification tree in Figure 9.3 has three leaves. Each *leaf* is a terminal node in the classification process; it represents the situation in which all the instances that follow that *branch* result in uniformity. The three leaves in Figure 9.3 are represented by the shaded boxes in the diagram. Data mining classification trees are *upside-down* in that the leaves are at the bottom, while the root of the tree is at the top; this is the convention in data mining circles. To begin a *scoring* process, all the instances are at the root (i.e., top) of the tree; these instances are partitioned by the rules we have determined with the known instances. The result is that the unknown instances move downward through the tree until reaching a leaf node, at which point they are (hopefully) successfully classified. In analytics software, the tree is "drawn" using rules from information theory that point the direction toward creating leaves that contain only homogeneous objects or instances. The tree representations of the solution can be drawn in most software (XLMiner© will do this), but that is primarily so the user can interpret and explain the result. It is the set of rules that the tree represents that allows rapid classifications of new unknowns.

Classification trees can become quite large and ungainly, but, more importantly, they will tend to overfit the data.

At times, the classification trees can become quite large and ungainly, but, more importantly, they will tend to overfit the data, much like the ARIMA models. It is common for data mining programs to *prune* the trees to remove branches to prevent this overfitting. An unpruned tree that was constructed using the training data set will sometimes match that data perfectly. Does that mean that this unpruned tree will do the best job in classifying new unknown instances? Probably not.

A good classification tree algorithm will make the best split (at the first decision node) first followed by decision rules that are made up with successively smaller and smaller numbers of training records. These later decision rules will become more and more idiosyncratic. The result may be (and usually will be) an overfit tree that will not do well in classifying new instances. Thus, the need for pruning. Each data mining package uses a proprietary pruning algorithm that usually takes into account for any branch the added drop in the misclassification rate versus the additional tree complexity. XLMiner© and other data mining programs use candidate tree formulations with the validation data set to find the lowest validation data set misclassification rate—that tree is selected as the final best-pruned tree. The actual process is more complicated than we have described here.

The best pruned tree is often used in actual practice.

In Figure 9.4, you can see that the error rate (misclassification rate) decreases on the training data as the number of splits increases, until finally each leaf contains only like items and the error rate is zero. But if we used this tree to classify unseen data (i.e., the validation data), the error rate bottoms out well before the error rate on the training data reaches zero. We use this property of decision trees as a basis for pruning. If we construct a tree with just enough splits to minimize the error rate on the unseen data, the resulting tree is called a "minimum error tree." If we choose the smallest tree within one standard error of the minimum error, the resulting tree is called the "best pruned tree." The best pruned tree is often used in actual practice; it is very similar to using the Akaike or Bayesian Information Criterions because it balances the complexity of the selected model

**FIGURE 9.4**
**Pruning Is Often Accomplished by Minimizing the Error Rate on the Unseen Data (Called a Minimum Error Tree) or Choosing a Tree within One Standard Deviation of That Point (Called a Best Pruned Tree)**

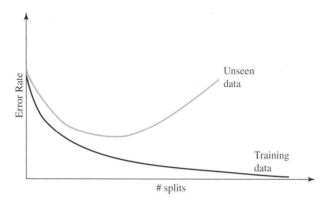

with its predictiveness. A data scientist who fails to use some form of pruning when employing a CART algorithm will almost certainly overfit the data and select a model that will perform poorly in the field.

Classification trees are very popular in actual practice because the decision rules are easily generated and, more importantly, because the trees themselves are easy to understand and explain to others. There are disadvantages as well, however. The classification trees can suffer from overfitting, and if they are not pruned well, these trees may not result in good classifications of new data (i.e., they will not score new data well). Attributes that are correlated will also cause this technique serious problems. It is somewhat similar to multicollinearity in a regression model. Be careful not to use attributes that are very closely correlated one with another. The more data you have available to build the model, the less chance the correlated attributes will cause problems.

## A Business Data Mining Example: Classification Trees

We can once again use the Universal Bank data from Table 9.2 in an attempt to classify customers into likely or unlikely personal loan clients. The first step, as always, would be to partition the data into training and validation data sets; the training data set was displayed in Table 9.3. Note that while the data scientist selects the attributes that are to be used, the CART algorithm selects the decision rules and the order in which they are executed using Shannon's information entropy approach. Table 9.7 displays a portion of the classification tree output from XLMiner© for the Universal Bank data. We have used a number of attributes to help in making up the decision rules; most of the attributes can be seen to intuitively affect whether a person is a likely personal loan candidate. Among the attributes used are:

- Customer's age
- Individual's average spending per month on credit cards
- Value of the individual's house mortgage
- Individual's annual income
- And others (but excluding ID and zip code).

**TABLE 9.7** Validation Classification Using the Best Pruned Tree on the Validation Data Set of the Universal Bank Data (C9T2)

## Validation: Classification Summary

| Confusion Matrix | | |
| --- | --- | --- |
| Actual\Predicted ▾ | 0 ▾ | 1 ▾ |
| 0 | 1783 | 29 |
| 1 | 16 | 172 |

| Error Report | | | |
| --- | --- | --- | --- |
| Class ▾ | # Cases ▾ | # Errors ▾ | % Error ▾ |
| 0 | 1812 | 29 | 1.600441501 |
| 1 | 188 | 16 | 8.510638298 |
| Overall | 2000 | 45 | 2.25 |

Source: Frontline Systems Inc.

The scoring summary format is identical to the one we saw with the k-Nearest-Neighbor technique. For the classification tree technique, the misclassification rate is just 2.25 percent; this is even lower than the 3.5 percent achieved with the k-Nearest-Neighbor model. A scant 29 individuals were expected to be likely to accept personal loans and yet did not do so.

Looking at the decile-wise lift chart on the left-hand side of Figure 9.5, we can see that if we were to choose the top 10 percent of the records classified by our best pruned classification tree model (i.e., the 10 percent most likely to accept a personal loan), our selection would include almost nine times as many correct classifications than if we were to select a random 10 percent of the database. That result is even more striking than the one we obtained with the k-Nearest-Neighbor model.

The lift chart on the right-hand side of Figure 9.5 is a cumulative gains chart. Recall that it is constructed with the records arranged on the *x*-axis *left to right from the highest probability of accepting a loan to the lowest probability of accepting a loan*. The *y*-axis reports the number of true positives at every point (i.e., the *y*-axis counts the number of records that represent actual loan acceptors). The fact that the cumulative personal loan line jumps sharply above the average beginning on the left side of the chart shows that our model does significantly better than choosing likely loan applicants at random. In other words, there is considerable lift associated with this model.

The actual topmost part of the classification tree that was produced by XLMiner© is displayed in Figure 9.6.

The classification tree first divides on the income variable. Is income greater than 92.5? That results in 2,162 of the records being sorted to the "less than 92.5" and 838 records sorted to the "greater than 92.5" side. XLMiner© then sorted on the basis of educational level on the "greater than" side and credit

**FIGURE 9.5** **Decile-Wise Lift Chart and Lift Chart (Cumulative Gains Chart) Using the Best Pruned Tree on the Validation Data Set of the Universal Bank** (C9T2)

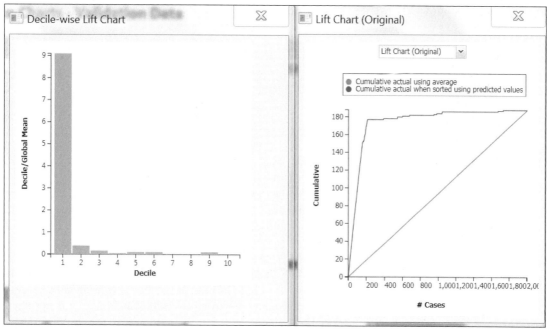

Source: Frontline Systems Inc.

**FIGURE 9.6** **A Portion of the Classification Tree Using the Best Pruned Tree on the Validation Data Set of the Universal Bank** (C9T2)

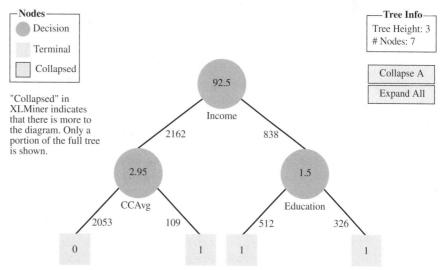

Source: Frontline Systems Inc.

**TABLE 9.8** **A Portion of the Tree Rules Using the Best Pruned Tree on the Validation Data Set of the Universal Bank** (C9T2)

**Fully Grown Tree Rules (Using Training Data)**

| Node ID | Parent ID | Left Child ID | Right Child ID | Split Var | Split Value/Set | Training Cases |
|---|---|---|---|---|---|---|
| 1 | N/A | 2 | 3 | Income | 92.5 | 3000 |
| 2 | 1 | 4 | 5 | CCAvg | 2.95 | 2162 |
| 3 | 1 | 6 | 7 | Education | 1.5 | 838 |
| 4 | 2 | N/A | N/A | N/A | N/A | 2053 |
| 5 | 2 | N/A | N/A | N/A | N/A | 109 |
| 6 | 3 | N/A | N/A | N/A | N/A | 512 |
| 7 | 3 | N/A | N/A | N/A | N/A | 326 |

Source: Frontline Systems Inc.

card average balance on the "less than" side and so on. While examining the partially drawn tree in Figure 9.6 is useful, it may be more instructive to examine the rules that are exemplified by the tree. Some of those rules are displayed in Table 9.8.

The rules displayed in Table 9.8 represent the same information shown in the tree diagram in Figure 9.6. Examining the first row of the table shows the split value as 92.5 for the split variable of income. It is called a decision node because there are two branches extending downward from this node (i.e., it is not a terminal node or leaf). The split on credit card average balance uses a split value of 2.95, while on education a split value of 1.5 is used. Row 2 shows that 2,162 cases are classified as going down the left branch, while 838 records travel down the right branch. It is the rules displayed in this table that the program uses to score new data, and they provide a concise and exact way to score new data in a speedy manner.

If actual values are predicted (as opposed to categories) for each case, then the tree is called a regression tree. For instance, we could attempt to predict the selling price of a used car by examining a number of attributes of the car. The relevant attributes might include the age of the car, the mileage the car had been driven to date, the original selling price of the car when new, and so on. The prediction would be expected to be an actual number, not simply a category. The process we have described could, however, still be used in this case. The result would then be a set of rules that would determine the predicted price.

*If actual values are predicted (as opposed to categories) for each case, then the tree is called a regression tree.*

## A Business Data Mining Example: Regression Trees

Regression trees (part of the CART family of algorithms) are used to predict actual numeric values rather than the category of a particular record. Consider the case of using Boston housing data to predict the median value of a home (i.e., the target is a variable denominated in thousands of dollars); the prediction will be made on a continuous variable, not a categorical variable as in the Universal Bank case. The attributes used will be items that are thought to affect housing prices in the area. For example, one attribute is the weighted distance to five

Boston employment centers (travel time to work is thought to affect housing prices). Another attribute is pupil-teacher ratio by town, which may be a proxy for school attractiveness, also thought to affect housing prices.

A "Regression Tree" algorithm is chosen for the prediction rather than a "Classification Tree" because the target is a continuous variable, but the algorithm works in much the same manner in constructing a tree that will probably require some pruning in order to prevent the disease of overfitting. The Regression Tree algorithm produces lift charts similar to a Classification Tree, but the confusion matrix will be replaced by the following diagnostic statistics: the root mean square error (RMSE as described on p. 30) and an R-squared calculation.

Consider Figure 9.7, which shows the upper portion of the regression tree as drawn by XLMiner©. The first split chosen by the algorithm was on the LSAT attribute. "LSAT" is the "% lower status of the population;" the greatest reduction in entropy was apparently achieved by using this attribute for the first split. Figure 9.7 shows that the split had a split value of 9.73. Entropy was reduced the most by splitting on the RM attribute and at a value of 9.73. Records would be sorted to the left if the RM value of a record is less than 9.73 (the actual split value is truncated in the diagrams drawn by XLMiner©) and sorted to the right if the value is greater. The next two splits suggested by the classification tree algorithm are on "RM" (number of rooms per dwelling) and on "CRIM" (per capita crime rate). The remainder of the tree is not shown in Figure 9.7, which is confined to displaying only the first three levels of the tree.

**FIGURE 9.7** **The Regression Tree (Only a Portion of the Full Tree) for the Boston Housing Data** (C9F7)

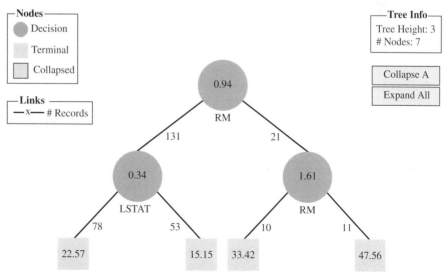

Source: Frontline Systems Inc.

**FIGURE 9.8** The Decile-Wise Lift Chart and The Cumulative Gains Chart for the Boston Housing Data (C9F7)

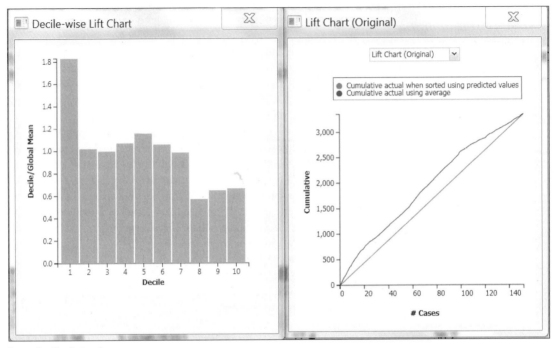

Source: Frontline Systems Inc.

We can, however, judge the appropriateness of the tree by examining the diagnostic statistics.

Figure 9.8 displays both the decile-wise lift chart as well as the cumulative gains chart for the best pruned regression tree on the Boston housing data. Both charts tell the story that there is some lift associated with the model. XLMiner© also makes available for regression tree estimates the RMSE and the R-squared calculations.

# NAIVE BAYES: A THIRD CLASSIFICATION TECHNIQUE

A third and somewhat different approach to classification uses statistical classifiers. This technique will also predict the probability that an instance is a member of a certain class. This technique is based on Bayes' theorem; we will describe the theorem below. In actual practice, these Naive Bayes algorithms have been found to be comparable in performance to the decision trees we have examined. One hallmark of the Naive Bayes model is speed, along with its high accuracy. Bayesian analytics techniques have been used successfully in many real-world situations. The Google self-driving car was based upon a Bayesian model predicting the state space of an unknown location. E-mail spam filters used at many universities and businesses are often based upon a Bayesian classification algorithm. The World War II codebreaking at Bletchley Park depicted in the movie *Enigma* used a technique titled Banburismus, which is a highly intensive Bayesian technique that allowed Alan Turing and his colleagues to guess a stretch of letters in a German Enigma-encoded message and measure their belief in the accuracy of these guesses (or classifications).

World War II codebreaking at Bletchley Park depicted in the movie *Enigma* used a technique titled Banburismus, which is a highly intensive Bayesian technique.

This model is called *naive* because it assumes (perhaps naively) that each of the attributes is independent of the values of the other attributes. Of course, this will never be strictly true, but in actual practice, the assumption (although somewhat incorrect) allows the rapid determination of a classification scheme and the accuracy does not seem to suffer appreciably when such an assumption is made.

To explain the basic procedure, we return to Eamonn Keogh's insect classification example. Our diagram may be of the same data we have used before, but we will examine it in a slightly different manner.

The known instances of katydids and grasshoppers are again shown in Figure 9.9, but only a single attribute of interest is labeled on the *y*-axis: antenna length. On the right-hand side of Figure 9.9, we have drawn a histogram of the antenna lengths for grasshoppers and a separate histogram representing the antenna lengths of katydids.

Now assume we wish to use this information about a single attribute to classify an unknown insect. Our unknown insect has a measured antenna length of 3 (as shown in Figure 9.10). Look on the problem as an entirely statistical problem. Is this unknown more likely to be in the katydid distribution or the grasshopper distribution? A length of 3 would be in the far-right tail of the katydid distribution (and therefore unlikely to be a part of that distribution). But a length of 3

**FIGURE 9.9**

**Insect Example**

This has only a single attribute displayed: antenna length. Abdomen length is still measured on the *x*-axis.

Courtesy of Eamonn Keogh.

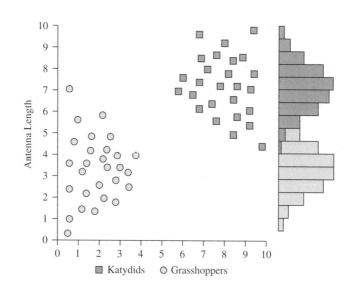

■ Katydids   ○ Grasshoppers

**FIGURE 9.10**
**Histograms**
**Representing**
**Antenna Lengths**
Katydids are on the
left and grasshoppers
on the right.

Courtesy of Eamonn Keogh.

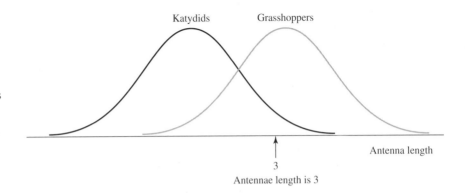

is squarely in the center of the grasshopper distribution (and therefore it is more
likely to be a member of that distribution). Of course, there is the possibility
that the unknown with an antenna length of 3 is actually part of the katydid
distribution (and therefore is actually a katydid), but that probability is small,
as evidenced by a length of 3 being in the small tail of the distribution. It is
far more likely that our unknown is part of the grasshopper distribution (and is
therefore truly a grasshopper). So far we have used only a single attribute. What
if we consider an additional attribute? Would that perhaps help our accuracy in
making classifications?

Figure 9.11 represents two attributes (antenna length on the *y*-axis and abdomen length on the *x*-axis) for the known katydids and grasshoppers. By using the
two attributes together, we effectively create a quadratic boundary between the

**FIGURE 9.11**
**Two Sets of**
**Histograms**
These represent the
antenna lengths of
katydids on the *y*-axis,
and abdomen lengths
on the *x*-axis.

Courtesy of Eamonn Keogh.

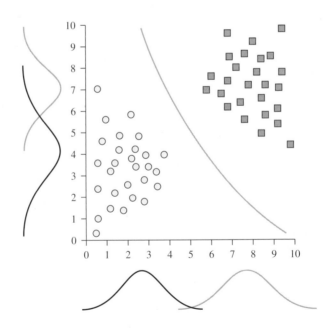

two classes of known insects. An unknown would be classified by its location above or below the boundary. One of the important features of the Naive Bayes model is that it handles irrelevant features quite well. If an irrelevant feature is included in the attributes list, it has little effect on the classifications the model makes (and thus introduces little error).

To examine this technique, we will use actual data from the passenger list of the HMS *Titanic*. On Sunday evening, April 14, 1912, the *Titanic* struck an iceberg. The ship sank a scant two hours and 40 minutes later. We have somewhat complete information on the 2,201 souls on the ship at the time of the accident. We say the information is "somewhat" complete because the data are based on a report made shortly after the event and the White Star line (the owners of the *Titanic*) kept their records in a peculiar manner.[10] For instance, boys are classified by the title "Master," but girls are not clearly distinguished from women. The data are not without some ambiguity, but we can still attempt to ascertain characteristics of the survivors. We are attempting to classify individuals as survivors of the disaster or nonsurvivors (i.e., those who perished). Our data looks like the following:

| Age | Sex | Class | Survived |
| --- | --- | --- | --- |
| Adult | Male | First | Alive |
| Adult | Male | First | Alive |
| Adult | Male | First | Alive |
| Adult | Male | First | Alive |
| Adult | Male | First | Alive |
| Adult | Male | First | Alive |
| Adult | Male | First | Alive |
| Adult | Male | First | Alive |
| Adult | Male | First | Alive |

The data set contains information on each of the individuals on the *Titanic*. We know whether they were adult or child, whether they were male or female, the class of their accommodations (first class passenger, second class, third class, or crew), and whether they survived that fateful night. In our list, 711 are listed as alive while 1,490 are listed as dead; thus, only 32 percent of the people on board survived.

What if we wished to examine the probability that an individual with certain characteristics (say, an adult, male crew member) were to survive? Could we use the Naive Bayes method to determine the probability that this person survived? The answer is yes; that is precisely what a Naive Bayes model will do. In this case, we are attempting to classify the adult, male crew member into one of two categories: alive or dead.

The Naive Bayes process begins like our two previous techniques; the data set is divided into a training data set and a validation data set. In Table 9.9, we

[10] The *Titanic* data set is used by permission of Professor Robert J. MacG. Dawson of Saint Mary's University, Halifax, Nova Scotia. See Dawson, "The Unusual Episode, Data Revisited," *Journal of Statistics Education*, vol. 3, no. 3 (1995).

**TABLE 9.9**  Validation Data Scoring for the Naive Bayes Model of *Titanic* Passengers and Crew  (C9T9)

## Validation: Classification Summary

| Confusion Matrix | | |
|---|---|---|
| Actual\Predicted ▼ | Alive ▼ | Dead ▼ |
| Alive | 130 | 149 |
| Dead | 50 | 551 |

| Error Report | | | |
|---|---|---|---|
| Class ▼ | # Cases ▼ | # Errors ▼ | % Error ▼ |
| Alive | 279 | 149 | 53.40501792 |
| Dead | 601 | 50 | 8.319467554 |
| Overall | 880 | 199 | 22.61363636 |

Source: Frontline Systems Inc.

present the validation summary report for the Naive Bayes model as computed in XLMiner©.

The misclassification rate on the validation data set that included 880 souls is computed by XLMiner© as 22.61 percent, but the lift chart and the decile-wise lift chart in Figure 9.12 show that the model does improve on naively selecting a class at random for the result. Note that the naive model would have us predict every individual as a casualty since that is the predominant result. Doing so, we would incorrectly classify the 279 survivors in the validation data set as dead; thus, the naive model validation data set misclassification rate is 31.70 percent (significantly higher than the Naive Bayes misclassification rate).

*Bayes' theorem* predicts the probability of a prior event (called a posterior probability), given that a certain subsequent event has taken place.

The Naive Bayes model rests on Bayes' theorem. Simply stated, *Bayes' theorem* predicts the probability of a prior event (called a posterior probability), given that a certain subsequent event has taken place. For instance, what is the probability that a credit card transaction is fraudulent, given that the card has been reported lost? Note that the reported loss preceded the current attempted use of the credit card.

The posterior probability is written as P(A | B). Thus , P(A | B) is the probability that the credit card use is fraudulent, given that we know the card has been reported lost. P(A) would be called the prior probability of A and is the probability that any credit card transaction is fraudulent, regardless of whether the card is reported lost.

The Bayesian theorem is stated in the following manner:

$$P(A \mid B) = \frac{P(B \mid A)P(A)}{P(B)}$$

where:

P(A) is the prior probability of A. It is *prior* in the sense that it does not take into account any information about B.

**FIGURE 9.12**   **Cumulative Gains Lift Chart and Decile-Wise Lift Chart for the Naive Bayes** *Titanic*
**Model**   (C9T9)

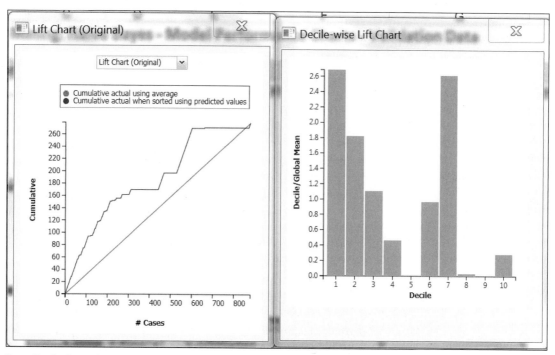

Source: Frontline Systems Inc.

$P(A \mid B)$ is the conditional probability of $A$, given $B$. It is also called the
*posterior probability* because it is derived from or depends upon the specified
value of $B$. This is the probability we are usually seeking to determine.

$P(B \mid A)$ is the conditional probability of $B$, given $A$.

$P(B)$ is the prior probability of $B$.

An additional example will perhaps make the use of Bayes' theorem clearer.
Consider that we have the following data set showing eight credit card transactions. For each transaction, we have information about whether the transaction was fraudulent and whether the card used was previously reported lost (see
Table 9.10).

Applying Bayes' theorem:

$$P(Fraud \mid Card\ Reported\ Lost) = \frac{P(Lost \mid Fraud)\ P(Fraud)}{P(Lost)}$$

$$= \frac{\left(\frac{2}{3}\right)\left(\frac{3}{8}\right)}{\frac{3}{8}} = 0.667$$

**TABLE 9.10**
Credit Card
Transaction Data Set

| Transaction No. | Fraudulent? | Reported Lost? |
|---|---|---|
| 1 | Yes | Yes |
| 2 | No | No |
| 3 | No | No |
| 4 | No | No |
| 5 | Yes | Yes |
| 6 | No | No |
| 7 | No | Yes |
| 8 | Yes | No |

and

$$P(NonFraud \mid Card\ Reported\ Lost) = \frac{P(Lost \mid NonFraud)P(NonFraud)}{P(Lost)}$$

$$= \frac{\left(\frac{1}{5}\right)\left(\frac{5}{8}\right)}{\frac{3}{8}} = 0.333$$

Thus, the probability of a fraudulent transaction if the card has been reported lost is 66.7 percent. The probability of a nonfraudulent transaction if the card has been reported lost is 33.3 percent.

Returning to the *Titanic* data and the Naive Bayes model calculated by XLMiner$^{©}$, we may now demonstrate the calculation of the posterior probabilities of interest. These are the answers to our question concerning the probability that an adult, male crew member would survive the disaster. XLMiner$^{©}$ produces an additional output for the Naive Bayes model displaying the prior class probabilities and the calculated conditional probabilities. These are displayed in Table 9.11.

To answer our question concerning the survival probability of an adult, male crew member we need once again to apply Bayes' theorem.

The statement of Bayes theorem would be:

$$P(alive \mid age = adult,\ sex = male,\ class = crew)$$
$$= \frac{P(adult,\ male,\ crew \mid alive)P(alive)}{P(adult,\ male,\ crew)}$$

We first need to calculate the conditional probabilities required in the Bayes' theorem:

Conditional probability of "alive" if you were a crew member, male, and adult:

$$P(alive) = (0.28440367)(0.495391705)(0.912442396)$$
$$(0.327024981) = 0.042040736$$

**TABLE 9.11**
Prior Probabilities
and Prior
Conditional
Probabilities
Calculated in
XLMiner© for the
*Titanic* Data   (C9T9)

Source: Frontline Systems Inc.

## Prior Probability

| Class | Probability |
|---|---|
| Alive | 0.327024981 |
| Dead | 0.672975019 |

## Prior Conditional Probability: Training

| Prior Conditional Probability: Training-Age | | |
|---|---|---|
| Value/Class | Alive | Dead |
| Adult | 0.912442396 | 0.970819304 |
| Child | 0.087557604 | 0.029180696 |

| Prior Conditional Probability: Training-Sex | | |
|---|---|---|
| Value/Class | Alive | Dead |
| Male | 0.495391705 | 0.912457912 |
| Female | 0.504608295 | 0.087542088 |

| Prior Conditional Probability: Training-Class | | |
|---|---|---|
| Value/Class | Alive | Dead |
| First | 0.279816514 | 0.085106383 |
| Second | 0.172018349 | 0.10862262 |
| Third | 0.263761468 | 0.356103024 |
| Crew | 0.28440367 | 0.450167973 |

Note that we are now multiplying probabilities, assuming they are independent. In like manner, we calculate the conditional "dead" probability:

Conditional probability of "dead" if you were a crew member, male, and adult:

$$P(dead) = (0.450167973)(0.912457912)(0.970819304)$$
$$(0.672975019) = 0.268364325$$

To compute the actual (or posterior) probabilities, we divide each of these conditional probabilities by their sum:

Posterior probability of "alive" if you were a crew member, male, and adult:

$$= (0.042040736)/(0.042040736 + 0.268364325) = 0.135438307$$

And

Posterior probability of "dead" if you were a crew member, male, and adult:

$$= (0.268364325)/(0.268364325 + 0.042040736) = 0.864561693$$

There are only two possible outcomes here ("dead" or "alive"), and the posterior probabilities should (and do) sum to 1 (0.135438307 + 0.864561693 = 1). The Bayes theorem calculation in this instance includes a sum in the denominator because the denominator includes all individuals who are adult, male, and crew, whether they are dead or alive (hence, the sum of two probabilities).

Naive Bayes has assumed the attributes have independent distributions. While this is not strictly true, the model seems to work well in situations where the assumption is not grossly violated. Use of larger data sets will all but eliminate the problem of including irrelevant attributes in the model. The effects of these irrelevant attributes are minimized as the data set becomes larger.

We can again use the Universal Bank data and apply the Naive Bayes model in order to predict customers who will accept a personal loan. Figure 9.13 displays the Naive Bayes results from XLMiner© for the Universal Bank data.

Once again, it is clear that the model performs much better than a naive selection of individuals when we try to select possible loan acceptors. Looking at the decile-wise lift chart on the right-hand side of Figure 9.13, we can see that if we were to choose the top 10 percent of the records reordered by our classification tree model (i.e., the 10 percent most likely to accept a personal loan), our selection would include approximately seven times as many correct classifications than if we were to select a random 10 percent of the database and count the number of acceptors included (i.e., the naive model). While Naive Bayes models do extremely well on training data, in real-world applications these models tend not to do quite as well as other classification models in some situations. This is likely due to the disregard of the model for attribute interdependence. In many real-world situations, however, Naive Bayes models do just as well as other classification models. While the Naive Bayes model is relatively simple, it makes sense to try the simplest models first and to use them

**FIGURE 9.13**  **The Naive Bayes Model Applied to the Universal Bank Data**
Included are the confusion matrix, misclassification rate, and lift charts for the validation data set   (C9F13)

## Validation: Classification Summary

| Confusion Matrix | | |
|---|---|---|
| Actual\Predicted ▾ | 0 ▾ | 1 ▾ |
| 0 | 1762 | 50 |
| 1 | 57 | 131 |

| Error Report | | | |
|---|---|---|---|
| Class ▾ | # Cases ▾ | # Errors ▾ | % Error ▾ |
| 0 | 1812 | 50 | 2.759381898 |
| 1 | 188 | 57 | 30.31914894 |
| Overall | 2000 | 107 | 5.35 |

**FIGURE 9.13**  (continued)

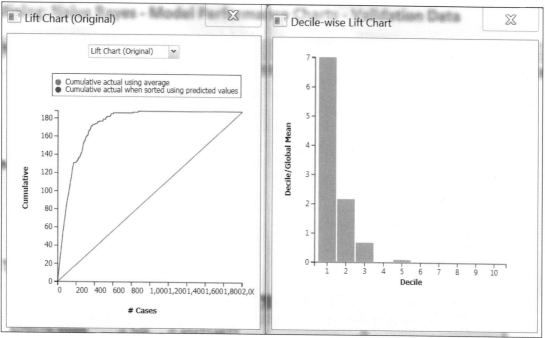

Source: Frontline Systems Inc.

if they provide sufficient results. Data sets (especially small data sets) that contain highly interdependent attributes may fare poorly with Naive Bayes.

## LOGIT: A FOURTH CLASSIFICATION TECHNIQUE

Logistic regression (or logit) is perhaps the most famous of the classification algorithms and is used in a variety of fields. It is the only classification algorithm to be associated with a Nobel Prize. Economist Daniel McFadden won the Nobel Memorial Prize in 2000 for his development of a discrete choice model, that is, a particular form of logit. The logit technique is a natural complement to linear least-squares regression. It has something in common with the ordinary linear regression models we examined in Chapters 4 and 5. Ordinary linear regression provides a universal framework for much of economic analysis; its simplified manner of looking at data has proven useful to researchers and forecasters for decades. But ordinary linear regression assumes a continuous numeric target variable and tries to estimate the functional relationship between the predictors and the target variable.

Economist Daniel McFadden won the Nobel Memorial Prize in 2000 for his development of a discrete choice model, that is, a particular form of logit.

Logistic regression serves much the same purpose for categorical data. The single most important distinction between logistic regression and ordinary regression is that the dependent variable in logistic regression is categorical (and not continuous numerical). The explanatory variables, or attributes, may be either continuous or categorical (as they were in linear least-squares models). Just like the ordinary linear regression model, logistic regression is able to use all sorts of extensions and sophisticated variants. Logistic regression has found its way into the toolkits of not only forecasters and economists but also of, for example, toxicologists and epidemiologists.

In situations where the target variable is categorical, ordinary linear regression models become inadequate. Thus, a different approach involving a very different estimating procedure is required. What logit does is to transform the concept of an ordinary linear regression into an equation able to predict the probabilities of the possible outcomes, not just the numeric value of the target variable itself.

The Universal Bank situation we have been examining provides a case in point. The dependent variable, the item we are attempting to forecast, is dichotomous—either a person accepts a loan or rejects the loan. There is no continuous variable here; it is more like an on/off switch. But why are we unable to use linear least-squares models on this data?

Consider Table 9.12: it contains information about 20 students, the hours they spent studying for a qualifying exam, and their results. If they passed the exam, the table shows a 1; if they failed the exam, the table shows a 0.

If we graph this data as a scatterplot (Figure 9.14), we see there are two possible outcomes: pass (shown as 1) and fail (shown as 0).

It appears from the scatterplot that students who spent more time studying for the exam did have a better chance of passing. We might seek to quantify this perception by running an ordinary least-squares regression using "hours of study" as the single independent variable (i.e., attribute) and "pass/fail" as the

**TABLE 9.12**

**Data on 20 Students and Their Test Performance and Hours of Study** (C10T12)

| Student No. | Hours of Study | Pass/Fail |
|---|---|---|
| 1 | 2.5 | 0 |
| 2 | 22.6 | 1 |
| 3 | 17.8 | 0 |
| 4 | 5.4 | 0 |
| 5 | 14 | 0 |
| 6 | 13.3 | 1 |
| 7 | 26 | 1 |
| 8 | 33.1 | 1 |
| 9 | 13.6 | 0 |
| 10 | 45.3 | 1 |
| 11 | 1.9 | 0 |
| 12 | 31.4 | 1 |
| 13 | 27 | 1 |
| 14 | 10.1 | 0 |
| 15 | 2.7 | 0 |
| 16 | 16.3 | 1 |
| 17 | 14.5 | 1 |
| 18 | 4.5 | 0 |
| 19 | 22.6 | 1 |
| 20 | 17.1 | 1 |

**FIGURE 9.14**
**Scatterplot of**
**Student Performance**
(C10T12)

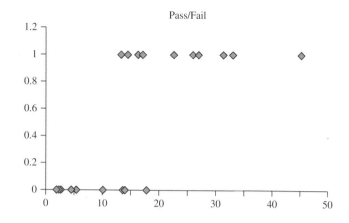

**TABLE 9.13**
**Linear Least-Squares**
**Regression**
(C10T12)

| | Coefficients | Standard Error | T-test | P-value |
|---|---|---|---|---|
| Intercept | 0.002053203 | 0.15 | 0.01 | 0.99 |
| Hours of Study | 0.032071805 | 0.01 | 4.47 | 0.00 |

dependent variable or target. Running this regression results in the output in Table 9.13.

Since the "hours of study" coefficient is positive (0.03), it appears to indicate that more study leads to a higher probability of passing. But is the relationship correctly quantified? Suppose a student studies for 100 hours. How well will this student do on the exam? Substituting into the regression equation, we have:

$$\text{Pass/fail} = 0.002053 + (0.032072) \text{ X } (100)$$

$$\mathbf{3.209253} = 0.002053 + (0.032072) \text{ X } (100)$$

What does this mean? Is the predicted grade 3.21 percent? That doesn't seem to make sense. Examining the regression line estimated and superimposing it on the data scatter may make the problem clear (see Figure 9.15).

The difficulty becomes clearer when examining the diagram. There are only two states of nature for the dependent variable (pass and fail). However, the regression line plotted in Figure 9.13 is a straight line sloping upward to the right and predicting values all along its path. When predicting the outcome from 100 hours of study, the regression chooses a number (i.e., 3.209253) that is much greater than the maximum value of 1 exhibited in the data set. Does this mean the individual has passed the test 3.21 times? Or does this mean that the expected score is 3.21 percent? Or does this have any meaningful explanation at all? This rather confusing result indicates that we have used an inappropriate tool in attempting to find the answer to our question. In earlier chapters, we assumed the dependent variable was continuous; this one is not. What we are attempting to estimate is

**FIGURE 9.15**
**Linear Least-Squares**
**Regression Plot**

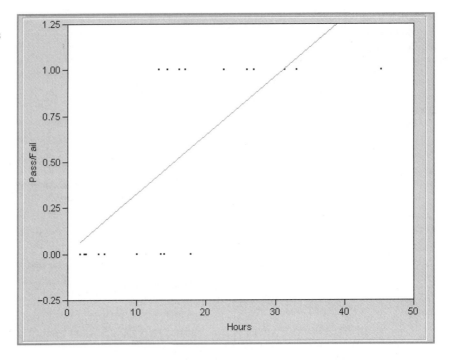

This function of the dependent variable is limited to values between zero and one. The function we use is called a *logit*.

actually the probability of passing the exam; that will be a number between zero and one. Linear least-squares regression does not restrict the predictions of the dependent variable to a range of zero to one as we would like in this case.

We would like to use this same data but predict the probability that an individual would pass the test given a certain number of hours of study, but that will require a different algorithm. To accomplish this, we modify the linear least-squares model by modifying what we use as the target variable. Ordinarily, we simply use *Y, a numeric variable,* as the target variable; in logit, we use a function of *Y* as the dependent variable instead. This function of the dependent variable is limited to values between zero and one. The function we use is called a *logit,* and that is the reason the technique is called logistic regression.

The logit is $\text{Log}(e^{\alpha+\beta_1 X_1+\beta_2 X_2+\cdots+\beta_p X_p})$. You will recognize this as being similar to our explanation of the logistic curve in Chapter 3. In fact, the concepts are one and the same. We are going to use some knowledge of how growth works in the real world just as we did in Chapter 3. Recall that the diffusion models' assumed growth proceeded along an s-curve. When we used these models to predict new product sales, we did so in the knowledge that real-world new products almost always follow such a path. We now make the same assumption that real-world probabilities will behave in a similar manner. This assumption has withstood the test of time, as logistic regression has proven very predictive and accurate in actual practice.

The logistic regression model will estimate a value for pass/fail as a probability with zero as the minimum and one as the maximum. If we were to look

**FIGURE 9.16**
**The Logit Estimated**
**for the Student Data**

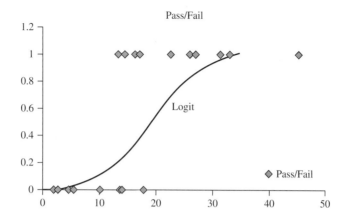

at the entire range of values that a logistic regression would estimate for the student data, it would appear like the s-curve in Figure 9.16. Recall that "hours of study" are represented on the *x*-axis, while "pass/fail" is represented on the *y*-axis. If for instance, an individual had studied for a scant 10 hours, the model would predict a probability of passing somewhere near 10 percent (since the *y*-axis represents the values from zero to one, it can be read directly as the probability of occurrence of the dependent event). However, if the individual in question were to have studied for 30 hours, the probability of passing is predicted to be near 90 percent.

# BANK DISTRESS

One example of the use of logit would be for a banking commission to predict the probability that any particular bank is likely to face distress in the near future. Bank distress is a condition where the bank cannot meet, or has difficulty paying off, its financial obligations to its creditors. Financial analysts wishing to assess the performance of a bank look for ways to measure the financial and economic consequences of past management decisions that have shaped the investments, assets, expenses, and financing of the bank. While there are many tools that address measurement in very specific and often narrow ways, analysts often "run the numbers" by calculating illuminating ratios. Ratios are easy to calculate, and a few selected ratios will often yield the information the analyst is seeking.

Ratios, to be useful, should have clear meaning and be predictive of the item being forecasted. In the past, analysts have looked at individual ratios as simple tests to be examined one at a time, but logit allows the ratios that have been useful in the past to be used together in a single predictive model with much more predictive power than any single ratio alone. While there are differences in accounting methods among various industries, there are often rigid standards applied by the government to the banking community.

Bank regulators need a way to identify banks that are in distress; the costs of a bank failing are quite costly, not only to the bank's investors and owners but also to the bank's customers. The effect on a single bank failure may also lead to failures in related banks. Because of this, the European Banking Authority (EBA) does stress testing on banks routinely (you can even see some of their methodology online[11]). Let's use a simplified example of how logit may be used with the ratios the EBA uses.

In our data set are 25 banks for which we have the values of two ratios; we also know whether each of these banks is in distress. The banks are shown in Table 9.14.

We will begin our analysis by using only a single ratio (total loans and leases divided by assets) as the attribute and using the "Distress" variable as the target. The goal is to create a model that is able to predict which banks are in distress by using ratio analysis. Running a logit on the entire data set of 25 banks with that variable gives the result shown in Table 9.15.

**TABLE 9.14**

**Stress Data. Stressed Banks (Ones in Distress) Are Labeled as "1," While Banks That Are Strong and Not Stressed (I.e., Strong Banks) Are Labeled as "0."** (C9T14)

| Obs | Stress | Total Loans and Leases to Assets | Total Expenses to Assets |
|-----|--------|----------------------------------|--------------------------|
| 1 | 1 | 0.65 | 0.12 |
| 2 | 1 | 0.7 | 0.12 |
| 3 | 1 | 0.66 | 0.11 |
| 4 | 1 | 0.92 | 0.09 |
| 5 | 1 | 0.69 | 0.11 |
| 6 | 1 | 0.74 | 0.14 |
| 7 | 1 | 0.75 | 0.12 |
| 8 | 1 | 0.75 | 0.12 |
| 9 | 1 | 0.7 | 0.16 |
| 10 | 1 | 0.64 | 0.13 |
| 11 | 1 | 0.64 | 0.11 |
| 12 | 1 | 1.01 | 0.11 |
| 13 | 0 | 1.04 | 0.1 |
| 14 | 0 | 0.51 | 0.09 |
| 15 | 0 | 0.3 | 0.08 |
| 16 | 0 | 0.55 | 0.1 |
| 17 | 0 | 0.6 | 0.13 |
| 18 | 0 | 0.54 | 0.08 |
| 19 | 0 | 0.43 | 0.08 |
| 20 | 0 | 0.52 | 0.07 |
| 21 | 0 | 0.54 | 0.08 |
| 22 | 0 | 0.3 | 0.09 |
| 23 | 0 | 0.67 | 0.07 |
| 24 | 0 | 0.79 | 0.12 |
| 25 | 0 | 0.46 | 0.08 |

[11] http://www.eba.europa.eu/risk-analysis-and-data.

**TABLE 9.15**   **Logit Model for Bank Distress Given Only One Ratio as a Predictor: Total Loans and Leases to Assets**   (C9T14)

| Predictor | Estimate | Confidence Interval: Lower | Confidence Interval: Upper | Odds | Standard Error | Chi2-Statistic | P-Value |
|---|---|---|---|---|---|---|---|
| Intercept | −5.1354956 | 4.884E-05 | 0.708943 | 0.005884 | 2.444695953 | 4.41280786 | 0.03567 |
| Total Loans and Leases to Assets | 7.84907599 | 1.7020223 | 3860606 | 2563.365 | 3.733363923 | 4.420143959 | 0.035517 |

Source: Frontline Systems Inc.

The P-value on the ratio is 0.035, indicating that there is a significant effect of the ratio on bank distress. To interpret the result, however, is probably best done by graphing the resulting logit.

The logit itself is not the probability. However, we are able to convert the logit (or log odds) into the probability by using the formula:

$$Probability = \frac{Odds}{1 + Odds}$$

Let's examine two different banks with different Total Loans and Leases to Assets ratios and predict the probability that each bank is in distress by calculating the probability that the bank is in the "1" class as opposed to the "0" class.

Bank number one has a Total Loans and Leases to Assets ratio of 0.6; Bank number two has a Total Loans and Leases to Assets ratio of 0.8. Note that the two financial ratios for the banks are quite close; they differ only by 0.2.

For bank number one, the probability of being in the "1" class (i.e., stressed) is:

$$Probability = \frac{e^{(-5.1355 + (7.8491 \, X \, 0.6))}}{(1 + -5.1355 + (7.8491 \, X \, 0.6))}$$

Probability = 0.3951 or **39.51%**

For bank number two, the probability of being in the "1" class (i.e., stressed) is:

$$Probability = \frac{e^{(-5.1355 + (7.8491 \, X \, 0.8))}}{(1 + -5.1355 + (7.8491 \, X \, 0.8))}$$

Probability = 0.7584 or **75.84%**

Notice that as the ratio increased only slightly, the probability that the bank was in distress increased by a much larger amount. Probabilities are not linear (they follow a logit pattern), and that is a compelling reason to use logit instead of ordinary least-squares regression in this case. Figure 9.17 makes this clear by examining the two different financial ratios for the two different banks; bank number one with only a 39.51 percent probability of being in distress would be classified by the logit

**FIGURE 9.17**
Logit Plot Using
the Attributes Total
Loans and Leases to
Total Assets

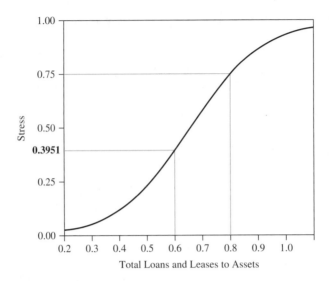

algorithm as "nonstressed." But bank number two with a 75.84 percent probability of being in distress would be classified by the logit algorithm as "stressed," assuming we used a cutoff value of 0.5 to separate stressed from nonstressed.

Table 9.16 also offers a second financial ratio that could be used in testing; Total Expenses to Assets. Could this second financial ratio also be useful in predicting bank stress? Once again, we will run a logit model with the dichotomous stress variable as the target and the financial ratio as the attribute. The goal again is to classify banks as either "stressed" or "nonstressed."

Let's examine the results of estimating the logit for the same two banks. They have different Total Expenses to Total Assets ratios. We wish again to predict the probability that each bank is in distress by calculating the probability that the bank is in the "1" class (stressed) as opposed to the "0" class (nonstressed).

**TABLE 9.16**  Logit Model for Bank Distress, Given Only One Ratio as a Predictor: Total Expenses to Assets  (C9T14)

| Predictor | Estimate | Confidence Interval: Lower | Confidence Interval: Upper | Odds | Standard Error | Chi2-Statistic | P-Value |
|---|---|---|---|---|---|---|---|
| Intercept | −9.8348255 | 3.616E-08 | 0.079321 | 5.36E-05 | 3.724852799 | 6.971321055 | 0.008283 |
| Total Expenses to Assets | 93.2988115 | 5.666E+10 | Inf | 3.3E+40 | 34.96924312 | 7.11835689 | 0.00763 |

Source: Frontline Systems Inc.

Bank number one has a Total Expenses to Total Assets ratio of 0.10; Bank number two has a Total Expenses to Total Assets ratio of 0.14. Note again that the two financial ratios for the banks are quite close; they differ only by 0.04 in this case.

For bank number one, the probability of being in the "1" class (i.e., stressed) is:

$$\text{Probability} = \frac{e^{(-9.8348 + (93.2988 \, X \, 0.10))}}{(1 + -9.8348 + (93.2988 \, X \, 0.10))}$$

$$\text{Probability} = 0.3763 \text{ or } \mathbf{37.63\%}$$

For bank number two, the probability of being in the "1" class (i.e., stressed) is:

$$\text{Probability} = \frac{e^{(-9.8348 + (93.2988 \, X \, 0.14))}}{(1 + -9.8348 + (93.2988 \, X \, 0.14))}$$

$$\text{Probability} = 0.9618 \text{ or } \mathbf{96.18\%}$$

Figure 9.18 displays the results of using the logit estimate to plot the probability that either bank will be in the "stressed" category. Bank number one with a Total Expenses to Total Assets ratio of 0.10 has only a 37.63 percent chance of being in the "stressed" category and would be classified by the logit algorithm as a "nonstressed" bank. Bank number two, however, with a Total Expenses to Total Assets ratio of 0.14 has a 96.18 percent chance of being in the "stressed" class; this bank would be classified by the logit algorithm as being "stressed."

Logistic regression is not limited to using only a single attribute; in our bank stress example, we could use both financial ratios at the same time, probably with even better results. Could more than two financial ratios be used? Yes, much as with multiple linear regression, we may use multiple attributes.

**FIGURE 9.18**
**Logit Plot Using the Attribute Total Expenses to Total Assets**

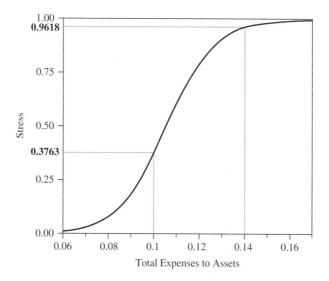

## Summary

In this chapter, we have covered four classification techniques that are commonly used by real data miners. Classification, however, is only a single aspect of data mining. In general, there is no one best classification technique; the individual data in a particular situation will determine the best technique to use. The diagnostic statistics will lead the researcher to choose an appropriate model; there may be no single optimal model.

Data mining also uses other tools such as clustering analysis, and this will be covered in Chapter 10. The growth in the use of commercial data mining tools rivals the growth in business forecasting software sales; SAS Enterprise Miner, Frontline Solver, and IBM/SPSS Modeler have become important additions to the forecaster's toolkit in recent years.

## Suggested Readings

Berry, Michael J. A.; and Gordon S. Linhoff. *Data Mining Techniques for Marketing, Sales, and Customer Relationship Management*. Indianapolis, IN: Wiley Publishing, Inc., 2004.

Cortada, James W. *The Digital Hand, Volume 2*. Oxford, U.K.: Oxford University Press, 2006.

Cramer, J. S. *Logit Models*. Cambridge, U.K.:Cambridge University Press, 2003.

De Ville, Barry. *Decision Trees for Business Intelligence and Data Mining*. Cary, NC: SAS Publishing, 2006.

Foreman, John W. *Data Smart*. Indianapolis, IN: John Wiley & Sons, Inc., 2014

Hilbe, Joseph M. *Logistic Regression Models*. Boca Raton, FL: Chapman & Hall/CRC, 2009.

Keating, Barry. "Analytics Off the Shelf." *Applied Marketing Analytics*, 2, no. 1 (Winter 2015–16), pp. 12–24.Keough, Eamonn. We would be remiss in not mentioning the tools Eamonn Keough has provided for this chapter to help explain the process of data mining; you may wish to examine his website (http://www.cs.ucr.edu/~eamonn/).

Mayer-Schonberger, Viktor; and Kenneth Cukier. *Big Data: A Revolution That Will Transform How We Live, Work, and Think*. New York: Houghton Mifflin Harcourt, 2013.

McGrayne, Sharon Bertsch. *The Theory That Would Not Die: How Bayes Rule Cracked the Enigma Code, Hunted Down Russian Submarines and Emerged Triumphant from Two Centuries of Controversy*. New Haven, CT.: Yale University Press, 2011.

SAS Institute. *Applied Analytics Using SAS Enterprise Miner*. Carey, NC.: SAS Institute, Inc., 2011.

Shannon, Claude. "A Mathematical Theory of Communication," *Bell System Techincal Journal*, 27 (July, October 1948). pp. 379–423, 623–656.

Shmueli, Galit; Nitin R. Patel; and Peter C. Bruce. *Data Mining for Business Analytics*. Hoboken, NJ: John Wiley & Sons, Inc., 2016.

Siegel, Eric. *Predictive Analytics*. Hoboken, NJ: John Wiley & Sons, Inc., 2013.

Singh, Simon. *The Code Book: The Science of Secrecy from Ancient Egypt to Quantum Cryptography*. New York: Anchor Books, 2000.

Wendler, Tito; and Soren Grottrup. *Data Mining with SPSS Modeler*. Switzerland: Springer International Publishing, 2016.

Witten, Ian H.; and Eibe Frank. *Data Mining: Practical Machine Learning Tools and Techniques*. Amsterdam: Elsevier, 2005.

**Exercises**

1. A data mining algorithm has been applied to a transaction dataset and has classified 88 records as fraudulent (30 correctly so) and 952 as nonfraudulent (920 correctly so). Which of the following situations represents the confusion matrix for the transactions data mentioned? Explain your reasoning.

    A.

    **Classification Confusion Matrix**

    | | Predicted Class | |
    |---|---|---|
    | Actual Class | 1 | 0 |
    | 1 | 58 | 920 |
    | 0 | 30 | 32 |

    B.

    **Classification Confusion Matrix**

    | | Predicted Class | |
    |---|---|---|
    | Actual Class | 1 | 0 |
    | 1 | 32 | 30 |
    | 0 | 58 | 920 |

    C.

    **Classification Confusion Matrix**

    | | Predicted Class | |
    |---|---|---|
    | Actual Class | 1 | 0 |
    | 1 | 30 | 32 |
    | 0 | 58 | 920 |

    D.

    **Classification Confusion Matrix**

    | | Predicted Class | |
    |---|---|---|
    | Actual Class | 1 | 0 |
    | 1 | 920 | 58 |
    | 0 | 30 | 32 |

2. Calculate the classification error rate for the following confusion matrix. Comment on the pattern of misclassifications. How much better did this data mining technique do compared to a naive model? What is the misclassification rate for the naive model?

    | | Predict Class 1 | Predict Class 0 |
    |---|---|---|
    | Actual 1 | 8 | 2 |
    | Actual 0 | 20 | 970 |

3. Explain what is meant by Bayes' theorem as used in the Naive Bayes model.

4. Explain the difference between a training data set and a validation data set. Why are these data sets used routinely with data mining techniques in the XLMiner© program and not used in the ForecastX™ program? Is there, in fact, a similar technique presented in a previous chapter that is much the same as partitioning a data set?

5. For a data mining classification technique, the validation data set lift charts are shown below. What confidence in the model would you express, given this evidence?

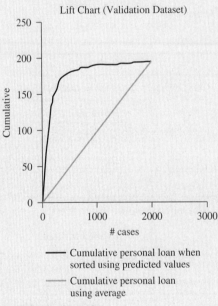

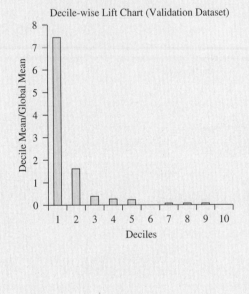

Cumulative personal loan when sorted using predicted values

Cumulative personal loan using average

Source: Frontline Systems Inc.

6. Wine (in this case, red wine) has been graded for many years by experts who actually taste a sample of the wine, examine its color and aroma, and assign a grade (in our case, high quality or lower quality). Would it be possible, however, to use attributes of the wine that are machine measurable such as fixed acidity and residual sugar to classify the wines?

Partition the data into two partitions (60 percent and 40 percent, respectively), the training data and the validation data. Estimate a kNN algorithm for the training data, and examine the resulting estimation.

Explain the overall misclassification rate for the validation partition and its calculation. What would have been the validation misclassification rate if you had used the naive model?

What does the validation confusion matrix tell the data scientist? Is the algorithm more likely to make one type of error than the other?

The lift chart is potentially the most important information provided by the algorithm. Examine either the cumulative gains chart, the lift chart proper, or the decile-wise lift chart. Do they each tell much the same story? How would you explain one of these lift charts to someone unfamiliar with predictive analytics?

7. Use the red wine data again with the same partition and estimate a classification model with Naive Bayes.

   Again explain the overall misclassification rate for the validation data. Is it different for the Naive Bayes algorithm and the kNN algorithm?

   Is the confusion matrix for the validation data different than the one obtained with the kNN algorithm?

   Finally, examine the lift chart and make a comparison with the kNN model.

8. The bank marketing data includes actual information for a direct marketing effort by a bank. We will attempt to construct a model with just a few of the available attributes. We are interested in classifying whether a customer will respond positively to the marketing effort offering a term deposit.

   The attributes you are to use are age, balance, duration, campaign, pdays, and previous; explanations of these numeric variables are in the file. After your initial analysis, you may wish to transform some of the remaining variables to attempt to estimate a more complete model.

   Use a logit model for the estimate, making sure to request an "analysis of coefficients" in XLMiner©. As usual, use a 60/40 split for the training and validation data sets, and request a full set of lift charts.

   Does this estimate, using only some of the available attributes, do better than a naive model in the overall misclassification rate? What if you examine the lift chart? Recall that the lift chart reorders the data from most likely to accept a marketing offer to least likely to accept such an offer. Now does the algorithm appear to have explanatory power (i.e., could you successfully use it to suggest who to market to in the first place)?

   Which of the attributes that you selected appear to have the greatest effect on the classification? How certain are you that these attributes have an effect on the classification?

   By creating dummy variables and categorical variables for the attributes that you did not use in this exercise already, you may extend the analysis in order to refine the algorithm. Evaluate the resulting output in the same manner described above and compare the two outputs. Did the addition of the extra attributes to the logit model add additional explanatory power?

9. The Boston housing data includes information from the 1970 U.S. census for the city of Boston and surrounding area. Note that there are two variables representing value; one is "Medv," which is a dollar value. The other is "Cat Medv," which is a binary variable indicating whether the house is of "high value" (signified by "1") or "lower value" (identified by "0").

   Estimate a classification tree using the Cat Medv variable as the target. You are trying to classify home as either high value or lower value by using the given attributes (such as the number of rooms in the house, the crime rate in the local area, and the age of the houses in the area). Use all of the attributes in the file to estimate the model requesting the "best pruned tree" to prevent overfitting. For display, however, request the "full tree."

   Evaluate the estimate for the best pruned tree using the confusion matrix, the misclassification rate, and, most importantly, the lift chart.

   By examining the full tree, you should be able to see how the CART algorithm will attempt to perfectly classify the records. In doing so, it may overfit the data, and that is the reason for using the pruning method.

   Now re-estimate the algorithm using the target Medv this time. In order to do so, you will have to use the "Prediction" menu in XLMiner© and select "Regression Tree."

The method is similar to the classification tree estimated earlier, but now an actual numerical prediction is being requested. Overfitting remains a possible problem, and so it will again be necessary to prune using either the best pruned tree or the minimum error tree.

10. The credit card fraud data is a small version (comprised of 14,240 records) of a much larger data set (containing 248,807 records); it is made up of 2013 European transactions. It is a very unbalanced data set in which there are only a few fraudulent transactions. Attempting to classify transactions as fraudulent will be difficult since there are very few instances of fraud.

    Use logit and a kNN model to create a predictive model for the credit card fraud data. Does either of these models have predictive power?

    Explain carefully the information provided by the lift chart or the decile-wise lift chart; how does this information differ from the information provided by the overall misclassification rate?

    What value to a firm could you see in creating such a model and using it in real time?

# Chapter **Ten**

# Ensemble Models and Clustering

Ensemble learning is the art of combining a diverse set of learners (individual models) together to improve on the stability and predictive power of a model.

## LEARNING OBJECTIVES

After reading this chapter, you should be able to:

- Explain the use of an ensemble type algorithm.
- Construct and employ three different ensemble type enhancements.
- Interpret the standard diagnostic statistics for these enhanced models.
- Explain how better decisions can be made through the use of ensembles.
- List and explain the advantages offered by clustering algorithms.
- Construct and employ the two basic methods used for clustering.
- Apply clustering to make business predictions.

## INTRODUCTION

The last decade has seen an explosion in the use among forecasters and data scientists of combining models (similar to the combination models in the Appendix of Chapter 5); the technique is called building "ensemble models." The single reason for this use of ensembles is the reduction in errors that results. By combining predictions, more robust and accurate models nearly always result in an improvement upon a single-model solution. This chapter will introduce the methods used by data scientists to create ensembles of the classification algorithms we have covered in Chapter 9. There are many methods today for creating ensembles, but we will confine ourselves to the three most popular methods, "bagging," "boosting" and the random forest method. Each of these methods may be applied to many data mining algorithms.

We will also examine "clustering," a set of algorithms for organizing data into sensible groupings; this is one of the most fundamental modes of understanding and learning. The use of clustering as a standard analytics technique has been made possible by the advances in storage and sensing technology and the extraordinary growth in applications such as Internet search capability, digital imaging, and high-quality sound and video capture. Most newly acquired data today are stored digitally, and that suggests the possibility of automatic retrieval and classification. The increases in the variety as well as the volume of such digital data require changes in our techniques for understanding, processing, and summarizing the data. There are many ways of summarizing such diverse and voluminous data: analysis of variance, linear regression, discriminant analysis, and correlation analysis are all useful. Clustering, however, has come to be the foremost manner of discovering natural groupings. The last portion of this chapter examines clustering.

# ENSEMBLES

Ensemble modeling
is a powerful way
to improve the
performance of
many classification
algorithms.

Ensemble modeling is a powerful way to improve the performance of many classification algorithms. Applying ensemble learning over and above the various algorithms you might be using often leads to better predictions. Data scientists have used ensemble models in competitions such as the KDnuggets Cup[1] and benefited from doing so. Ensemble learning is a broad topic and is only confined by your own imagination. For the purpose of this chapter, we will cover the basic concepts and ideas of ensemble modeling. Since ensemble features are included in all popular analytics software, including XLMiner©, IBM/SPSS Modeler, and SAS Enterprise Miner, it is possible for you to begin exploring ensembles immediately and employing them in practice.

Every analytics algorithm trades off bias and variance; we would like to minimize both at the same time but, as we shall see, that is not usually possible. Both bias and variance are sources of error in our models, but these are two different sources of error operate differently.

## Error Due to Bias[2]

The error due to bias is taken as the difference between the expected (or average) prediction of our model and the correct value that we are trying to predict. Due to randomness in the underlying data sets, models will have a range of predictions. Bias measures how far off in general these models' predictions are from

---

[1] KDnuggets is a website for data scientists that holds an annual competition to "further knowledge discovery in data mining." Previous iterations of their competition, especially the 2009 version, have made clear that ensemble models are effective in improving accuracy and stability in prediction (http://www.kdnuggets.com/datasets/kddcup.html).

[2] The discussion of bias and variance is the work of data scientist Scott Fortmann-Roe in a paper titled "Understanding the Bias-Variance Tradeoff," June 2012 (http://scott.fortmann-roe.com/docs/BiasVariance.html).

the correct value (with bias usually resulting in a consistently high or consistently low prediction).

## Error Due to Variance

The error due to variance is the variability of a model prediction for a *given* data point. Imagine you can repeat the entire model building process many times. The variance is how much the predictions for a given point vary between different builds of the model.

It might be easier to see the relationship between bias and variance with a diagram. Figure 10.1 is a graphical visualization of bias and variance using a bull's-eye. Imagine that the center of the target is a model that perfectly predicts the correct values. The further away we move from the bull's-eye for a given model's prediction, the worse the prediction. Now imagine we can repeat our entire model building process to get a number of separate hits (predictions) of the model. Each hit represents an individual estimation of our model. At times we will get a good distribution of training data so we predict very well, and the predictions are close to the bull's-eye, while sometimes our training data might be full of outliers or nonstandard values, resulting in poorer predictions. These different realizations result in a scatter of hits on the target.

The *x*-axis in Figure 10.1 represents variance; the variance around the bull's-eye is measured as greater divergence from the bull's-eye. This is displayed by the

**FIGURE 10.1**
**Bias and Variance**

Source: Fortmann-Roe, S.
"Understanding the Bias-
Variance Tradeoff," June 2012.

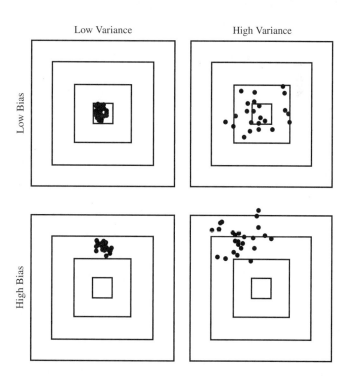

two bull's-eyes on the right of the diagram. The *y*-axis in Figure 10.1 represents the bias; bias is represented as being on one side of the bull's-eye or the other, or the top or bottom of the bull's-eye. Note that for the two bull's-eyes at the bottom of the diagram there is a clear bias toward the top of the target. However, there is little partiality left, right , up, or down in the upper two bull's-eyes. So, bias and variance are two different ways of being "off target" or incorrect about a prediction. Every algorithm we use in analytics will exhibit these two characteristics, and we would prefer to reduce or eliminate both types of error but there is unfortunately often a trade-off in doing so.

Most people think that they should minimize bias even at the expense of variance. The thinking goes that the presence of bias indicates something basically and most seriously wrong with their model or algorithm. They acknowledge variance is also bad, but a model with high variance could at least predict well on average; at least, it will not be fundamentally wrong.

This is mistaken logic. It is true that a high variance and low bias model can perform well in a long-run average sense. However, in practice, modelers are always dealing with a single data set, and long-run averages are irrelevant. What is important is the performance of the model on the data you actually have at hand, and in this case, *bias and variance are both important,* and one should not necessarily be improved at an excessive expense to the other.

## THE CASE FOR BOOSTING AND BAGGING

At its root, dealing with bias and variance takes us back to our discussion of over- and under-fitting. Bias is reduced and variance is increased as algorithms become more complex. As more and more attributes are added to a model, the complexity of the model rises, and variance becomes our primary concern while bias steadily falls. Figure 10.2 graphs the bias- and variance-caused errors for a particular

**FIGURE 10.2**
**Bias and Variance Related to Error and Model Complexity**

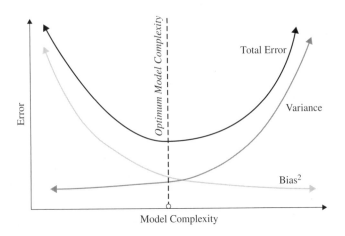

model; the line labeled "Total Error" is the summation of these two types of error. If we desire minimum error, it will be impossible to achieve by either minimizing bias or variance. So what are we to do? Both types of error are bad, but how do we "split the difference," as it were?

"Splitting the difference" in the two types of error or finding the "sweet spot" is accomplished most often by using two tools called "bagging" and "boosting." We are interested not in decomposing the error but in minimizing the total error; we want more predictive accuracy.

In Chapter's 5 and 7, we discussed the Akaike Information Criterion (and its companion, the Bayesian Information Criterion). When a model is overfit one may obtain an almost perfect error reduction in the historical period accompanied by large errors in the forecast period. We implemented a measure (the Akaike) to handle the trade-off between model complexity and error. In much the same manner, we are introducing here two techniques of ensemble model construction (i.e., bagging and boosting) that will help in solving the same sort of problem, but now for analytics algorithms.

> "Splitting the difference" in the two types of error or finding the "sweet spot" is accomplished most often by using two tools called "bagging" and "boosting."

# BAGGING

> Bagging is properly called bootstrap aggregation; it is a method of creating "pseudo-data" from the data in an original data set.

One computationally intensive method used to minimize error, trading off between bias and variance errors, is called bagging. It is not the only technique in this category, but it is one of the most often used; we will also consider boosting. Bagging is properly called bootstrap aggregation; it is a method of creating "pseudo-data" from the data in an original data set. These pseudo-data sets, or artificial data sets, are constructed to mimic the process originally used to select the real sample. We can then use these pseudo-data sets to improve the accuracy of a single instance of model estimation by creating an ensemble model.

To illustrate the bootstrap portion of the process, consider the data in Table 10.1.

The X and Y values in Table 10.1 are positively related to each other; that is, we believe as the observed value of X rises, the corresponding value of Y is greater. It is quite likely, however, that the true relationship between the two variables is not a perfectly proportional one. We desire to know how close the relationship between the two variables is to proportionality. We do not, however,

**TABLE 10.1**

| X | Y | X | Y | X | Y |
|---|---|---|---|---|---|
| 3 | 7 | 4 | 14 | 6 | 24 |
| 1 | 3 | 2 | 4 | 4 | 12 |
| 1 | 2 | 6 | 25 | 3 | 7 |
| 3 | 8 | 5 | 20 | 3 | 9 |
| 2 | 4 | 7 | 30 | 2 | 5 |

have every value for X and Y that exists; we have only the 15 records we are able to measure and list in Table 10.1. What we would really like to know is whether the sample of 15 values we have observed allows us an accurate picture of the true relationship between all the X and Y values.

Since we have collected only a small sample of all the existing X and Y values, the classical statistical measure of the proportionality between X and Y would be the sample correlation coefficient (as described in Chapter 2). Remember that the correlation coefficient measures the degree to which the plotted pairs of the sample data cluster along a straight line (it is a linear relationship that the correlation coefficient measures).

Some values in the real world we expect to be perfectly proportional; for example, inches are perfectly proportional to the same distance measured in centimeters. The correlation coefficient for various lengths measured in both centimeters and inches would be +1. A given distance measured in centimeters is directly proportional to the same distance measured in inches.

Other variables in the real world are related but not directly proportional to one another. The miles per gallon an automobile achieves is roughly (inversely) proportional to the gross weight of the car. The proportionality is not exact, because other factors such as engine displacement and aerodynamic characteristics, also affect mileage.

For the sample in Table 10.1, the correlation coefficient is 0.983. This calculation indicates that there appears to be a strong positive linear association between Y and X. Recall that the correlation coefficient measures only the linear associations. If the two variables were associated in nonlinear fashion, the plotted points would not tend to cluster along a straight line. In such cases, the calculated correlation coefficient might well be close to zero.

Since we have examined only a sample of the XY combinations (with only 15 records in our sample), what certainty do we have that the true relationship between X and Y is represented by the calculated correlation coefficient of 0.983? The population from which the sample of 15 observations was drawn might very well have a true correlation coefficient larger or smaller than 0.983. Since a sample with only 15 records is quite small, the calculated value of 0.983 could be quite inaccurate.

In like manner, if we estimate our analytics model (no matter whether it is a kNN model, decision tree model, etc.) with only a single estimation procedure, how sure are we that the parameter estimates provided are close to the true real-world population parameters? There is a set of methods for us to use that offer the possibility of estimating the true parameter estimates, even if we only have access to a small portion of the XY population. Bagging (bootstrap aggregation) is one procedure that will allow such a measure.

We could get a better (but still not perfect) idea of what the real parameter values are if we were to obtain a few more samples of the XY pairs. Suppose we were able to obtain 10 more samples of 15 records each on X and Y. We could calculate a new correlation coefficient for each sample. If all the coefficients were quite close to our original number of 0.983, we would feel more confident that our original estimate was in the ballpark.

If, on the hand, the coefficients for the new samples ranged from $-1$ to $+1$ and were spread out evenly along the spectrum, we would be much less confident that our original estimate of 0.983 was representative of the true relationship between all X and Y combinations in the population.

The most common situation data scientists face in the real world is that only limited (even though it might seem quite voluminous) data are available. You may be able to obtain only a single sample of 15 records to represent a much larger population of XY combinations.

This is the precise situation in which bagging is perfect for determining a more accurate set of estimated parameters than those estimated from a single sample; building an ensemble aids us in estimating more accurate and true estimates. The essence of the bagging procedure is to imitate the process of selecting our original sample of 15 observations. In fact, we will imitate the process not once but many times over. This gives us many "artificial samples" of 15 observations, from each of which we may find the probability that the values of their correlation coefficients fall within various intervals.

The process of selecting the artificial samples is called bootstrapping and consists of making many copies of each of our 15 data points. Pretend that the XY coordinates of a single data point, say, the first observation of (3, 7) are written on a note card. This card is then duplicated many times over (say, $10^9$ times), and the resulting large stack of cards is placed in a hopper.

We continue this process, producing $10^9$ duplicates of every one of our original 15 data points. All the note cards are placed in the hopper. The hopper is then turned a sufficient number of times to ensure that the cards are truly randomly mixed. Figure 10.3 depicts the process.[3]

In order to create the first artificial sample, we draw one card from the hopper, list its represented point as the first record in the artificial sample, and replace the card in the hopper. After again turning the hopper to randomize, we continue the process (with replacement) until we have created a single artificial sample with 15 data points.

We repeat the process, creating more artificial samples. Each time we create an artificial sample, we calculate the correlation coefficient between the X and Y for the sample. Of course, the process outlined is actually carried out in software with a computer-intensive statistical technique when we are bagging.

We will now have a large number of correlation coefficients, each one calculated from an artificial sample that in turn was generated from the 15 records in the original sample. This large number of correlation coefficients (one for each artificial sample) can be viewed as if they were the product of real samples drawn from the real population.

Table 10.2 displays just three of these artificial data sets and their respective correlation coefficients. It is the combination of these correlation coefficients (one way would be to simply average them) that gives us what we believe is a truer measure of the true population correlation coefficient. For demonstration purposes, we actually created 100 artificial data sets using the method described

---

[3] The example we use here is modeled after Persi Diaconis and Bradley Efron, "Computer Methods in Statistics," *Scientific American*, May 1983, pp. 116–30.

**FIGURE 10.3** The Bootstrap Procedure

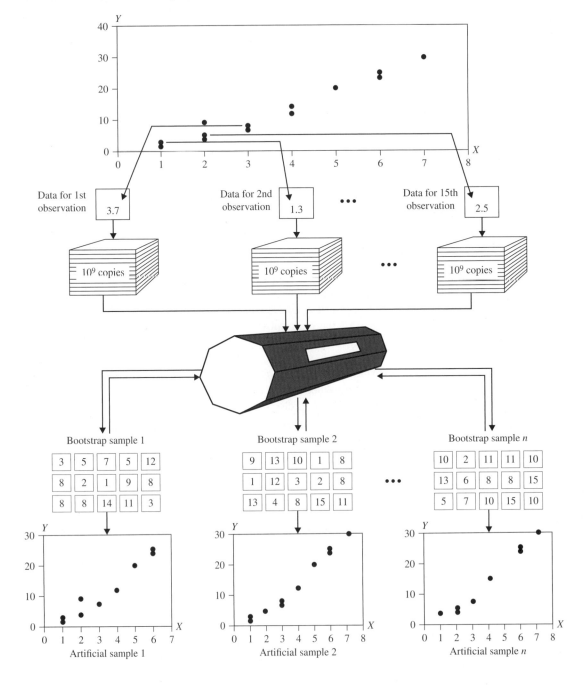

**TABLE 10.2**
**Bootstrapped**
**Samples (Artificial**
**Data Sets)** (C10T2)
How Dependable
Is This Bootstrap
Aggregation (Bagging)
Procedure? It Has
Been Shown That
the Accuracy of
the Measure Is
"Dependable in a Wide
Variety of Situations."

| 1st Bootstrapped Artificial Sample | | 2nd Bootstrapped Artificial Sample | | 100th Bootstrapped Artificial Sample | |
|---|---|---|---|---|---|
| X | Y | X | Y | X | Y |
| 1 | 2 | 5 | 20 | 7 | 30 |
| 2 | 4 | 3 | 7 | 1 | 3 |
| 2 | 4 | 7 | 30 | 6 | 24 |
| 2 | 4 | 3 | 7 | 6 | 24 |
| 4 | 12 | 6 | 25 | 3 | 7 |
| 6 | 25 | 3 | 7 | 3 | 7 |
| 1 | 3 | 4 | 12 | 4 | 14 |
| 3 | 7 | 1 | 2 | 6 | 25 |
| 6 | 25 | 3 | 7 | 3 | 7 |
| 1 | 3 | 4 | 12 | 4 | 14 |
| 3 | 7 | 1 | 2 | 6 | 25 |
| 5 | 20 | 1 | 3 | 6 | 25 |
| 6 | 25 | 6 | 25 | 2 | 5 |
| 6 | 25 | 3 | 7 | 2 | 4 |
| 6 | 25 | 3 | 8 | 2 | 4 |
| 2 | 9 | 6 | 25 | 7 | 30 |
| 6 | 24 | 2 | 5 | 2 | 5 |
| 1 | 2 | 6 | 24 | 7 | 30 |
| r | 0.983 | r | 1.00 | r | 0.994 |

Diaconis, Persi, and Efron, Bradley, "Computer Methods in Statistics," *Scientific American*, May 1983, 116–30.

(three of those data sets are shown in Table 10.2). Of the 100 correlation coefficients we computed, 68 percent fell between 0.945 and 1.00. This interval (0.055) can be thought of as the bootstrap measure of the range over which we are confident that the true correlation coefficient exists.

Bagging combines outputs from classification models generated from bootstrap samples (with replacement) of a training data set. Models are combined by a simple voting (or averaging) of the individual model output predictions. In software such as XLMiner© and Modeler, models are usually combined using a simple voting mechanism, with each algorithm model having one vote. To break ties, however, a slight weighting factor is often used: model weights are created so that the models that performed best during training are given slightly more weight than others. Bagging will work with algorithms such as CART, kNN, and Logit. In 2009, Orange (a telecommunications corporation) offered €10,000 for the best classification algorithm to classify churn of telecommunications customers (from one provider to another). The challenge was to beat the in-house system developed by Orange Labs. It was an opportunity for data scientists to strut their stuff.[4]

[4] Isabelle Guyon, Vincent Lemaire, Marc Boullé, Gideon Dror, and David Vogel. "Analysis of the KDD Cup 2009: Fast Scoring on a Large Orange Customer Database," *JMLR: Workshop and Conference Proceedings* 7: 1-22, 2009.

*Ensembles* of decision trees were the most widely used classification method in this challenge, with IBM winning the top prize. In fact, more than two-thirds of the entries employed bagging or boosting (including the winning entry).

# BOOSTING

Boosting, like bagging, is an ensemble technique that may be used on the classification models we have already seen. Boosting does not involve bootstrap sampling. In one sense, it is a weighting technique. Boosting is an iterative technique that adjusts the weight of any record based upon the last classification. If a record was incorrectly classified, it tries to increase the weight of this observation and vice versa. In other words, if you get it wrong (i.e., the classification), just boost and try it again! While this sounds counter intuitive, boosting in general decreases the bias error and builds strong predictive models by combining a set of "weak learner" models. New weak learners focus more on the examples that previous weak learners misclassified; this is the source of the increased classification accuracy.

> Boosting is an iterative technique that adjusts the weight of any record based upon the last classification.

Bagging, we have seen, is working with random selections (i.e., artificial data sets); boosting, on the other hand, does much the same thing but with weights. Both, however, are clearly ensemble models in that they combine a number of models to obtain the best result. Boosting does not look at a random portion of the records in our data; it uses the whole data set for each iteration. But, with each iteration, boosting concentrates on training the decision stump that determines some of the sins committed by the previous classifiers. A "decision stump" is just a decision tree with a single root node (and that is certainly a "weak learner"). In boosting, each attribute may be the basis for a weak learner.

In boosting, each record originally counts the same; all records have equal weights, in other words. With boosting, we use the entire data set to choose the best classifier. Boosting is a true machine learning algorithm; it performs supervised learning by attempting to improve the model with each iteration. Each record is given a weight. At each iteration, a new hypothesis is learned and all the records are reweighted to focus the algorithm on records that the most recently learned classifier got wrong. These "weak learners" do just better than a naive model at first, but the process iterates concentrating on the mistakes made previously.

The boosting process takes these steps:

1) Learn a single, very simple classifier (a "weak learner");
2) Classify the data;
3) Look at where it makes errors;
4) Reweight the data so that the inputs where we made errors get higher weight in the learning process;
5) Now learn a second simple classifier on the weighted data;

6) Combine the first and second classifiers and weight the data according to where they make errors;

7) Learn a third classifier on the weighted data;

8) ... and so on, until we learn T simple classifiers.

9) Final classifier is the combination of all T classifiers.

XLMiner© and other software use a version of these stylistic steps. While this may seem a bit vague, recall that the 2009 KDD Cup proved rather conclusively that both bagging and boosting work to improve prediction in real-world settings!

# RANDOM FOREST®

A third form of ensemble algorithm is the "random forest"; the random forest is based on applying bagging to a decision tree algorithm with one important change: in addition to sampling the records, the algorithm also samples the attributes. The specific term *random forest* is actually a trademark of Leo Breiman and Adele Cutler and licensed to Salford Systems.[5] There is no alternative (but nontrademarked) name in common use, but "random tree" is used by XLMiner©.

In the traditional CART algorithm, to determine how to create a split at any point, the algorithm makes the choice of an attribute and a split value for the attribute by minimizing entropy (see Chapter 9, CART models). The random forest algorithm is then a collection of many CART trees that are independent when constructed. The sum of the predictions made from this collection of trees determines the overall prediction of the random forest. The overall prediction is determined by voting for classification and by averaging for regression (remember from Chapter 9 that CART stands for "classification and regression tree," depending upon whether the target is continuous or categorical). With random forests, at each stage of the algorithm, the choice of an attribute is limited to a random subset of attributes. Compared to the basic CART, the random forest algorithm adds two more steps: a bagging operation and a bootstrap sampling of variables at each split.

The random forest method is a bit obtuse when compared to the standard CART. It produces more accurate predictions than a simple CART, but the simple intuition of CART is lost. Over-fitting was a problem with standard CART, and it can also be a problem with random forest models.

# A BAGGING EXAMPLE

The data set we will use to demonstrate bagging contains information collected by the U.S. Census Bureau concerning housing in the area of Boston, Massachusetts.[6] The data set has 506 records, with each record representing the value of a

---

[5] https://www.salford-systems.com/.

[6] D. Harrison and D. L. Rubinfeld, "Hedonic prices and the demand for clean air," *Journal of Environmental Economics and Management*, vol. 5, 1978, pp. 81–102. The data was obtained from the StatLib archive: http://lib.stat.cmu.edu/datasets/boston.

**TABLE 10.3** A Portion of the Boston Housing Data. "CAT. MEDV" Is Used as the Target

This dataset contains data collected in 1970 by the U.S. Census Service concerning housing in the Boston, MA area. The dataset is provided with the XLminer software. (C10T3)

| CRIM | ZN | INDUS | CHAS | NOX | RM | AGE | DIS | RAD | TAX | PTRATIO | B | LSTAT | MEDV | CAT. MEDV |
|------|-----|-------|------|-------|-------|------|--------|-----|-----|---------|--------|-------|------|-----------|
| 0.00632 | 18 | 2.31 | 0 | 0.538 | 6.575 | 65.2 | 4.09 | 1 | 296 | 15.3 | 396.9 | 4.98 | 24 | 0 |
| 0.02731 | 0 | 7.07 | 0 | 0.469 | 6.421 | 78.9 | 4.9671 | 2 | 242 | 17.8 | 396.9 | 9.14 | 21.6 | 0 |
| 0.02729 | 0 | 7.07 | 0 | 0.469 | 7.185 | 61.1 | 4.9671 | 2 | 242 | 17.8 | 392.83 | 4.03 | 34.7 | 1 |
| 0.03237 | 0 | 2.18 | 0 | 0.458 | 6.998 | 45.8 | 6.0622 | 3 | 222 | 18.7 | 394.63 | 2.94 | 33.4 | 1 |
| 0.06905 | 0 | 2.18 | 0 | 0.458 | 7.147 | 54.2 | 6.0622 | 3 | 222 | 18.7 | 396.9 | 5.33 | 36.2 | 1 |
| 0.02985 | 0 | 2.18 | 0 | 0.458 | 6.43 | 58.7 | 6.0622 | 3 | 222 | 18.7 | 394.12 | 5.21 | 28.7 | 0 |

The attribute descriptions are listed below:

| | |
|---|---|
| CRIM | Per capita crime rate by town |
| ZN | Proportion of residential land zoned for lots over 25,000 sq. ft. |
| INDUS | Proportion of nonretail business acres per town |
| CHAS | Charles River dummy variable (1 if tract bounds river; 0 otherwise) |
| NOX | Nitric oxides concentration (parts per 10 million) |
| RM | Average number of rooms per dwelling |
| AGE | Proportion of owner-occupied units built prior to 1940 |
| DIS | Weighted distances to five Boston employment centers |
| RAD | Index of accessibility to radial highways |
| TAX | Full-value property-tax rate per $10,000 |
| PTRATIO | Pupil-teacher ratio by town |
| B | 1000(Bk - 0.63)^2 where Bk is the proportion of African-Americans by town |
| LSTAT | % lower status of the population |
| MEDV | Median value of owner-occupied homes in $1000 (not used) |
| CAT. MEDV | Dichotomous version of median value (target) |

house and its related attributes (such as the number of rooms, age of the structure, property tax rate, etc.). The target variable is dichotomous and represents homes of high median value and those of low median value (set by the data scientist). Our goal is to construct a classifier that uses the available attributes to correctly predict whether a structure will be of low or high median value ("CAT. MEDV" in the data).

Using a standard logistic regression and a bagged logistic regression, validation partition results in the ROCs (receiver operating curve) shown in Figure 10.4.

Recall from Chapter 8 that the AUC (area under the curve) calculated from the ROC curve is often used to compare the predictive power of analytics algorithms. This is not the only comparison method that may be used, but it is the one most commonly used. The higher the AUC, the more predictive the model on average. The standard logistic regression result is shown on the left-hand side of Figure 10.4 where the AUC = 0.966. The bagged logistic regression is shown on the right-hand side of Figure 10.4 and AUC is 0.973, indicating an increase in the predictive power of the bagged algorithm. Specifically, the AUC is equal to the probability that a classifier will rank a randomly chosen "success" instance higher than a randomly chosen "failure."

The validation lift charts for the same two models show similar results. Remember that the lift charts contain reordered data (reordered from most successful to least successful), and the upper-left hand corner of each chart in Figure 10.5

**FIGURE 10.4** **ROC for the Standard Logit Model of the Boston Housing Data on the Left and the Logit Model with Bagging on the Right**

Both AUCs Are Validation Data Results. (C10T3)

Source: Frontline Systems Inc.

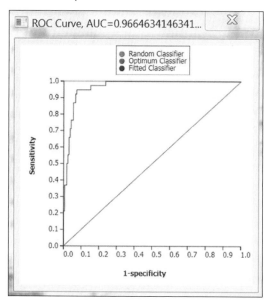
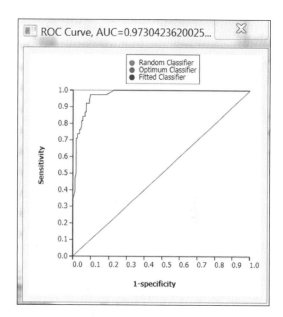

**FIGURE 10.5** **Validation Lift Charts for the Standard Logit Model on the Left and the Bagged Logit Model on the right** (C10T3)

Source: Frontline Systems Inc.

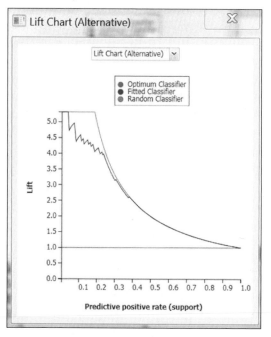
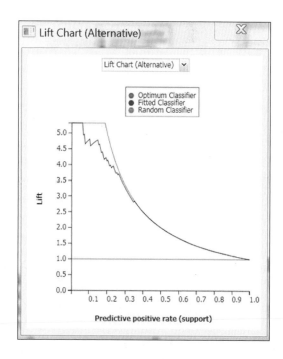

is illustrative of the improvement in the bagged Logit model. While we have used a Logit model as the classifier in this example, it would also be possible to use other classification algorithms and employ the bagging procedure as an enhancement.

# A BOOSTING EXAMPLE

We are able to use the same Boston housing data as an example of boosting. This time we use as a classifier, a classification tree. The model is pruned by using the "best pruned tree" method to prevent over-fitting. The same model is then boosted in XLMiner© using the standard AdaBoost method (this method of calculation appears in virtually all analytics software; there are, however, a number of alternative methods for boosting).

The AUC of 0.985 for the boosted tree in Figure 10.6 is greater than the AUC of 0.853 for the standard tree, indicating an improvement in predictive power. In addition, an examination of the lift charts in Figure 10.7 also shows an improvement in predictive power.

**FIGURE 10.6** **Validation ROC for Best Pruned Classification Tree on the Left and the Boosted Best Pruned Classification Tree on the Right** (C10F6)

Source: Frontline Systems Inc.

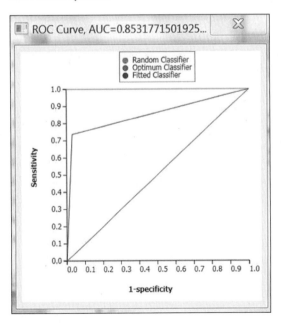
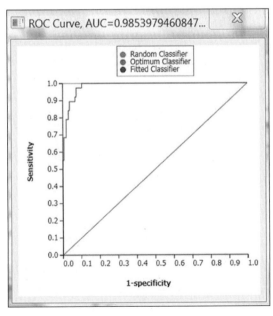

**FIGURE 10.7** **Validation Lift Chart for the Best Pruned Tree on the Left and Validation Lift Chart for the Boosted Best Pruned Tree on the Right** (C10F6)

Source: Frontline Systems Inc.

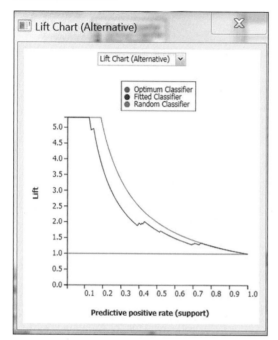 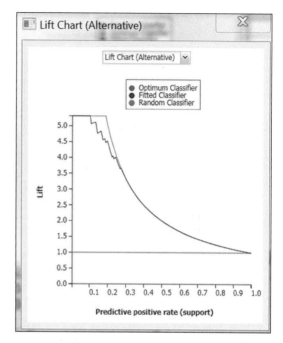

# A RANDOM FOREST (i.e., TREE) EXAMPLE

The random forest (or random tree) algorithm has become a standard ensemble tool for data scientists. It has worked well in settings where the number of attributes is much larger than the number of records, can cope with highly correlated attributes and returns measures of attribute importance. Random forest methodology is used to address two main classes of problems: to construct classification rules for a learning problem and to assess and rank attributes with respect to their ability to predict the classification. The random forest algorithm is a classification and regression method (CART) based on the aggregation of a large number of trees. Specifically, it is an ensemble of trees constructed from the training data and validated to yield a classification given the attributes for future observations.

The Boston housing data will again provide the data for the random forest example (C10F6). In XLMiner©, the random tree is selected from the classify/ensemble menu. For the example, we selected classification tree as the weak learner (10 weak learners were used).

Figure 10.8 demonstrates the ROC curve and the AUC estimate for both the standard CART algorithm and the random forest. Note that the AUC is much better for the random forest. Figure 10.9 displays the lift chart for both algorithms.

**FIGURE 10.8**  **ROC for the Standard CART on the Left and the ROC for the Random Forest on the Right**  (C10F6)

Source: Frontline Systems Inc.

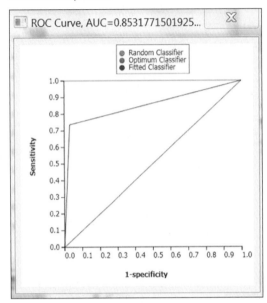 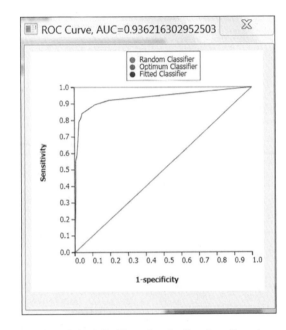

**FIGURE 10.9**  **Lift Chart for the Standard CART on the Left and the Lift Chart for the Random Forest on the Right**  (C10F6)

Source: Frontline Systems Inc.

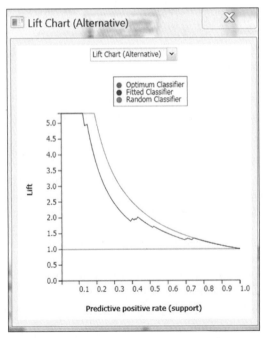 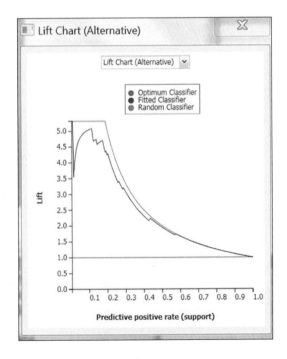

**FIGURE 10.10**
**The Features**
**Importance for the**
**Random Forest**
**Model of the**
**Boston Housing**
**Data** (C10F6)

Source: Frontline Systems Inc.

**Features Importance**

| Feature ▾ | importance ▾ |
|---|---|
| CRIM | 0.100126521 |
| ZN | 0.050939069 |
| INDUS | 0.16850648 |
| NOX | 0.019736842 |
| RM | 0.237731335 |
| AGE | 0.070143736 |
| DIS | 0.046659535 |
| RAD | 0.032196538 |
| TAX | 0.012482675 |
| PTRATIO | 0.045544661 |
| B | 0.010454111 |
| LSTAT | 0 |
| CHAS | 0.039923425 |

Here the improvement is not quite as apparent. Figure 10.10 displays the features importance output from XLMiner for the random forest model that ranks the attributes with a score indicating their importance in predicting a correct classification.

Not surprisingly, when examining the features importance output, the average number of rooms in the house (RM) is the most important attribute in the classification.

# CLUSTERING

Clustering is the assignment of a set of observations into subsets so that observations in the same subset are similar in "some sense."

Clustering is the assignment of a set of observations into subsets so that observations in the same subset are similar in "some sense." Things that are similar in "some sense" are quite difficult to define, but at times, we understand intuitively that objects are similar. Take the two objects in Figure 10.11; they are obviously quite different! But they are also somewhat similar, and some would place them in the same cluster. While we suspect that the real meaning of "similar" is philosophical, we will take a more pragmatic approach.

Clustering finds patterns of similarities among objects; it tries to create groupings in which every member is very similar to the other members of the same cluster but very different from the members of every other cluster. Market researchers immediately recognize clustering as an important step in any marketing segmentation study. To marketers, the notion of clustering people is familiar territory.

If you think of what people do, what they purchase, and how they view the world, you can see many individuals fall naturally into groups. Take food as an example; there are individuals who care deeply about their own nutrition and commonly make decisions on the basis of nutrition. They read labels carefully; they avoid certain ingredients; they may only eat organic food. And then there is another group that will eat just about anything at any time. There may be a third group that eats carefully at times and cavalierly at other times, a sort of

**FIGURE 10.11   What Is Clustering?**

half-and-half group. By asking people a large number of questions and assuming that they will tell the truth, we might collect enough data on attributes to be able to classify everyone we know into one of the three "nutritional" groups. Members of each group would not be perfectly alike, but they would be more alike members of their assigned group than members of the other two groups if our clustering mechanism were successful.

In normal conversation similarity is elusive. Data scientists also find similarity elusive; there are numerous clustering algorithms, different methods for creating sets of objects in a cluster. For these different algorithms, the results often differ, and that begs the question of which clustering algorithm is the best one. We can only scratch the surface here by suggesting that it probably depends upon how you intend to use the clustering results. There are two basic types of clustering algorithms; k-means methods and hierarchical methods.

There are two basic types of clustering algorithms; k-means methods and hierarchical methods.

K-means methods are iterative; to find the best clustering arrangement, the algorithm makes an initial pass through the data assembling clusters based upon some "best" criterion and then makes additional passes through the data checking to see if it can improve the clusters. Typically the process will be repeated.

Hierarchical clustering algorithms are quite different; they create a tree-like structure showing the objects most closely related to each other, creating a "dendrogram."

## Usefulness of Clustering

There are many examples of where clustering algorithms, whether of the k-means type or the hierarchical type, are useful. Marketing and business strategy probably have been the most popular subjects for clustering analysis. If we had a data set of items purchased and attributes of the individuals who purchased them (i.e., age, income, sex, timing of the purchase, etc.), it would be possible to cluster customers into similar groups. It might be possible to predict what a particular customer cluster is likely to purchase next and to provide them with attractive offers in order to manipulate their purchases.

Universities have successfully used clustering to create student clusters; groups of students who are similar end up in one cluster and those less alike in other clusters. With performance attributes included in the data, administrators are able to identify groups that may require more attention and effort to ensure success.

Likewise, banking authorities cluster banks as similar and unalike to identify classes of banks with firm specific attributes (e.g., size, loan structure, financial ratios, etc.) that may lead to failure in the near future. It is much easier and less costly to help a failing bank than to dissolve the bank and distribute its assets, but that depends upon successfully clustering banks.

Insurance companies group policyholders according to their attributes to identify groups that are likely to commit insurance fraud. Those clusters would likely receive more attention when a claim is filed against the insurance company. By limiting fraud, the company may be able to better service all their customers and achieve lower premiums.

Customer segmentation in its many forms is one of the most common uses of clustering analysis. When used in this manner, clustering is called "market segmentation." When a market is divided into subsets of customers who have similar attributes, the results may be used to target customers or to reduce risks in some manner. Airlines create "fare buckets" that are clusters of their customers (and potential customers) who have similar characteristics. The fare buckets are individuals roughly willing to pay a particular price for a certain flight on a certain day. By dividing up the customers, the airline can dynamically price tickets and reach higher profits than if it were to charge a single price.

If you use a "news aggregator" to read the news, you probably identified some broad areas of interest as part of the selection process. But how did the aggregator (say, Google News) know how to divide up the hundreds of thousands of newsfeeds into those that you would like to read and everything else? A cluster algorithm would solve the problem very neatly; most of the algorithms can even be "trained" by you as you receive stories you don't want to read (and you so identify those to the algorithm) and, likewise, identify stories related to topics about which you would like to see more articles.

## How Clustering Works

Clustering is the most common form of unsupervised learning; it is unsupervised learning because there is no classification of examples provided to the algorithm as we used in our (supervised) classification algorithms. When we used a kNN model, the training partition of the data already had correct classifications included, and the kNN algorithm attempted to use that information to assemble a classifier that would work well on the validation partition of the data.

One of the key question in clustering is how to choose how many clusters to create in a given situation. You (or the algorithm) do not want to have such broad clusters that little information is provided, but you also do not want clusters to be so small that each record is almost an individual cluster because that provides no information at all.

Without specifying exactly how the clusters are formed, a few examples will make clear the ease with which the process may be used and how useful the results might be.

The data in Figure 10.12 are depicted with only two attributes considered; one attribute is represented by the scale on the *x*-axis and the second attribute is represented by the scale on the *y*-axis. We have used metric attributes to make the clusters clear. To measure the similarity or dissimilarity between objects, we measure the distance (or "nearness") between objects. Thus, those records in the lower right-hand corner of the figure (high x and low y values) would be quite unlike those in the middle of the y values and with low x values. The important point is that the basis of all clustering algorithms is to measure in some manner the similarity and dissimilarity of records. In our figure, records near to one another would be

*Clustering is the most common form of unsupervised learning.*

**FIGURE 10.12**
**The Structure of Clustering**

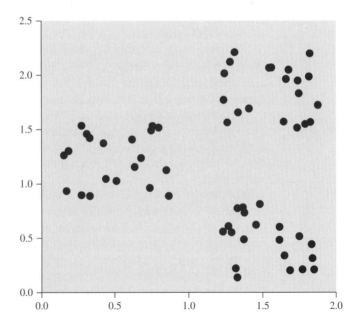

assigned to the same cluster. With a recursive procedure, an algorithm would then calculate the distance between the groups and merge them by distance again. This simple representation only shows two attributes; an actual clustering model would most likely use many attributes (and therefore be impossible to show graphically).

In the k-means algorithm, the data scientist starts by picking "k," the number of clusters.

The question data scientists must ask is, "How do I determine the 'nearness' of clusters?" The simplest answer (but not necessarily the best in all situations) might be to represent each cluster by a "centroid," or the average of its points. Each cluster's centroid could be compared to the intercluster distance to another cluster's centroid. But what do we mean by closeness or nearness? Euclidean distance is the meaning most of us would use as a default. But "closest" could also mean the smallest maximum distance to the other points. Alternatively, it could also mean the smallest average distance to the other points. It could also mean the smallest sum of the squares of distances to other points, and so on. In other words, there are many ways to define the "closest" point; there are many ways to measure distance. In the k-means algorithm, the data scientist starts by picking "k," the number of clusters. The k-means algorithm terminates when the cluster centers for the last iteration are identical to the cluster centers for the previous iteration.

## A Clustering Example (k-Means Clustering)

As a clustering example, we will take a set of data available to a human resources manager covering a workforce of 14,999 individuals who either are currently working with the firm or were employees who have left. The employees are in a firm that is an outfitter like EMS or REI; they are customer service employees whose job is not an easy one. Representatives commonly spend six hours per day handling customer requests, complaints, or issues (these are the "projects" listed in the data set). Workdays are highly structured with specified frequency, length, and number of breaks allowed. Breaks are often curtailed at peak ordering times, causing stress on the employees. In similar companies, the turnover rate per year for the organization is quite high with newly hired employees, sometimes in the 50 percent range. The manager has a number of attributes available for each of the individuals:

- The self-reported satisfaction level of the employee
- The score of the last evaluation performed on the individual
- The number of projects they have handled in the most recent period
- The employee's average monthly hours worked
- The length of time the employee has been with the company
- Whether the employee has had a work accident
- Whether the employee has had a promotion in the last five years
- The employee's department assignment
- Salary of the employee
- Whether the employee has left the firm

The manager wishes to organize the mass of data into clusters that might suggest why some good employees have left the firm. Note that there is no target in this

**FIGURE 10.13**
**The Distribution
of Employees Who
Have Left the Firm
and Those Who
Are Currently
Employed** (C10F10)

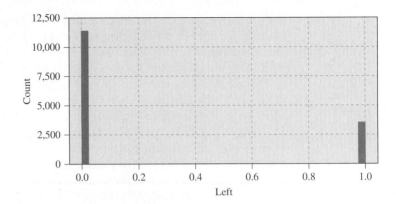

analysis; all of the attributes will be used to construct clusters of employees that are simply more alike their clustermates than those employees assigned to different clusters. Relatively few of the employees have left (3,571 of 14,999) the firm, as shown in the distribution in Figure 10.13.

The particular algorithm we will use to create the clusters is called k-means clustering; like kNN, it is based roughly upon cluster center distances measured from cluster to cluster. Each point is placed in the cluster whose current centroid is nearest. After all the points are assigned, the centroids of the resulting clusters are fixed, and the algorithm may reassign some points to their closest centroid. Thus, the choice of a distance measure plays a significant role in cluster analysis. In most cases, Euclidian distance is used by the algorithm, and the standardization (or normalization) of units is commonly performed, just as we did when using a kNN classification algorithm. Some software may use other measures of distance, and because of proprietary routines used by the various software producers, the results may differ somewhat from one piece of software to the next. The clusters created by the algorithm will contain one or more of the records with the distance (however measured) from one cluster to another measuring their similarity or dissimilarity. The "distance" that is used may vary from one version of the algorithm to another; it could be the minimum distance between two pairs of records, the average distance between records in one cluster to another, the maximum distance between records (called complete linkage) in one cluster and another cluster, squared distances if greater weight is to be placed upon objects far apart, or some version of a centroid distance (the distance between the two cluster centroids). Complete linkage and average distance are the two most commonly used and work well if the clusters are spherical (with customers segmented on the basis of a number of attributes). Using XLMiner© and requesting four clusters, we obtain the results outlined in Table 10.4.

The cluster summary shows four clusters (labeled 0 through 3) with cluster 1 being the largest cluster and containing 8,606 of the employees and former employees. The "average distance" measure is used here.

**TABLE 10.4** The Clusters Produced by XLMiner© Using k-Means Clustering and Requesting Four Clusters (C10F10)

Source: Frontline Systems Inc.

### Cluster Summary

| Cluster | Size | Average Distance |
|---|---|---|
| Cluster 0 | 2505 | 2.681219171 |
| Cluster 1 | 8606 | 2.401600394 |
| Cluster 2 | 2045 | 2.661165082 |
| Cluster 3 | 1843 | 1.707441435 |
| Total | 14999 | 2.398394838 |

In order to see how these clusters differ, it would be instructive to observe how the cluster centers of the most important predictors looked in each cluster. Cluster centers use a distance metric or dissimilarity measure with distances defined in multiple ways that are beyond the scope of this explanation. The distance measure chosen is influenced by the scale of each attribute; it is customary to normalize or standardize distance measures before computing Euclidean distance. All measurements are converted to the same scale for each attribute. Some qualitative variables, however, may be binary or categorical; in such instances the most useful measures of similarity are matching coefficients and Jaquard's coefficient (again, beyond the scope of this explanation). Remember that the clustering algorithm is based on a method to measure the similarity of each object. Based on this measure, objects that are similar are included in a subgroup called a cluster with the goal being to cluster records into homogeneous subgroups.

Table 10.5 presents those cluster centers.

Note that cluster 3 has the highest instance of employees leaving; it also has the lowest number for satisfaction rating of employees, low salaries, and very few projects. Cluster 3 employees are also those with the firm for the shortest period of time. This is quite dissimilar from other clusters! The other cluster with the most leave takers is cluster 0, also with quite low satisfaction numbers and low

**TABLE 10.5** Cluster Centers of Five Most Important Predictors in the k-Means Clustering Model (C10F10)

Source: Frontline Systems Inc.

| Cluster | left | satisfaction_level | number_project | Factorized_salary | time_spend_company |
|---|---|---|---|---|---|
| Cluster 0 | 1.216648 | -0.708184777 | 1.142595534 | -0.176490304 | 1.060200545 |
| Cluster 1 | -0.55434 | 0.327918712 | -0.037685501 | 0.100336065 | -0.248792558 |
| Cluster 2 | -0.50502 | 0.220583179 | -0.000890438 | 0.044377476 | 0.00204726 |
| Cluster 3 | 1.483334 | -0.806768196 | -1.370820289 | -0.27574472 | -0.282795558 |

relative salary but a very high number of projects. Cluster 0 also includes those employees with the firm for the longest period of time.

Apparently, there is more than a single footprint denoting a leave taker! Clusters 1 and 2 have few leave takers (someone who left the company), relatively higher salaries, and fewer projects than the average. A human resource manager might take these findings along with those for the other less important predictors as an indicator for future action.

## A Hierarchical Clustering Example (Agglomerative Bottom-Up Clustering)

Hierarchical clustering starts by computing a distance between every pair of re-cords that you are clustering. Table 10.6 would be an example of a distance matrix (or dissimiliarity matrix). The numbers in the matrix represent the distance (how-ever measured) between records. For instance, between records 4 and 5, there is a distance of 8, while between records 4 and 3, there is a distance of 9.

In order to begin clustering the five records in Table 10.6, we note that the smallest distance is between record 3 and record 5 and we combine them into a new cluster called "35." That's not the number 35 but simply records 3 and 5.

Records 3 and 5 are removed in Table 10.7 and combined to form a new "cluster" labeled "35." The distance between cluster 35 and every other record becomes the maximum of the distance between this record, and record 3 or record 5. For example, the distance between record 2 and record "35" is listed as 10 in Table 10.7; the 10 is the greater of the distances between record 2 and record 3

*Hierarchical clustering starts by computing a distance between every pair of records that you are clustering.*

**TABLE 10.6**
**Distance Matrix**

|   | 1 | 2 | 3 | 4 | 5 |
|---|---|---|---|---|---|
| 1 | 0 | | | | |
| 2 | 9 | 0 | | | |
| 3 | 3 | 7 | 0 | | |
| 4 | 6 | 5 | 9 | 0 | |
| 5 | 11 | 10 | 2 | 8 | 0 |

**TABLE 10.7**
**The First Reconstituted Matrix after the First Clustering**

|    | 35 | 1 | 2 | 4 |
|----|----|---|---|---|
| 35 | 0 | | | |
| 1 | 11 | 0 | | |
| 2 | 10 | 9 | 0 | |
| 4 | 9 | 6 | 5 | 0 |

**FIGURE 10.14**

**Complete Linkage Dendrogram for the Records Listed in Table 10.6**

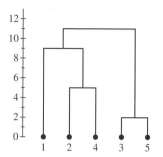

(the distance between records 2 and 3 is 7 from Table 10.6) and record 5 (the distance between 5 and 2 is 10 from Table 10.6). The larger distance between 7 and 10 is, of course, 10 and that is shown in Table 10.7. The method described here is called "complete linkage clustering." There are other methods available to form the clusters (single linkage, group average linkage, etc.), but they all are similar to this method. Continuing in this way, after a number of steps, every record is assigned a cluster. Figure 10.14 is the dendogram (or cluster representation) for the result. In Figure 10.14, the *y*-axis shows the distance between the records at the time they were clustered. This is called the cluster height.

One of the problems with hierarchical clustering is that there is no objective way to say how many clusters there are. If we "cut" the single linkage tree at a value of, say, 10 (see Figure 10.14), we would say that there are two clusters. One cluster would be made up of records 1, 2, and 4, while the second cluster would be made up of records 3 and 5. The idea of hierarchical or agglomerative clustering is to start with each cluster being a single record, much like we did in Table 10.6. Then, we agglomerate (or combine) the two nearest clusters (or records in the case of Table 10.6) again and again until there is just one cluster left at the end; that final cluster would include all the records in the data set!

By "cutting" the dendrogram as we do in Figure 10.15, we created two clusters that represented the entire data set. There is no agreed-upon correct number of clusters in any situation. The goal, of course, is to come up with meaningful clusters. There are many clusters that can be constructed from any data set; the distance measures used may be changed, the "cut" in the dendrogram may be selected at different levels, etc. For valid clusters, we would expect that in some sense they create insight. That, after all, is the reason for the exercise in the

**FIGURE 10.15**

**The Dendrogram with a "Cut" at a Value of 10, Resulting in Two Clusters**

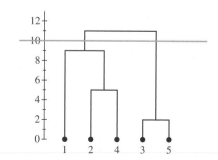

first place. Often the clusters will have a common attribute (that was not used in the clustering algorithm). Assigning labels to each cluster can be an illuminating exercise; often the label you choose will define the salient uniqueness of the clusters. Summary statistics on each cluster are also a good way of seeing if there is some validity in the clustering mechanism.

Consider another example (different from the example above) of a human resources manager who has data available on employees from the enterprise resource planning system used in the firm. Many characteristics of each employee are available, including measures of their output, estimations of the quality of their work, and self-reported job satisfaction data. Could the employees be grouped into meaningful clusters? We will use just two employee attributes to see if a clustering algorithm could group employees. The two chosen attributes are "performance quality," a measure of the quality of the employee's performance, and "job satisfaction," the self-reported satisfaction of the employee. Using the 305 employee records, XLMiner© is instructed to use a single linkage hierarchical clustering algorithm using Euclidean distance measures. Figure 10.16 and Table 10.8 are XLMiner© outputs of this process.

Table 10.8 shows the 10 clusters created that now include all 305 employee records. A meaningful clustering may be constructed using the dendogram in Figure 10.16. Consider "cutting" the dendogram at 0.65. This results in two clusters and two singletons (clusters made up of only a single record). One cluster is made up of subclusters 1, 9, 2, 10, 3, and 4. That cluster would include all the records shown in Table 10.8 as being members of any of these subclusters. A second cluster is defined by the cut as being made up of subclusters 5 and 6; all five records in those two subclusters would become members of this second cluster. Finally, there are the two singletons, subclusters 7 and 8, that would each be considered a cluster of their own. Now, whether this particular cut at a distance measure of 0.65 produces meaningful clusters would be the call of the human resource manager. If this clustering provides meaningful clusters in any sense, the effort was worthwhile.

**FIGURE 10.16**

**Dendrogram of the Single Linkage Hierarchical Clustering Using Euclidean Distance** (C10F12)

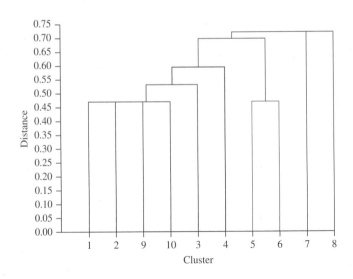

**TABLE 10.8** A Portion of the Cluster Legend Created in XLMiner© for the Human Resource Hierarchical Clustering (C10F12)

Source: Frontline Systems Inc.

| Cluster Legend (Numbers show the record sequence relative to the original data) | | | | | | | | | |
|---|---|---|---|---|---|---|---|---|---|
| Sub-Cluster 1 | Sub-Cluster 2 | Sub-Cluster 3 | Sub-Cluster 4 | Sub-Cluster 5 | Sub-Cluster 6 | Sub-Cluster 7 | Sub-Cluster 8 | Sub-Cluster 9 | Sub-Cluster 10 |
| 1 | 3 | 32 | 41 | 49 | 76 | 86 | 178 | 184 | 255 |
| 2 | 215 | 42 | 166 | 219 | 126 | | | | 259 |
| 4 | 281 | 46 | 189 | | 291 | | | | |
| 5 | | 190 | 244 | | | | | | |
| 6 | | 232 | | | | | | | |
| 7 | | 290 | | | | | | | |
| 8 | | 293 | | | | | | | |
| 9 | | 305 | | | | | | | |
| 10 | | | | | | | | | |

**Suggested Readings and Web Sites**

Diaconis, Persi; and Bradley Efron. "Computer Methods in Statistics." *Scientific American*, May 1983, pp. 116–30.

Foreman, John W. *Data Smart: Using Data Science to Transform Information into Insight*. Indianapolis: John Reilly & Sons, 2014

Fortmann-Roe, Scott. "Understanding the Bias-Variance Tradeoff." http://scott.fortmann-roe.com/docs/BiasVariance.html, June 2012, pp. 1–10.

Gan, Guojun, Chaoqun Ma, and Jianhong Wu. *Data Clustering: Theory, Algorithms, and Application*. Philadelphia: ASA-SiAM, 2007.

Guyon, Isabelle; Vincent Lemaire; Marc Boullé; Gideon Dror; and David Vogel. "Analysis of the KDD Cup 2009: Fast Scoring on a Large Orange Customer Database." *JMLR: Workshop and Conference Proceedings*, 7 (2009), pp. 1–22.

Harrison, D.; and D. L. Rubinfeld. "Hedonic prices and the demand for clean air." *Journal of Environmental Economics and Management*, vol. 5 (1978), pp. 81–102.

Jain, A. K.; M. N. Murty; and P. J. Flynn. "Data Clustering: A Review." *ACM Computing Surveys*, 31(1999), pp. 264–323.

Keating, Barry. "Analytics Off the Shelf." *Applied Marketing Analytics*, 2, no 1 (Winter 2015–16), pp. 12–24.

Keating, Barry; and Maryann O. Keating. "Well-Being Across Indiana: Is It Related to Good Governance?" *Indiana Policy Review* (Summer 2017), pp. 8–22.

Linden, Greg; Brent Smith; and Jeremy York. "Amazon.com Recommendations: Item-to-Item Collaborative Filtering." *IEEE Internet Computing* (January–February 2003):76–80.

Linden, Greg; J. A. Jacobi; and E. A. Benson. "Collaborative Recommendations Using Item-to-Item Similarity Mappings, U.S. Patent 6,266,649 (to Amazon.com), Patent and Trademark Office, Washington, D.C., 2001.

Surowiecki, James. *The Wisdom of Crowds*. New York: Doubleday, 2004.

Xiao, Jin; Ling Xie; Changzheng He; and Xiaoyi Jiang. *"Dynamic Classifier Ensemble Model for Customer Classification with Imbalanced Class Distribution."* *Expert Systems with Applications*, 39, no. 3 (15 February 2012), pp. 3–10.

Xie, Jianjun; Viktoria Rojkova; Siddharth Pal; and Stephen Coggeshall. "A Combination of Boosting and Bagging for KDD Cup 2009—Fast Scoring on a Large Database." *JMLR: Workshop and Conference Proceedings* 7 (2009), pp. 35–43.

http://www.kdnuggets.com/datasets/kddcup.html

## Exercises

1. What is the basic concept underlying an "ensemble" model?

2. Explain the fundamental difference between "boosting" and "bagging."

3. What are "weak learners" and are they used by bagging or boosting? Explain the concept of a weak learner.

4. "Bagging" is a short form of "bootstrap aggregation." Explain conceptually how bagging is accomplished in software. Why might bagging increase the predictive capacity of an underlying algorithm?

5. Boosting may only be used with Naive Bayes algorithms. Is this a true statement?

6. What method explained in this chapter is a concept in analytics of approximating the sampling distribution of a statistic by repeatedly sampling from a given sample of size n.

7. In the ensemble algorithms XLMiner© uses, there is a third model listed (in addition to boosting and bagging). The third model is a "random tree." Apply this ensemble algorithm to any data for classification and compare the results to a standard CART algorithm on the same data.

8. The Credit Card Fraud data was used in Chapter 9. It is a small version of a much larger data set; it is made up of 2013 European transactions. It is a very unbalanced data set in which there are only a few fraudulent transactions. Attempting to classify transactions as fraudulent will be difficult since there are very few instances of fraud. (C10P8)

   Use a best-pruned CART algorithm this time to create a predictive model for the Credit Card Fraud data. Does this model have predictive power?

   Explain carefully the information provided by the lift chart or the decile-wise lift chart; how does this information differ from the information provided by the overall misclassification rate?

   Now, separately, use bagging and boosting on the CART algorithm to determine if either of these enhancements to the original model result in an improvement in predictive capacity. Remember to selected "decision tree" as the underlying model.

9. In Chapter 9, we used red wine data to predict wine quality. Recall that wine has been graded for many years by experts who actually taste a sample of the wine, examine its color and aroma, and assign a grade (in our case, high quality or lower quality). Would it be possible, however, to use attributes of the wine that are machine measurable such as fixed acidity and residual sugar (and other attributes) to classify the wines? (C10P9)

   Partition the data into two partitions (60 percent and 40 percent, respectively), the training data and the validation data. Estimate a best-pruned CART algorithm for the training data and examine the resulting estimation.

Explain the overall misclassification rate for the validation partition and its calculation. What would have been the validation misclassification rate if you had used the naive model? What is the reason for using a "best-pruned" tree?

What does the validation confusion matrix tell the data scientist? Is the algorithm more likely to make one type of error rather than the other?

The lift chart is potentially the most important information provided by the algorithm. Examine either the cumulative gains chart, the lift chart proper, or the decile-wise lift chart. Do they each tell much the same story? How would you explain one of these lift charts to someone unfamiliar with predictive analytics?

Now, use the same wine data to estimate a bagged and a boosted CART model (i.e., the underlying model selected should be "decision tree"). Evaluate these versions of the CART algorithm by comparing them to the "base" results of the best-pruned model.

10. A telecommunication company wants to segment their customers into distinct groups in order to send appropriate subscription offers. Is this an example of "supervised" learning or "unsupervised" learning? Explain using the concepts of this chapter.

11. Hierarchical clustering algorithms compute a dendrogram; what is a dendrogram?

12. Describe the method and ideas regarding hierarchical agglomerative clustering as described in the chapter. Show the different steps of the algorithm using the distance or dissimilarity matrix below, and complete link clustering as described in the chapter. Give the partial results after each step, and create the complete dendrogram.

Now "cut" the dendrogram to create two clusters. Which records are in each of the clusters?

**Distance Matrix**

|   | 1 | 2 | 3 | 4 | 5 |
|---|---|---|---|---|---|
| 1 | 0 |   |   |   |   |
| 2 | 2 | 0 |   |   |   |
| 3 | 4 | 3 | 0 |   |   |
| 4 | 10 | 7 | 9 | 0 |   |
| 5 | 8 | 5 | 6 | 1 | 0 |

13. Which of the following statements about clustering are true?
- Clustering analysis is unsupervised learning since it does not require labeled training data.
- It is impossible to cluster objects in a data stream. We must have all the data objects that we need to cluster ready before clustering can be performed.
- When clustering, we want to put two dissimilar data objects into the same cluster.

14. Three different wineries (or cultivars) in a particular Italian region have produced 178 unique wines. We have information on the various characteristics of each of these wines (e.g., the amount of alcohol, the amount of ash, the alkalinity of the ash, etc.). Without using the "type" variable (which indicates the winery that produced the wine), perform a clustering of the wines. Do the clusters match the winery of origin of the wine? (C10P14)

# Chapter **Eleven**

# Text Mining

Since much of the data business managers encounter is in the form of text, using predictive analytics techniques requires that the text is in some manner transformed into data that can be actually used by the standard data mining techniques covered in Chapters 8-10. How exactly does this "transformation" or "datafication" take place? Once transformed, how is the resulting numerical data used in an analytics algorithm? This chapter will answer these two questions and present examples of the process described. Also, important and common errors encountered in text mining are explained.

©VLADGRIN/Getty Images

## LEARNING OBJECTIVES

After reading this chapter, you should be able to:

- Explain the concept of "dimension reduction."
- Construct and employ two different dimension reduction algorithm types.
- Explain and apply a "bag of words" type algorithm.
- Explain and use a "natural language processing" algorithm.
- Interpret the standard diagnostic statistics for text mining algorithms.
- Explain how better decisions can be made through the use of text mining.
- Apply text mining to make business predictions.

## INTRODUCTION

Our intent in this chapter is to introduce how text mining software turns ordinary text into numbers and thereby reduces the dimensions of the original data. Once the text data is in numerical form, any of the standard data mining algorithms from previous chapters may be applied to obtain greater explanatory power than is obtained by only using numerical data.

# WHY TURN TEXT INTO NUMBERS?

International Business Machines Corporation (IBM) has partnered with Twitter to collect and use tweets worldwide to aid in making business decisions. Tweets, recall, are unstructured pieces of textual data sent via Twitter that are a limited number of characters in length; Twitter registered users post and interact with these short messages, and even unregistered users can read them. This arrangement between a social media company and a business technology company may seem to be a strange combination. "IBM will help businesses predict trends in the marketplace and consumer sentiment about products and brands and will train 10,000 employees to consult businesses on the best use of Twitter data."[1] According to IBM Chief Executive Officer Ginni Rometty, this is an attempt to help transform IBM from its traditional hardware-based position into a higher-valued cloud and data analytics firm. This alignment of an old-line company with a new tech company is unusual. Will it create value? The jury is out on that question, but more and more firms are attempting (and succeeding) to gain value from analyzing textual data.

*Transforming text into numbers has been termed "datification."*

IBM and its clients will now be able to filter Twitter data based on geography, public biographical information, and the emotion expressed in the tweet. "Twitter has created something extraordinary. When you bring this together with other kinds of information and leverage IBM's innovations in analytics, Watson and cloud, business decision-making will never be the same," said IBM's Rometty. And IBM is not the only company to use Twitter; Thomson Reuters has access to Twitter data and sells sentiment analysis of that data that measures the emotional sentiment behind the tweets directed toward companies and their products. Prevedere, a software analytics company that makes data in more than 3.5 million time series available to customers, also provides information on what individuals are searching for on Google. Those search terms are text, and knowing what terms people are searching on may provide valuable information to forecasters and business decision makers.

Transforming text into numbers has been termed "datification" by Mayer-Schonberger and Cukier,[2] as we discussed in Chapter 8. This is not simply counting the letters in words or counting the words in a document but includes analyzing what the words and phrases mean and transforming that meaning into numbers that can be used in the standard data mining models.

# WHERE TO START—THE "BAG OF WORDS" ANALYSIS

The most difficult decision to make when considering the use of text as data is to formally define the problem you are trying to solve. Your odds of having success in analyzing any text data will suffer considerably if the problem you are trying to solve is not well defined at the outset. As part of defining the problem to be solved, you will also need to determine how much time you are willing to invest and what

---

[1] "IBM, Twitter to Partner on Business Data Analytics," Technology News, October 29, 2014.
[2] Viktor Mayer-Schonberger and Kenneth Cukier, *Big Data: A Revolution That Will Transform How We Live, Work, and Think* (New York, Houghton Mifflin Harcourt 2013), p. 85.

resources you are willing to employ. Both time and resources may be quite expensive because the commercial software is still relatively expensive and the human expertise to use the tools effectively at present is scarce. All that will change over the next few years, but it's best to get a head start now because there is likely to be useful information in business data. Even today, there are very low-cost software alternatives; XLMiner© includes a "bag of words" type set of tools that we will employ in this chapter. A "bag of words" analysis looks at the unprocessed text as a collection of words without regard to grammar. This will be the first approach we take to begin text mining; historically, it was also the first approach used by data scientists.

In some instances, defining your problem may seem quite simple, but in data mining (and text mining in particular), the objective is often initially quite vague. If we are using a clustering analysis such as those explained in Chapter 10, for example, we would not know the precise outcome the information might provide; that's why we use a clustering algorithm. This unsupervised algorithm often gives us unseen and unexpected information. The simpler situation would be when we use a classification algorithm (Chapter 9); here, we initially have some idea of the likely outcomes and are attempting to score records into the different classes with some prescribed purpose in mind.

Text mining is also not what data scientists are doing when engaged in simple information retrieval; for example, "find all the Idahoan Foods products purchasers in South Bend, Indiana." A SQL (Structured Query Language) statement to perform this task is strictly not text mining in a predictive analytics sense. It is a database management concept. Likewise, text mining is also not Boolean searching as we often do on the Internet when using Google; it is not, for example, searching for the conjunction of "Idaho" and "river." However, we would be data mining (and possibly text mining), if we were using textual attributes and if we were attempting to discern the "sentiment" of the public for Idahoan Food products.

Text mining is the automated algorithmic analysis of a single document or a group of documents to extract useful information.

Text mining is the automated algorithmic analysis of a single document or a group of documents to extract useful information. Text mining takes unstructured text and transforms it into structured data by analyzing the patterns derived from the text. The results of a text mining algorithm can be used by any of the classification methods we have covered in Chapter 9 or the clustering methods of Chapter 10.

Perhaps the most common misconception regarding text mining, or text analytics as it is sometimes called, is that a great deal of what data scientists do in this area most people would not call "analytics" at all in a strict sense. The process of counting the number of words in a document is part of what we do, but by itself, counting words is not analytics. In the same way, looking at how one word of interest is either close to or far from another word in a document is also strictly not analytics in the way we have been using the term, but it also is a part of what we do in text mining. All text is hard to analyze in any manner. That is why we break down the analysis of this unstructured data into small parts; we divide and conquer.

Our goal in text analytics is to reduce the dimensions of the unstructured text to manageable attributes we can use in data mining algorithms.

Overall, our goal in text analytics is to reduce the dimensions of the unstructured text to manageable attributes we can use in data mining algorithms. Consider the representation of the London Tube (subway) in the bottom of Figure 11.1. This is not an actual map depicting the precise routes run by the various Tube lines; it is, rather, an abstract view of the Tube lines in central London. An engineering map

**FIGURE 11.1** **London Tube Actual and Abstract Depictions**

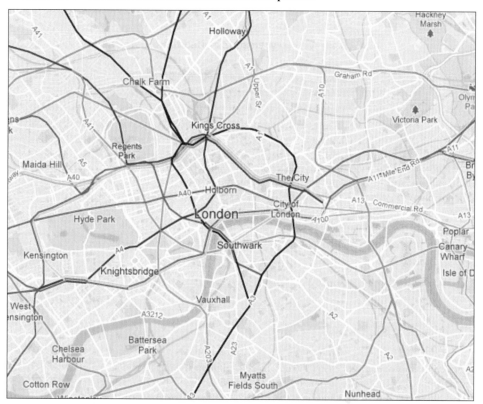

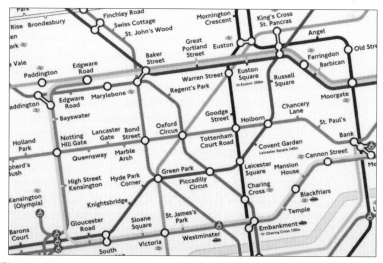

(shown in the top of Figure 11.1) of the same Tube lines would show the actual routes run by the lines; none of the lines run in straight lines like the abstract map in the bottom of Figure 11.1. The lines twist around and change elevation to avoid underground objects and other lines. But does this abstract map convey useful information? Which map (the abstract version shown at the bottom of Figure 11.1 or the "true" engineering version shown at the top of Figure 11.1) would you find helpful in making trip plans? It is no coincidence that the Transport for London hands out free tube maps like the one depicted at the bottom of Figure 11.1. That depiction is not an accurate representation of the precise routes run by the various lines; the routes are "incorrectly" shown as going in straight lines with clear intersections. But this abstraction, which reduces the information that is available in an engineering map, makes entirely clear how you might navigate the different lines to arrive easily at your destination. The Transport for London map depends upon "dimension reduction" for its usefulness. In precisely the same manner, we will use dimension reduction to clear away the clutter in raw text documents and extract some useful characteristics that may serve as attributes in a standard data mining algorithm.

When we deal with text (either in Excel or text files or databases), we treat rows as "documents," even if the row is huge. These rows might contain the comments of a single person, as we will use in our first example.

# NEWSGROUPS

As an example of text analytics in this chapter, we will use newsgroup data from the UCI Machine Learning Repository; Tom Mitchell originally collected this data at Carnegie Mellon University. These are Usenet comments from 1998 postings.[3] Usenet was a worldwide discussion group begun in 1980; users posted messages to different subject categories. We use as examples a sample of the "autos" group postings and a sample of the "electronics" group postings. Our goal will be to take the collection of postings and predict (classify) which are from the autos group and which are from the electronics group.

One method of approaching the goal for a classification scheme would be to use structured data we have about past postings. What characteristics did these Usenet users exhibit when posting to the two different newsgroups? Any one of many standard classification algorithms might work to provide the information, but our classification algorithms expect structured numerical data and the Usenet postings are in unstructured text format.

The difficulty, of course, is how to turn thousands of comments like the four examples in Table 11.1 into meaningful structured numerical data for analysis by our classification algorithm. We have words, phrases, sentences, and whole paragraphs; none of it is in the structured numerical form required of the classification algorithms of Chapter 9. The ultimate goal is to "reduce the dimensions" that now exist in the unstructured text into structured numerical categories that we are able to use in a classification algorithm. Data scientists have been working for decades

[3] T. M. Mitchell, *Machine Learning* (New York: McGraw-Hill, 1997).

**TABLE 11.1**

**Four Postings from the Two Usenet Newsgroups**
The Goal is to Use Text Analytics to Identify the Comment as Coming from the "Autos" Newsgroup or from the "Electronics" Newsgroup. (c11T1)

---

Subject: Ford Explorer 4WD - do I need performance axle?

We're considering getting a Ford Explorer XLT with 4WD and we have the following questions (All we would do is go skiing—no off-roading):

1. With 4WD, do we need the "performance axle" - (limited slip axle). Its purpose is to allow the tires to act independently when the tires are on different terrain.
2. Do we need the all-terrain tires (P235/75X15) or will the all-season (P225/70X15) be good enough for us at Lake Tahoe?

Thanks,
Tom

---

Subject: Radio for Toyota Tercel

I'm looking for a replacement radio/tape player for a 1984
Toyota Tercel. Standard off-the-shelf unit is fine, but
every place I've gone to (Service Merchandise, etc.) doesn't
have my car in its model application book. I want to just
take out the old radio, and slide in the new, with minimal time
spent hooking it up and adjusting the dashboard.
If you have put in a new unit in a similar car, I'd like to hear
what brand, how easy it was to do the change, and any other relevant information.

Please answer via E-mail.
Thanks, Tom

---

Subject: Re: Help with ultra-long timing

Thanks for the resposes as they were all good ideas and I am looking at using a couple of the ideas. I recieved in the mail today the spec sheets on the mil. spec version of Exar's XR-2240 timer/counter chip. It is stable down to -50 C and sucks very little power. They show an application for a ultra-long time delay (up to several years depending on the RC time constant). In this application, they have two of them cascaded together. The reset and trigger pins of both chips are tied together and the timebase of the second chip is disabled. In this configuration, the output is high when the system is reset.

Thanks again everyone...
-=-= Wes =-=-

---

Subject: WANTED: DRAM Controller for use with MC68HC16

For an upcoming project I want to use 4 Megs of DRAM configured as two 2 Meg banks of 16 bit data. I was wondering if anyone out there knows of a DRAM controller which will handle refreshing the data. It's ok if the controller doesn't handle bank switching - that part is easy.

Wayne

---

on "dimension reduction," and only recently has the power of the tools they have created been made accessible in commercial software. While some contend that only "coders" are able to manipulate text to obtain dimension reduction adequately, the commercial software packages have done an impressive job in making serious text mining available to anyone willing to learn the specifics of a particular piece of software (without a knowledge of coding). With a modest knowledge of what the software is capable of doing and with some reasonable direction on the part of the user, some beneficial text mining results may be achieved.

Examining the four sample comments in Table 11.1, a human could quite easily assign each to the appropriate Usenet group. Our goal should be to reduce the dimension of the text to structured numerical attributes that may be used to classify each comment.

Text mining is more than simply identifying words in a document; the text mining software must also

1) remove "stop words";
2) perform a process called "stemming"; and
3) correct spelling errors.
4) break the text into "tokens."

Text mining is more than simply identifying words in a document.

The sample posts in Table 11.1 will require all four cleanup procedures. We usually remove the "stop words" (such as *the*, *and*, *a*, and so on) from the text. These stop words are so numerous in text that they tend to swamp out more meaningful words in an analysis (much like a trend in an ARIMA model swamps out the other more subtle patterns). Stop words are so common in natural language that, if left in the text, they would dominate all other words. The list of words that are considered stop words is usually editable (it is in XLMiner©), and this allows for customization for particular bodies of text. We remove them to reduce the text dimensions and yet retain the original meaning of the author.

We also need to reduce the text dimensions by "stemming," which is the process of making regular the remaining words by reducing them to their stem. For example, stemming terms such as *agree, agreed, agrees, agreeable, agreeing*, and *agreement* would result in the stem "agree." Even if not a real word, "agree" would be the token remembered and used in place of all the other forms of the word. The stem need not be a real word. Each different text mining software you use will stem differently, and the procedure is always evolving in the upgrades to each software package. Stemming reduces the dimensions of the text by treating all versions of the same (or a very similar) concept identically.

Spelling errors (which are all too common and are evident in the examples in Table 11.1) also need correction, such as is commonly done when one sends a text message to a smartphone. The text is finally broken up into tokens through "tokenization," which makes essential elements out of the words, phrases, and symbols in the original text.

Some other procedures are also often used to reduce the text dimensions to prepare for analysis. Words of more than, say, 20 letters in length are removed from the document. These are often not actual words in the English language but URLs or computer-generated jargon. XLMiner© also allows the user to specify exact terms that are to be excluded, such as *subject, from,* and anything that appears to be an email address. Numbers and items that appear to be monetary values are removed as well. We also remove terms occurring in almost every document; these terms might be headers and would help little in classification. The text is usually "normalized" as well; all text is converted to lower case so that *car, Car,* and

**FIGURE 11.2**    Term Count Information on the Usenet Newsgroups Data After Performing the Data Cleansing Procedures   (C11T1)

Source: Frontline Systems Inc.

**Term Count Info**

| Text Var | Original (Total) | Final (Total) | Reduction, % | Vocabulary |
|----------|------------------|---------------|--------------|------------|
| TextVar  | 8586             | 1583          | 18.43699045  | 200 |

"Tokens" are the words finally extracted from a block of text.

*CAR* would be recognized as a single word. The size of the vocabulary examined is also commonly limited; we might, for instance, limit the vocabulary to 200 or 300 concepts, those most frequently mentioned in the text.

In text mining, "tokens" are the words finally extracted from a block of text once these procedures have been performed. The process is called "tokenization." In some cases, text mining software will carry out the process of "entity extraction," which identifies a group of words as a single item; people's names are often characterized in this way. Users may help the software by engaging in phrase reduction; you might identify the phrase "subcompact" as being synonymous with *car* for instance. Or, the terms *car, motor car, passenger car, limousine, hatchback, sedan, coupe,* and *jalopy* might all be reduced to *auto.* This form of directed learning (i.e., you are aiding the software in reducing the text dimensions) may have a significant impact on the accuracy of the outcome.

Figure 11.2 shows about an 18 percent reduction in terms found in the Usenet newsgroups data as a result of the data cleansing processes of removing stop words, stemming, and so on. In our example, we will limit the vocabulary to 200 different terms.

The term document matrix illustrated in Figure 11.3 displays some of the terms (after cleansing) that are present in the various documents. Each document ID represents a single Usenet posting. To see which are the most common terms across all documents, examine Figure 11.4. "Numbertoken" refers to any number appearing in the document. The term *auto* appeared in 14 of the 40 documents. Each row of the term document matrix represents the narrative of a single Usenet post. Each column represents one word or term extracted from the body of all the Usenet postings.

**FIGURE 11.3**    A Small Portion of the Term-Document Matrix Shows the Terms Present in the Selected Documents   (C11T1)

Source: Frontline Systems Inc.

**Term-Document Matrix**

| Doc ID | accur | activ | addit | advanc | air | applic | articl | australia | auto |
|--------|-------|-------|-------|--------|-----|--------|--------|-----------|------|
| 101551 | 0 | 1.59603 | 0 | 0 | 0 | 0 | 0.679859 | 0 | 2.515777 |
| 101552 | 0 | 0 | 1.59603 | 0 | 0 | 0 | 0.679859 | 0 | 0.679859 |
| 101553 | 0 | 0 | 0 | 0 | 0 | 0 | 0 | 0 | 0 |
| 101554 | 0 | 0 | 0 | 0 | 0 | 0 | 0 | 0 | 0 |
| 101555 | 0 | 0 | 0 | 0 | 0 | 0 | 0.679859 | 0 | 1.75741 |
| 101556 | 0 | 0 | 0 | 0 | 0 | 0 | 0 | 0 | 0 |

**FIGURE 11.4**    **The Most Common Terms in the Documents Selected**    (C11T1)

Source: Frontline Systems Inc.

## Top Terms Info

TextVar

| Term | Collection Frequency | Document Frequency | Top Documents |
|---|---|---|---|
| numbertoken | 458 | 29 | 434, 52743, 101555 |
| auto | 42 | 14 | 76, 101558, 101560 |
| time | 32 | 12 | 2739, 52434, 52464 |
| write | 23 | 18 | 1580, 52464, 52739 |
| articl | 18 | 14 | 464, 52739, 101551 |
| dealer | 17 | 6 | 56, 101558, 101576 |
| problem | 15 | 11 | 51, 101554, 101574 |
| thing | 14 | 11 | 739, 101558, 52464 |
| work | 14 | 10 | 559, 101576, 52434 |
| power | 13 | 9 | 42, 101560, 101577 |

# IN PICTURES

We could also examine the Usenet documents in pictures. A "Wordle" displays the most often used words in a single document or set of documents by displaying the words in different size type (see http://www.wordle.net/); the larger the display of a word, the more often it appears. Wordles are the most well-known form of output from text; in a simple sense, they represent dimension reduction. The Wordle for the 40 Usenet postings covering both autos and electronics is shown in Figure 11.5. Stemming is rudimentary in the Wordle routines available on the Internet; notice that *car* and *cars* both appear separately in this Wordle. Not surprisingly, the term *subject* is the largest word; it appears in every document. The word *subject* is one of the words that the data cleansing procedures of a text mining program would have eliminated; it is of little use in trying to differentiate the postings since it appears in every Usenet posting. The other words displayed, however, begin to tell a story about the documents we are examining. If we did not know that there are two newsgroups represented (autos and electronics), we might begin to guess their subject areas from the size of the word *car* or the fact that *Tesla* is present. While Wordles are interesting and give some rudimentary information about text data, we probably would not consider them a text analytics tool. Wordles simply count words; it is just a frequency count and not particularly useful in text mining in general.

XLMiner©, on the other hand, is a true analytics software package and provides graphics representing the data under analysis that help to provide more insight and allow us to create numerical variables representing concepts from the individual words.

XLMiner© uses a "singular value decomposition" (SVD) method for text mining; this allows us to reduce the dimensionality of the data matrix. If a text data set includes 500 attributes or predictors, SVD allows XLMiner© to construct a much

SVD is a concept extraction tool; it will take a large number of words and compress or summarize them into a much smaller, and thus more manageable, number of linear combinations that will represent the majority of the information represented by the original words.

**FIGURE 11.5**  **Wordle of the 40 Documents in the Two Usenet Newsgroups: Autos and Electronics**

Source: "Wordle," wordle.net.

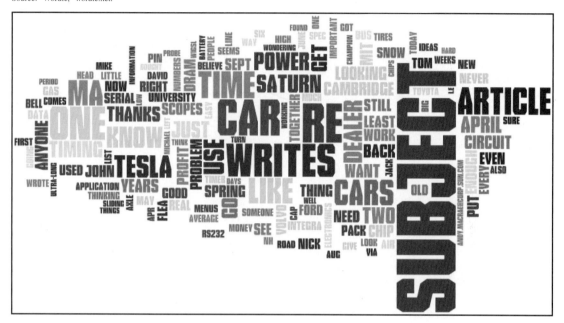

smaller number of linear combinations of the attributes called "concepts." These linear combinations will be weighted sums and may be used to build predictive models (i.e., classification models). The SVD tool employed by XLMiner© (and other text mining software) is a concept extraction tool; it will take a significant number of words and compress or summarize them into a much smaller, and thus more manageable, number of linear combinations that will represent the majority of the information described by the original words. This is a method not unique to text mining, but it is especially useful in text mining.

## UNDERSTANDING SVD

To understand singular value decomposition (SVD), consider the following situation: you have collected data on both the height in centimeters and weight in kilograms of 100 individuals. We thus have two dimensions (or terms) for each: the height of the person and the weight of the person. If we were to plot this information, it would look like Figure 11.6.

However, we may also represent the same information about the 100 individuals with the reduced form of a regression line like that shown in Figure 11.7. All the points in Figure 11.7 can roughly (roughly, because not every point is exactly on the line) be represented by the line. The points on the regression line might be thought of as a combination of the two pieces of information we had for

**FIGURE 11.6**
**Height and Weight
of 100 Individuals
as a Scatterplot.
The Regression Line
Shown, However,
May Be Used to
Represent as the
Single Concept
"Size."**

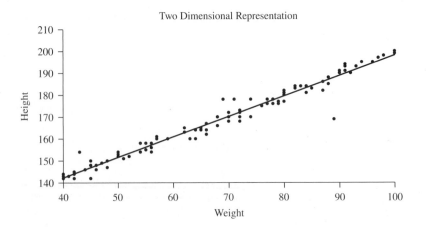

each individual; the line represents a latent dimension that we could call "size." The "size" concept extracts the information from all the data we originally had.

This is the basic mechanism of singular value decomposition. We started with two dimensions (height and weight) and now have a single dimension or concept titled "size" that contains "most" of the information in the original data but has the advantage that the dimensions are reduced.

## BACK TO THE USENET EXAMPLE

Returning to our Usenet postings classification problem, a Zipf plot (Figure 11.7) shows the most frequently appearing terms (i.e., words) in the set of posts; moving from left to right displays the most frequent term to the least frequent term. Note that the curve drops quite steeply. The term *auto* is represented by the third data point from the left and appears in 14 documents (out of the total of 40 documents) and 42 times in total. The first data point from the left (the highest data point) represents the term *numbertoken*, which appears in 29 of the documents and 458 times overall. These values are used in the creation of the documents concept matrix that displays the numeric representation of the concepts derived from the text; this is what we will use in the classification models to follow.

This Zipfs plot follows Zipf's law, an empirical law formulated using mathematical statistics. The law is named for the linguist George Kingsley Zipf. The law states that given a large sample of words used (in any language), the frequency of any single word is inversely proportional to its rank in the frequency table.

The Concept Importance table lists the 200 most important concepts calculated by using SVD. The table is used to create the Scree plot in Figure 11.8. This plot is a graphical exhibition of the import (i.e., the contribution) of each concept. The largest "drop" or "hinge" in the plot appears between the first and second concept. This suggests that the first concept explains the leading topic in our collection of documents from the two Usenet groups. The rest of the concepts have less importance than the

**FIGURE 11.7** **Zipf Plot of the Usenet Newsgroup Data** (C11T1)

Source: Frontline Systems Inc.

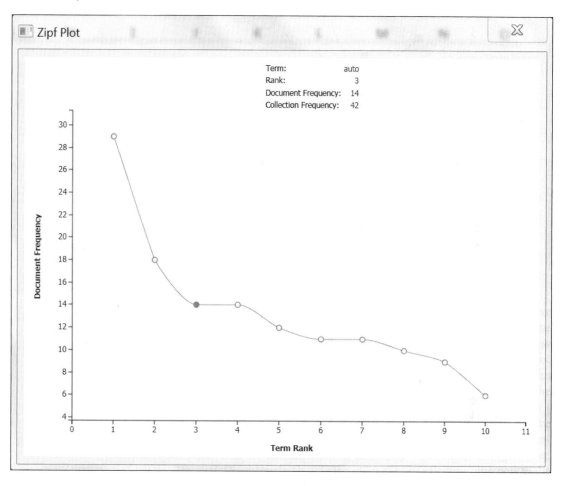

first concept. *Scree* is a geological term that describes the debris that collects on the lowest part of a rocky slope where the slope flattens out. In our example, most of the variability in a document is suggested to occur in just a few dimensions or concepts. In actual text mining, we usually find that no more than a few dimensions (sometimes single digits) are required to extract most of the information from a document.

"Latent semantic indexing" collates the most common words and phrases and identifies them as keywords

Once the most relevant terms have been identified, XLMiner© uses "latent semantic indexing" to determine the relationship between terms and concepts in the content of the documents (Usenet postings in our example). Latent semantic indexing collates the most common words and phrases and identifies them as keywords for particular postings; it is an indexing and retrieval method that uses the mathematical technique called singular value decomposition to identify patterns in the relationships between the terms and concepts contained in an unstructured

**FIGURE 11.8** **Scree Plot** (C11T1)

Source: Frontline Systems Inc.

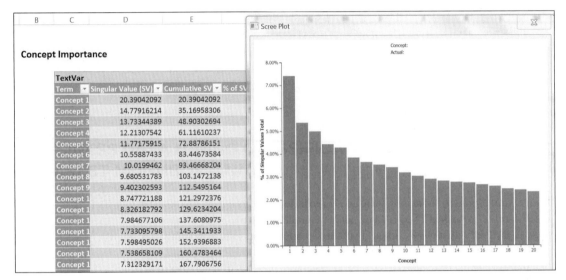

collection of text. SVD is routinely used in statistical natural language processing to identify "latent dimensions of meaning" that organize documents in the body of words, terms, or phrases used in the original documents. The result of the process can be displayed as either a table or a plot. Figure 11.9 is the concept-document

**FIGURE 11.9**
**The Concept-**
**Document**
**Matrix** (C11T1)

Source: Frontline Systems Inc.

## Concept-Document Matrix

| Doc ID | Concept 1 | Concept 2 | Concept 3 | Concept 4 | Concept 5 |
|---|---|---|---|---|---|
| 101551 | -0.365394 | 0.08523673 | -0.7643377 | 0.29206233 | -0.4355564 |
| 101552 | -0.5900338 | -0.2149373 | -0.7625902 | 0.12535718 | -0.0916727 |
| 101553 | -0.9102068 | -0.109168 | 0.26332622 | -0.1380866 | -0.2668282 |
| 101554 | -0.663527 | -0.5461936 | -0.3848488 | 0.15705947 | -0.2977048 |
| 101555 | -0.5775238 | -0.2798862 | -0.6827411 | 0.3464294 | 0.04451146 |
| 101556 | -0.5288995 | -0.0991888 | -0.7080417 | 0.19843499 | -0.4119799 |
| 101557 | -0.6417256 | -0.1452084 | -0.3346327 | -0.645239 | 0.19695278 |
| 101558 | -0.6703883 | -0.1025042 | -0.7331143 | -0.0447765 | 0.02471806 |
| 101559 | -0.6656735 | -0.2013315 | -0.4397669 | -0.544104 | -0.1640135 |
| 101560 | -0.5142766 | -0.2583275 | -0.6637505 | 0.45154424 | 0.15597918 |
| 101571 | -0.5534198 | -0.0264743 | -0.6141913 | -0.0914658 | 0.55446252 |
| 101572 | -0.7605116 | -0.6461916 | 0.0599811 | 0.01324113 | -0.0168941 |
| 101573 | -0.6835975 | -0.0402968 | -0.548398 | -0.2787154 | -0.390702 |
| 101574 | -0.8188538 | 0.12732937 | -0.4657913 | 0.02814612 | -0.30905 |
| 101575 | -0.8524468 | -0.2851402 | -0.3491554 | 0.06917474 | -0.255607 |
| 101576 | -0.6075946 | -0.4590983 | -0.5500782 | 0.19499523 | -0.2818659 |
| 101577 | -0.4899644 | -0.251011 | -0.684355 | 0.45387457 | 0.15028108 |

**FIGURE 11.10**  **Concept Scatter Plot for Concepts 1 and 2**  (C11T1)

Source: Frontline Systems Inc.

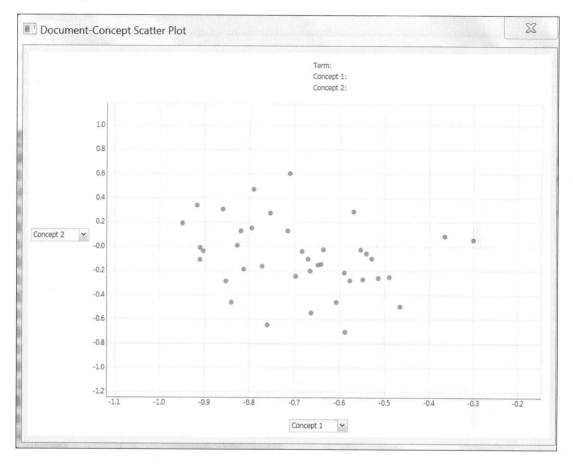

matrix for the Usenet documents; this matrix displays the top concepts as columns of the matrix, and the individual Usenet posting ID numbers form the rows of the matrix.

Figure 11.10, the concept scatter plot, is the visual representation of the concept-document matrix. The further the magnitude of a plotted point from zero, the more effect that particular concept has for the corresponding document. XLMiner© normalizes each document representation, so it lies on a unit hypersphere. Documents that appear in the middle of the plot, with concept coordinates near 0, are not explained well by either of the shown concepts.

In our Usenet example, we identify a concept having a set of terms that can be divided into two groups—one related to autos and the other to electronics. If these groups are distant from each other on the axis corresponding to this concept, we would have evidence that this particular concept represents a pattern in the document collection that is capable of identifying the group to which the documents belong (either autos or electronics).

We are now ready to use the values from the concept-document matrix (that have been calculated using SVD) to attempt to classify the Usenet postings.

# A LOGISTICS REGRESSION CLASSIFICATION OF THE USENET POSTINGS

The concept values in Figure 11.8 are used as the attributes in a logistic regression (they could, however, be used in other classification algorithms as well). Recall that we are attempting to generate a model that will classify text postings on Usenet into one of two possible categories: autos or electronics. As always, we start with a known data set of 40 total postings of which 20 are from the autos group, and 20 are from the electronics group. We will partition the data and train the logit model.

Both the confusion matrices and the lift charts (cumulative gains charts) of Table 11.2 and Figure 11.11 indicate that the logistic regression algorithm has performed well in classifying the postings into the correct Usenet group.

**TABLE 11.2**
**Training and Validation Confusion Matrices for the Usenet Postings Classification Logistic Regression** (C11T1)

Source: Frontline Systems Inc.

**Training: Classification Summary**

Confusion Matrix

| Actual\Predicted | Auto | Electronics |
|---|---|---|
| Auto | 16 | 1 |
| Electronics | 3 | 12 |

Error Report

| Class | # Cases | # Errors | % Error |
|---|---|---|---|
| Auto | 17 | 1 | 5.882352941 |
| Electronics | 15 | 3 | 20 |
| Overall | 32 | 4 | 12.5 |

**Validation: Classification Summary**

Confusion Matrix

| Actual\Predicted | Auto | Electronics |
|---|---|---|
| Auto | 3 | 0 |
| Electronics | 1 | 4 |

Error Report

| Class | # Cases | # Errors | % Error |
|---|---|---|---|
| Auto | 3 | 0 | 0 |
| Electronics | 5 | 1 | 20 |
| Overall | 8 | 1 | 12.5 |

**FIGURE 11.11** Training (Left) and Validation (Right) Lift Charts for the Usenet Postings Classification Logistic Regression (C11T1)

Source: Frontline Systems Inc.

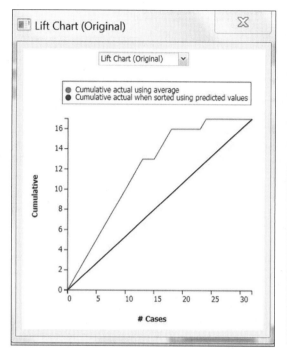
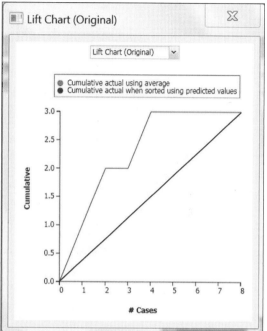

Recall that the "raw material" we started with was the actual text postings from the two groups as shown in Table 11.1. We reduced the dimension of the textual data into numbers representing four concepts and their relationship to the Usenet group category (autos or electronics). The logistic regression used those concepts to create a model that could be employed to classify thousands, hundreds of thousands, or even millions of postings. All of this could be accomplished without any human reading even a single posting. The key is dimension reduction.

# NATURAL LANGUAGE PROCESSING

While the "bag of words" analysis that we performed with the Usenet postings provides a great deal of useful information, another form of text mining is available in some commercial software such as IBM/SPSS Modeler and SAS Enterprise Miner. We will use IBM/SPSS Modeler as the example for natural language processing (NLP). The powerful capabilities of NLP to rapidly process a great variety of unstructured text data, reduce the dimensions of that data, and extract key concepts such as sentiment from the data have widened the scope of text analytics uses. Natural language processing is the ability of an algorithm to understand human speech as it is written or spoken. NLP is a component of artificial intelligence (AI) mechanisms that recognize voice commands. The Hal 9000 was a fictional AI mechanism in Arthur C. Clarke's *2001: A Space Odyssey*. The Hal computer interacted in an almost human manner with the astronaut; while Hal was an entirely fictional device, like much that has been written as science fiction, today we take for granted our voice interactions with our automobiles and smartphones.

Commercial data mining/text mining software that employs natural language processing adds prebuilt dictionaries to the tools available to data scientists. These dictionaries are not like the ones we use to look up the meaning or spelling of a particular word; these dictionaries cover specific domains such as consumer sentiment for products or consumer sentiment for services. Sometimes they include only accurate information for a single industry such as banking or insurance. They are also available in different languages (IBM/SPSS Modeler includes eight languages at present; that will increase). Each of the dictionaries contains not just words and phrases but also synonyms and analysis rules for the treatment of text in a specific domain. Context, which was ignored in the "bag of words" analysis, becomes essential in natural language processing. The dictionaries are also customizable; terms and phrases specific to an industry or firm can be added, new synonyms may be defined, and specific phrases can be recognized. The fine-tuning feature of the commercial dictionaries is a particularly powerful rationale for using their software, and the commercial providers update their current selection of dictionaries and expand the number and range of dictionaries available each year.

Extracting complex concepts is aided in the commercial packages by features that allow minimal human intervention if that is what is wanted; the commercial programs also allow maximum customization by the user and the insertion of coding for specific circumstances. We will see, however, that even with virtually no intervention or coding, powerful insights may be gained.

The interfaces of the two primary commercial packages are quite different from the menu-driven approach we have seen in forecasting and data mining software so far. Both IBM/SPSS and SAS use graphical user interfaces. Students have commented that using either IBM/SPSS Modeler or SAS Enterprise Miner is a bit like building with Lego blocks; the user places the blocks in a specific sequence and "runs" or executes the model from left to right. The menu options are "hidden" beneath the various icons but accessible with a click.

Figure 11.12 is an example of the "canvas" on which a model stream is formed in IBM/SPSS Modeler. On the left is a node titled "Facebook Wall." This node is not a data file or a pointer to a static database but rather a pointer to Chipotle's Facebook wall. The node includes directions about what portion of the wall to collect data from (i.e., text from the comments section) and how much data to collect. This process of collecting text data from websites is sometimes called "scraping," "web scraping," or "harvesting." Depending upon when the scraping node executes, the resulting text collected will change.

Natural language processing is the ability of an algorithm to understand human speech as it is written or spoken.

**FIGURE 11.12** **IBM/SPSS Modeler Stream to Gather Information (i.e., Text) from Facebook and Reduce the Dimensions Using Natural Language Processing**

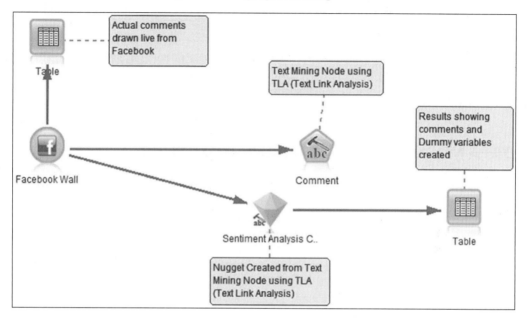

Clicking on the Facebook node of Figure 11.12 opens up the comments collected in real time by the software. The twenty-ninth and thirtieth comments (truncated) are displayed in Figure 11.13. Examine the thirtieth comment; the full comment reads

> *"My 7 year old son has decided that Chipotle is the best restaurant out there!! Want to know why??? He's been doing a no sugar added summer and nothing at Chipotle has added sugars (other than the salad dressing). Thanks Chipotle for having a healthy option for us!"*

By using the Text Link Analysis that performs the natural language processing, the two dummy variables on the right-hand side of Figure 11.13 are created; only two of the dummy variables are shown here, but several more were created. What do you think of the thirtieth comment? Was it a positive or negative comment? And what was the subject of the comment? Modeler identified the comment as "Category Positive with respect to product functioning." Most of you would probably agree this comment is positive, and most would also agree that

**FIGURE 11.13** **A Portion of The Textual Data Drawn from the Facebook Node**

| | Comment | Category_Neg: Service: Attitude | Category_Pos: Product Functioning |
|---|---|---|---|
| 29 | Need a third location in ft collins. Theres a perfect space available right next to the brand new starbucks at college and horsetooth. Thanks in a... | F | F |
| 30 | My 7 year old son has decided that Chipotle is the best restaurant out there!! Want to know why??? He's been doing a no sugar added summe... | F | T |

the comment has to do with the operation of Chipotle. Modeler has gone beyond a "bag of words" analysis and assigned consumer sentiment to the comment as well as defining the subject of the sentiment. Both pieces of information are created as dummy variables with the value of either true or false (or zero and one) being the only alternatives. The dimensions of the text have been reduced, and the text has been "datified" and is thus capable of being used as additional attributes in any data mining algorithm we have seen so far. Numeric attributes now represent the text comments and may be used with other attributes that were not derived from text.

## DATA MINING AND TEXT MINING COMBINED

Data mining and text mining are most often combined in an ensemble model, one containing attributes derived from text as well as attributes like those we used in the classification models in Chapter 9. Consider the example of a rental car company that has structured data representing past customers but also has unstructured customer satisfaction comments that may have come from a survey or may be text gleaned from customer hotline telephone interviews. The structured data looks like that in Table 11.3.

The data in Table 11.3 are in a familiar format, rows and columns. Even the text aspects of the data can easily be transformed into dummy variables; female and male become one and zero, and active and inactive likewise become one or zero. For the target classification variable, we will use customer status; we are trying to classify customers as currently active or inactive.

**TABLE 11.3**
**A Portion of the Structured Data Available About Customers for the Auto Rental Agency** (C11T3)

| ID | Gender | Status | Children | Age | Customer_Status |
|---|---|---|---|---|---|
| 149... | Male | S | 0.000 | 32.000 | Active |
| 149... | Male | M | 2.000 | 49.987 | Inactive |
| 154... | Male | S | 1.000 | 14.640 | Active |
| 154... | Male | S | 2.000 | 56.473 | Active |
| 155... | Male | M | 0.000 | 60.367 | Active |
| 164... | Male | S | 1.000 | 56.047 | Inactive |
| 164... | Male | S | 2.000 | 62.753 | Active |
| 164... | Male | S | 0.000 | 55.340 | Inactive |
| 167... | Male | M | 2.000 | 52.627 | Active |
| 173... | Male | M | 0.000 | 42.347 | Inactive |
| 174... | Female | S | 2.000 | 55.000 | Active |
| 175... | Male | M | 1.000 | 47.853 | Active |
| 176... | Male | M | 0.000 | 42.167 | Inactive |
| 177... | Female | M | 1.000 | 62.000 | Active |
| 178... | Female | S | 2.000 | 43.000 | Active |
| 180... | Female | S | 0.000 | 39.787 | Inactive |
| 180... | Female | M | 2.000 | 33.493 | Active |
| 183... | Female | S | 0.000 | 53.013 | Inactive |
| 185... | Male | S | 0.000 | 40.180 | Inactive |
| 189... | Male | M | 1.000 | 46.827 | Inactive |

**TABLE 11.4** **A Portion of the Unstructured Text Comments Available to the Auto Rental Agency** (C11T4)

| ID | Car_Owner | Customer_Service |
|----|-----------|------------------|
| 759.... | No | I haven't actually spoken with anyone from a car rental organization for quite a while. When I did (probably about three years ago), I believe they we... |
| 771.... | Yes | Customer Service was fine. They were able to upgrade me for $2 a day to the next class...that was nice. |
| 772.... | Yes | They were too pushy in trying to sell insurance. |
| 782.... | No | They were helpful and accommodating when I wanted to change the color of the car. |
| 803.... | Yes | speed up the rental process! |
| 827.... | Yes | The counter girl seemed confused and she had lost our reservations. They directed us to one car and then came running out to tell us that was the... |
| 841.... | No | The representatives were helpful and considerate; the only problem encountered was finding the rental car in the parking lot. I really would have a... |
| 900.... | No | Excellent response dealing with child seat. |
| 916.... | Yes | For the most part, they it's been really good service. I usually rent from the airports because it's much cheaper. Once they charged me over and I h... |
| 930.... | No | The customer service was excellent |
| 931.... | No | Customer service was average. They did not go above and beyond. They did, however, do more than the minimum. |
| 954.... | No | I HATE how they pressure you to buy add-on service. |
| 956.... | No | Experience was fine |

The unstructured text data we have available appear like that in Table 11.4. Would an analysis of these comments help us differentiate between active and inactive customers?

Two IBM/SPSS Modeler streams are pictured in Figure 11.14. At the bottom of Figure 11.14 is the stream representing a kNN model using only structured data like that in Table 11.3. The stream at the top of the figure depicts a similar model but includes text data as well from the customer satisfaction survey like that in Table 11.4. The model at the top of Figure 11.14 is a true ensemble model because it merges information from two very different sources.

The nodes are read from left to right (as you usually read a line of text), and they execute in that order as well. The results from the first node execution are

**FIGURE 11.14** **Two IBM/SPSS Modeler Streams. Both Are kNN Classification Models. The Top Stream Includes Both Structured and Unstructured (Text) Data. The Bottom Stream Includes Only Structured Data.** (C11F14)

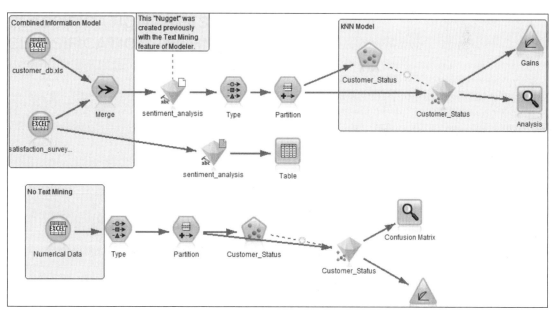

passed to the node to its right, and so on. In the bottom stream in Figure 11.14, the first node is an Excel source node (designated "Numerical Data"); this node instructs the software to load data from a particular Excel spreadsheet (in this case, the Excel spreadsheet contains only structured data like that in Table 11.3). The next node is a type node; this is where the data scientist identifies the attribute variables and the target variable (and which variables might be disregarded). The following partition node performs the familiar function of randomly dividing the data into two partitions (a training data portion and a testing or validation portion). The "Customer Status" node is a classification model request; this node specifies that you wish to estimate a kNN classification model with the data. We could have chosen from any number of the classification models of Chapter 9. The "Customer Status nugget" is the resulting rule set that the software creates; it is the actual model estimated for use in classification of both the training data and the validation data. The final two nodes, one with a magnifying glass icon and the other with a stylized cumulative gains chart, create the diagnostic statistics we will examine.

Examining the node with the magnifying glass icon (which is called an "analysis" node) displays the confusion matrices for both the training and validation data. Note that IBM/SPSS Modeler refers to confusion matrices as "coincidence" matrices and the two partitions of the data are called "training" and "testing". These results appear in Table 11.5.

The 53 and 32 records displayed on the diagonal of the training coincidence (i.e., confusion) matrix and the 38 and 18 records displayed on the diagonal of the testing (i.e., validation) matrix represent the model's correct classifications; the off-diagonal numbers represent the records incorrectly classified. For instance, in the testing matrix, the 20 represents 20 records that were classified by the algorithm as "inactive" but were actually "active" customers. The overall misclassification rate for the training data is seen to be 24.78 percent, the misclassification rate for the testing data is 35.63 percent.

Would adding unstructured text data in the model construction process by way of text mining in any way aid the classification model? We can see the execution procedure of the combined or "ensemble" model represented in the top half of

**TABLE 11.5**

The "Coincidence Matrix" or Confusion Matrix Produced by IBM/SPSS Modeler Using Only the Structured Data. Also Displayed Are the Misclassification Rates   (C11F14)

Results for output field Customer_Status
Comparing $KNN-Customer_Status with Customer_Status

| 'Partition' | 1_Training | | 2_Testing | |
|---|---|---|---|---|
| Correct | 85 | 75.22% | 56 | 64.37% |
| Wrong | 28 | 24.78% | 31 | 35.63% |
| Total | 113 | | 87 | |

Coincidence Matrix for $KNN-Customer_Status (rows show actuals)

| 'Partition' = 1_Training | Active | Inactive |
|---|---|---|
| Active | 53 | 14 |
| Inactive | 14 | 32 |
| 'Partition' = 2_Testing | Active | Inactive |
| Active | 38 | 11 |
| Inactive | 20 | 18 |

**TABLE 11.6**
A Partial List Showing Just Two of the Variables Created by Text Mining and Used in the Classification Stream (C11F14)

| Category_Neg: Pricing and Billing | Category_Neg: Product: Availability/Variety/Size |
|---|---|
| F | F |
| F | F |
| F | F |
| F | F |
| F | F |
| F | T |

Figure 11.14. In this case, the two sources of data are first combined using a merge node. The combined data (now including structured data like that in Table 11.3 *and* unstructured data like that in Table 11.4) are fed into the remaining nodes that are precisely like those used in the structured data–only estimation. The type, partition, and model nodes that follow are exactly like those in the stream that represented only the structured data.

The numeric variables created by text mining represent the concepts that we used from the "Customer Satisfaction" dictionary resident in Modeler. They include attributes representing concepts such as the two concepts shown in Table 11.6. One of the variables shown here identifies negative comments regarding pricing and billing; the other variable identifies negative comments regarding availability (note that the last individual represented had a negative comment on availability). These variables were not available when we performed the initial kNN analysis. We are using all the data previously available and adding to it the attributes created through the text mining process.

But did the additional effort to create numeric variables from the text and merging them with the original structured data result in any improvement?

Yes, there is significant improvement in the results. The results for the ensemble model are shown in Table 11.7. For the testing (i.e., validation) data, the misclassification rate has fallen from 35.63 percent to 23.53 percent. While this is impressive, recall that the overall misclassification rate should not be the only diagnostic statistic you should examine. What about the lift charts for each model?

**TABLE 11.7**
The "Coincidence Matrix" or Confusion Matrix Produced by IBM/SPSS Modeler Using Both the Structured Data and the Unstructured (Text) Data. Also Displayed Are the Misclassification Rates. (C11F14)

Results for output field Customer_Status

Comparing $KNN-Customer_Status with Customer_Status

| 'Partition' | 1_Training | | 2_Testing | |
|---|---|---|---|---|
| Correct | 109 | 82.58% | 52 | 76.47% |
| Wrong | 23 | 17.42% | 16 | 23.53% |
| Total | 132 | | 68 | |

Coincidence Matrix for $KNN-Customer_Status (rows show actuals)

| 'Partition' = 1_Training | Active | Inactive |
|---|---|---|
| Active | 69 | 9 |
| Inactive | 14 | 40 |
| 'Partition' = 2_Testing | Active | Inactive |
| Active | 33 | 5 |
| Inactive | 11 | 19 |

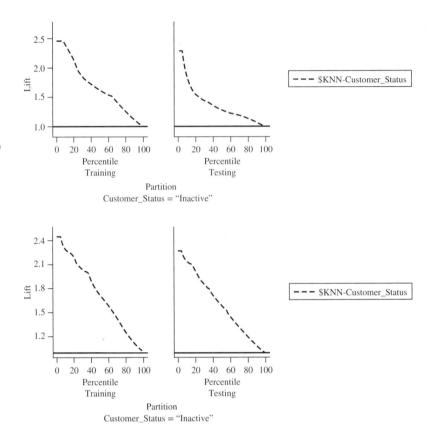

**FIGURE 11.15**
**The Lift Charts for the Structured Data Only Model (Top) and the Combined Structured and Unstructured (Text) Model (Bottom)** (C11F14)

Will adding text data to record consumer sentiment always improve model results? No!

Shown in Figure 11.15 are the lift charts for both models; the model using only structured data is shown in the top two charts, and the results for the combined model that adds the text data are shown in the bottom two charts. The lift is 1.54 at the 20 percent level for the structured data model; the lift is 2.03 for the combined model at the same level. Since the data are reordered when drawing the lift charts, this may be the better measure for evaluating the difference between the two models. Clearly, the combined model added predictive power. Will adding text data to record consumer sentiment always improve model results? No, only when the added attributes actually provide extra information will the process work. But in actual practice, the added variables almost always add predictive power if they are constructed in a sophisticated manner. Even a "bag of words" approach would probably have resulted in improvement, but the use of natural language processing has resulted in a dramatic improvement. Consider too that most of the data in the world are unstructured; the greater part of that data remains untapped by data scientists at the current time. That will change. As the value of accessing unstructured data of all types (i.e., text, graphics, audio, etc.) becomes evident and as your competitors begin to do so, firms will have little choice but to use unstructured data.

# TARGET LEAKAGE

One further consideration bears mentioning for those interested in text mining. "Target leakage"[4] is the term given to the introduction of information about the text mining target that should not legitimately be available to the algorithm. Recall that in regression analysis, it is a capital mistake to have the same variable on both sides of the equation; that would be called *model misspecification* and would clearly result in a meaningless regression. Much the same thing apparently often occurs in data mining and most especially in text mining. It is common because it is difficult to detect and possibly even harder to eliminate, but to overlook it would surely be folly. An algorithm that makes predictions that are "too good to be true" is probably an indication that target leakage has occurred. According to Edward Kwartler of Liberty Mutual Insurance, target leakage may be the number one source of difficulty in text mining. The paper by Kaufman, Rosset, and Perlich[5] gives numerous examples of the debilitating effects of target leakage that went unchecked in analytics efforts. Indeed, some of the examples occurred in analytics competitions where even the expert judges with extensive experience in the field failed to detect the target leakage until well after the competitions had ended and the prizes had been awarded!

One simple example occurred in a churn prediction algorithm similar to the classification presented in this chapter. In that situation, an innocuous attribute titled "interviewer name" was used. However, since a particular interviewer was routinely assigned to all clients when they churned, the model results were "fantastically predictive." Of course, in this instance, the model had access to information that should not have been legitimately available to it. Perhaps the best method for preventing target leakage is exploratory data analysis at the very beginning of a project; expert domain knowledge is the best medicine for preventing leakage. Know you data!

# CONCLUSION

Over a decade ago, James Surowiecki wrote convincingly in *The Wisdom of Crowds*[6] that given the correct conditions, the predictions of the crowd will almost always outperform the comments of any number of individuals. When we access the population of comments available on a topic on social media or in customer help line comments, how could we not expect that therein lies some predictive power? It is the individual and independent opinions represented, not crowd psychology, that contains the predictive power. Until recently, we have been hampered in efficiently using the large amount of textual data available; we had no cheap and useful way to reduce the dimensions of the unstructured data to a usable format.

---

[4] Shachar Kaufman, Saharon Rosset, and Claudia Perlich, "Leakage in Data Mining: Formulation, Detection, and Avoidance," *KDD '11*, August 21–24, 2011.

[5] Ibid.

[6] James Surowiecki, *The Wisdom of Crowds* (New York: Anchor Books, 2005).

Text mining has changed our ability to assimilate useful dimensions from a seemingly incomprehensible amount of textual data. Text analytics and natural language processing in particular have become commercially viable. Since at least 80 percent of all the world's data is unstructured, that commercial viability is a sea-change in the way analytics will look in the future. While textual data represents the greatest challenge to predictive analytics, it also holds out the greatest opportunity for innovation. You have already been subjected to one version of natural language processing if you have used Apple's Siri, Microsoft's Cortana, IBM's Watson, or Amazon's Alexa. Each of these applications (all of which are now used every day commercially) is an example of the power of natural language processing.

But Siri and Cortana make mistakes all the time. Yes, they do, but they provide the answers to most questions correctly and over time "learn" from their mistakes. Your use of text analytics should have the same characteristics; your first cut at analyzing text will likely end with mixed results. But over time and with a bit of supervised learning and appropriate software, your processes for handling text will get better.

In the early days of the venerable Apple II microcomputer, many users ran a program called Eliza. The small program emulated a psychologist with what, at the time, seemed like almost human responses from the computer in response to the user's typed statements. Many of us were surprised that the Apple II could produce such seemingly meaningful interactions in text. We knew the computer was powerful in performing repetitive numerical calculations with unerring accuracy, but the surprising part of Eliza was that we were using text to "communicate" with the Apple II. How was this possible? That was the very beginning of the study of natural language processing and the ability to reduce the dimensions of text.

In the near future, we will get a great deal of the meaning of the mountains of text exactly wrong! But it seems clear that we are getting better at deducing the meaning and even the sentiment in text; that alone appears evident from the perception that the commercial use of text mining appears to be growing exponentially each year. The success of Siri and Cortana have spawned Amazon Echo and Google Home, the unsolicited emails you receive seem surprisingly accurate in covering your interests, and even Amazon's suggestions seem to get better and better.

## Suggested Readings

Barbier, G., and H. Liu. "Data Mining in Social Media." In *Social Network Data Analytics*. Edited by Charu C. Aggarwal. Boston: Springer, 2011. pp. 327–352.

Elder, John; Gary Miner; and Bob Nisbet. *Practical Text Mining and Statistical Analysis for Non-Structured Text Data Applications*. Waltham, MA: Academic Press, 2012.

Feldman, R., and J. Sanger. *The Text Mining Handbook*. Cambridge, U.K.: Cambridge University Press, 2007.

Good, I. J. *The Estimation of Probabilities: An Essay on Modern Bayesian Methods*. Cambridge, MA: MIT Press, 1965.

Good, I. J. *Good Thinking: The Foundations of Probability and Its Applications*. Minneapolis: University of Minnesota, 1983.

He, Wu; Shenghua Zha; and Ling Li. "Social Media Competitive Analysis and Text Mining: A Case Study in the Pizza Industry." *International Journal of Information Management* (June 2013), pp. 465–472.

Kaufman, Shachar; Saharon Rosset; and Claudia Perlich. "Leakage in Data Mining: Formulation, Detection, and Avoidance." *KDD '11*, August 21–24, 2011.

Keating, Barry. "Text Into Numbers: Can Marketers Benefit from Unstructured Data?" *Applied Marketing Analytics,* vol. 2, no. 2 (May 2016), pp. 111–120.

Mayer-Schonberger, Viktor, and Kenneth Cukier. *Big Data: A Revolution That Will Transform How We Live, Work, and Think.* New York: Houghton Mifflin Harcourt, 2013.

Mitchell, T. M. *Machine Learning.* New York: McGraw-Hill, 1997.

Mooney, Raymond J., and Razvan Bunescu. "Mining Knowledge from Text Using Information Extraction." *SIGKDD Explorations*, vol. 7, no. 1 (June 2005), pp. 3–10.

Radovanovic, Miloš, and Mirjana Ivanovic. "Text Mining: Approaches and Applications." *Novi Sad J. Math,* vol. 38, no. 3 (2008), pp. 227–234.

Struhl, Steven. *Practical Text Analytics: Interpreting Text and Unstructured Data for Business Intelligence.* London: Kogan Page, 2015.

Schumaker, R., and H. Chen. "Textual Analysis of Stock Market Prediction Using Breaking Financial News: The AZFinText System." *ACM Transactions on Information Systems,* vol. 27, no. 2 (April 2009). pp. 1–29.

Surowiecki, James. *The Wisdom of Crowds.* New York: Anchor Books, 2005.

Van de Cruys, Tim. "A Comparison of Bag of Words and Syntax-Based Approaches for Word Categorization." In *Proceedings of the Lexical Semantics Workshop: Bridging the Gap between Semantic Theory and Computational Simulations.* Edited by M. Baroni, S. Evert, and A. Lenci. 2008. pp. 47–54.

## Exercises

1. What is meant by the term *dimension reduction*?
2. What is meant by "bag of words" analysis?
3. What is meant by "natural language processing"?
4. In the chapter, the two different text mining approaches were both used to mine text: "bag of words" analysis and "natural language processing." What is the significant difference between the two approaches? Which approach preceded the other historically?
5. In previous chapters, we used data mining diagnostic statistics such as confusion matrices and lift charts to evaluate models. Are these types of statistics useful in text mining?
6. Why mine text at all? Isn't language so complex that little useful insight can be gained through machine learning methods?
7. In the chapter example, we used a very small sample taken from two Usenet newsgroups (autos and electronics). Use the much larger data set that includes many postings from each of the two groups and again use XLMiner© to attempt to classify the groups as either "auto"-related or "electronics"-related.

   First, text mine the postings and then use the SVD-derived concept document matrix" from XLMiner© to estimate a classification model that you believe will predict each posting's category correctly (as either "autos" or "electronics"). Some classification models may work better than others.

   Evaluate the resulting classification model(s) using the standard diagnostic statistics and explain their meaning (C11P7).

8. Trivago is a German technology company that is essentially a hotel price comparison website. It claims to be the world's largest online hotel search site. As part of the information on their website Trivago displays the Trivago Rating Index (TRI), a number between 0 and 100 for every hotel (with 100 being the highest rating and 0 the lowest).

In the data provided are over 4,500 text comments from Trivago for various hotels and lodges. Also in the data is a variable titled "Score High/Low" that translates to a "1" if the TRI is above 49 and a "0" if the TRI is 49 or below.

Use a sample of 500 of the text comments to attempt to classify a hotel as either a "1" or "0." After mining the text, you will need to apply a classification model to the SVD-derived concept document matrix. The target for the classification model will be the "Score High/Low" variable.

Be aware that there are few negative reviews, and so the naive model would be to simply rate every hotel as a "1." Try to estimate a model using the text comments alone that does a better job than a naive model. Use standard diagnostic statistics to evaluate the model (C11P8).

# Chapter **Twelve**

# Forecast/Analytics Implementation

In this chapter, we discuss the forecasting/analytics process and provide a framework that will help you get the most out of any prediction effort. While every prediction problem has unique features, there is enough commonality in forecasting/analytics that guidelines can be helpful in several ways. First, the guidelines we provide will help you come to grips with some of the nuts-and-bolts issues related to data problems. Second, these guidelines will help you in making certain that the effort that goes into forecasting and analytics has the desired result in terms of the decision process. Finally, the guidelines discussed in this chapter will help you make logical choices regarding the technique(s) you should use for any particular situation.

©VLADGRIN/Getty Images

## LEARNING OBJECTIVES

After studying this chapter, you should be able to:

1. Discuss how forecasting has evolved from being purely judgmental to using highly complex methods and how predictive analytics can be considered an extension of forecast methods.
2. Explain the flow of the prediction process from raw data to action.
3. Discuss the two groups that must communicate well concerning forecasts and explain why this communication is important.
4. Explain the nine-step forecast/analytics process.
5. Explain the two major areas to consider when selecting a prediction method.

# FORECASTING INVOLVES A DEFINITE FLOW

Both quantitative and qualitative information should be valued and, when possible, combined in preparing a forecast.

You have now learned numerous quantitative forecast methods. You have spent considerable time and effort developing a working knowledge of many quantitative techniques and how they can be implemented using a software package. Our own personal experiences, as well as the experiences of others, provide convincing evidence that quantitative forecasting and analytics methods outperform qualitative predictions. However, the best software cannot automatically take into account the specific industry, marketing, and economic knowledge that a business professional may have. To obtain the best forecast outcomes, both quantitative and qualitative information should be valued and, when possible, combined in preparing a forecast.

It is important for everyone involved with forecasting and analytics to be clear about the distinction between forecasts, plans, and goals. In a recent discussion, a veteran forecaster in the automobile industry commented: "I prepared what I thought was a logical and well-thought-out forecast, but when it was presented to management, the response was that the forecast was wrong and that I should go back and redo it." In this individual's case, what management wanted was a plan (what the company intends to do) or a goal (the company target) rather than an objective projection of what is likely, given the current business environment. This scenario is not uncommon. What it points out is a serious confusion on the part of many between a prediction (or projection), a plan, and a goal. The prediction should be one piece of objective information that plays a part in the development of plans and/or goals, but it should not be confused with the planning or goal-setting functions.

The forecast should be one piece of objective information that plays a part in the development of plans and/or goals, but it should not be confused with the planning or goal-setting functions.

The emergence of widely available and sophisticated forecasting software (such as the ForecastX Wizard™ you have been using) and predictive analytics software (such as XLMiner©) has made it possible for people to implement complex forecasting and analytics methods quickly and easily. However, there is danger in implementing a technique about which one does not have a reasonable level of understanding. For example, suppose that you are a brand manager who has some forecasting responsibility for certain brands but that this function is only about 10 percent of your overall workload. In this situation, you might be inclined to make relatively simple judgmental forecasts, or if you have come to realize that quantitative methods can improve forecast accuracy, you might be tempted to use an automated forecast "black box" to develop your forecasts. In either case, you are likely to have difficulty explaining and/or justifying the forecast to those to whom you report. However, if you have a basic understanding of forecast methods (which you have now developed), you can articulate the reasoning behind your forecast and how the quantitative methods employed are well suited to the type of data that represent sales of your products. You will be able to make qualitative judgments and adjustments to the forecasts and be able to explain why such adjustments may be necessary. You may not be able to derive the formulas for the Winters' exponential smoothing model or for developing an ARIMA forecast that does not overfit, but you know enough about how these methods work to know when they are appropriate.

Communication, cooperation, and collaboration are important if the forecasting effort is to be successful. Many times, the people who develop a prediction do so in a vacuum of sorts. They look at the data and prepare a forecast, which is then sent to users who have had little or no input into the forecast process. The forecast may not be in a form that is useful to the end user, or the units forecast may be inappropriate for their use, or the wrong series may have been forecast, or they may simply not have enough understanding of the forecast to use it properly.

Two particular groups that need to communicate well are the analysts (or data scientists) and the end users of a forecast (people in sales, marketing, finance, production and others). Each of these groups may have quite different perspectives on the forecasting process and the desired results. Collaboration among interested parties is essential for the forecasting process to truly meet an organizations' needs.

There may be substantial savings if inventory levels can be reduced.

For collaborative forecasting to be successful, all parties need to work together by treating the perspectives and biases of others as valuable inputs rather than as obstacles to overcome.[1] These days, the need for communication, cooperation, and collaboration goes beyond company boundaries. To maximize the benefits to be derived from the forecast process or analytics effort, communication, cooperation, and collaboration should involve the entire supply chain.

Everyone is well aware that inventory is expensive and there may be substantial savings if inventory levels can be reduced. Such reduction was the premise upon which "just-in-time" processes were developed.

# THE FORECAST PROCESS

Data are the foundation, or base, for all predictions. There was a time when only numeric data were considered useful. Now useful data come in many forms. Much of the data used is still numeric, and the volume of available numeric data seems to grow almost without bounds. The "Internet of things" (IoT) drives a good part of this increased flow of numeric data. Cars talk to computers, refrigerators talk to tablets and phones, phones talk to thermostats, and on it goes. Sensors in one business can talk to sensors in another business, facilitating real time knowledge about inventories, production schedules, delays, and any other events that may affect forecasts. Adjustments can be made on the fly, saving time and money all along a supply chain.

An important way to look at the forecasting process is shown in Figure 12.1. Data are the starting point for all forecasts. Having reliable, clean, accurate data

---

[1] Sean Reese, "The Human Aspects of Collaborative Forecasting," *Journal of Business Forecasting*, Winter 2000–2001, pp. 3–9.

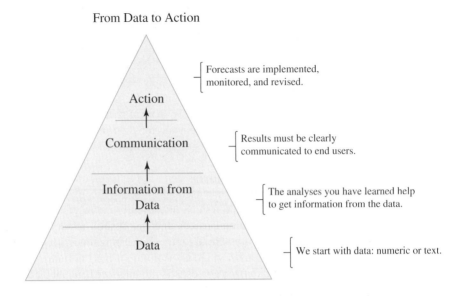

**FIGURE 12.1**

**Data to Action in Forecasting**

Forecasting begins with data that eventually drives actions.

From Data to Action

Action — Forecasts are implemented, monitored, and revised.

Communication — Results must be clearly communicated to end users.

Information from Data — The analyses you have learned help to get information from the data.

Data — We start with data: numeric or text.

forms the bedrock of a successful forecasting process. Often people confuse data with information. Data are not information. Data are simply the raw materials that allow us to build forecasts. The raw data contain information, but the information is hidden in a forest of detail. The various tools you have learned allow you to glean information from the clutter of the details in the data.

Think about the thousands of SKUs that companies such as Walmart and Amazon must order, track, and sell. The sheer volume of the related data is so large that no human can make sense of what meaning is hidden in the vastness of the detail. This is where data analysis comes into play. Using various tools, one can dig into the data to find the information that is necessary to make sound business decisions.

A key role for analysts is to be able to communicate succinctly and with clarity the information derived from the data. This usually means no complex equations, limited quantitative jargon, and relatively few numbers (certainly not all the statistics your software can compute). Visualization using various graphics is the key to helping others understand the results of complex analyses. All predictions should be communicated in a manner that is easily understood by the end user. Long, complex tables will numb the mind. Try to boil the important results down to the essentials and present that information with clarity in terms the end user understands. Almost always, graphics are a great help in this communication process.

End users of forecasts will take action based on the forecast only if they trust and understand the forecast. Too often, analysts do a wonderful job of teasing information from the data, only to fail when it comes to communicating actionable results.

**FIGURE 12.2**
**A Nine-Step**
**Forecasting Process**

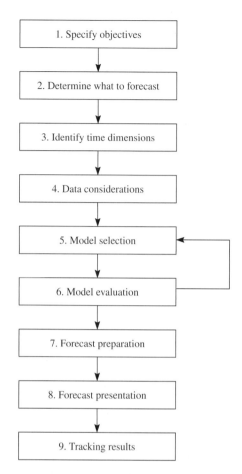

## A Nine-Step Forecasting Process

Communication, cooperation, and collaboration are critical if forecasting is to have the desired positive effect on decisions.

In Chapter 2, we suggested a nine-step forecasting process. This is shown again in Figure 12.2. These steps begin and end with communication, cooperation, and collaboration between the managers who use the forecasts and the technicians who prepare them. This communication and cooperation are critical if forecasting is to have the desired positive effect on decisions.

### Step 1. Specify Objectives

The objectives related to the decisions for which a prediction is important should be stated clearly. Management should articulate the role that the forecast will have in the decision process. If the decision will be the same regardless of the forecast, then any effort devoted to preparing the forecast is wasted. This may sound too obvious to deserve mention. However, it is not uncommon for a manager to request a forecast only to ignore it in the end. One reason that this happens is that the manager does not understand or have faith in the forecast. This issue will be addressed more fully in steps 7, 8, and 9, but a grounding of faith and understanding should begin here in step 1. If the manager who needs the information from a forecast and the data scientist who prepares the forecast take the opportunity to discuss the objectives and how the forecast will be used, there is increased likelihood that the ultimate forecast will be one that the manager understands and has faith in using.

## Step 2. Determine What to Forecast

Once your overall objectives are clear, you must decide exactly what to forecast. For example, it is not sufficient to say that you want a sales forecast. Do you want a forecast of sales revenue or unit sales? Do you want an annual forecast or a quarterly, monthly, or weekly forecast? Is the prediction about which specific customers will "churn"? Is the forecast needed on a global basis, by global regions (such as Asia and North America), on a national level, on a sales territory level? What level of product aggregation is desired? All of these issues must be made clear at the start. It is generally better to base sales forecasts on units rather than dollars so that price changes do not cloud actual variations in unit sales. The unit sales forecast can then be converted to a dollar figure easily enough. If the effect of price on sales is important, you may want to use a regression-based technique that incorporates causality. Good communication between the forecast user and the analysts who prepare the forecast is important in making certain that the appropriate variables are being forecast.

## Step 3. Identify Time Dimensions

There are two types of time dimensions to consider. First, one must establish the length of the forecast horizon. For annual forecasts, this might be from one to five years or more, although forecasts beyond a few years are likely to be influenced by unforeseen events that are not incorporated into the model used. Quarterly forecasts are probably best used for one or two years (four to eight quarters), as are monthly forecasts (perhaps as long as 12 to 18 months). The objectives dictate the time interval (year, quarter, and so forth) that is appropriate in preparing the forecast. For inventory control, short time periods are often necessary, whereas an annual forecast may be sufficient for the preparation of an estimated profit-and-loss statement for the coming year.

Second, the manager and the forecaster must agree on the urgency of the forecast. Is it needed tomorrow? Is there ample time to explore alternative methods? Proper planning is appropriate here. If a forecasting process is integrated into ongoing operations, then the forecasting personnel can plan an appropriate schedule, which will contribute to better forecasts.

## Step 4. Data Considerations

The data necessary in preparing a forecast may come from within or may be external. Let us first consider internal data. Some people may believe that internal data are readily available and easy to incorporate into the forecasting process. It is surprising how often this turns out to be far from correct. Data may be available in a technical sense yet not readily available to the person who needs them to prepare the forecast. Or the data may be available but not expressed in the right unit of measurement (e.g., in sales dollars rather than units sold).

Data are often aggregated across both variables and time, but it is best to have disaggregated data. For example, data may be kept for refrigerator sales in total but not by type of refrigerator, type of customer, or region. In addition, what data are maintained may be kept in quarterly or monthly form for only a few years and annually thereafter. Such aggregation of data limits what can be forecast and may limit the appropriate pool of forecasting techniques. Data storage has become relatively inexpensive, so all data should be kept for as long as possible. Communication and cooperation among the personnel involved in database maintenance, forecast preparation, and forecast use can help alleviate many unnecessary problems in this regard.

External data are available from a wide variety of sources, many of which have been discussed in Chapter 1 and some of which are discussed in Chapter 5 (Prevedere, for example). Data from national, state, and local government agencies are generally available at low cost. The more local the level of government unit, the more likely it is that the data will not be available as quickly as you might like or in the desired detail. Other sources of secondary data include industry or trade associations and private companies, such as some of the major banks. Most secondary data are available on the Internet.

## Step 5. Model Selection

There are many methods to select from when you set out to make any forecast. There are subjective or judgmental methods, some of which were reviewed in Chapter 1, and a growing set of quantitative methods is becoming available. The most widely used of these quantitative methods have been discussed in the previous chapters. The emergence of data and text mining in a forecasting environment is an exciting new horizon. Some of the things that should be included in making the selection are:

1. The type and quantity of data available
2. The pattern that the data have exhibited in the past
3. The urgency of the forecast
4. The length of the forecast horizon
5. The technical background of the people preparing and using the forecast

This issue of selecting the appropriate methods to use is of sufficient importance that we will come back to it in the next section. There, we provide specific guidelines for each of the methods discussed in the text.

## Step 6. Model Evaluation

Once the methods that we want to use have been selected, we need to do some initial evaluation of how well they work. For quantitative methods, we should apply the techniques to historical series and evaluate how well they work in a retrospective sense. We have referred to this as an evaluation of the "fit" of the model. If they do not work well in the historical context, there is little reason to believe that they will perform any better in the unknown domain of the future.

If we have sufficient historical data, a good approach to model testing is to use a "holdout" period for evaluation. For example, suppose we have quarterly data on sales for 10 years. We might use only the earliest nine years (36 data points) and make a forecast for the tenth year. If the model performs well when the forecast values are compared with the known values for the four quarters of year 10, we have reason to believe that the technique may also work well when the forecast period is indeed unknown. Out-of-sample evaluations such as this provide a preliminary measure of potential forecast "accuracy." Recall that in predictive analytics, the concept of a "holdout" is built into the basic process as you always partition the data into "training" and "validation" partitions. It is the lift and misclassification results for the validation partition that are most useful for model evaluation.

Once you are satisfied with a model based on historical and holdout period (or validation partition) evaluations, you should respecify the model using all the available data (historical and holdout) and then use it for your actual forecast.

Suppose a technique turns out not to perform well when tested. The purpose of testing is, at least in part, to help us avoid applying a method that does not work well in our unique situation. Therefore, we should go back to step 5 and select another method that is appropriate to the problem at hand. It is not always possible to tell ahead of time how well a particular method will actually perform in a specific forecasting environment. We can apply reasoned judgment to our initial selection, but ultimately, the proof is in the pudding. We must apply the method to see whether it performs adequately for the purpose at hand.

> Once you are satisfied with a model based on historical and holdout period evaluations, you should respecify the model using all the available data (historical and holdout) and then use it for your actual forecast.

## Step 7. Forecast Preparation

At this point, some method or set of methods has been selected for use in developing the forecast, and from testing, you have reasonable expectations that the methods will perform well. We recommend using more than one forecasting method when possible, and it is desirable for these to be of different types (e.g., a regression model and Holt's exponential smoothing, rather than two different regression models). The methods chosen should be used to prepare a range of forecasts. You might, for example, prepare a worst-case forecast, a best-case forecast, and a most-likely forecast. The latter may be based on a combination of forecasts (ensembles) developed by following the procedures suggested in the Appendix to Chapter 5. In predictive analytics, the concept of ensemble models is again built into the process and most of the commercial software; consider boosting and bagging as well as alternative algorithms. And always remember that more data (and better data) will almost always make better predictions.

## Step 8. Forecast Presentation

For a forecast to be used as intended, it must be presented to management clearly, in a way that provides an understanding of how the forecast was obtained and that elicits confidence in the forecast. It does not matter how much work is put into

"The forecaster must be capable of communicating the findings in language which the functional managers can understand. . . ."

developing the forecast. It does not matter how confident the preparer is in the results. It does not matter how sophisticated the methodology may be. What matters is whether or not the manager understands and has confidence in the forecast. All too often, quantitative analyses are put on a shelf and do not play the role in decision making that they should, because the results are not effectively presented to management. Decades ago Mark J. Lawless, who has been involved with forecasting within a number of corporations, including Chrysler, NCR, Ponderosa, and Hanson Industries Housewares Group, commented that:

> In communicating the forecast results to management, the forecaster must be capable of communicating the findings in language which the functional managers can understand and which is compatible with the corporate culture.[2]

The forecast should be communicated to management both in written form and in an oral presentation. Visuals should dominate. The written document should be at a level that is appropriate to the reader. In most cases, the managers who read the forecast document will have little interest in technical matters. They need the information necessary so that they use the forecast appropriately. They do not need the amount of background and detail to be able to prepare the forecast themselves.

Tables should be kept relatively short. Rarely would it be desirable to include an entire history of the data used and historical forecasts. The most recent observations and forecasts are usually sufficient. The long series should, however, be shown graphically and should include both actual and forecast values. In such graphic displays, colors and/or patterns can be used effectively to distinguish actual and forecast values.

The oral presentation should follow the same form and be made at about the same level as the written document. Generous use should be made of flip charts, slides, overheads, or projections of computer displays to heighten interest and involvement in the presentation. This oral presentation provides an excellent opportunity for discussion and clarification, which helps the manager gain a more complete understanding of the forecast and confidence in its usefulness.

## Step 9. Tracking Results

Neither the preparer nor the user is done with the forecast after the presentation and incorporation of results into the relevant decisions. The *process* continues. Deviations from the forecast and the actual events should be discussed in an open, objective, and positive manner. The objectives of such discussions should be to understand why errors occurred, to determine whether the magnitude of the errors was sufficient to have made a difference in the decisions that were based on the forecast, and to reevaluate the entire process with the intent of improving performance in the next round of forecasts. Input from both managers and technicians is important for the continual refinement of the forecasting process.

---

[2] Lawless, Mark J. "Effective Sales Forecasting: A Management Tool," *Journal of Business Forecasting* 9, no. 1 (Spring 1990), 10.

It is important to stress once more the critical role that communication and cooperation between managers and technicians play in building and maintaining a successful forecasting process. This is true whether forecasts are prepared in house or by outside suppliers. Without a commitment to communication and cooperation, it is not likely that any organization can get a maximum return from the forecasting effort.

## CHOOSING A FORECASTING TECHNIQUE

There a great many techniques that can be used to make forecasts. In this text, you have learned about many of the most commonly used methods. These methods are not only commonly used, but they are also the basis upon which many other methods have been developed. You started learning about some subjective (qualitative or judgmental) methods that were once the core of forecasting. More recently, quantitative methods have come to dominate the forecasting landscape.

Quantitative methods have evolved from simplistic methods, such as moving averages, to highly complex tools, such as data and text mining. Figure 12.3 illustrates the increasing complexity of forecasting methods. With the increasing complexity, we also gain richer information.

Now that you have an understanding of a variety of forecasting techniques, you need a general framework that will help you determine when to use each method.

**FIGURE 12.3** **Complexity of and Information from Forecast Methods**

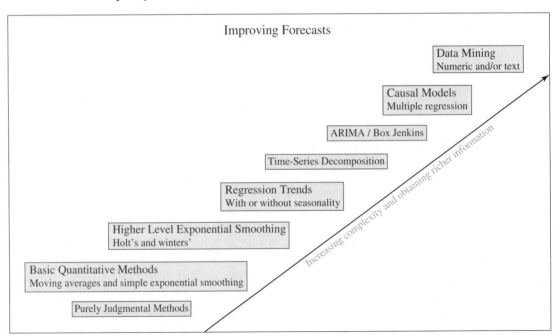

There are few hard-and-fast rules in this regard, but there are guidelines to assist in making the determination. If you understand how to use the methods discussed in this text, you have a good start toward determining when each method is likely to be useful. For example, if you are preparing a quarterly forecast of sales for a product that exhibits considerable seasonality, you would want to use one of the methods that is designed to handle such seasonal fluctuations.

In this section, we evaluate the forecasting methods presented earlier in the text relative to the underlying conditions for which they are most likely to be useful. There are many characteristics of a forecasting situation that might be considered in selecting an appropriate method. We will focus attention on two major areas: data and time. For data, we consider the type and quantity of data that are available as well as any pattern that may exist in the data (e.g., trend, cycle, and/or seasonality). Time includes the amount of historical data and the forecast horizon. We begin with the methods discussed in Chapter 1 and progress sequentially through the text, ending with data and text mining techniques. Table 12.1 provides a quick reference summary of the data and time issues.

## Sales Force Composite (SFC)

In using the sales force composite method, little or no historical data are necessary. The data required are the current estimates of salespeople regarding expected sales for the forecast horizon. Historical data may be considered by the sales force, but not necessarily. Thus, this method may not reflect patterns in the data unless they are obvious to the sales force (e.g., holiday season sales of jewelry). The method may, however, provide early warning signals of pending change (positive or negative) because of the closeness of the sales force to the customer. The SFC method is probably best used for short- to medium-term forecasts.[3] The preparation time is relatively short once a system for gathering data from the sales force is in place.

## Customer Surveys (CS)

Forecasts that are based on surveys of buyers' intentions require no historical data, and thus, the past plays no explicit role in forecasting the future. Customer surveys are most appropriate for medium- to long-term forecasting. For example, a natural gas utility has used this method to help in long-term planning by gathering survey data on customers' plans for future energy use, including long-term capital expansion plans. The time necessary to develop, conduct, and analyze a survey research project can be relatively extensive. Rarely can such a project be completed in less than two to three months. If the same survey is used year after year, however, this time can be shortened considerably. CS is not a method to consider if there is a sense of urgency in getting the forecast.

---

[3] Short-term, medium-term, and long-term forecasts will be mentioned throughout this section. Short-term forecasts include up to three months, medium-term forecasts cover four months to about two years, and long-term forecasts are for periods longer than two years

**TABLE 12.1**  Guide to Selecting an Appropriate Forecasting Method

| Forecasting Method | Data Pattern | Quantity of Historical Data No. of Observations | Forecast Horizon |
|---|---|---|---|
| **Subjective Methods** | | | |
| Sales force composite | Any | Little | Short to medium |
| Customer surveys | Not applicable | None | Medium to long |
| Jury of executive opinion | Any | Little | Any |
| Delphi | Any | Little | Long |
| **Quantitative Methods** | | | |
| Naive | Stationary[a] | 1 (or number of seasons) | Very short |
| Moving averages | Stationary[a] | Number equal to the number of periods in the moving average | Very short |
| **Exponential Smoothing** | | | |
| Simple | Stationary[a,b] | 5 to 10 | Short |
| Adaptive response | Stationary[a,b] | 10 to 15 | Short |
| Holt's | Linear trend[b] | 10 to 15 | Short to medium |
| Winters' | Trend and seasonality | At least 4 or 5 per season | Short to medium |
| Bass model | S-curve | Small, 3 to 10 | Short, medium, and long |
| **Regression-Based** | | | |
| Trend | Linear and nonlinear Trend with or without seasonality | Minimum of 10 with 4 or 5 per season if data are seasonal | Short to medium |
| Causal | Can handle nearly all data patterns | We desire 10 per independent variable. | Short, medium, and long |
| **Time-Series Decomposition** | | | |
| | Can handle trend, seasonal, and cyclical patterns | Enough to see 2 peaks and troughs | Short, medium, and long |
| **ARIMA** | | | |
| | Stationary[a] | Minimum of 50 | Short, medium, and long |
| **Data Mining** | | | |
| | Any | Used with large databases | Prediction usually for near-term use |
| **Text Mining** | | | |
| | Any | Used with large databases | Prediction usually for near-term use |

[a] Or data that have been transformed to a stationary series.
[b] May be used for seasonal data if the data are first deseasonalized.

### Jury of Executive Opinion (JEO)

The executives included do not need a formal data set. They need only the body of experience that they have developed to make judgments concerning the most likely value of the forecast variable during the period of interest. Historical data patterns may or may not be reflected in the opinions expressed, although regular patterns such as seasonality are very likely to receive attention, albeit implicit attention. A JEO may be used for any forecast horizon and is generally a relatively quick procedure. This method requires a substantial base of expertise on the part of the participants.

### Delphi Method

The Delphi method does not require a historical data series, other than what is in the knowledge base of the panel members, and therefore does not necessarily reflect patterns that may have existed in the past. It is most often applicable for long-range forecasting but can be applied to medium-term projects as well. In these respects, it is much like JEO. However, the time to develop the Delphi forecast can be considerable unless the responses of panel members stabilize quickly. Use of the Internet speeds the flow of information and thus shortens the time considerably. The Delphi approach, as well as a jury of executive opinion and customer surveys, are sometimes useful in forecasting the sales of new products.

### Naive

The basic naive model requires only one historical value as a basis for the forecast. An extended naive model that takes the most recent trend into account requires just two past values. This method is best suited to situations in which the data are stationary. Seasonality can sometimes be accounted for in a reasonably stationary series using a seasonal time lag. The naive approach is suited only for very short-term forecasts.

### Moving Averages

Moving averages are most appropriate when the data are stationary and do not exhibit seasonality. Relatively few historical data are necessary. The number of past observations must be at least equal to the number of periods in the moving average. For example, if a four-period moving average is used, you need at least four historical data points. Moving averages are normally used to forecast just one period ahead.

### Simple Exponential Smoothing (SES)

Historical data are necessary to establish the best weighting factor in simple exponential smoothing, but thereafter, only the most recent observed and forecasted values are required. Five to ten past values are sufficient to determine the weighting factor. The data series should be stationary (i.e., have no trend and no seasonality) when SES is used. This method is appropriate for short-term forecasting. While the arithmetic work can be done by hand, a computer can be helpful in determining the best weighting factor. Once the weighting factor is known, forecasts can be developed very quickly.

## Adaptive–Response-Rate Single Exponential Smoothing (ADRES)

The adaptive–response-rate single exponential smoothing model may be used when the data are stationary and exhibit no seasonality but have a shift in level. Ten to 15 historical observations should be available when ADRES is used, and forecasts should be for only a short forecast horizon, typically one or two periods ahead.

## Holt's Exponential Smoothing (HES)

As with SES, Holt's exponential smoothing model requires historical data to determine weighting values, but only the very recent past is required to apply the model. It is desirable to have at least 10 to 15 historical observations in determining the two weights. HES can be used effectively with data series that exhibit a positive or negative trend; thus, this method has a much wider scope of application than SES. However, it should not be used when the data contain a seasonal pattern unless the data have been deseasonalized. HES is appropriate for short- and medium-term forecasts and, like SES, can be implemented rapidly once the weights have been selected.

## Winters' Exponential Smoothing (WES)

Sufficient historical data to determine the weights are necessary in using Winters' exponential smoothing model. A minimum of four or five observations per season should be used (i.e., for quarterly data, 16 or 20 observations should be used). Because this method incorporates both trend and seasonal components, it is applicable to a wide spectrum of data patterns. Like HES, this method is most appropriate for short- to medium-term forecasts. Once the weights have been determined, the process of making a forecast moves quickly. The use of professional forecasting software (such as ForecastX™) is recommended for the process of selecting the best values for the weights in the WES model.

## Regression-Based Trend Models

The data requirement for using a regression-based trend depends to a considerable extent on the consistency in the trend and whether or not the trend is linear. We look for enough data that the $t$-statistic for the slope term (i.e., the trend) is significant (a $t$-value of 2 or more in absolute value is a handy rule of thumb). For a simple linear trend, 10 observations may be quite sufficient. A simple trend model can be effective when the series being forecast has no pattern other than the trend. Such a model is appropriate for short- to medium-term forecasts and can be developed and implemented relatively quickly.

## Regression-Based Trend Models with Seasonality

To include seasonality in a regression-based trend model, it is desirable to have at least four or five observations per season. Thus, for quarterly data, a minimum of 16 observations would be appropriate. For monthly data, 48 or more observations should be used. Regular seasonal patterns in the series are often modeled quite well by using dummy variables. As with simple trend models, linear or nonlinear forms can be used; the models are best for short- to medium-term forecasts, and the time necessary for preparation is short. A computer regression program is a virtual necessity, however.

## Regression Models with Causality

The quantity of data required for the development of a causal regression model depends on the number of independent variables in the model and on how much contribution each of those variables makes in explaining variation in the dependent variable. One rule of thumb is that you should expect to have a minimum of 10 observations per independent variable. Thus, for a model with three independent variables, you should have at least 30 observations. However, in practical applications, the length of the data set may be less. No matter how many observations are used, a statistical evaluation should be the guide for model acceptability. Developing and maintaining a database for multiple-regression models can be a significant undertaking. The effort may be worthwhile, however, since multiple-regression models are often effective in dealing with complex data patterns and may even help identify turning points. Seasonality can be handled by using dummy variables. Causal regression models can be useful for short-, medium-, or long-term forecasts. Because the causal variables must usually be forecast as well, regression models may take more effort to develop.

## Time-Series Decomposition (TSD)

The quantity of data needed for time-series decomposition should be enough for you to see at least two peaks and two troughs in the cycle factor, if the cycle factor is important. If the cycle factor does not appear important (i.e., has not been far above or below 1.0 during the historical period), then the quantity of data needed should be determined by what is necessary to adequately identify the seasonal pattern. A rule of thumb would be at least four or five observations per season (e.g., for quarterly data, you should have at least 16 to 20 observations). TSD is quite good at picking up patterns in the data. The challenge is for the analyst to successfully project the patterns through the forecast horizon. This is generally fairly easy for the trend and seasonal pattern but more difficult for the cyclical pattern. TSD is especially appropriate for short-term and medium-term forecasting. If the cycle pattern is not important or if it can be projected with confidence, the method can also be used effectively for long-term forecasts. This method may be one of the best in terms of being able to identify and incorporate turning points. Doing so is dependent on the analyst's ability to correctly interpret when the cycle factor may turn up or down.

## ARIMA

A long data series (at least 50 data points—more if data are seasonal) is necessary to make use of the ARIMA models. These models can handle variability in the data as long as the series is stationary or can be transformed to a stationary series. This method can be applied to short-, medium-, or long-term forecast horizons. Because of the complexity of model identification, forecast preparation can take an extended period of time. This complexity also means that the preparer needs a highly sophisticated technical background. Users of ARIMA forecasts must also be quite sophisticated, because even achieving a basic understanding of the method is not easy. It is rare to find a manager who has a good feel for how an ARIMA forecast is developed and rarer still to find a manager capable of explaining the forecast derivation to others who must use the results. This may be part of the reason that ARIMA models have often had relatively low ratings in terms of importance, accuracy, and use by business managers.

## Data Mining

The data used in predictive analytics is usually not time series data like that used in most of the forecasting models. The size of the data set may also differ in that analytics depends more upon very large data sets; in most situations, the more data, the better the prediction. Two very different types of data mining algorithms were examined; classification algorithms and clustering algorithms. Classification is the most used type of analytics algorithm; it is used extensively in business and many different forms of classification were examined. Ensembles of different classification algorithms or modifications that created ensembles such as boosting and bagging are often used to improve accuracy. The clustering type models are less used but also have their place in business usefulness.

## Text Mining

The types of data used in text mining were a stark departure from the data previously examined. Text was unstructured, not arranged in neat columns and rows with only numbers populating the various locations. Text, since it is so available for analysis, offered a new and larger frontier for prediction. The bag of words analysis that we examined is useful and will often yield useful results but that is only the frontier of examining unstructured data. Video, photo, and audio data will also offer possibilities for building predictive models. Text is just the tip of the data that data scientists will find useful and predictive in the future.

# SPECIAL FORECASTING CONSIDERATIONS

In the text, a number of situations have been discussed for which special forecasting techniques are appropriate. Four of these are: (1) situations in which we must make forecasts if "events" of some type influence the forecast; (2) situations in which we have multiple forecasts, each of which may contain valuable information that we do not want to ignore; (3) situations in which we need to forecast a new product for which we have little historical information; and (4) situations in which we need to predict some outcome and we have very large, often somewhat unrelated, databases that hold hidden keys to the likely outcome. Here, we review some important aspects of each of these four.

## Event Modeling

When forecasting sales or demand in a highly promoted market, using event modeling can often significantly improve forecast accuracy. Event modeling is a feature within many forecasting programs, such as ForecastX™. This feature allows the user to specify the time of one or more special events, such as irregular promotions and natural disasters, in the calibration data. For each type of special event, the effect is estimated and the data adjusted so that the events do not distort the trend and seasonal patterns of the time series.

The method of event modeling follows in the same pattern as the other smoothing models except that the event model adds a smoothing equation for each of the events being considered. Event models are analogous to seasonal models: just as each month is assigned its own index for seasonality, so, too, each event type is assigned its own index. Event adjustments are created through the use of an indicator variable that assigns an integer for each event type to the period during which it recurs. An example of integer value assignment would be that 0 indicates a period in which no event has occurred, 1 indicates a period in which a free-standing advertising insert was used, 2 indicates a period in which instantly redeemable coupons were used, and so on. The event indicator variable must be defined for each historical period and future period in the forecast horizon.

## Combining Forecasts (Ensembles)

Instead of choosing the best model from among two or more alternatives, a more reasoned approach, according to the empirical evidence, is to combine the forecasts in order to obtain a forecast that is more accurate than any of the separate predictions. Any time a particular forecast is ignored because it is not the "best" forecast produced, it is likely that valuable independent information contained in the discarded forecast has been lost. The information lost may be of two types:

1. Some variables included in the discarded forecast may not be included in the "best" forecast.
2. The discarded forecast may make use of a type of relationship ignored by the "best" forecast.

In the first of these cases, it is quite possible for individual forecasts to be based on different information; thus, ignoring any one of these forecasts would necessarily exclude the explanatory power unique to the information included in the discarded model. In the second situation, it is often the case that different assumptions are made in different models about the form of the relationship between the variables. Each of the different forms of relationship tested, however, may have some explanatory value. Choosing only the "best" of the relationships could exclude functional information. To prevent this loss of useful information requires some method for combining the two forecasts into a single *better* forecast. We should expect that combinations of forecasts that use very different models are likely to be effective in reducing forecast error.

Combining forecasts is not guaranteed to reduce error, but one does not know until forecasts are combined and the combination results compared with results for individual forecasts. When combining forecasts, it is important that one check to be sure that doing so will not create a forecast bias.

## New-Product Forecasting (NPF)

Most products for which we are likely to have to prepare a sales forecast are products with a substantial amount of sales history for which the methods you have learned in earlier chapters will work quite well. However, often we are faced with new, or substantially altered, products with little sales history. These new products pose particularly difficult issues for a forecaster. Understanding the concept of a product life cycle (PLC) can be helpful in developing a forecast for a new product. During the introductory stage of the product life cycle, only consumers who are *innovators* are likely to buy the product. Sales start low and increase slowly. Near the end of this stage, sales start to increase at an increasing rate. As the product enters the growth stage of the PLC, sales are still increasing at an increasing rate as *early adopters* enter the market. In this stage, the rate of growth in sales starts to decline. Near the end of the growth stage, sales growth starts to level off substantially as the product enters the maturity stage. Businesses may employ marketing strategies to extend this stage; however, all products eventually reach the stage of decline in sales and are, at some point, removed from the market.

Product life cycles are not uniform in exact shape or duration and vary from industry to industry. Think, for example, about products that are fashion items or fads in comparison with products that have real staying power in the marketplace. Fashion items and products that would be considered fads typically have a steep introductory stage followed by short growth and maturity stages and a decline that is also very steep. High-tech products, such as cell phones, often have life cycles that are relatively short in comparison with low-technology products. For high-tech electronic products, life cycles may be as short as six to nine months.

Methods such as analog forecasts, test marketing, and product clinics are often useful for new-product forecasting. The Bass model for sales of new products is probably the most notable model for new-product forecasting. The Bass model was originally developed for application only to durable goods. However, it has been adapted for use in forecasting a wide variety of products with short product life cycles and new products with limited historical data.

## Data Mining

Sometimes people think of forecasting only in the context of time-series data. In some manner, past data are used to help predict the likely outcomes in the future. These include univariate time-series methods, such as exponential smoothing, as well as causal models, such as multiple regression. We have seen that at times regression models may be useful with cross-sectional data to predict some out-come, such as sales volume. Data mining is another technique that has been de-veloped to help one predict outcomes when there is a great deal of data available that might contain hidden information.

Data mining techniques work often with very large and somewhat unrelated databases. There was a time when decision makers had too little data upon which to base decisions. Now that has changed dramatically, and decision makers have so much data that it is difficult to find the information content from the data. This is where data mining becomes a useful tool.

Data mining has become a new application for some types of forecasting in which we have huge amounts of data but we know little about the structural re-lationships contained therein. Data mining is a tool that helps us uncover rela-tionships that are often quite unexpected yet useful in making predictions. For example, a California retailer found through data mining that shoppers who buy diapers are also likely to buy beer.[4] Such knowledge would not be likely to be un-covered using more simplistic data analysis but can be useful in predicting sales of both items and in developing new ways to structure marketing communications involving both products.

Suppose you wanted to forecast the number of sports cars an insurance com-pany would insure. It is obvious to us that one factor would be the price (premium) charged for coverage, which in turn would be influenced by the number of claims filed by sports car owners. Conventional wisdom might suggest that sports car own-ers would have more claims for accidents and/or thefts. However, through data min-ing, Farmers Group found that sports cars owned by people who also owned another vehicle have fewer insurance claims. As a result, they restructured their premiums in these situations with a resulting increase in premium revenue of over $4 million in two years without having a substantial increase in claims.[5] It was only possible to make the prediction about the potential new market by using data mining.

## Text Mining

Text mining is truly the frontier of prediction. The suggestions you receive from Amazon and the ability of firms to react almost immediately to customer complaints (or compliments) are likely due to some text mining algorithm. The uses of digital assistants such as Siri and Alexa are examples of text mining (in which the audio has been converted to text and then analyzed) that have become commonplace. As we obtain access to more data from the Internet of Things, sensors, and the mining of social media, the uses of text mining will grow. And with more data to work with, the usefulness of the predictions will likely become better.

[4] Donald R. Cooper and Pamela S. Schindler, *Marketing Research*, McGraw-Hill/Irwin, 2006, p. 261.

[5] Carl McDaniel and Roger Gates, *Marketing Research Essentials*, 6th ed. New York: John Wiley & Sons, 2008, pp. 79–80.

# USING PROCAST™ IN FORECASTX™ TO MAKE FORECASTS

We generally recommend that you think carefully about your forecast objectives and about the nature of your data to select a forecast method. However, there are situations in which you might allow ForecastX™ to select the method for you. Suppose you have hundreds or thousands of SKUs to forecast. Rather than analyzing each individually, you might want to let the software take on that task. There is a way to do this within ForecastX™ by using a feature called **ProCast™**.

**ProCast™** will search through a subset of methods to determine the method that will work best for your data. You can select the criteria to use in selecting the best method. In the example shown below, we selected to minimize the absolute error. There is a downside to using **ProCast™** in that you may not be familiar with the method selected and so would have trouble explaining it to an end user. Also, causal models would not be included in the decision set because ForecastX™ would not have access to the desired independent variables.

To use ProCast™, begin by opening your data file in Excel. Place your cursor in any cell with the data to be forecast. In the example below, we selected cell B3.

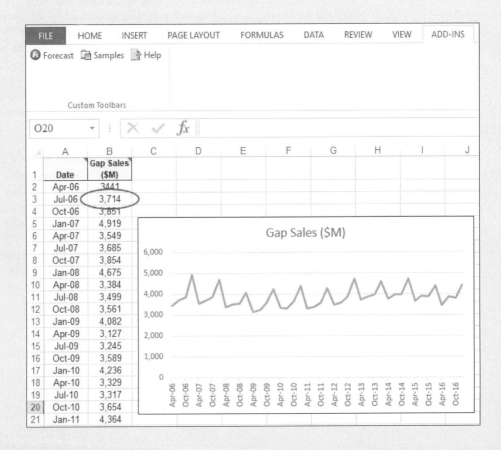

Then start ForecastX$^{TM}$. In the **Data Capture** dialog box, identify the data you want to use, as shown below.

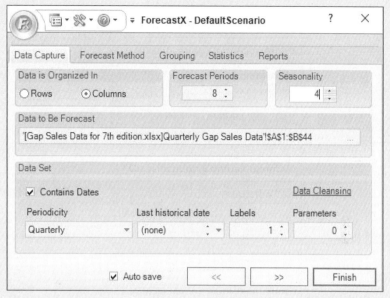

Source: John Galt Solutions

Then click the **Forecast Method** tab. In the **Method Selection** dialog box, click the down arrow in the **Forecasting Technique** box and select **ProCast**$^{TM}$. Click the down arrow in the **Error Term** box and select **Mean Absolute Error** (or another error term you want to use).

Source: John Galt Solutions

Then click the **Statistics** tab. In this dialog box, select the statistics that you desire. Re member that there are more statistics choices if you click the **More Statistics** button near the bottom right of the dialog box.

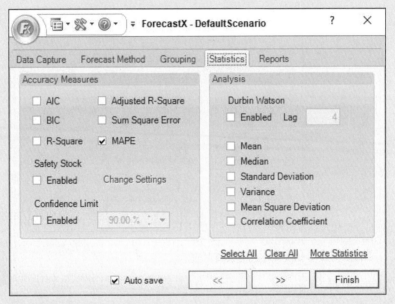

Source: John Galt Solutions

After selecting the statistics you want to see, click the **Reports** tab.

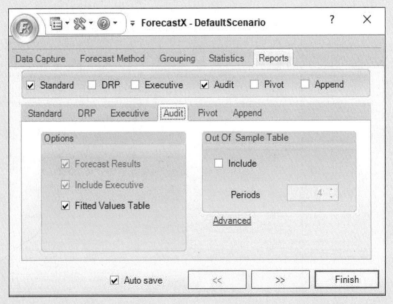

Source: John Galt Solutions

In the **Reports** box, select those you want. Typical selections might be those shown here. When you click the **Standard** tab, select the **Show Chart** and **Classic.** In the **Audit Trail** tab (the active tab shown here), click the **Fitted Values Table.**

Then click the **Finish** button. In the Audit Trail output, you will find the method that ProCast™ used to make the requested forecast.

Using an automated forecasting method such as ProCast™ is all right if you understand the selected method well enough to evaluate whether it is truly a logical choice. It is wise to exercise some caution when allowing any software to select a method automatically. By using a software package, such as ForecastX™, over a period of time, you may develop confidence in the selections it makes. Then using an automated process may provide considerable time savings—such as in situations where there are hundreds or thousands of items that must be forecast frequently.

**Suggested Readings**

Armstrong, J. Scott. "Research Needs in Forecasting." *International Journal of Forecasting* 4, no. 3 (1988), pp. 449–65.

Chase, Charles W., Jr. "Business Forecasting: A Process Not an Application." *Journal of Business Forecasting* 11, no. 3 (Fall 1992), pp. 12–13.

Fisher, Marshall; and Kumar Rajaram. "Accurate Retail Testing of Fashion Merchandise: Methodology and Application." *Marketing Science* 19, no. 3 (Summer 2000), pp. 266–78.

Harrington, Lisa H. "Retail Collaboration: How to Solve the Puzzle." *Transportation and Distribution,* May 2003, pp. 33–37.

Keating, Barry; and J. Holton Wilson. "Forecasting Practices and Teachings." *Journal of Business Forecasting* 7, no. 4 (Winter 1987–88), pp. 10–13, 16.

Larréché, Jean-Claude; and Reza Moinpour. "Managerial Judgement in Marketing: The Concept of Expertise." *Journal of Marketing Research* 20, no. 2 (May 1983), pp. 110–21.

Lawless, Mark J. "Effective Sales Forecasting: A Management Tool." *Journal of Business Forecasting* 9, no. 1 (Spring 1990), pp. 2–11.

———. "Ten Prescriptions for Forecasting Success." *Journal of Business Forecasting* 11, no. 4 (Spring 1997), pp. 3–5.

LeLee, Gary S. "The Key to Understanding the Forecasting Process." *Journal of Business Forecasting* 11, no. 4 (Winter 1992–93), pp. 12–16.

Lynn, Gary S.; Steven P. Schnaars; and Richard B. Skov. "Survey of New Product Forecasting Practices in Industrial High Technology and Low Technology Businesses." *Industrial Marketing Management* 28 (November 1999), pp. 565–71.

Mentzer, John T.; and Kenneth B. Kahn. "State of Sales Forecasting Systems in Corporate America." *Journal of Business Forecasting* 11, no. 4 (Spring 1997), pp. 6–13.

Moon, Mark A.; and John T. Mentzer. "Improving Salesforce Forecasting." *Journal of Business Forecasting* 18, no. 2 (Summer 1999), pp. 7–12.

Moon, Mark A.; John T. Mentzer; Carlo D. Smith; and Michael S. Garver. "Seven Keys to Better Forecasting." *Business Horizons* (September–October 1998), pp. 44–52.

Pammer, Scott E.; Duncan K. H. Fong; and Steven F. Arnold. "Forecasting the Penetration of a New Product—A Bayesian Approach." *Journal of Business & Economic Statistics* 18, no. 4 (October 2000), pp. 428–35.

Raghunathan, Srinivasan. "Interorganizational Collaborative Forecasting and Replenishment Systems and Supply Chain Implications," *Decision Sciences* 30, no. 4 (Fall 1999), pp. 1053–71.

Reese, Sean. "The Human Aspects of Collaborative Forecasting." *Journal of Business Forecasting* 19, no. 4 (Winter 2000–2001), pp. 3–9.

Reyes, Luis. "The Forecasting Function: Critical Yet Misunderstood." *Journal of Business Forecasting* 14, no. 4 (Winter 1995–96), pp. 8–9.

Szmania, Joe; and John Surgent. "An Application of an Expert System Approach to Business Forecasting." *Journal of Business Forecasting* 8, no. 1 (Spring 1989), pp. 10–12.

Tkacz, Greg. "Neural Network Forecasting of Canadian GDP Growth." *International Journal of Forecasting* 17, no. 1 (January–March 2001), pp. 57–69.

Weitz, Rob R. "NOSTRADAMUS—A Knowledge-Based Forecast Advisor." *International Journal of Forecasting* 2, no. 1 (1986), pp. 273–83.

Wilson, J. Holton; and Hugh G. Daubek. "Marketing Managers Evaluate Forecasting Models." *Journal of Business Forecasting* 8, no. 1 (Spring 1989), pp. 19–22.

# Exercises

1. Discuss how forecasting has moved from purely judgmental methods to highly complex methods.

2. Explain the process of going from raw data to actions based on a forecast.

3. What two groups must communicate well in order for the forecast process to be effective? Explain why.

4. Describe the nine-step forecast process presented in the chapter.

5. What are the two main things to consider when selecting a forecast method? Why?

6. The forecast process begins with a need to make one or more decisions that depend on the future value of some variable. Think about this as it relates to the daily weather forecast you hear, and write a list of five decisions that might depend on such a forecast.

7. The availability and form of data to be used in preparing a forecast are often seen as especially critical areas. Summarize, in your own words, the database considerations in the forecasting process (step 4).

8. Suppose that you have been asked to recommend a forecasting technique that would be appropriate to prepare a forecast, given the following situational characteristics:

   *a.* You have 10 years of quarterly data.

   *b.* There is an upward trend to the data.

   *c.* There is a significant increase in sales prior to Christmas each year.

   *d.* A one-year forecast is needed.

   *e.* You need to have the forecast done and the presentation ready in just a few days.

   *f.* What method(s) would you consider using and why?

9. Write an outline of what you would like to see in a forecast presentation from the perspective of a manager who needs to use the forecast.

10. Explain how the predictions made using analytics are somewhat different than those from traditional forecasting models. Are the data used differently? Are the types of predictions different?

# Index

# S

# T

## W

Wanamaker, John, 421–432
Warming up a model, 103
Warren, Neil Clark, 432
Weighted-average models, 340
Weighted averages, 100
WES. *see* Winters' exponential smoothing
White noise (Box-Jenkins), 337–339
Whitlark, David B., 19
Wigley, Chris, 398
Williams, Billy, 376
Wilson, J. Holton, 6, 8, 18
Winters' exponential smoothing (WES), 111–115, 544, 546
Wordles, 514–515

## X

XLMiner©
  area under the curve in, 427
  bagging, 485
  boosting example, 490
  data mining, 418–421
  hierarchical clustering, 502–503
  k-means clustering, 498–499
  lift chart in, 423, 424–425
  random forest, 487
  text mining tools, 508, 514–515

## Z

Z-distribution, 63–65
Zipf, George Kingsley, 516
Zipf plot, 516–517